THE PHYLA
SIPUNCULA AND ECHIURA

THE PHYLA

SIPUNCULA

AND

ECHIURA

By

A. C. STEPHEN

Formerly Keeper of Natural History
Royal Scottish Museum, Edinburgh

and

S. J. EDMONDS

Department of Zoology, University of Adelaide

TRUSTEES OF
THE BRITISH MUSEUM (NATURAL HISTORY)
LONDON : 1972

CONTENTS

A LIST OF TABLES

PREFACE

The publication of this monograph, the first in any language on either of the two phyla, realizes a long-held ambition of the late Dr A. C. Stephen who at the time of his death in 1966 had completed the first draft of the descriptions of genera and species together with their synonymies and distributions and the bibliography. Much, however, remained to be done and it is fortunate that Dr S. J. Edmonds not only was as anxious as other friends of Dr Stephen that the work on the monograph should be completed but also had the scholarship and energy to do the work.

Dr Edmond's share of this important contribution to marine studies has been a large one. As far as possible he has checked the descriptions, records and translations with the original specimens and data. He has brought the information up-to-date, completed the arrangement of species into genera and formed the Sipuncula into families. He has also largely provided the keys for identification, the general information and the appendices.

Dr Edmonds is alone responsible for the many illustrations since Dr Stephen left no notes of his intentions with regard to them. Here, I gratefully acknowledge the initiative of Mr A. Rodger Waterston, Dr Stephen's former colleague and successor as Keeper of Natural History for making a generous grant available from the funds of the Royal Scottish Museum for the employment of an artist. Mrs M. Schaffer is the artist.

J. P. Harding

Keeper of Zoology

British Museum (Natural History)

I. INTRODUCTION

Although the phyla Sipuncula and Echiura are considered to be minor phyla (Hyman, 1959) sipunculans and echiurans are not uncommon and are well known inhabitants of the shores of polar, temperate and tropical seas. They have also been collected from the floor of the oceans at great depths. Our records show that about 320 species of sipunculans and about 130 species of echiurans have been described.

The identification of sipunculans and echiurans is not always an easy matter, for a number of reasons. In the first place most of the species lack hard parts and skeletal structures, like the plates of holothurians and the setae of annelids, which on account of their more or less fixed shape and size can be used as specific characters. Moreover, the bodies of living sipunculans and echiurans are soft and highly muscular. Consequently preserved specimens, unless they have been carefully relaxed or narcotized before fixation, are often much contracted and distorted. In this condition they are not easy to dissect and describe. It becomes difficult, for instance, to ascertain the number, nature and arrangement of the tentacles and whether hooks are present on the introvert. In addition, the descriptions of the species are written in many different journals, some of which are not well known. Therefore it is not always easy to obtain the necessary information about a species unless one has access to a large library. No book which gives a detailed account of the systematics of either phylum has been written this century.

The aim of the authors has been to bring together into a single account information which deals with the collection, narcotization, fixation and dissection of sipunculans and echiurans, along with descriptions of all the known species organized into genera and families. We have also included for each phylum a glossary of anatomical terms that are important in identifying the worms.

The Sipuncula and Echiura, although now regarded as separate phyla, were for a long time grouped together in the Gephyrea. Systematists have tended to work in both groups and consequently much of the literature is common to the two phyla. It is for these reasons that we thought it convenient to monograph the two phyla in a single volume. We have, however, treated them except for the bibiliography as separate groups.

Although they are often confused by collectors on account of their superficial resemblances, sipunculans and echiurans can be easily distinguished from each other.

In a sipunculan

    (i) the highly muscular introvert can be invaginated and completely retracted into the body cavity

    (ii) the mouth is situated at the anterior extremity of the introvert

    (iii) a group of tentacles usually surrounds, partly surrounds or lies near the mouth

(iv) the anus is situated dorsally in the anterior region of the trunk (rarely on the introvert)

(v) setae are never present

(vi) anal vesicles are never present.

In an echiuran

(i) the proboscis, although highly muscular and extensible, cannot be invaginated or retracted into the body cavity

(ii) the mouth is situated on the trunk at the base of the proboscis

(iii) tentacles are not present

(iv) the anus is situated at the posterior extremity of the trunk

(v) one or two ventral setae usually lie just posterior to the mouth

(vi) a pair of tubular, sac-like or branching anal vesicles is attached to the cloacal region of the intestine.

II. Phylum **SIPUNCULA**

1. GENERAL INFORMATION

(1) *Status and name of the group*

Amongst the earliest records of sipunculans is that of Bohadsch (1761) who described a specimen from Naples as *Syrinx* without giving it a specific name. He described it as a new kind of zoophyte 'corpore reticulato, pyramidali, apice globosa, impervio ornato, et ore, in medio baseos sito atque in eo syphunculo mobili praeditum est'. Linnaeus (1766 : 1078) gave it the name *Sipunculus nudus* and also gave a brief description of another species *Sipunculus saccatus* from the Indian Ocean. The identity of the latter is uncertain. Pallas (1774) described *Lumbricus edulis* (=*Siphonosoma edule*) and *L. phalloides* (=*Sipunculus phalloides*). Montagu (1804) described *Sipunculus strombi* (=*Phascolion strombi*) from the shell of *Strombus*.

Sipunculans were recognized as a group in their own right first by Delle Chiaje (1823) who called them Sifunculacei and later by de Blainville (1827) who called them the Sipunculidia. Quatrefages (1847) placed sipunculans, echiurans and priapulans in a group which he called the Gephyrea (Greek 'gephyros'—a bridge) under the impression that they formed a link between the annelids and the holothurians. In systematic zoology the Gephyrea were sometimes regarded as a class and sometimes as an appendix of the Annelida. A glance through a few pages of the bibliography at the end of this monograph will show that the term was widely used by zoologists. At least one textbook of zoology published as recently as 1965 still refers to the Gephyrea. The term, however, has no standing in zoological nomenclature and Hyman (1959) bluntly states that 'the name and the concept of Gephyrea must be obliterated from zoology'. Sipunculans were first promoted to the rank of a phylum by Sedgwick (1898) and the phyletic status of the group is now generally accepted (Zoological Records, Vermes Section 1961 : 81; Hyman, 1958; Fisher, 1952; Stephen, 1964; Clark, 1969; Florkin & Scheer, 1969). The phylum is distinguished from the Annelida chiefly because sipunculans show no sign of segmentation either in their larval or adult stage.

During the last 70 years three different names have been given to the phylum. Sipunculoidea was used by Sedgwick (1898) and is still in use today (Biological Abstracts, 1968). Sipunculoidea, however, is not a very satisfactory name in view of Recommendation 29A of the International Code of Zoological Nomenclature (1961) that the suffix '-oidea' be used to denote only a superfamily. Hyman (1959) had previously realized that the name was unsatisfactory and used the term Sipunculida for the phylum. However, she kept 'sipunculoid' as a common name. In an attempt to comply with Recommendation 29A and at the same time follow the 'Pearse' system of nomenclature (Chitwood, 1958 : 888), Stephen (1965) proposed the name Sipuncula for the phylum. Whether or not the name is likely to be adopted is not yet clear. It has been used by Stephen (1965 and 1966), by Rice (1967), by Florkin & Scheer (1969) and is being used in the Zoological Records (Vermes Section) and in the present monograph.

Two common names, 'sipunculoid' and 'sipunculid', exist for an animal that belongs to the phylum. Neither seems to us to be entirely satisfactory, 'sipunculoid' because the term Sipunculoidea should refer to a superfamily and 'sipunculid', as Hyman (1959 : 611) points out, because it is the name of an animal that falls within the family Sipunculidae, a family already proposed by Baird (1868 : 77). If the phylum is to be called Sipuncula it seems reasonable and logical to use the term 'sipunculan'. If the new term is adopted, the confusion that exists over the use of the terms sipunculoid and sipunculid will be avoided. Throughout this monograph we use the term sipunculan. In parts of the U.S.A. sipunculans are known as pea-nut worms. Table I gives a summary of the terms used by some previous workers.

TABLE I

A summary of terms used for Sipuncula by some previous authors

Author	Name	Rank	Common name
Sedgwick, 1898	Sipunculoidea	phylum	—
Ikeda, 1905b	Sipunculoidea	—	—
Théel, 1905	Sipunculacea	suborder	sipunculid
Gerould, 1913	—	—	sipunculid
Sato, 1934b	Sipunculoidea	—	—
Sato, 1937b	—	—	sipunculid
Pickford, 1947	Sipunculida	phylum	sipunculid
Fisher, 1952	Sipunculoidea	phylum	sipunculoid
Hyman, 1959	Sipunculida	phylum	sipunculoid
Wesenberg-Lund, 1963	Sipunculoidea	—	sipunculid
Stephen, 1965	Sipuncula	phylum	—
Stephen & Edmonds	Sipuncula	phylum	sipunculan

(2). *Biology and distribution*

Sipunculans are found only in the sea. They are soft-bodied, almost defenceless creatures that live in protected places. Some like *Sipunculus nudus* Linn. and *S.*

robustus Keferstein live in temporary burrows which they make in the sand near
or below the level of low water in semi-protected bays along an ocean coast.   Others
like *Themiste cymodoceae* (Edmonds) and *T. zostericola* (Chamb.) live amongst the
tangled roots of marine angiosperms, the former in a more or less permanent cavity.
Species of *Phascolosoma, Aspidosiphon* and *Paraspidosiphon* are often found in
burrows in calcareous rocks.   Species of *Cloeosiphon* and *Lithacrosiphon* occur
only in coral rock and those of *Phascolion* inhabit the discarded shells of some
molluscs.   Some species are found amongst beds of mussels, in masses of serpulid
worm tubes and even in sponges.   One species of *Phascolosoma* lives in galleries
or burrows amongst mangroves where it is immersed only occasionally; other species
are often dredged from the mud that lies on the floor of the oceans.

The gut of sipunculans usually contains some of the following; sand, mud, small
particles of rock or coral, pieces of algae, fragments of molluscan shells and echino-
derm exoskeleton, frustules of diatoms and skeletal parts of foraminferans.   This
suggests that sipunculans are detritus feeders that extract from the material which
they swallow any food that it may contain.   The presence of the highly ciliated
tentacles that some species possess suggests that they may waft or direct small
particles from the water or the surface of the substratum into their mouths.   There
is, however, very little experimental information about their feeding habits.   One
species, *Golfingia procera* (Möbius), is said to be a temporary parasite that feeds
by introducing its introvert into the body cavity of the polychaet, *Aphrodite
aculeata* (Thorson, 1957).

The size of sipunculans varies considerably.   The trunk of mature specimens of
Onchnesoma steenstrupii Kor. & Dan. is reported to be only 3 mm long although
the introvert may extend up to 30 mm (Selenka & de Man, 1883 : 130).   Specimens
of *Sipunculus, Siphonosoma* and *Siphonomecus* grow to be the largest sipunculans.
The trunk of *Siphonosoma ingens* Fisher may reach a length of 500 mm and the
introvert 90 mm (Fisher, 1952 : 382), the trunk of *Siphonomecus multicinctus*
Fisher a length of 510 mm and the introvert 150 mm and one of us has a specimen
of *Sipunculus indicus* Sluiter from Guam the trunk of which (in the preserved state)
measures 550 mm and the introvert 30 mm.

Sipunculans live in tropical, temperate and polar seas and their bathymetric
range is wide.   They are collected along the sea-shore and are dredged from the
abyssal depths of the oceans.   A list of some golfingids that occur at considerable
depths is given on page 79.   Species of other genera, too, can be added e.g.

Species	Depth	Record
Phascolion lutense Selenka	3315–6850 m	Selenka (1885), Murina (1961, 1957a)
Phascolion pacificum Murina	5080–6860 m	Murina (1957c)
Sipunculus nitidus Sluiter	4400 m	Sluiter (1900)
Onchnesoma steenstrupii Kor. & Dan.	3318 m	Murina (1968)

The deep-sea sipunculans resemble very closely the species of the same genus
that live in the intertidal zone and lack the adaptations that are found in some of

the deep-sea bonellids (phylum Echiura) of the genera *Vitjazema, Prometor, Jakobia* and *Choanostomellia.*

There is no doubt that some species have a wide geographical distribution. Some like *Siphonosoma cumanense* (Keferstein) and especially those like *Phascolosoma nigrescens* Keferstein and *Cloeosiphon aspergillus* Grübe, that are associated with coral reefs, are circumtropical. *Sipunculus nudus* is known from the Mediterranean Sea, the Atlantic coasts of northern Europe and northern America and the Pacific coasts of the United States, China and Japan. *Golfingia anderssoni* (Théel) is circumpolar in the Antarctic. It is claimed by a number of authors experienced in the taxonomy of the phylum that some sipunculans, particularly *Golfingia margaritacea* (Sars), are bipolar (Fischer, 1920; Théel, 1911; Stephen, 1941b). A list of these species is given by Stephen, 1941b : 243. Whether or not there is a continuous distribution of the species between the polar regions is not known. However, the more recent study of specimens collected during deep-sea and widely ranging expeditions shows that some species are much more widely distributed than was formerly believed (Murina, 1957, 1958, 1961, 1964c, 1968). Some of the most widely distributed species in addition to those already mentioned are the following, the details of their distribution being given in this monograph at the end of their specific descriptions; *Sipunculus robustus* Keferstein, *Phascolion strombi* (Montagu), *Phascolosoma perlucens* Baird (=*P. dentigerum* Selenka & de Man), *Phascolosoma scolops* (Selenka & de Man) and *Golfingia eremita* (Sars).

(3). *Collection, relaxation, fixation and preservation*

It is difficult to pull or force a sipunculan out of the substratum in which it lives without damaging the animal. If it lives in sand or mud it is best to dig out the worm with a fork. Sipunculans that live in masses of tangled roots or that bore into rock or coral are usually much more difficult to collect especially if they are flask-like or rounded in shape. If the worm lives in tangled roots it is probably best to dig out a square or sod of the material and either break it up into smaller pieces or examine the undersurface of the sod for the worm. If it is still wedged tightly pull or break away the material that is holding it. Animals that live in rock are often difficult to dislodge. Sometimes a sharp blow with a hammer will break the rock or coral along the fissure, gallery or tube which the animal inhabits, so that it can be removed with the aid of forceps. If the rock does not break easily it is sometimes worthwhile to try soaking it in very weak solutions (about 0·5%) of formalin in sea-water. The sheltering animals will then sometimes partly or completely dislodge themselves in a period of 3–12 hours.

After it has been collected the animal should be placed in plenty of cool sea-water until it is to be narcotized. It is highly desirable to relax or narcotize a specimen before it is fixed in order to prevent it from becoming distorted and contracted when it is directly plunged into fixatives. Sipunculans can be narcotized (1) by placing them in a shallow dish containing cool sea-water on top of which some crystals of menthol have been sprinkled, (2) by placing them in a 7% solution of magnesium chloride (made up in tap or distilled water), (3) by placing them in sea-water to which alcohol is added very carefully (drop by drop, if the volume of

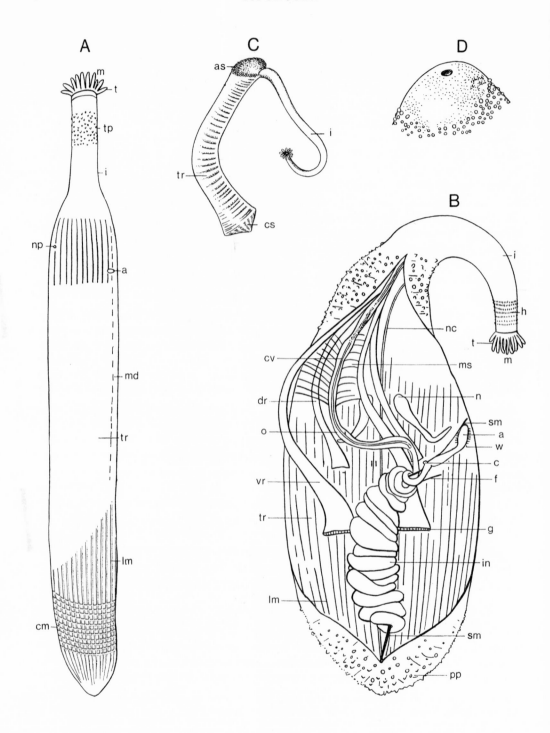

liquid is small) or (4) by immersing them in 1% solution of propylene phenoxetol. Often it is necessary to leave the animal in the relaxing agent for 2–12 hours, depending on its size. When the animal no longer responds to touch it can be transferred to a 5% solution of neutral formol in order to kill it and fix its tissues. After it has been fixed for 24 hours it should be placed in 70% alcohol for storage.

(4). *Dissection, external and internal characters*

Sipunculans usually must be dissected before they can be identified. The dissection is performed by first pinning out an animal under water in a dish that contains a layer of solidified wax. The animal is placed with its ventral side down on the wax so that the dorsally placed anus is on the upper surface. With the aid of a scalpel and forceps the body wall is cut longitudinally along a line a little to one side of the anus. The body wall should be held up before it is cut so that the incising does not damage the organs and fixing muscles in the body cavity. It is usually necessary to cut along almost the whole length of the trunk. The flaps are then pinned back clear of the internal organs. By cutting to one side of the anus, the rectum, wing muscles and spindle muscle are usually preserved. Sometimes the blood and reproductive cells of the animal are found to have coagulated in the body cavity during fixation thereby obscuring some of the finer structures. It is often possible to wash away some of the coagulated matter by directing on it a stream of water from a wash bottle. If the specimen is dissected in this way the characters that are important taxonomically are preserved.

One way of examining the shape and size of the hooks on the introvert is to snip out a small segment of the introvert, place it in a drop of glycerine on a slide and tease it up with two fine needles. When a cover slip is now placed on the preparation and pushed down it often happens that single hooks stand out clearly. In drawing and measuring hooks it is important to remember that they must lie flat and not be inclined at an angle. In order to examine the structure of papillae it is usually best to cut off a piece of skin where they are grouped and mount it under a coverslip in glycerine.

The morphology and anatomy of a 'generalized' sipunculan is shown in Fig. 1A–D. The external characters are shown in Fig. 1A, the internal characters in Fig. 1B,

FIG. 1. (A) The external characters of a sipunculan. The musculature of the body wall may form a continuous sheet or be thickened into longitudinal and circular bands. The dotted line in the diagram marks the mid-dorsal line of the specimen. (B) A specimen dissected from the dorsal side. Some rings of hooks are shown on the introvert and some papillae and glands are shown on the anterior and posterior surfaces of the trunk. (C) Diagram to show the positions of an anal shield and a caudal shield. (D) One kind of gland from the skin of a sipunculan. Glands may be hemispherical, globular, conical or almost flat. *a*, anus; *as*, anal shield; *c*, caecum; *cs*, caudal shield; *cm*, circular muscle; *cv*, contractile vessel; *dr*, dorsal retractor; *f*, fastening muscle; *g*, gonad; *h*, hooks; *i*, introvert; *in*, intestine; *lm*, longitudinal muscle; *m*, mouth; *md*, mid-dorsal line; *ms*, mesentery; *n*, nephridium; *nc*, nerve cord; *np*, nephridiopore; *o*, oesophagus; *pp*, papillae; *sm*, spindle muscle; *t*, tentacles; *tp*, triangular papillae; *tr*, trunk; *vr*, ventral retractor; *w*, wing muscle.

the position of the anal and caudal shields in the genera *Aspidosiphon* and *Para-spidosiphon* in Fig. 1C and a papilla from the surface of the body in Fig. 1D.

An explanation of the terms used in the figures and in the descriptions of the species is given in the next section.

(5). *Explanation of terms as used for sipunculans*

anal shield or anterior cap – A thickened and hardened area of the skin, circular to oval in shape, at the anterior region of the trunk just in front of the anus. In the genera *Aspidosiphon*, *Paraspidosiphon* and *Lithacrosiphon* the shield is placed on the dorsal side of the anterior region and usually consists of irregular or polygonal, horny or calcareous plates (Fig. 1C). The shield may be furrowed or grooved and is usually much darker in colour than the trunk (Fig. 26B). The introvert in the three genera arises ventral to the shield. In the genus *Cloeosiphon* the structure, which is always calcareous, is more like a cap and is placed terminally (Fig. 32B); the introvert then arises from the middle of the cap.

anus – The posterior extremity of the alimentary canal but situated in all sipunculans, except those of the genera *Onchnesoma* and *Nephasoma*, on the anterior, dorsal surface of the trunk. In *Onchnesoma* and *Nephasoma* it lies on the introvert.

brain – A bilobed structure that lies on the dorsal side of the intestine at the anterior extremity of the introvert. It is connected by two commissures to a median, ventral nerve cord. It is a prominent structure in many of the Sipunculidae (Fig. 2B).

buschelförmigen Körper – A term used by Selenka and others for the tufted organs that appear on each side of the rectum of species of *Sipunculus*. See under 'racemose glands'.

caecum – See under 'rectal caecum'.

caudal shield – A horny cap or shield at the posterior extremity of the trunk of species of *Aspidosiphon* and *Paraspidosiphon*. It is usually either flat and circular or sub-conical in shape and it is generally furrowed or grooved (Fig. 1C).

cerebral ganglion – See 'brain'.

cerebral organ – The anterior margin of the cerebral ganglion consisting largely of high columnar epithelium. According to Akesson (1958 : 74) its function is probably not sensory.

chloragen or *chloragogue cells* – Cells found on the peritoneal surfaces of sipunculans, particularly the surface of the intestine. They are made yellow-brown in colour by the substances which they ingest. Their function is not known with certainty.

ciliated groove – A long ciliated channel on the ventral surface of the intestine; it runs from the anterior region of the pharynx or oesophagus to the rectum, usually terminating at the rectal caecum if the latter is present. Usually readily observable to the naked eye as a reddish line in fresh specimens or a white line in preserved specimens. The cilia beat towards the anus.

ciliated sense organ – See 'nuchal organ'.

circular muscles – The outermost of the layers of muscle that constitute the body wall. In some genera, particularly *Sipunculus*, *Xenosiphon* and *Siphonomecus*, the circular musculature is grouped into well defined bands or fascicles. In some other genera there is a tendency for the circular muscles to form sheets.

coelomic canals and sacs – Dermal canals, spaces or diverticula connected with the body cavity (coelom) through small pores; the spaces contain coelomic fluid. The structures are present in the genera *Sipunculus*, *Xenosiphon*, *Siphonosoma* and *Siphonomecus* but not in *Phasco-lopsis*. The presence of the spaces can be demonstrated by injection with a dye or diluted Indian ink. Manwell (1960 : 277) has shown that the surface of *Siphonosoma ingens* is an important respiratory site. It is possible that the presence of fluid in the canals or sacs aids respiration at the surface of the animal. Dermal canals have recently been found in *Phascolosoma arcuatum* by Rice & Stephen, 1970.

coelomic papillae – Small, flat, leaf-like processes of unknown function which develop on the coelomic surface of the body wall, usually just anterior to the point of attachment of the nephridia (Fig. 7A).

compensatory sac – See 'contractile vessel'.

contractile vessel(s) – A single tube (dorsal) or a pair of tubes (lateral) attached to the surface
of the oesophagus. Anteriorly it communicates with the fine vessels in the tentacles and
posteriorly it ends blindly. Short villi or tubules may arise from the surface of the vessel;
in some species of *Themiste* the tubules or villi may be very long and slender. The
vessel, which is contractile, contains fluid which closely resembles that found in the body
cavity. Hyman (1959 : 635) states that the vessels act as compensatory sacs for the
tentacles 'receiving the fluid from the latter when they contract and sending it into the
tentacles when they expand'. She prefers the term 'compensatory sac' to the more usual
terms, contractile or polian vessel, and considers the view, that the system is circulatory,
is wrong. Hyman's term, however, is not completely satisfactory because Manwell
(1960 : 277) has shown that in species like *Themiste* (=*Dendrostomum*) *zostericola* the
fluid in the contractile vessel has some vascular function. We consider the terms polian
vessel, compensatory sac and contractile vessel to be the same.

contractile tubules – Branches which arise from the contractile vessel and extend into the body
cavity. They may be few or very numerous, short and simple or longer and branching.
In some species of *Themiste* they are very long.

dendritic – Branching or tree-like (Fig. 23A).

digitate processes – A group of fine, finger-like processes or a few leaf-like projections that arise
from the anterior dorsal surface of the brain and which are particularly noticeable in some
species of Sipunculidae. Akesson (1958 : 136) considers them to be neurosecretory and
not sensory structures (Fig. 2E, Fig. 3D).

dissepiments – A series of layers of peritoneal tissue situated transversally across the coelom
of some species of *Siphonosoma* e.g. *S. cumanense* (Keferstein) (Fig. 5B).

dorsal vessel – Contractile vessel.

eyespots or *eyes* – Pigment spots (pigmented cup-ocelli)—usually two in number—embedded
in the brain of many sipunculans. The pigment is present at the base of a tubular depression, the ocular tube.

fascicles – Small bundles.

fastening or fixing muscle – A thin strand or filament of muscle which joins or fastens some part
of the alimentary canal, either the oesophagus or the posterior region of the intestine, to
the body wall.

frons or frontal organ – As used by Gerould (1939 : 315) these terms are synonymous with the
term 'cerebral organ' of Ward (1891). At one time Fisher (1947 : 356 and pl. 10, fig. 2)
uses 'frons' as equivalent to 'digitate processes' and at another (Fisher, 1952 : 380) as
equivalent to 'cerebral organ'.

glandular organ – A prominent structure situated on the ventral, median part of the oral disc
of pelagosphaeric larvae (Akesson, 1961 : 12). The gland and its ducts may be about
1 mm long. Jägersten (1963 : 30) prefers to call it a 'lip gland' and reports that a ciliated
groove runs from the pore to the tip of the lip.

glans – The posterior extremity of the trunk of some species of *Sipunculus* may become acorn-
shaped. The structure so formed is referred to as the glans.

gonads – Reproductive cells which develop at the base of the retractor muscles, usually the
ventral pair. Fisher thinks that a strand of fine tissue attached to the body and stretching
from the rectum to the nerve cord may be a gonad in *Xenosiphon*.

Hautkörper – See 'skin bodies'.

introvert – The anterior, invaginable part of the animal. At its anterior extremity are the
mouth and usually numerous tentacles.

Keferstein bodies – Small, though rather prominent, oval bodies (diameter 0·1–0·5 mm) which
lie on the inner or coelomic surface of the body wall of some species of *Siphonosoma*,
Described by Keferstein (1867 : 53) as enclosing small hooks or spines insoluble in either
acetic acid or caustic soda solution (Fig. 5B).

longitudinal muscle – The innermost of the layers of muscle that make up the body wall of the
trunk. The longitudinal muscles of some genera form prominent bands or bundles

B

e.g. *Sipunculus, Siphonosoma, Xenosiphon, Siphonomecus, Phascolopsis, Phascolosoma, Paraspidosiphon* and *Lithacrosiphon*. In some genera, especially the last four, the bundles tend to anastomose, sometimes considerably.

nephridia – A pair of tubular sacs which serve as excretory sacs and gonoducts. Their external opening, the nephridiopore, lies on the ventral surface of the animal near the anus. Posteriorly or distally they end blindly in the body cavity. In some species they are attached to the body wall only at the nephridiopore but in others they are attached for all or part of their length by a thin mesentery. Their coelomic opening is a nephrostome. In *Phascolion* and *Onchnesoma* there is only one nephridium.

nephridiopore – The external opening of the nephridium. Usually placed near the anal aperture.

nephrostome – The internal or coelomic opening of the nephridium.

nerve cord – A single, median, unsegmented mass of nervous tissue that runs along the ventral surface of the body wall from the brain to the posterior extremity of the trunk.

nuchal organ – A lobed cushion of ciliated epidermal cells usually situated at the mid-dorsal edge of the oral disc (Fig. 17B). It is richly supplied with nerves which arise from the adjacent anterior surface of the brain. The function of the organ is believed to be sensory. In phascolosomatids the ring of tentacles almost encloses the nuchal organ (Fig. 34D).

ocular tube – See 'eyespots'.

oblique muscles – A thin layer of diagonally placed muscles lying between the circular and longitudinal muscles of some species.

oesophagus – The region of the gut lying between the pharynx and the descending loop of the intestine.

papillae – Elevations of the surface of the trunk or introvert which are usually associated with glandular cells. They are usually conical to hemispherical in shape and they may be comparatively tall or flat. In some species they are mamillate. Very often they are largest and most densely placed on the anterior and posterior regions of the trunk. In some genera, e.g. *Phascolosoma* the papillae are very prominent and usually dark in colour. The shape, structure and to some extent the size of the papillae on a particular region of the body are useful in identifying species.

paraneural muscle – A pair of longitudinal muscles which lie on each side of the anterior part of the nerve cord, especially of the genera *Sipunculus, Xenosiphon* and *Siphonosoma*.

pelagosphaera – A name given to a larval stage of some sipunculans that is often collected in samples of plankton. Rice (1967 : 164) has suggested that the meaning of the term should be broadened to include not only the planktotrophic pelagic larva but 'any sipunculan larva resulting from the metamorphosis of a trochophore that swims by means of a prominent, ciliated metatroch, and in which the prototroch either has been lost or has undergone a marked regression'.

pharynx – Anterior-most region of the alimentary canal.

polian vessel – See 'contractile vessel'.

polian tubules or villi – See 'contractile tubules'. The polian vesicles of holothurians are rounded or elongated sacs that arise from the ring canal and that are suspended in the body cavity. The term seems to have been borrowed to describe the club-like caeca, swellings or villi which arise from the contractile vessel of many sipunculans. Hyman (1959 : 638, 639) calls the sipunculan structures 'diverticula of the compensatory sac'.

post-oesophageal loop – An extra loop in the foregut of all species of the genus *Sipunculus* and some species of *Xenosiphon*.

protractor muscles – An extra pair of retractor muscles attached to the introvert near the brain and attached to the body wall of the anterior part of the trunk; found in adult specimens only in the genus *Xenosiphon* (Fig. 4C). Akesson (1958) points out that additional or protractor-like muscles are attached to the introvert of some larval sipunculans.

racemose glands – Glandular structures, usually a pair, which lie on each side of the rectum of some species of *Sipunculus*. They often lie on a muscle that attaches the rectum to the base of the dorsal retractors. Their function is unknown. The term is a synonym of Selenka's 'büschelförmigen Körper' (Fig. 2B).

rectal caecum – A small blind tube of uncertain function present on the posterior or rectal section of the gut of many species of sipunculans (Fig. 2B). It is usually situated at the posterior extremity of the ciliated groove. In *Sipunculus nudus* the caecum may become exceptionally long and then it contains a mucous substance. It is usually assumed that the presence or absence of a rectal caecum is a systematic character. Often the spindle muscle makes contact with the caecum. In some species, e.g. *Siphonosoma vastum* many caeca arise from the rectum. Their function is also unknown.

rectum – The posterior-most region of the alimentary canal. It is usually straight and may carry a caecum or more rarely numerous caeca.

retractor muscles – Longitudinally arranged bands of muscle tissue, the contraction of which invaginates the introvert. At one extremity they are fixed to the anterior end of the introvert near the brain and at the other extremity to the body wall. In many species there are two pairs of retractor muscles, one ventral and the other dorsal, the former arising nearer the nerve cord than the latter. In some species the retractors arise from the body wall at the same level and in others one pair arises more anteriorly than the other. In some species the dorsal pair is lacking and only the ventral pair is present. In the genera *Onchnesoma*, *Nephasoma* and *Cloeosiphon* and in some species of *Phascolion* there is only one retractor. In some species of *Aspidosiphon* and *Paraspidosiphon* what appears to be a single retractor arises from two short roots.

segmental organs – An older term for the nephridia; it is no longer used for sipunculans.

sipunculus loop – See 'post-oesophageal loop'.

skin bodies – This appears to be a general term for groups of glandular cells that are often present on the surface of the trunk. The term is Keferstein's 'Hautkörper'.

spindle muscle – A long thread-like muscle that arises anteriorly in the musculature of the body wall or in the wall of the rectum. It supports the coils of the intestine. It may or may not be fixed posteriorly to the body wall. Some species are said to lack a spindle muscle. In the genus *Siphonosoma* the spindle muscle has anteriorly two additional lateral roots.

tentacles – Extensions of the body wall which arise at the anterior extremity of the introvert and which are associated with the mouth. They may be fingerlike, threadlike or dendritic in shape and form and in *Sipunculus* they are replaced by a tentacular fold. They are reduced to a few lobes in some species and in a few others they are lacking. One surface of the tentacles usually bears a ciliated groove along which food is moved to the mouth. The cavities of the tentacles are extensions of the contractile vessel and it seems certain that in some species, e.g. *Themiste* (=*Dendrostomum*) *zostericola* they have a respiratory function as well (Manwell, 1960 : 277).

terminal organ – A small sac-like invagination at the terminal extremity of the trunk of species of *Sipunculus* and *Xenosiphon*. The structure is able to evaginate. The organ and the surrounding tissue is innervated by nerves from the terminal ganglion of the nerve cord. Akesson (1958 : 163) considers that the structure is primarily a secreting organ. A terminal organ is present in some larval sipunculans also (Rice, 1967).

trunk – The part of the animal that is wider and into which the introvert invaginates.

villi – See 'contractile tubules'.

(5). *General references*

Of the several general accounts that have been written about the phylum those of Baltzer, 1931 (in German), Pickford, 1947, Hyman, 1959 and Tetry, 1959 (in French) are the most informative. That of Hyman is particularly comprehensive and discusses the anatomy, histology, physiology, embryology, ecology and taxonomy of the phylum. A considerable amount of information about the natural history of sipunculans is contained in Macginitie & Macginitie, 1968. A recent study of the phylogeny of the phylum is that of Clark (1969).

2. CLASSIFICATION

(1). *Systems of classification*

a. Genera of sipunculans

The information in Table 2 shows the genera of sipunculans that have been created during the last 90 years. Selenka, de Man & Bülow (1883) recognized 10 genera and Fisher (1952) 13, two of the older genera having disappeared and five new ones having been proposed. The new genera were *Lithacrosiphon* Shipley, 1902, *Siphonosoma* Spengel, 1912, *Siphonomecus* Fisher, 1947, *Xenosiphon* Fisher, 1947 and *Siphonides* Fisher, 1952. Stephen, 1965, erected three new genera, *Fisherana*, *Phascolopsis* and *Paraspidosiphon*, by splitting off from the parent genera three groups in which the longitudinal musculature of the body wall was different from that of the parent.

TABLE 2

Systems of Classification of Sipuncula

Selenka & de Man, 1883	Fisher, 1952	Stephen, 1965	Stephen & Edmonds
Sipunculus Linn.	*Sipunculus* *Xenosiphon* Fisher *Siphonosoma* Spengel *Siphonomecus* Fisher	*Sipunculus* *Xenosiphon* *Siphonosoma* *Siphonomecus*	*Sipunculus* *Xenosiphon* *Siphonosoma* *Siphonomecus*
Petalostoma Kef. *Phascolosoma* authors	*Golfingia* Lank.	*Phascolopsis* *Golfingia*	*Phascolopsis* *Golfingia*
Onchnesoma Kor. & Dan.	*Onchnesoma*	*Onchnesoma*	*Onchnesoma* *Nephasoma* Perg.
Tylosoma Kor. & Dan. *Phascolion* Théel	*Phascolion*	*Phascolion*	*Phascolion*
Dendrostoma Kef.	*Dendrostomum*	*Themiste* Gray	*Themiste*
Phymosoma Quatr.	*Phascolosoma* Leuck. *Siphonides* Fisher	*Fisherana* Stephen *Phascolosoma* *Siphonides* Fisher	*Fisherana* *Phascolosoma*
Aspidosiphon Diesing	*Aspidosiphon*	*Aspidosiphon* *Paraspidosiphon* Steph.	*Aspidosiphon* *Paraspidosiphon*
	Lithacrosiphon Ship.	*Lithacrosiphon*	*Lithacrosiphon*
Cloeosiphon Grübe	*Cloeosiphon*	*Cloeosiphon*	*Cloeosiphon* *Centrosiphon* Ship.

In this monograph we have recognized 17 genera, (1) 12 of the 13* which were included in Fisher (1952), (2) the three new genera of Stephen (1965), (3) *Nephasoma* Pergament, 1940 erected for a species closely resembling but standing apart from *Onchnesoma* Kor. & Dan. and *Golfingia* Lankester and (4) *Centrosiphon* Shipley (1903). The distinction between the 17 genera is based on the following characters; (1) the presence or absence of integumentary canals or sacs, (2) the condition of the longitudinal musculature of the body wall, (3) the presence of a cap or shield at the anterior extremity of the trunk, (4) the presence of a shield at the posterior extremity of the trunk, (5) the arrangement of the tentacles relative to the mouth, (6) the number of retractor muscles of the introvert, (7) the number of nephridia, (8) the presence of a pair of protractor muscles attached to the introvert and (9) the presence of a postoesophageal loop in the intestine. The 17 genera, their authors, the differences between the genera and the number of species that each contains is shown in Table 3.

Gf the genera erected since Fisher (1952) *Phascolopsis* contains one species, *Fisherana* four and *Paraspidosiphon* 23. The generic position of *Phascolopsis gouldii* (Pourtalès) has always been uncertain, the species having been assigned a plaee at different times in *Sipunculus* and *Golfingia*. We consider that it stands apart from both and is best regarded as belonging to a different genus. The separation of *Paraspidosiphon* from *Aspidosiphon*, *Phascolopsis* from *Golfingia* and *Fisherana* from *Phascolosoma*, each on account of the condition of the longitudinal musculature, we think is both logical and consistent. *Nephasoma* Pergament, 1940, specimens of which we have not examined, differs from *Onchnesoma* in possessing two nephridia and from *Golfingia* in possessing only one retractor muscle and an anus which is placed on the introvert.

Two of the genera, *Golfingia* with 96 species and *Phascolosoma* with 60, are very large. The systematics of *Golfingia*, however, has been considerably simplified by the subdivision of the genus into seven subgenera by Fisher (1950a), Wesenberg-Lund (1959), Stephen (1965) and Murina (1967a). The subgenera are described on p. 80. We have divided the genus *Phascolosoma* into four subgenera, using as a basis for subdivision, similar criteria to those used for subdividing *Golfingia*. The subgenera are described on p. 271. Even then the subgenus *Phascolosoma* (*sensu stricto*) contains 30 species which we have not been able to subdivide further. Two other genera have also been divided into subgenera, *Siphonosoma* into three by Fisher (1950b) and *Xenosiphon* into two by Fisher (1954). These subgenera are described in this monograph on p. 44 and p. 39 respectively.

(2). *The recognition of families*

We have attempted to arrange the genera into families, something which previous authors, except Baird (1868), have seemed reluctant to do. Baird divided the subclass Gephyrea into two orders, Gephyrea inermia (which included the sipunculans) and the Gephyrea armata (or echiurans). The first order he split into four families (a) Sipunculidae, to contain *Sipunculus*, *Phascolosoma*, *Themiste* and *Petalosoma*

---

* *Siphonides* Fisher, 1952 for reasons set out on p. 287 we consider to be synonymous with *Phascolosoma* Leuckart.

TABLE 3
Genera of the phylum Sipuncula

Genus and Author	Integumental canals or sacs	Longitudinal musculature	Anterior cap or shield	Posterior cap or shield	Tentacles	Retractor muscles	Protractor muscles	Post oesophageal loop	Nephridia	Species
Sipunculus Linnaeus, 1766	present	bundles	—	—	encircle mouth	4	—	present	2	18
Xenosiphon Fisher, 1947	present	bundles	—	—	encircle mouth	4	2	present or absent	2	3
Siphonosoma Spengel, 1912	present	bundles	—	—	encircle mouth	4	—	—	2	20
Siphonomecus Fisher, 1947	present	bundles	—	—	encircle mouth	2	—	—	2	1
Phascolopsis Fisher, 1950	—	bundles	—	—	encircle mouth	4	—	—	2	1
Golfingia Lankester, 1885	—	continuous	—	—	encircle mouth	2–4	—	—	2	96
Onchnesoma Kor. & Dan., 1875	—	continuous	—	—	few or absent	1	—	—	1	2
Nephasoma Pergament, 1940	—	continuous	—	—	absent	1	—	—	2	1
Phascolion Théel, 1875	—	continuous	—	—	encircle mouth	1–2	—	—	1	32
Themiste Gray, 1828	—	continuous	—	—	encircle mouth; often dendritic	2–4	—	—	2	25
Phascolosoma Leuckart, 1828	—	bundles	—	—	form a ring dorsal to mouth	2–4	—	—	2	60
Fisherana Stephen, 1965	—	continuous	—	—	form a ring dorsal to mouth	4	—	—	2	4
Aspidosiphon Diesing, 1851	—	continuous	present	present	wholly or partly encircle mouth	1–4	—	—	2	24
Paraspidosiphon Stephen, 1965	—	bundles	present	present	wholly or partly encircle mouth	1–4	—	—	2	24
Lithacrosiphon Shipley, 1902	—	bundles	present	—	encircle mouth	2	—	—	2	8
Cloeosiphon Grübe, 1868	—	continuous	present	—	encircle mouth	1	—	—	2	1
*Centrosiphon** Shipley, 1903	—	continuous	present	present	encircle mouth	4	—	—	2	1

*The introvert of *Centrosiphon* arises from the centre of the anterior shield but the introvert of *Aspidosiphon* arises ventrally to the anterior shield.

(=*Golfingia*), (b) Aspidosiphonidae, to contain *Aspidosiphon* and *Pseudaspido-siphon*, (c) Loxosiphonidae, to contain *Loxosiphon* (=*Cloeosiphon*) and *Diesingia*, (d) Priapulidae, now a separate phylum.

During the succeeding 100 years the only attempt to group the genera into higher categories was made by Pickford (1947) who suggested that they fell into four groups. She, however, assigned no name to her groups. She suggested;

> Group A, genera with horny or calcareous plates, *Aspidosiphon* and *Lithacro-siphon*
>
> Group B, genera with only preanal plates, *Cloeosiphon*
>
> Group C, genera without plates but with longitudinal muscles thickened into bundles, *Sipunculus*, *Xenosiphon*, *Siphonosoma*, *Phascolosoma*
>
> Group D, genera without plates but with longitudinal muscles continuous *Themiste*, *Golfingia* and *Onchnesoma*.

The chief criticism of Pickford's grouping is that it attaches too much importance to the presence of anal and caudal plates and that it ignores the arrangement of the tentacles of the genera.   Pickford (1947 : 722) remarks that 'Since the Sipunculida are so frequently treated as a family of the Gephyrea, there has been no attempt to group the genera into families and in view of the close interrelationships it is possible that any such attempt would be doomed to failure'.

Akesson (1958 : 230) considers that before the genera are grouped into families 'some new distinguishing characters in addition to those which have been used by previous writers should be employed'. He suggests that the structure of the epidermal organs and the central nervous system might give valuable information about the grouping of the genera. His careful study of 14 specimens led him to believe that they could be placed in three groups;

a. *Golfingia*-group including *Golfingia* (*G. vulgaris*, *G. elongata*, *G. margaritacea*, *G. minuta* and *G. procera*) and *Phascolion* (*P. strombi*).

b. *Phascolosoma*-group including *Phascolosoma* (*P. granulatum*), *Aspidosiphon* (*A. muelleri*), *Siphonosoma* (*S. cumanense*) and *Onchnesoma* (*O. steenstrupii*).

c. *Sipunculus*-group including *Sipunculus* (*S. nudus*, *S. robustus* and *S. nor-vegicus*).

In spite of Pickford's warning we have divided the phylum into four families, Sipunculidae Baird (in part), Golfingiidae n. fam., Phascolosomatidae n. fam. and Aspidosiphonidae Baird (in part), using as a basis the following criteria; (1) the presence of integumentary or coelomic sacs, (2) the condition of the longitudinal musculature of the body wall, (3) the arrangement of the tentacles relative to the mouth and (4) the presence of a cap or shield at the anterior extremity of the trunk. The families are described on pages 19, 77, 216 and 269 and the differences between them are shown in Table 4.

In presenting the families of the Sipuncula in the sequence Sipunculidae, Golfingiidae, Aspidosiphonidae and Phascolosomatidae we have been influenced by two considerations. The first, and one that seems to be accepted generally, is that the archetype of the phylum was probably a *Golfingia*-like animal (Selenka, 1883 : 6; Fisher, unpublished communication but quoted by Cole, 1952). Gerould (1913 : 378) considered *Golfingia* to be the 'central genus' and Akesson (1958 : 226)

Tentacles that surround or partly surround the mouth

 Tentacles form a tentacular fold or lie in one or more rings around the mouth; *Sipunculus*, *Siphonosoma*, *Golfingia*, *Phascolion*.

 Tentacles in groups of 4–5 or more; *Golfingia*.

 Tentacles in 4–6 branching groups; *Themiste*.

 Ring of tentacles broken in the mid-dorsal line; *Golfingia*.

 Tentacles in two groups; *Onchnesoma*.

 Ring of tentacles broken in the mid-ventral line; *Aspidosiphon*, *Paraspidosiphon*.

 Ring of tentacles reduced to half or quarter circle. Mouth ventral: *Aspidosiphon*.

Tentacles that lie in a ring dorsal to the mouth

 Ring of tentacles lies dorsal to the mouth and encloses the nuchal organ, if present; *Phascolosoma* and *Fisherana*.

TABLE 4

Families of the phylum Sipuncula

Family	Integumentary canals or sacs in the body wall	Longitudinal musculature of the body wall	Arrangement of the tentacles	Anterior cap or shield	Genera
Sipunculidae	present (except in *Phascolopsis*)	grouped into bundles	numerous tentacles or a tentacular fold surround the mouth	absent	*Sipunculus* *Xenosiphon* *Siphonosoma* *Siphonomecus* *Phascolopsis*
Golfingiidae	absent	continuous	basically tentacles surround the mouth, but may be in groups, be dendritic or reduced to a few lobes or in two genera may be absent	absent	*Golfingia* *Onchnesoma* *Nephasoma* *Phascolion* *Themiste*
Aspidosiphonidae	absent	either continuous or in bundles	surround or partly surround the mouth but never in a ring dorsal to the mouth	present	*Aspidosiphon* *Paraspidosiphon* *Lithacrosiphon* *Cloeosiphon* *Centrosiphon*
Phascolosomatidae	absent (except in one species)	either continuous or in bundles	always in a horseshoe-shaped ring that is dorsal to the mouth: tentacles always enclose the nuchal organ, if present	absent	*Phascolosoma* *Fisherana*

agreed that it was the 'most primitive genus'. The second consideration, one that probably stems from Baltzer (1931 : 58) and one which is supported by Fisher (as quoted by Cole, 1952), is that the genus *Phascolosoma*, on account of the arrangement of its tentacles, is most removed from the archetype. Using this information we have assigned the families Golfingiidae a central and Phascolosomatidae an extreme position in the order of the families. In placing the family Sipunculidae first and Aspidosiphonidae between Golfingiidae and Phascolosomatidae we have followed the lead of Fisher (1952). When more complete embryological studies have been carried out on the different genera, especially *Aspidosiphon*, it may be found that our rather tentative sequence should be changed.

We have included a number of figures which show the arrangement of the tentacles relative to the mouth and nuchal organ of some genera. The relation is an important family character (see page 16). (X = nuchal organ; O = mouth.)

(2). *Characters of the phylum and key to the families*

Phylum SIPUNCULA

Sipunculoidea Sedgwick, 1898 : 534; Fisher, 1952 : 371.
Sipunculida Pickford, 1947 : 717; Hyman, 1959 : 611.
Sipuncula Stephen, 1965 : 457.

The phylum Sipuncula consists of a group of unsegmented, coelomate, bilaterally symmetrical and wormlike invertebrates that are found only in the sea. The body of a sipunculan consists of two parts, a muscular trunk that is usually cylindrical, globular, sac-like or flask-like in shape and an anteriorly placed, highly extensible and comparatively slender introvert which may be completely retracted within the trunk. The mouth is situated at the anterior extremity of the introvert and is usually wholly or partly surrounded by a group of tentacles or by a tentacular fold. The tentacular system in some species is complex but in a few others it may be either reduced to form a few lobes or absent. A long alimentary canal lies within a large coelom and is usually wound into a spiral for a considerable part of its length. The anal aperture is situated anteriorly on the mid-dorsal surface of the trunk, more rarely on the introvert. Setae are absent. Hooks or spines, occasionally both, may be present on the anterior surface of the introvert. Small glandular openings and papillae, often very prominent, are usually present on the trunk or introvert, sometimes on both. A pair of nephridia lies in the body cavity and opens to the exterior anteriorly on each side of the nerve cord usually near the anus. In a few genera only one nephridium is present. A contractile (Polian or compensatory) vessel runs along the surface of the oesophagus of many species and branches anteriorly in the tentacles. The vessel may be single and dorsal or double when the vessels are lateral. From the vessel of some species tubules (villi) arise which may be small to very long in length and branched or unbranched in structure. The contractile vessel in some species is simple (without tubules) and in others is absent. The fluid in the coelom and contractile vessel is made light-red in colour by the presence of the respiratory pigment, haemerythrin, which is contained in blood

cells. An unsegmented, ventral nerve cord is connected anteriorly by two circumoesophageal commissures to a cerebral ganglion which lies dorsally near the
anterior extremity of the introvert. Sensory structures including tactile organs,
eyespots, a cerebral organ, a cephalic tube and a nuchal organ are present in many
species. The sexes are separate, except in one species which is a protandrous
hermaphrodite, and indistinguishable externally. The gonads develop usually
at the base of the ventral retractor muscles of the introvert. Fertilization is external, cleavage of the zygote is spiral and the larva is a trochophore. The developing
larva is unsegmented. Two species, at least, are able to reproduce asexually (Rajula
& Krishnan, 1969; Rice, 1970).

KEY TO FAMILIES

1 Horny or calcareous shield, cone or cap present at the anterior extremity of the
   trunk; tentacles surround or partly surround the mouth but never in a horseshoe-
   shaped ring situated dorsal to the mouth; longitudinal musculature of body wall
   may be in bands or be continuous . . . **ASPIDOSIPHONIDAE** (p. 215)
– No horny or calcareous shield, cone or cap present at the anterior extremity of the
   trunk 2
2 Tentacles basically surround or partly surround the mouth and may be simple or
   branched (dendritic), in groups, reduced to a few lobes or even absent but never
   in a horseshoe-shaped ring situated dorsal to the mouth; nuchal organ, if present,
   lies dorsal to the tentacles and is not enclosed by them 3
– Tentacles arranged in a horseshoe-shaped ring which does not surround the mouth
   but lies dorsal to it and which encloses the nuchal organ, if present; longitudinal
   musculature of body wall grouped into bands except in one genus of four species;
   skin bears conical to hemispherical papilliform glands which may be very prominent
   at the anterior and posterior extremities of the trunk
                                        PHASCOLOSOMATIDAE (p. 269)
3 Longitudinal musculature of body wall thickened to form well defined bands;
   integumentary canals or coelomic sacs present in the body wall except that of one
   species . . . . **SIPUNCULIDAE** (p. 19)
– Longitudinal musculature of body wall is continuous and never thickened into
   bands . . . . **GOLFINGIIDAE** (p. 77)

(3). Family **SIPUNCULIDAE**

Sipunculidae Baird, 1868 : 77 (in part); Sedgwick, 1898 : 539 (in part).

DESCRIPTION. Species usually large: body wall of trunk contains either longitudinally arranged integumentary canals or independent coelomic sacs or diverticula
(except in *Phascolopsis* where canals and coelomic extensions are lacking). Numerous tentacles or a tentacular fold always surrounds the mouth; tentacles may form
clusters or be arranged in meridional rows (but never in a horseshoe-shaped ring
dorsal to the mouth). Longitudinal muscles always separated into prominent
bands. Anterior region of trunk not modified to form a cap or shield. Retractor
muscles four (in *Siphonomecus* there are two); nephridia two.

TYPE GENUS. *Sipunculus* Linnaeus, 1766.

REMARKS. Baird's Sipunculidae contained the following genera; *Sipunculus* Linn., *Phascolosoma* Leuck. and others, *Petalostoma* Kef., *Themiste* Gray and three genera which are no longer considered valid. The family is now considered to contain the following genera; *Sipunculus* Linn., 1766, *Xenosiphon* Fisher, 1947, *Siphonosoma* Spengel, 1912, *Siphonomecus* Fisher, 1947 and *Phascolopsis* Fisher, 1950.

Sipunculids are usually large and either stout or elongate worms that generally live in sand. The presence of coelomic canals or diverticula and prominent bands of longitudinal muscle are important characters of the family. Manwell (1960) has shown that the body surface is a more important respiratory site in *Siphonosoma ingens* than in *Themiste* (=*Dendrostomum*) *zostericola*. It is possible that the presence of body fluid in the coelomic canal plays an important part in the respiratory exchanges of the family.

The position of *Phascolopsis* in the family is not as secure as that of the other four genera. We have not found any coelomic extensions in the body wall of transverse sections that we have made from two specimens. The condition of its longitudinal muscles and the general appearance of the worm has led us to place the genus with the Sipunculidae rather than the Golfingiidae. Gerould (1906) considered that the development of *Phascolopsis* resembled that of *Golfingia* more closely than that of *Sipunculus*. Fisher (1952) regarded *Phascolopsis* as a subgenus of *Golfingia*.

FAMILY SIPUNCULIDAE—KEY TO GENERA

1   Introvert with subtriangular, scale-like papillae but without hooks; skin of trunk
     strongly marked into rectangles by longitudinal and transverse furrows   .   .   2
 — Introvert without subtriangular, scale-like papillae; hooks or spinelets may be
     present or absent; skin of trunk not strongly marked off into rectangles (except in
     Siphonomecus)   3
2   Four retractor muscles and an additional pair of protractor muscles, the latter arising
     from the body wall near the anus and connecting with the introvert near the brain;
     spindle muscle arises anteriorly from the wall of the rectum; gonad in the form of
     a loop attached to the body wall and rectum   .   **XENOSIPHON** Fisher (p. 38)
 — Four retractor muscles but no additional pairs of protractor muscles; spindle
     muscle arises from body wall anterior to anus; gonads at the base of the ventral
     retractors   .   .   .   .   **SIPUNCULUS** Linn. (p. 21)
3   Four retractor muscles; skin of trunk not divided into rectangles by furrows   .   .   4
 — Two retractor muscles; skin of trunk strongly marked into rectangles by furrows;
     spines present on the introvert; anteriorly two roots of spindle muscle arise from
     body wall posterior to the anus and a third is attached to the oesophagus
                                              SIPHONOMECUS Fisher (p. 73)
4   Spindle muscle not fixed to body wall posteriorly; no coelomic extensions in the body
     wall; no hooks or spines on the introvert   .   **PHASCOLOPSIS** Fisher (p. 74)
 — Spindle muscle fixed posteriorly; coelomic extensions present in the body wall;
     hooks or spines may be present or absent on the introvert
                                              SIPHONOSOMA Spengel (p. 43)

Genus *SIPUNCULUS* Linnaeus, 1766

Syrinx Bohadsch, 1761 : 93–97.
Sipunculus Linnaeus, 1766 : 1078; Quatrefages, 1865b : 613; Keferstein, 1865a : 418–419;
   Selenka & de Man, 1883 : 88; Gerould, 1913 : 427; Sato, 1930 : 2; 1939 : 365; Fisher, 1952 :
   375.

DESCRIPTION. Species usually large. Introvert usually short, sharply marked
off from the trunk and covered with flat, triangular papillae. Trunk long and
cylindrical and its posterior region may be swollen slightly, rounded or bluntly
pointed. Longitudinal and circular musculature thickened into well formed, regular
bands or fascicles, the furrows between the muscle bands usually dividing the skin
into a large number of rectangular or square areas. Mouth surrounded by a flat,
tentacular fold, the margins of which are drawn out to form more or less distinct
tentacles. Introvert without hooks. Longitudinal coelomic or integumentary
canals lie between the muscle bands and communicate with the coleom. Retractor
muscles four, usually arising at the same level. Spindle muscle usually present but
reported to be absent in some species. Contractile vessel double. Post-oesophageal
or 'sipunculus' loop present in the alimentary canal between the oesophagus and
the first spiral of the intestine. Oesophagus and alimentary canal held in position
by numerous mesenteries and fixing muscles. Paraneural muscle usually well
developed and brain conspicuous. A median dorsal, unpaired epithelial tube opens
on the surface of the introvert immediately behind the tentacular fold and leads
backwards to the cerebral sense organ anterior and ventral to the brain.

TYPE SPECIES. *Sipunculus nudus* Linn., 1766.

REMARKS. The genus is readily identified by the presence of (1) numerous,
posteriorly directed scale-like papillae on its comparatively short introvert, (2) well
developed longitudinal and transverse muscle bands in the wall of the trunk and
(3) a post-oesophageal or 'sipunculus' loop in the intestine. *Sipunculus nudus*
Linn., the best known species of the genus, is found along the Atlantic coast of
France, in the Mediterranean Sea and on the shores of southern California and is
considered by some authors to be cosmopolitan.

We have re-examined the type specimen of *S. robustus* Keferstein and found
that it possesses both a rectal caecum and racemose glands. These findings help
to clear up some uncertainties about *S. robustus* and bring *S. angasii* Baird into the
synonymy of *S. robustus*. Also they narrow the gap between *S. nudus* and *S.
robustus* and make them very close species. The main difference between the two
now is that in *S. robustus* the digitate processes on the brain are much larger and
more prominent and the longitudinal muscles are fewer in number.

S. norvegicus Danielssen and *S. titubans* Selenka & Bülow are also closely allied
to *S. robustus* and *S. nudus* but appear to possess fewer longitudinal muscles. *S.
delphinus* Murina we consider is synonymous with *S. titubans*. We have placed
S. tesselatus Rafinesque in the synonymy of *S. nudus* and *S. discrepans* Sluiter in
that of *S. indicus* Peters. *S. indicus* is one of the most clearly defined species in
the genus. *S. porrectus* Selenka is unusual in that it possesses 120 tentacles and
strands of muscle that freely traverse the body cavity. As far as we know only two

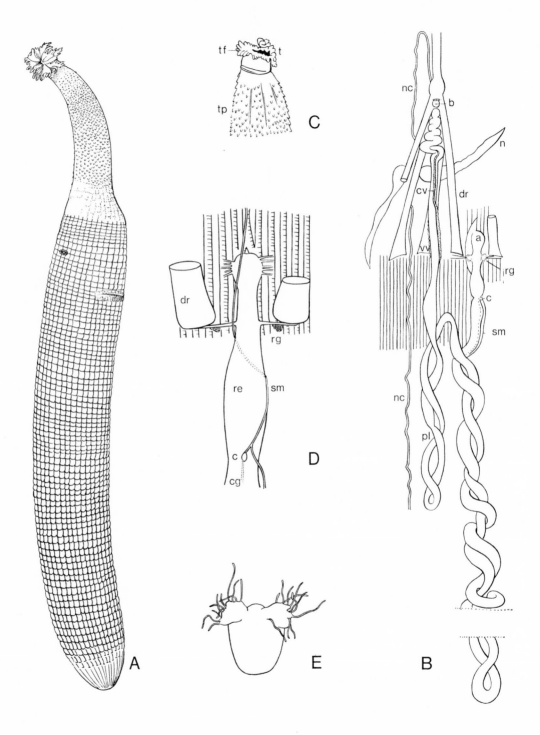

specimens have ever been reported. S. *phalloides* Pallas is a better known species and has been described from the West Indies and the Atlantic coast of South America by a number of authors. S. *galapagensis* Fisher is very close to and not easily distinguishable from S. *multisulcatus* Fischer. S. *natans* Fisher and S. *polymyotus* Fisher are clearly defined.

We have re-examined Sluiter's holotypes of S. *claviger*, S. *pellucidus*, S. *inclusus* and S. *infrons* and consider that S. *claviger* is synonymous with *Siphonosoma cumanense* (Keferstein) and that S. *pellucidus* is a species of *Siphonosoma* near S. *amamiense* (Ikeda). S. *inclusus* is closely related to S. *robustus* but possesses a greater number of longitudinal muscles in the posterior part of its trunk. The type specimen of S. *infrons*, while undoubtedly that of a *Sipunculus*, is very thin and fragile and its internal structures are missing. We have been unable to locate the holotype of S. *nitidus* Sluiter, a species which needs to be re-examined and redescribed. S. *gravieri* Hérubel we consider to be a *Xenosiphon*, most likely *X. branchiatus* Fischer.

TABLE 5

Species of *Sipunculus* arranged according to their number of longitudinal muscles

Number of muscle bands	Species
21	*Sipunculus aequabilis* Sluiter
21	*Sipunculus infrons* Sluiter
22–24	*Sipunculus norvegicus* Danielssen
22–28	*Sipunculus nitidus* Sluiter
25–30	*Sipunculus titubans* Selenka & Bülow
26–30	*Sipunculus robustus* Keferstein
29–33	*Sipunculus nudus* Linnaeus
32	*Sipunculus porrectus* Selenka
31–37	*Sipunculus inclusus* Sluiter
37–38	*Sipunculus phalloides* Pallas
39–43	*Sipunculus indicus* Peters
41–42	*Sipunculus galapagensis* Fisher
41–42	*Sipunculus multisulcatus* Fischer
49–52	*Sipunculus natans* Fisher
53–61	*Sipunculus polymyotus* Fisher

FIG. 2 (A–C). *Sipunculus nudus*. (A) Entire animal, natural size. (B) Dissection of the anterior region of the trunk. (c) Anterior region of introvert (after Ward). (D–E). *Sipunculus robustus*. (D) Rectal structures of the type specimen. (E) Brain and digitate processes. *a*, anus; *ac*, anal caeca; *ag*, aboral gland; *b*, brain; *c*, caecum; *cc*, circular canal; *cg*, cilitate groove; *cm*, circular muscle; *cp*, coelomic papillae; *cv*, contractile vessel; *dr*, dorsal retractor; *dp*, digitate process; *ds*, dissepiments; *e*, eye-spot; *f*, *f*$_1$, etc., fastening muscles; *g*, gonad; *k*, Keferstein body; *l*, wing-like, lateral branch of spindle muscle; *lc*, lateral canals; *n*, nephridium; *nc*, nerve cord; *no*, nuchal organ; *ns*, nephrostome; *o*, oesophagus; *pl*, post-oesophageal loop; *pm*, protractor muscle; *re*, rectum; *rg*, racemose gland; *rm*, retractor muscle; *sm*, spindle muscle; *so*, sensory organ; *t*, tentacles; *tf*, tentacular fold; *tp*, triangular papillae; *tr*, trunk; *vr*, ventral retractor; *w*, wing muscle.

According to our revision the genus contains 15 species, seven species formerly
assigned to the genus having been either referred to other species within the genus
or transferred to another genus.   The seven are *S. delphinus* Murina which becomes
S. titubans Selenka, *S. tesselatus* Rafinesque which becomes *S. nudus* Linn., *S.
discrepans* Sluiter which becomes *S. indicus* Peters, *S. angasii* Baird which becomes
S. robustus Keferstein, *S. claviger* Sluiter which becomes *Siphonosoma cumanense*
Keferstein, *S. gravieri* Hérubel which becomes *Xenosiphon branchiatus* Fischer
and *S. pellucidus* Sluiter which becomes *Siphonosoma pellucidum.*

We have given a key to the genus although it has been difficult to find reliable
distinguishing characters for some species.

GENUS SIPUNCULUS—KEY TO SPECIES

1 Anal aperture posterior to the nephridiopores   2
– Anal aperture well in front of the nephridiopores (large species, longitudinal muscles
        39–43, spindle muscle free posteriorly, nephridia long and thin and fastened to
        body wall for their whole length) .   .   .   .   .   .   **S. indicus** (p. 27)
2 Longitudinal muscles grouped into 20–21 bands   3
– Longitudinal muscles grouped into more than 21 bands   4
3 Skin smooth and transparent so that viscera are visible (on skin are minute papillae
        which are largest at the posterior end of the body, ventral retractors from bands
        3–4 and dorsals from 8–9, two intestinal fasteners at the beginning of the intestinal
        coil)   .   .   .   .   **S. infrons** (p. 28)
– Skin not transparent but translucent (no anastomosation of longitudinal muscles,
        ventral retractors arise from three bands and dorsals from bands 8–9, rectal
        caecum present; specimens dredged at 330–959 m) .   .   .   **S. aequabilis** (p. 25)
4 Longitudinal muscles in 22–40 bands   5
– Longitudinal muscles in more than 40 bands   12
5 Circular musculature poorly developed (longitudinal muscles 22–28, body wall
        transparent, introvert with eight lappets, contractile vessel single, ventral
        retractors from three bands and dorsal from band 11)   .   .   **S. nitidus** (p. 32)
– Circular musculature in well developed bands   6
6 Nephridia completely free and not attached to the body wall   7
– Nephridia attached to the body wall for about half their length (longitudinal
        muscles 26–30, ventral retractors from bands 3–5 and dorsals from 8–11, spindle
        muscle probably present)   .   .   .   .   **S. titubans** (p. 37)
7 Body cavity freely traversed by 20–25 strands of muscle which arise from the
        longitudinal muscles   .   .   .   .   **S. porrectus** (p. 35)
– Body cavity not traversed by free muscle strands   8
8 Longitudinal muscles 24 (rectal caecum present, no racemose glands (?), posterior
        part of nerve cord dilated)   .   .   .   .   .   .   **S. norvegicus** (p. 29)
– Longitudinal muscles more than 24   9
9 Longitudinal muscles 26–30, usually 27–29 (large species, ventral retractors arise
        from bands 3–5, dorsal from 9–11, rectal caecum and racemose glands present,
        a number of long filamentous or digitate processes arise from the anterior, dorsal
        surface of the brain)   .   .   .   .   **S. robustus** (p. 36)
– Longitudinal muscles more than 30   10
10 Longitudinal muscles 28–33, usually 31–32 (large species, ventral retractors arise
        from bands 2–5 and dorsal from 9–12, rectal caecum and racemose glands present;
        digitate processes very short)   .   .   .   .   .   .   **S. nudus** (p. 32)
– Longitudinal muscles greater than 32   11

11 Longitudinal muscles, 31–37 (ventral retractors from bands 2–5 and dorsal from
      10–14, rectal caecum present) .   .   .   .   .   .   *S. inclusus* (p. 26)
–   Longitudinal muscles, 37–38 (ventral retractors from bands 3–4 and dorsal from
      11–15, no spindle muscle, no caecum and no racemose glands)   *S. phalloides* (p. 34)
12 Longitudinal muscles, 41–42   13
–   Longitudinal muscles, more than 42   14
13 Introvert covered with blunt, leaf-like papillae directed backwards (ventral re-
      tractors arise from bands 2–5 and dorsal from 12–16, racemose elements reduced,
      caecum present, spindle muscle absent, cerebral organ prominent)
                                             S. galapagensis (p. 26)
–   Introvert covered with hemispherical papillae (ventral retractors arise from bands
      2–5 and dorsal from 16–18, spindle muscle absent but two fixing muscles present)
                                             S. multisulcatus (p. 28)
14 Longitudinal muscles, 49–52 (skin nearly transparent, ventral retractors from 1–9
      and dorsal from 15–22, brain conspicuous) .   .   .   .   *S. natans* (p. 29)
–   Longitudinal muscles, 53–61 (ventral retractors from bands 2–8 and dorsal from
      16–24, spindle muscle fastened posteriorly, racemose elements and caecum
      present, cerebral organ conspicuous) .   .   .   .   *S. polymyotus* (p. 35)

Sipunculus aequabilis Sluiter, 1902

Sipunculus aequabilis Sluiter, 1902 : 7; Prashad, 1936 : 236–237, pl. 9, fig. 3; Murina, 1964c :
   73–75.

TYPE LOCALITY. Indonesia, Siboga stations, 5, 52 (7°46′S, 114°30′30″E;
9°3′15″S, 119°57′42″E, at 330–959 m).

DESCRIPTION. Small. Trunk 80 mm long and swollen posteriorly. Introvert
about one eighth as long as the body. Tentacular fold is deeply cut into ten
feather-like tentacles, the largest two of which are placed dorsally. Longitudinal
musculature split into 21 bands which do not anastomose. Transverse furrows
slight. Two pairs of short, slender retractors, the ventral pair arising from the third
muscle band and the dorsal pair from the eighth and ninth. Intestine with 14
convolutions. Small rectal caecum and two contractile vessels present. Spindle
muscle not fixed posteriorly to the body wall. Two short, stout nephridia which
open to the exterior between the fourth and fifth muscles about 8 mm anterior to
the anus.

REMARKS. Described originally from two specimens. Prashad examined others
from deep water, but added little to Sluiter's original description. There are two
specimens of this species, reg. nos. 21495 and 21496, in the U.S. National Museum,
both from the Philippines and identified by W. K. Fisher. One from Chocolate Is.
has a trunk about 54 mm long and an introvert about 9 mm, 22 longitudinal muscles
and a rectal caecum. The retractor muscles arise at the same height, the ventral
pair from muscle 3 and the dorsal pair from muscle 9. The spindle muscle is not
fixed posteriorly; the nephridiopores lie between muscles 4–5 and are anterior to
the anus. The other undissected specimen from Deepon Bay, Leyte possesses
posteriorly a prominent glans with a circular rim like that shown in Prashad (1936,
pl. 9, fig. 3).

C

DISTRIBUTION. Indonesia (Sluiter, 1902); Laccadive Is. (Prashad, 1936); Mediterranean Sea (Murina, 1964c). It appears to be a deep-water species, 330–959 m (Sluiter), 637–870 m (Prashad), 26–1234 m (Murina).

Sipunculus galapagensis Fisher, 1947

(Fig. 3A)

Sipunculus galapagensis Fisher, 1947 : 358–360, pl. 2.

TYPE LOCALITY. Indefatigable Island, Galapagos Islands. *Type*. U.S.N.M. no. 20835.

DESCRIPTION. Introvert 30 mm long, covered with blunt leaf-like papillae which are directed backwards and largest anteriorly. Trunk 320 mm long with about 170 annuli. Longitudinal muscles gathered into 41–42 bands. Retractors short and free; the ventral pair arises from bands 2–5 and the dorsal pair from bands 12–16. From each side of the rectum a short strong muscle runs to the base of the dorsal retractors; racemose elements very much reduced. Rectal caecum present. Spindle muscle absent. Nephridia long, free, slender tubes 80 mm in length, which open well in front of the anus; the muscles on each side of their base have thin lobed crests. Digitate processes consisting of two irregular, folded sheets of tissue arise from the brain.

REMARKS. Known only from the holotype.

DISTRIBUTION. As for the type locality.

Sipunculus inclusus Sluiter, 1902

Sipunculus inclusus Sluiter, 1902 : 6.

TYPE LOCALITY. Kwandang Bay, Pajunga Island, Indonesia. *Type*. Zoologisch Museum, Amsterdam.

DESCRIPTION. Introvert about one sixth of the length of the body. Trunk and extended introvert 100 mm long. Skin smooth, without papillae. Longitudinal muscles anastomose, 31–37 in number. Two pairs of short, stout retractors; the ventral pair arises from muscles 2–5 and the dorsal from 10–14. Spindle muscle not attached posteriorly. Intestine fastened throughout its length to the body wall by mesenteries. Rectal caecum present. Two nephridia, free for their whole length, open between muscles 4–5 anterior to the anus.

REMARKS. Only two specimens of this species are known. A re-examination of the type specimen shows that the species is closely allied to *S. nudus* and *S. robustus*. A post-oesophageal loop is present in the gut but we could not find racemose glands or a rectal caecum. It is possible that they were present when the specimen was first dissected. There are 32 longitudinal muscles at the base of the retractor muscles and about 37–38 towards the base of the trunk. The introvert is completely retracted. We are not sure whether this is a valid species.

DISTRIBUTION. As for the type locality.

Sipunculus indicus Peters, 1850

Sipunculus indicus Peters, 1850 : 382–383; Selenka & de Man, 1883 : 111–112; Keferstein, 1865a : 421, pl. 31, fig. 1; Sluiter, 1886 : 475–481, pl. 1, figs 1 & 2, pl. 2, figs 1–7; 1891 : 122; 1902 : 5; Fischer, 1892 : 86–88, figs 6–7; 1893 : 1–12; 1895 : 8; Shipley, 1902d : 136; Lanchester, 1905a : 29; Sato, 1939 : 367–368, pl. 19, fig. 4; Stephen & Robertson, 1952 : 433–435; Wesenberg-Lund, 1963 : 102–103; Murina, 1964b : 265; Cutler, 1965 : 56.
Sipunculus discrepans Sluiter, 1898 : 445–450; 1902 : 6; Fischer, 1913 : 95–98, pl. 1, fig. 2; 1914b : 1; Leroy, 1942 : 29–30, pl. 3; Sato, 1935b : 302–303, pl. 2, fig. 2.

TYPE LOCALITY. Mozambique.

DESCRIPTION. Introvert short, up to 30 mm in length, with scale-like papillae on more than half of its surface; tentacular membrane divided into eight lappets. Trunk long, slender, up to 270 mm in length and 10–15 mm in breadth. Posterior end slightly swollen, ending in a truncated cone. Pinkish-white in colour when alive. The surface of the trunk is cut into rectangular areas by the circular and longitudinal muscles. Longitudinal muscles gathered into 39–43, usually 39–41 bands. Two pairs of short retractors arise at about the same level just posterior to the nephridiopores; the ventral pair from muscle bands 2–4 and the dorsal from bands 10–12. Spindle muscle strong and free posteriorly. Digestive tract fastened to the body wall by numerous mesenteries. Rectum held by a pair of broad wing muscles; no rectal caecum (?). Nephridia long and thin, fastened to the body wall by mesenteries for almost their whole length; both open posterior to the anus.

REMARKS. There are a number of specimens of this species in the British Museum (Natural History). One from Andaman Is. (reg. no. 97.2.26.16) possesses 38–43 anastomosing longitudinal muscles, a post-oesophageal or 'sipunculus' loop, a spindle muscle that arises behind the anus, a small rectal caecum (to which is attached the spindle muscle) and a short contractile vessel with numerous small villi that give the organ a bushy appearance. The trunk of another specimen from Billiton is 450 mm long and the introvert 15 mm. The anal slit in this species is placed very far forward on the trunk and well in front of the nephridiopores.

S. indicus is a well known species that is distributed in warmer seas. Cutler (1965) reports that the species is used as bait by fishermen in Madagascar and describes how it is caught by them.

We are placing *S. discrepans* Sluiter, 1898 in the synonymy of *S. indicus* Peters, 1850. Sluiter (1886) first described his specimen as *S. indicus* but later (1898) made it a new species. His reasons were (1) that the papillae on the introvert were rather larger anteriorly instead of being of uniform size, (2) that the rectangular areas of the trunk were not arranged in lines parallel to the body-axis and (3) that the retractors arose from a single band rather than from several bands. We consider that these differences can reasonably be regarded as intraspecific variations. Sato's description (1935b : 302) seems to us to fit *S. indicus* in all respects. Apparently Sato thought so too because in 1939 he changed his 1935 record to *S. indicus*. It is worth mentioning that Sato (1935b) describes a rectal caecum for the species. He states also that the natives of Palau Is. use the animal as food.

DISTRIBUTION. Cape Province (Wesenberg-Lund, 1963); Zanzibar (Fischer, 1892; Stephen & Robertson, 1952); Madagascar (Cutler, 1965); Pemba Is. (Lanchester, 1905); Mozambique (Fischer, 1895; Peters, 1850); Billiton (Sluiter, 1891, 1898, 1902; Fischer, 1913, 1914b); South-Chinese seas (Leroy, 1942; Murina, 1964b); West Caroline Is. (Sato, 1935b).

Sipunculus infrons Sluiter, 1902

Sipunculus infrons Sluiter, 1902 : 10, pl. 1, fig. 4.

TYPE LOCALITY. Indonesia. 5°40′42″S, 120°45′30″E. *Type.* Zoologisch Museum, Amsterdam.

DESCRIPTION. Introvert strong, rounded, 8 mm in length, bearing papillae which are visible only under the microscope; tentacular membrane entire. Trunk 32 mm long. Skin smooth and transparent so that both viscera and muscle bands are visible. Longitudinal musculature split into 21 bands. The retractors are weak and arise near each other in the middle of the body; the ventral pair arises from the third and fourth muscle bands, the dorsal pair from the eighth and ninth and are joined for most of their length. The gut reaches only to the middle of the body and has a long straight portion before it begins to coil; about 10 convolutions present. Spindle muscle arises in front of the anus and is not fixed posteriorly. Two fixing mesenteries at the beginning of the intestinal coil. Two bladder-shaped nephridia are about a quarter the length of the body and open just anterior to the anus. Nephridiopore distinct.

REMARKS. This is another poorly known species, the holotype being the only specimen. We have re-examined Sluiter's dissected holotype which is very thin and fragile and which has lost most of its internal structures. Although the specimen is damaged it is clear that it possesses a tentacular fold, well spaced triangular papillae in the introvert and in the middle of the trunk, about 21 longitudinal muscles which anastomose posteriorly. The weak circular musculature is definitely grouped into bundles. We were not able to find the papillae which Sluiter mentions in his type description. The external appearance of the specimen differs markedly from that of *S. aequabilis* Sluiter, the only other species of *Sipunculus* with 21 longitudinal muscles.

DISTRIBUTION. As for the type locality.

Sipunculus multisulcatus Fischer, 1913

Sipunculus multisulcatus Fischer, 1913 : 93–94, figs 1, 2, 7; 1914b : 1.

TYPE LOCALITY. Santos, Brazil.

DESCRIPTION. Introvert 25 mm long, covered with small hemispherical papillae. Trunk 110–130 mm long; 41–42 longitudinal muscle bands but with no anastomoses. Two pairs of retractors which arise at the same level in the anterior third of the body, the ventral pair from bands 2–5 and the dorsal from bands 16–18. The retractors join near the tentacles. Oesophagus with two contractile vessels. Spindle muscle absent but two fixing muscles present. The nephridia open between longitudinal muscle bands 5 and 6 just anterior to the anus; they are short, light yellow-brown, free for their whole length and reach to the base of the retractors.

REMARKS. Described from two specimens. No other records.

DISTRIBUTION. As for the type locality.

Sipunculus natans Fisher, 1954
(Fig. 3B)

Sipunculus natans Fisher, 1954a : 238–240, figs 1–2.

TYPE LOCALITY. Santa Inez Bay, Baja California. Surface net, night lamp. *Type.* U.S.N.M., Washington.

DESCRIPTION. Introvert about 15 mm long; papillae small, obtuse, decreasing in number towards the tentacles. Trunk 150 mm in length and very slender; skin nearly transparent. Longitudinal muscles gathered into 49–52 bands which are weak and widely spread. Two pairs of retractor muscles, the ventral pair arising from bands 1–9, the dorsal from bands 15–22. The retractors remain separate to the tentacles. Brain conspicuous and bears numerous slender lobes.

REMARKS. Described from a single specimen taken by a surface net at night with the aid of a lamp. The species is closely allied with *S. polymyotus*, possessing a large number of longitudinal muscle bands and extensive wing muscles.

DISTRIBUTION. As for the type locality.

Sipunculus norvegicus norvegicus Danielssen, 1868
(Fig. 3C)

Sipunculus norvegicus Danielssen, 1869 : 541; Koren & Danielssen, 1875 : 128; 1877b : 123–125; Selenka & de Man, 1883 : 95–96; Sluiter, 1900 : 17; 1912 : 21–22; Théel, 1905 : 53–54; Southern, 1913b : 8–10, pl. 5, fig. 7; Fischer, 1914a : 63; 1920 : 421; 1922c : 4–6, pl. 1, fig. 1; 1925 : 27; Stephen, 1934 : 174; Leroy, 1936 : 434; Wesenberg-Lund, 1930 : 18, pl. 3, fig. 27; pl. 6, fig. 63; 1937a : 16–19, figs 4–5; 1937b : 6–8, fig. 2; 1939b : 27; 1959a : 180.
Sipunculus priapuloides Koren & Danielssen, 1877 : 126–128; Roule, 1896b : 473; 1906 : 65; Shipley, 1899a : 158; Sluiter, 1900 : 17, pl. 1, figs 6–7; Théel, 1905 : 52, 54, pl. 9, figs 137–145, pl. 10, figs 146–150, pl. 15, fig. 213.
Phallosoma norvegicus Levinsen, 1884 : 268.
Phallosoma priapuloides Levinsen, 1884 : 268; Roule, 1898a : 384; 1907 : 65–70, pl. 9, figs 85, 91–94.

DESCRIPTION. Introvert short, about a quarter as long as the body and with conical papillae; tentacular membrane divided into eight lappets. Body cylindrical, up to 79 mm long and translucent; posterior region is constricted. Longitudinal muscles split into 24 bands. Two pairs of retractor muscles arise posteriorly to the anus from four bands. Gut long and fastened along its length by mesenteries. Rectal caecum present. Spindle muscle arises near the anus, traverses the intestinal coils and is fixed to the caecum. Two contractile vessels on the oesophagus. Two thin nephridia. Part of the posterior region of the nerve cord dilated; branches from the nerve cord run right and left to each circular band.

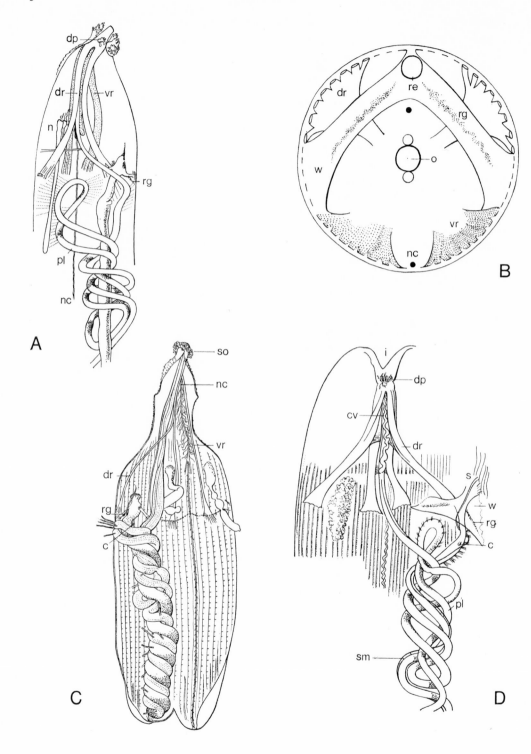

REMARKS. According to Selenka's key to the genus *Sipunculus* (Selenka, 1883 : 13) this species lacks 'Zottenbildung am Enddarm', which we take to mean racemose glands, and the nephridia are free. Wesenberg-Lund (1930 : 18) redescribed five specimens, 47–79 mm long, from Iceland. She reported that a caecum and racemose glands are present, that the nephridia are free and that the nerve cord 'ends in a rather distinct pear-shaped bulb at the hindermost tip of the trunk'. She reported the presence of 22 longitudinal muscles. Théel's excellent figure (1905 : 150) does not show racemose glands.

There are two specimens in the U.S. National Museum (reg. no. 21487) both collected in the vicinity of Kanai Is., Hawaii and identified by W. K. Fisher. This record is very interesting. The trunk of the dissected specimen is about 140 mm long and the introvert about 20 mm. The posterior region of the trunk forms a distinct glans with a circular ridge or annulation; there also appears to be a small posterior invagination. There are 23 longitudinal muscles which anastomose only slightly. The retractors arise at the same level, the ventral pair from muscles 3–4 and the dorsal pair from muscles 7 (part), 8, 9 and 10 (part). The spindle muscle arises in front of the anus, makes contact with a rectal caecum but is not attached posteriorly. Two racemose glands are present. Two nephridia which are swollen towards the nephridiopore open anteriorly to the anus between muscles 4–5. Para-neural muscle well developed. Two well developed and tubular contractile vessels. No pear-shaped or bulb-shaped swelling was observed at the posterior extremity of the nerve cord.

DISTRIBUTION. East Greenland (Wesenberg-Lund, 1930); Iceland (Wesenberg-Lund, 1937); Norway (Koren & Danielssen, 1877b); Northern North Sea (Stephen, 1934); South-west Ireland (Southern, 1913); West Africa (Sluiter, 1900; Roule, 1898a; Wesenberg-Lund, 1959a; Stephen, 1960); Loyalty Islands (Shipley, 1899a); Hawaii.

Sipunculus norvegicus americanus Gerould, 1913

Sipunculus priapuloides var. *americana* Gerould, 1913 : 429–432.

TYPE LOCALITY. Eastern coast, U.S.A. *Type.* U.S.N.M. 1379.

DESCRIPTION. This subspecies differs from *S. norvegicus norvegicus* only in minor respects. The glans is not marked off by an annular fold and there are 22–24, usually 22 longitudinal muscle bands. The retractors also show a difference in attachment; the dorsal pair arise from a single band and the ventral from two.

FIG. 3. (A) *Sipunculus galapagensis*. Dissection of the anterior region of the trunk, about half natural size (after Fisher). (B) *Sipunculus natans*. Semi-diagrammatic section to show the relation of the wing muscles to the retractors and rectum. The longitudinal muscle bands are indicated by the black dashes round the periphery (after Fisher). (C) *Sipunculus norvegicus*. Dissected specimen (after Théel). (D) *Sipunculus polymyotus*. Dissection of the anterior region of the trunk, about half natural size (after Fisher). KEY: *See* Fig. 2, page 23.

REMARKS. Described from several specimens. Gerould gave a detailed description.

DISTRIBUTION. Several stations off the East coast of the U.S.A. in depths of 883–1765 m.

Sipunculus nitidus Sluiter, 1900

Sipunculus nitidus Sluiter, 1900 : 14–16, pl. 1, figs 4–5, pl. 3, figs 10–11.

TYPE LOCALITY. Princess Alice station 650 (36°54′N, 23°06′30″W); at 4400 m.

DESCRIPTION. Short introvert with triangular papillae, the papillated part about 7 mm in length. Tentacular membrane divided into eight lappets. Trunk 80 mm in length, dark grey with a pearly iridescence. Body wall translucent, so that the intestine can be seen indistinctly through it. Under a microscope, small corpuscular bodies can be seen on its surface; they have a small central orifice, surrounded by a smooth margin, followed by several irregular circles of small chitinous plates. Two pairs of retractors; the ventral pair arises from three muscle bands, the stronger dorsal arises from the eleventh band. The retractors arise 8 mm behind the anus and join only at the extreme anterior part of the introvert. The oesophagus is long and the spire begins to form about 5 mm behind the insertion of the dorsal retractors. About 14 intestinal convolutions, fixed to the body-wall by numerous mesenteries; the spindle muscle does not emerge from the spire and the intestine is free posteriorly. A single contractile vessel. The two nephridia are short, but voluminous, bladder-like anteriorly, deep brown in colour, and open between the fifth and sixth bands.

REMARKS. This species is known only from the holotype which was dredged at 4400 m. Although Sluiter does not state the number of longitudinal muscle bands possessed by the species his illustration (pl. 1, fig. 4) shows the number to be about 28 anteriorly and about 22 posteriorly. His diagram shows that there is a post-oesophageal or sipunculus loop present. The circular muscle bands seem to be developed rather poorly. Sluiter considered the species to be near *S. norvegicus*. We have not been able to find the holotype.

DISTRIBUTION. Known only from the type locality.

Sipunculus nudus Linnaeus, 1766

(Fig. 2A–C)

Sipunculus nudus Linnaeus, 1766 : 1078; de Blainville, 1827 : 309; Gray, 1828 : 8; Keferstein, 1865a : 419; Andreae, 1882 : 477; Selenka & de Man, 1883 : 92–94; Ward, 1891 : 143; Fischer, 1895 : 9; 1914b : 1; 1922b : 5; 1925 : 26–27; Shipley, 1899a : 158; Metalnikoff, 1900 : 261, 12 pls, 74 figs; Sluiter 1902 : 5; Cuénot 1902 : 13–15; Ikeda, 1904 : 31–32; 1905a : 169; Hérubel, 1904a : 563; Gerould, 1913 : 418; Southern, 1913b : 8; ten Broeke, 1925 : 82; 1929 : 159–160, figs 2, 3; Sato, 1930b : 2–5, pl. 1, text-fig. 1; 1934b : 1–2, pl. 1, fig. 1; Wesenberg-Lund, 1933 : 11–12; 1954a : 2; 1957b : 2; Leroy, 1936 : 424; 1942 : 28; Prashad, 1936 : 232–233; Stephen, 1941b : 256; 1958 : 129; 1960a : 514–515; Chin, 1947 : 100; Stephen & Robertson, 1952 : 432–433; Fisher, 1952 : 376–377, pl. 18; Chen & Yeh, 1958 : 273; Murina, 1964b : 266.

Syrinx tesselatus Rafinesque, 1814 : 32.
Sipunculus nudus var. *tesselatus* Costa, 1853 : 17–20, pl. 2.
Sipunculus tesselatus Keferstein & Ehlers, 1861 : 38, pl. 7, fig. 1.
Sipunculus tesselatus: Selenka & de Man, 1883 : 96–97.
Sipunculus robustus (part): Stephen, 1941 : 402, pl. 1, fig. 1.
Sipunculus eximioclathratus Baird, 1868 : 81–82; Rice & Stephen; 1970 : 58.

DESCRIPTION.   Introvert relatively short, bearing triangular scale-like papillae.
A large species with trunk up to 300 mm; surface cut into a very large number
of small rectangles by the intersection of the longitudinal and circular muscles.
Longitudinal muscles normally gathered into 28–33 bands; circular muscles also
divided into numerous narrow bands.   Two pairs of short retractors arise at the
same level; the ventral pair usually from bands 2–5 and the dorsal from bands
9–12.   The spindle muscle arises in front of the anus, is attached to the rectal
caecum but is not attached posteriorly.   About 15 intestinal convolutions fixed
to the body wall by numerous mesenteries.   Anterior part of the intestine forms a
characteristic post-oesophageal or 'sipunculus' loop.   Two contractile vessels without
villi.   A tufted organ or 'racemose' gland occurs on each side of the rectum, actually
lying on a mesentery which helps to keep the rectum in position.   Nephridia
fairly short and attached for about a fifth of their length to the body wall.   Nephridiopores anterior to the anus.   Longitudinal integumentary canals, which communicate with the coelom, lie in the body wall between the muscle bands.   Brain,
bilobed and conspicuous on the dorsal surface of the introvert of dissected specimens.
Paraneural muscle well developed.   Digitate processes short (Akesson, 1958 : 138).

REMARKS.   *S. nudus* is a 'classical' species and is known to generations of students
if only as a figure in a text-book.   Specimens are easy to dissect and the dissection
supplies a great deal of information about the structure of some invertebrates,
particularly the muscular and nervous systems and the importance of an hydro-
static skeleton.   The species is well known in Europe, especially along the Atlantic
coast of France at places like Morgat and Arcachon, and in the Mediterranean.
At Morgat it occurs in great numbers (Edmonds, 1962).   The species is also reported
from the Californian coast of North America.

The anatomy and histology of the animal have been described very fully by a
number of writers but more particularly by Andreae (1881, 1882), Ward (1891)
and Metalnikoff (1900) and the embryology and development by Gerould (1904)
and Hatschek (1883).

We have noticed that the size of the caecum of the species may vary considerably.
In most specimens from Morgat and Arcachon we have found that it is small.
Occasionally, however, the caecum appears as a long, white narrow tube that
extends 30–40 mm along the posterior part of the intestine close to the spindle muscle.
This is the type of caecum shown by Metalnikoff (1900, fig. 1) and Sato (1930,
fig. 1).   The elongated structure is filled with a mucous substance.   The smaller
type of caecum is much more common than the longer form.

An examination of four specimens of *S. nudus* in the U.S. National Museum,
collected on the western coast of north America shows that about one quarter to
one third of a nephridium lies anterior to the nephridiopore, sometimes making

the nephridium appear bilobed. This is not the usual condition of the organ in specimens from France. How general the condition is in the north American specimens is not known.

We have added *S. tesselatus* Rafinesque to the synonymy of *S. nudus*, because it is very difficult to find a character that will distinguish between the two species. The specimens in the British Museum of Natural History labelled *S. tesselatus* (reg. no. 98.5.6.153–154) from the Zoological Station, Naples we consider to be *S. nudus* and to match specimens of the latter from French and Italian localities. The trunk of one of the above specimens is about 220 mm long and the introvert 30 mm and there are 29–31 longitudinal muscles which anastomose slightly. The ventral retractors span muscles 1–7 and the dorsal 8–12. The nephridiopores lie between muscles 4–5 and are anterior to the anus. A caecum and racemose glands are present on the rectum. The brain, however, is not as prominent as in most specimens of *S. nudus*.

DISTRIBUTION. *Eastern Atlantic*: Plymouth, Ireland (Southern, 1913b), France (Cuénot, 1922; Edmonds, 1962), Senegal (Stephen, 1960a), Gough Is. (Stephen, 1941b).

Western North Atlantic: Florida (Gerould, 1913), North Carolina (Gerould, 1913; Pearse, 1942), Bermuda (Verrill, 1904), West Indies (ten Broeke, 1925).

Mediterranean: Ibiza (Fischer, 1922b), Sardinia (Marcialis, 1892), Israel (Stephen, 1958).

Red Sea: (Wesenberg-Lund, 1957b).

Indian Ocean: Zanzibar (Stephen & Robertson, 1952), Indo-China (Leroy, 1942), Andaman Islands (Prashad, 1936).

Pacific Ocean: China (Chen & Yeh, 1958; Murina, 1964b), Japan (Ikeda, 1904; Sato, 1930, 1934b, 1937a, 1939), Fukien (Chin, 1947), Philippines (Ikeda, 1924), New Britain (Shipley, 1899a), Sunday Island (Benham, 1912), California (Chamberlain, 1919; Fisher, 1952).

Sipunculus phalloides (Pallas, 1774)

Lumbricus phalloides Pallas, 1774 : 12–15, pl. 1.
Sipunculus phalloides: Blainville, 1827 : 311, fig. 1; Keferstein, 1865a : 420; Baird, 1868 : 78; Selenka & de Man, 1883 : 99–100; Fischer, 1895 : 9; 1922b : 5–7, fig. 1; Leroy, 1936 : 424.

TYPE LOCALITY. Grenada, West Indies.

DESCRIPTION. Tentacular membrane much as in *S. nudus*, with two large flaps on the dorsal side and four small ones on the ventral side. Total length up to 170 mm. Light yellow-brown; only in the anterior part are the raised bands darker than the body. Circular and longitudinal bands everywhere about equally strong. Longitudinal muscles, 37 anteriorly, 38 posteriorly. Two pairs of retractors arise at the same level, the ventral pair from bands 3–4, the dorsal from bands 11–15. The oesophagus is attached by mesenteries to the retractors. No spindle muscle but numerous mesenteries. Two contractile vessels. The nephridia open anterior to the anus; they are free and reach to the base of the retractors.

REMARKS. Keferstein (1865a : 420) says that the species lacks a spindle muscle, a rectal caecum and racemose glands.

DISTRIBUTION. West Indies (Pallas, 1774; Fischer, 1922b); Chile (Leroy, 1936).

Sipunculus polymyotus Fisher, 1947

(Fig. 3D)

Sipunculus polymyotus Fisher, 1947 : 354–358, pl. 10.

TYPE LOCALITY. Key West, Florida. *Type.* U.S.N.M. no. 20612.

DESCRIPTION. Introvert 25 mm, relatively short and closely set with small blunt posteriorly directed papillae which increase in size posteriorly. Four relatively short tentacles. Body 300 mm long, posterior end blunt or pointed. Longitudinal muscles split into 53–61 bands. Over 200 circular annuli. Two pairs of retractors arise at about the same level just posterior to the anus; the ventral pair arises from bands 2–8 and the dorsal from bands 16–24. A slender spindle muscle arises just in front of the anus and is attached by many strands to the mid-intestine and to the body wall posteriorly. 'Sipunculus' loop present in the intestine; the rectum bears a small caecum. Nephridia about 40 mm in length. A thin, fan-shaped mesentery present on the rectum; racemose elements appear on the mesentery on each side of the rectum. Cerebral organ and its processes conspicuous.

The larva (pelagosphaera) is also described.

REMARKS. Described originally from three specimens. No other records.

DISTRIBUTION. Type locality; also Long Bay, South Carolina (Fisher, 1947).

Sipunculus porrectus Selenka, 1888

Sipunculus porrectus Selenka, 1888 : 221–222; Hérubel, 1907 : 225; Prashad, 1936 : 245–236.

TYPE LOCALITY. Mergui Archipelago, Bay of Bengal. *Type.* Indian Museum, Calcutta.

DESCRIPTION. Introvert covered with papillae; tentacles numerous, about 120 in number arranged in two half circles. Body up to 320 mm in length and 15 mm in diameter. Musculature strong. Longitudinal muscles split into 32 bands; anastomoses few and feeble. Two pairs of retractors; the ventral pair is a few mm shorter than the dorsal pair and each arises from 3, 4 or 5 longitudinal muscle bands. They join just before insertion into the introvert. Twenty to 25 muscle strands in the anterior part of the body freely traverse the body cavity; they apparently arise from the longitudinal muscles by subdivision, for each is inserted in front of the same band from which it arises. Oesophagus with two contractile vessels. Spindle muscle slight and intestine not fixed posteriorly. Anus placed unusually far forward. The rectum is attached by a mesentery for a length of 5 mm. Nephridia lacking (?).

REMARKS. Described originally from two damaged specimens. Prashad re-examined one and confirmed Selenka's description. It is a poorly known species.

The presence of strands of muscle that freely traverse the anterior part of the body cavity is very uncommon amongst sipunculans.

DISTRIBUTION.   As for the type locality.

Sipunculus robustus Keferstein, 1865

(Fig. 2D–E)

Sipunculus robustus Keferstein, 1865a : 421; Baird, 1868 : 80; Sluiter, 1881 : 482, pl. 2, figs 8–9; 1891 : 122; 1902 : 4; Selenka & de Man, 1883 : 97–99, pl. 12, fig. 170; Selenka, 1888 : 221; Fischer, 1895 : 7–8, fig. 4; 1896 : 337; 1922b : 7; Augener, 1903 : 313–315; 1906 : 193; Lanchester, 1905a : 27; ten Broeke, 1925 : 82–83; Monro, 1931 : 34; Sato, 1935b : 301–302, pl. 2, fig. 1; Leroy, 1936 : 424; Prashad, 1936 : 233–235, pl. 9, fig. 2; Stephen, 1941a : 402–404, pl. 1, figs 1–2, pl. 2, fig. 3; Stephen & Robertson, 1952 : 433; Wesenberg-Lund, 1954a : 3–5, pl. 1, fig. 1; Murina, 1964b : 266; Cutler, 1965 : 52.
Sipunculus priapuloides : Robinson, 1927 : 359.
Sipunculus angasii Baird, 1868 : 76; Edmonds, 1955 : 83–86, pl. 1, text-figs 1–4.
Sipunculus nudus : Fischer, 1914b : 1.
Sipunculus sp. Fisher, 1952 : 376.

TYPE LOCALITY.   Uea, Wallis Is.; Pacific Ocean.

DESCRIPTION.   Introvert 20–50 mm long and bearing numerous small, flat, triangular papillae directed backwards.   Mouth surrounded by a wrinkled and bushy tentacular fold.   Trunk up to 280 mm long and about 20 mm broad; posterior extremity sometimes slightly swollen and rounded or sharply pointed.   The whole surface is divided into small rectangular or square areas by longitudinal and transverse furrows.   Longitudinal musculature thickened into about 27–30 bands. Two pairs of retractor muscles arise at the same level, the ventral pair usually from bands 3–5 (range 2–6) and the dorsal pair from bands 9–11 (range 9–13).   The oesophagus is bound to the retractors by mesenteries and the intestine to the body wall by numerous threads.   A well-developed post-oesophageal loop is present. Contractile vessel single (Keferstein, 1865) but all other authors who have described the structure say that it is double.   The rectum is 20–30 mm long and the anus is situated just anterior to the insertion of the retractors.   The anus is a conspicuous slit and according to many authors it is bounded anteriorly by two muscles and posteriorly by one.   A prominent strand of muscle arises at the base of each dorsal retractor and joins the rectum in a fan-like manner.   Racemose glands or 'tufted' organs are lacking according to the type description (Keferstein, 1865), Selenka (1883) and ten Broeke (1925) but most authors maintain that they are present. A re-examination of the type specimen shows that they are present.   Rectal caecum absent (Keferstein, 1865) but clearly present in the type specimen.   Nephridia open between muscles 4–5 or 5–6 anterior to the level of the anus and reach to the roots of the retractors.   The spindle muscle arises anterior to the anus and is fixed posteriorly according to many authors.   Longitudinal coelomic spaces occur in the body wall between the longitudinal muscles.   Paraneural muscle well developed.   The brain is a bilobed structure from the anterior surface of which are given off a number of slender digitate processes up to 2 mm long and noticeably larger than those given off from the brain of *S. nudus* (Akesson, 1958 : 138).

REMARKS. Keferstein (1865) described *S. robustus* from Uea (Uvea?) Wallis Is. in the Pacific Ocean as possessing a single contractile vessel, no caecum and no racemose glands. This information has proved troublesome to a number of different authors. The occurrence of a *'robustus-*like' sipunculan with a caecum, with racemose glands and double contractile vessel has been reported particularly in the Indo-Pacific area on a number of occasions. *S. angasii* Baird, well known in southern Australia, is such a species.

In order to throw light on the problem the type specimen (reg. no. 2081) from the Hamburg Museum was re-examined. It is from Uea, Wallis Is. (12°5′S and 176°5′W), and although it had been dissected was still in a good state of preservation. It possesses 26–29 longitudinal muscles (27 just posterior to the retractors), ventral retractors that arise from muscles 2–4 and 2–5, dorsal retractors that arise from muscle 8–11 and 9–11, nephridia (about 50–60 mm long) which arise from between muscles 4–5, two contractile vessels, a rectal caecum, two racemose glands which are concealed to some extent by a twisting of the strand of muscle to which they are attached and a brain with two flaps of tissue from which arise several digitiform processes.

It now becomes evident that (1) *S. angasii* Baird, 1868 is synonymous with *S. robustus* Keferstein, 1865 and (2) that *S. nudus* Linnaeus and *S. robustus* Keferstein are very closely related species. The chief differences between the two are in the number of longitudinal muscles that they possess and in the structure of the digitate processes that arise from the brain.

DISTRIBUTION. *Indo-Pacific*: Mergui (Selenka, 1888; Prashad, 1936), Amboina (Sluiter, 1902; Selenka, 1883; Augener, 1903), Singapore (Lanchester, 1905a), Maldive Is. and Gulf of Oman (Stephen, 1941a), Andaman and Nicobar Is. (Prashad, 1936), Zanzibar (Stephen & Robertson, 1952), Madagascar (Cutler, 1965), Timor (Selenka, 1883), China (Leroy, 1942; Murina, 1964b), Palau Is. (Sato, 1935b), southern and eastern Australia (Edmonds, 1955), Madras (Prashad, 1936), Great Barrier Reef (Monro, 1931), Marquesas (Fischer, 1922b), Pelew Is. (Fischer, 1895), Solomon Is. (Leroy, 1936).

West Indies: Curaçao (ten Broeke, 1925).

Sipunculus titubans titubans Selenka and Bülow, 1883

Sipunculus titubans Selenka & Bülow, 1883 : 100–101; Fischer, 1895 : 6–7; 1914a : 61–62; 1923b : 24; Lanchester, 1905c : 29–30; Gerould, 1913 : 428–429; Stephen & Robertson, 1952 : 433; Stephen, 1960a : 515; Wesenberg-Lund, 1954a : 5; 1957a : 1–2; 1959a : 179–180; 1959c : 209–210.

Sipunculus delphinus Murina, 1967a : 1336–7, fig. 5.

TYPE LOCALITY. Puntarenas (Costa Rica?).

DESCRIPTION. Integument opaque on the introvert. Tentacular membrane with two large dorsal lappets and a number of small ventral ones. Colour dark brown. Integument in rectangular areas. Cuticle very iridescent, especially at the anterior and posterior extremities of the trunk. Skin bodies not visible to the eye. Longitudinal muscles split into 26 well-spaced bands; no anastomoses. Two pairs

retractors arising at the same level; the ventral pair arises from bands 3–5 or sometimes from 1–5, the first and fifth being attached by a fine strand.   Dorsal retractors
from bands 8–11.   Oesophagus bound to all four retractors by mesenteries.   Intestinal coils as in *S. nudus*.   Spindle muscle absent, according to Selenka, but
present according to Gerould (1913), Fischer (1895) and Wesenberg-Lund (1957c).
Two contractile vessels.   Nephridia open anteriorly to the anus between bands 4
and 5 and are fixed for the anterior half of their length to the body wall.   Nervous
system as in *S. nudus*.

REMARKS.   This is a troublesome species.   The type locality is 'Puntarenas'
according to Selenka, 1883 : 101, presumably Puntarenas, Costa Rica and not Punta
Arenas, Chile but this is by no means certain.   Fischer's (1895) specimens possessed
26–32 muscles, Gerould's (1913) specimens 27–30 and Wesenberg-Lund's 28.
Fischer (1895 : 6) says that a rectal caecum is present but Gerould and Wesenberg-
Lund make no mention of the structure.   Gerould (1913 : 429) suggests that '*S.
titubans* is a variable form closely resembling *S. nudus* and *S. robustus* from which,
in some cases at least, it can hardly be distinguished'.   According to Selenka's key
(1883 : 13) the nephridia of *S. titubans* are fixed to the body wall for half of their
length while those of *S. robustus* are free.

DISTRIBUTION.   North-west Africa, Cape Verde, Canaries, French Guinea, Gold
Coast, Nigeria, Lagos (Wesenberg-Lund, 1959c), Senegal (Stephen, 1960a), Zanzibar
(Lanchester, 1905c; Stephen & Robertson, 1952), Madagascar (Fischer, 1923b),
Siam (Fischer, 1923b), West Indies (Gerould, 1913), Guatemala (Fischer, 1895).

Sipunculus titubans diptychus Fischer, 1895

Sipunculus titubans var. *diptychus* Fischer, 1895 : 7, fig. 3; 1914a : 61–62; Longhurst, 1958 : 85;
    Wesenberg-Lund, 1954a : 5.

TYPE LOCALITY.   Accra, West Africa.

DESCRIPTION.   Longitudinal muscles divided into 30 bands anteriorly, 32–33
posteriorly.   Ventral retractors arise from bands 2–5, the dorsals from bands 11–14.
A spindle muscle is present.

REMARKS.   The characters that distinguish this subspecies from the nominate
form are the attachment of the dorsal retractors to bands 11–14, the number of
longitudinal muscle bands, presence of a spindle muscle and the attachment of the
ventral retractors (Fischer, 1914a : 61–62).

DISTRIBUTION.   Accra, Ghana (Fischer, 1895), French Guinea (Wesenberg-Lund,
1954), Sierra Leone (Longhurst, 1958).

GENUS *XENOSIPHON* Fisher, 1947

Xenosiphon Fisher, 1947b : 360; 1954b : 311; Edmonds, 1955 : 87–89, 1960b : 160.

DESCRIPTION.   Large animals resembling *Sipunculus* but with an extra pair of
small 'protractor' muscles which arise from the posterior border of the introvert

near the level of the brain.   Introvert short and covered with squamiform, triangular papillae.   Longitudinal and circular muscles grouped into bands so that
the surface of the animals appears divided into numerous rectangles or squares.
Tentacles very numerous and pad-like.   Papilliform dermal outgrowths may or
may not be present.   Integumental canals or sacs present.   Gonad is a filamentous
loop.   Rectum unusually long and anus situated anterior to the nephridiopores.
Rectal caecum present.

TYPE SPECIES.   *Sipunculus mundanus* var. *branchiatus* Fischer, 1895.

REMARKS.   Fisher (1954) amended his original description of the genus after
examining specimens of *X. mundanus*.   Further, he divided the genus into two
subgenera; (1) *Xenosiphon* (*sensu stricto*) in which (a) the subcutaneous, coelomic
system consists of independent, irregular sacs some of which carry papilliform gills,
(b) no post-oesophageal loop is present in the foregut and (c) the nephridia are very
long and attached to the body; *X. branchiatus* and *X. caribaeus*, and (2) *Austrosiphon*
in which (a) the subcutaneous, coelomic system is in the form of longitudinal canals
that lie between the longitudinal ridges of the body wall, (b) a post-oesophageal
loop is present in the foregut and (c) the nephridia are short and free; *X. mundanus*.

The external appearance of the species in the genus is very much like that of a
Sipunculus.   A dissected specimen can be identified readily by the extra pair of
protractor muscles, the unusually long rectum and the filamentous, gonadal loop.
The genus contains only three species.

DISTRIBUTION.   Caribbean Sea, west coast of north America, New Zealand,
Australia and Burma.

GENUS XENOSIPHON—KEY TO SPECIES

1	Nephridia small and free (longitudinal muscle bands 27–30) .	**X. mundanus** (p. 42)
–	Nephridia long and attached to the body wall	2
2	Longitudinal muscle bands 29–34	**X. branchiatus** (p. 39)
–	Longitudinal muscle bands 37–38	**X. caribaeus** (p. 41)

Xenosiphon branchiatus (Fischer, 1895)

(Fig. 4D–E)

Sipunculus mundanus var. *branchiatus* Fischer, 1895 : 3, pl. 1, figs 1, 1a, 2.
Sipunculus branchiatus: Spengel, 1913a : 74.
Xenosiphon branchiatus: Fisher, 1947b : 360–363, pl. 12; 1952 : 377–380, pl. 19; 1954b : 312,
    pl. 8.
Sipunculus gravieri Hérubel, 1904a : 476–480; 1904b : 690; 1904c : 562; Leroy, 1936 : 434.

TYPE LOCALITY.   Ecuador.

DESCRIPTION.   Introvert 20–25 mm covered with squamiform papillae which
increase in size anteriorly but decrease in a narrow zone just behind the tentacles.
Trunk up to 420 mm; the middle third is closely covered with slender, pointed
papilliform outgrowths, giving it a furry appearance.   Longitudinal muscles split
into 29–30 bands which rarely anastomose; circular muscles banded.   Three pairs
of retractors.   A small pair, the 'protractors', lies at the base of the introvert and

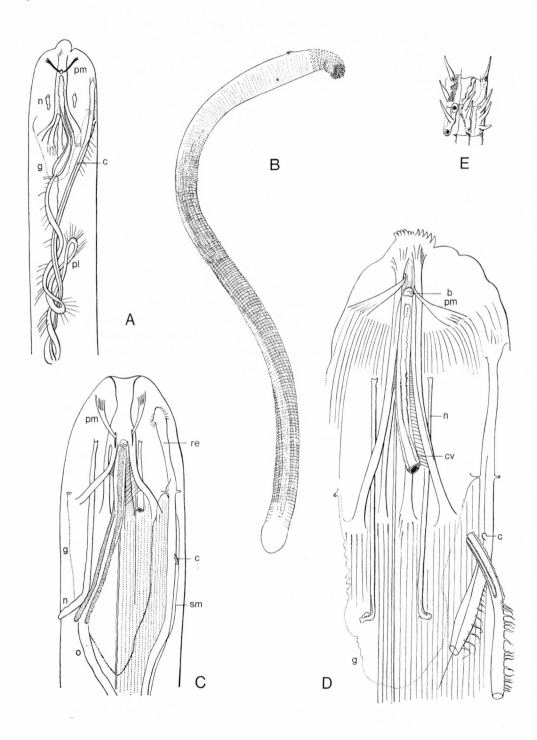

arises from bundles 12–15. The ventral pair arises from bands 1–4, the dorsal from bands 12–15. The anus opens near the protractors. Fan-shaped rectal muscles absent. A slender spindle muscle arises near the anus and is attached to a small caecum on the rectum. Nephridia long and slender, attached by mesenteries to the body wall and open posterior to the anus. A delicate filament passes obliquely and ventrally from the rectum to the base of each dorsal retractor. Brain bilobed with a prominent bushy cerebral organ. The presence of papilliform outgrowths gives the skin a furry appearance.

REMARKS. Originally described from four specimens. There are about 20 specimens of a *Xenosiphon* from Burma in the British Museum (Natural History) which resemble *X. branchiatus* very closely. No papilliform outgrowths, however, are present on the surface of the trunk in any of them.

We have placed *Sipunculus gravieri* Hérubel, 1904 from the Red Sea in the synonymy of this species. The anteriorly placed anus, the long rectum, the long nephridium and the strand of racemose-like elements stretching across the base of the dorsal retractors to the nerve cord and the number of longitudinal muscle bands point to this conclusion. Hérubel (1904 : 479), himself, said that his specimen resembled *Xenosiphon mundanus*. The length of the nephridia shows that it is more likely to be *X. branchiatus*.

DISTRIBUTION. West coast of North America; Ecuador (Fischer, 1895). Baja California; Panama (Fisher, 1947b, 1952); Red Sea (Hérubel, 1904).

Xenosiphon caribaeus Fisher, 1954

(Fig. 4C)

Xenosiphon caribaeum Fisher, 1954b : 312–315, pl. 8.

TYPE LOCALITY. Punta de Cerro, San Juan, Porto Rico. *Type.* U.S.N.M. no. 23789.

DESCRIPTION. Introvert about one tenth of the total length and covered with squamate oval papillae. Tentacles very numerous in 16–18 groups. Body up to 230 mm and delicate. Longitudinal muscles gathered into 37–38 bands with few anastomoses; the eight mid-ventral bands are broader than the laterals. The protractors arise from bands 13–16 or 17; they are delicate and translucent. The ventral retractors arise from bands 2–4 and the dorsals from bands 10–13. Papillae extend from about the middle of the body to near the posterior extremity; they

---

FIG. 4 (A–B). *Xenosiphon mundanus.* (A) Dissection of the anterior part of the trunk; longitudinal muscles not shown (after Fisher). (B) Entire animal (specimen from Sydney, Australia). (c) *Xenosiphon caribaeus.* Dissection of the anterior region. The gonad is in the form of a long loop attached to the rectum of the body wall (after Fisher). (D–E) *Xenosiphon branchiatus.* (D) Dissection of the anterior region of the trunk. (E) A single rectangle of skin about 25 mm anterior to the papularium showing a skin canal filled with material, × about 5. At either end, the dark spot marks the canal that leads to the coelom (after Fisher). KEY: *See* Fig. 2, page 23.

D

are up to 1 mm in height and give this part of the body a furry appearance. Rectum attached by a dorsal mesentery and two lateral muscles. The spindle muscle is delicate and originates in the ventral side of the rectum giving off strands to the slender caecum; it is not attached posteriorly. Nephridia long, slender and attached by mesenteries to the body wall.

REMARKS. Described originally from two specimens. No other records.

DISTRIBUTION. As for the type locality.

Xenosiphon mundanus (Selenka & Bülow, 1883)

(Fig. 4A–B)

Sipunculus mundanus Selenka & Bülow, 1883 : 108–109, pl. 12, fig. 174; Fischer, 1922b : 5–7; Shipley, 1899a : 158.
Sipunculus maoricus Benham, 1904 : 303–305, pl. 15, fig. 3; pl. 16, figs 11, 17, 20; Edmonds, 1960 : 160.
Xenosiphon mundanum: Fisher, 1954b : 314, pl. 7; Edmonds, 1955 : 87–89, fig. 5; 1960 : 160, pl. 1.

TYPE LOCALITY. Sow and Pig Bank near Sydney, Australia. *Type*. British Museum (Nat. Hist.).

DESCRIPTION. Introvert comparatively short, about 22·5 mm long, bearing on its surface numerous squamiform, triangular papillae and at its anterior extremity numerous digitiform tentacles. Trunk long, up to 340 mm and in preserved specimens light yellow in colour. Longitudinal and circular muscles are banded so that most of the surface appears to consist of numerous squares or rectangles. The dorsal surface of the posterior half of the body, where the bands are not so clearly separated, has a slightly different appearance from the ventral surface where the banding is strong. Longitudinal musculature split into 31 bands with few anastomoses. Four main retractors arising about the same level; the right ventral arises from bands 2–4, the left from bands 1–4 and the dorsals from bands 7–10. An additional pair of protractors arises near the brain. Intestine and rectum fixed by numerous mesenteries. Post-oesophageal or 'sipunculus' loop present; rectum long and bears a caecum which is attached to the spindle muscle. Spindle muscle not attached posteriorly. Dorsal and ventral contractile vessels prominent. Gonads lie along a long filamentous loop. Nephridia small, stout and free. The integumental canals are longitudinally placed between the ridges of the muscles. No papilliform gills present on the surface of the trunk.

REMARKS. This is a species well known in Australia and New Zealand. *Sipunculus maoricus* Benham, 1904 is a junior synonym (Edmonds, 1960).

DISTRIBUTION. Australia: New South Wales (Selenka & de Man, 1883; Fischer, 1922b); New South Wales, Victoria, Western Australia, Lord Howe Island (Edmonds, 1955); New Britain (Shipley, 1899); New Zealand (Benham, 1904; Edmonds, 1960).

Genus *SIPHONOSOMA* Spengel, 1912

Siphonosoma Spengel, 1912 : 264; Gerould, 1913 : 432; Sato, 1939 : 369; Fisher, 1950b : 805; 1952 : 380–381.

DESCRIPTION. Usually large in size and cylindrical in shape. Introvert relative to the trunk is usually short and lacks scale-like, triangular-shaped papillae; it may be smooth or armed with hooks or spines. Tentacles filiform or fingerlike, usually numerous, often forming a dense cluster and arranged like those in *Golfingia*. Longitudinal musculature divided into bands. Circular musculature usually divided into anastomosing bundles, which may not be noticed externally. Coelomic sacs present in the body wall of larger species. Four retractor muscles. Spindle muscle arises anteriorly from three roots and is fixed posteriorly to the body wall. Contractile vessel single and dorsal and usually with numerous tubules. Two nephridia usually with large semi-lunar nephrostomes. Paraneural muscle less well developed than in *Sipunculus*.

TYPE SPECIES. *Sipunculus australis* Keferstein, 1865.

REMARKS. Although many species of *Siphonosoma* resemble superficially those of *Sipunculus*, the two genera can be readily distinguished. The tentacles of *Siphonosoma* do not form a fold, the body wall is not usually furrowed into rectangles by the longitudinal and circular muscles and the introvert lacks scale-like papillae. The alimentary canal of *Siphonosoma* does not form a post-oesophageal loop and its spindle muscle arises anteriorly from three roots.

The presence of coelomic sacs or pockets in the body wall is generally considered to be a character of the genus. We are also assuming this although Fisher (1952 : 381) says that they 'are perhaps absent in small species having a thin body wall'. We have observed the sacs in *S. australe*, *S. cumanense*, *S. boholense* and *S. vastum* and their presence is reported in at least *S. ingens* (Fisher, 1952 : 384) and *S. eniwetoki* (Fisher, 1950b : 806).

Fisher's division of the genus into three subgenera (Fisher, 1950b : 805) helps to simplify the identification of species of *Siphonosoma*. We have followed his subdivision in preparing keys and in arranging specific descriptions.

TABLE 6
Subgenera of *Siphonosoma*

Subgenera	Transverse dissepiments	Numerous rectal caeca	Type Species
Siphonosoma s. s.	absent	absent	*S. australe* (Kef.)
Hesperosiphon	absent	present	*S. vastum* (Sel. & Bülow)
Damosiphon	present	absent	*S. cumanense* (Kef.)

KEY TO THE SUBGENERA OF SIPHONOSOMA

1 Transverse dissepiments present on the ventral wall of the coelom
DAMOSIPHON (p. 44)
– Transverse dissepiments not present on the ventral wall of the coelom . . 2

2   Numerous club-shaped or elongated caeca on the rectum
                                  HESPEROSIPHON (p. 53)
–   Numerous club-shaped or elongate caeca not present on the rectum
                                  SIPHONOSOMA (p. 58)

Sub-genus ***DAMOSIPHON*** Fisher, 1950

Damosiphon Fisher, 1950b : 805.

DESCRIPTION. Numerous transverse dissepiments attached to the coelomic surface of the body; rectum without numerous caeca and introvert without hooks.

TYPE SPECIES.   *Siphonosoma cumanense* (Keferstein).

REMARKS.   The species in this subgroup are remarkably alike and it is possible that they are synonymous.   For reasons that are stated in the remarks under the separate species *S. billitonense* (Sluiter) has been placed in the synonymy of *S. edule* (Sluiter), *S. formosum* in the synonymy of *S. cumanense* (Keferstein) and *S. hataii* Sato in the synonymy of *S. carolinense* Fischer.   The chief difference between *S. edule* and *S. cumanense* is that the length of the introvert of the former is about one tenth that of the trunk while that of the latter is about one third.   Just how good a character this is for separating the two species is uncertain.   *S. carolinense* differs from both *S. edule* and *S. cumanense* because it possesses 60–80 tentacles while the latter possess about 25–30.

The information set out in Table 6 is a summary of the characters of the six species of the subgenus *Damosiphon* which we consider should be reduced to three, *S. edule*, *S. cumanense* and *S. carolinense*.

DISTRIBUTION.   Known mostly from warmer waters.

SUBGENUS DAMOSIPHON—KEY TO THE SPECIES

1   Length of introvert relative to length of trunk about one eighth to one fourteenth
                                  S. edule (p. 51)
–   Length of introvert relative to length of trunk about one third to one seventh   .   2
2   Tentacles about 25–30   .   .   .   .   .   .   ***S. cumanense*** (p. 46)
–   Tentacles about 60–80   .   .   .   .   .   .   ***S. carolinense*** (p. 44)

Siphonosoma (Damosiphon) carolinense Fischer, 1928

Siphonosoma carolinense Fischer, 1928a : 138-140.
Siphonosoma hataii Sato, 1935b, pl. 3, fig. 7, text-figs 3–7; 1939 : 373.

TYPE LOCALITY.   Yap Island, Caroline Islands.

DESCRIPTION.   Introvert 58 mm, pale grey in colour; tentacles numerous, 60–80, thread-like and arranged in bundles.   Hooks absent but small ball-shaped skin bodies present.   Trunk 160 mm, blue grey to red grey in colour.   Longitudinal muscles freely anastomosing and gathered into 21 bands in the middle of the body and 18 posteriorly.   Two pairs of retractors; the ventral pair arises 20 mm behind the anus from muscle bands 1–3 and the dorsal pair somewhat more anteriorly

TABLE 7

A summary of the characters of six previously described species of the subgenus *Damosiphon*

	S. edule	*S. billitonense*	*S. cumanense*	*S. formosum*	*S. carolinense*	*S. hataii*
ratio of length of introvert to length of trunk	$\frac{1}{8}$–$\frac{1}{16}$	$\frac{1}{14}$	$\frac{1}{3}$	$\frac{1}{4}$	$\frac{1}{3}$	$\frac{1}{4}$
tentacles	24–30	?	20–25	numerous	60–80	80
papillae or skin bodies		elliptical	elliptical	large and tall to small		flat, elliptical
bands of longitudinal muscle	20–21 no anastomosing	19–21 no anastomosing	18–21	18 rarely anastomosing	18–21 some anastomosing	20–21 little anastomosing
dorsal retractors	7–8	8	8	6–7	7–8	8–9
ventral retractors	1–3	2–3	2–3	1–3	1–3	1–3
spindle muscle anteriorly with		3 roots	3 roots	3 roots	3 roots	3 roots
rectal caecum	present	present	present	present	present	present
nephridiopores	in front of anus	between 2–3	in front of anus	between 3–4	between 2–3	between 3–4
nephridia	short	long	short	almost free	free	posterior free
wing muscle	present	present	present	present	present	present
transverse dissepiments	present	present	present	present	present	present
contractile tubules or villi	present	present	present	present	present	present
type locality	Batavia (Indonesia)	Billiton (Indonesia)	Venezuela	Hattosi (Formosa)	Yap Is. (Caroline Is.)	Palau (West Caroline Is.)

from muscle bands 7–8. Contractile vessel with numerous villi. The oesophagus is fastened by two mesenteries; one arises from the first right and the other from the second left bands on a level with the roots of the ventral retractor. Spindle muscle arises anteriorly from three roots and posteriorly from one. The anus opens between muscle bands 9 and 10 and is fixed by a strong mesentery which covers four to five muscle bands. Rectal caecum large. The two nephridia open between muscle bands 2 and 3 about the same level as the anus. They are free for their whole length and reach to the roots of the ventral retractors. Keferstein bodies also present.

REMARKS. *S. carolinense*, according to Fischer, was named but never described by Spengel. Fischer's description is based on a single specimen. Fischer (1928 : 140) stated that the species is very close to *S. cumanense* but considered that the two were different on account of (1) the colour of its inner musculature, (2) the anastomosation of its longitudinal musculature, (3) the fact that the roots of the ventral retractors arise from slightly different heights and (4) the fact that the nephridia arise from between 2–3 instead of 3–4. Most of the differences, however, are only slight. Fischer appears to have overlooked the fact that the number of tentacles present is 60–80 while in *S. cumanense* there are 25–30.

S. hataii was described in considerable detail and well illustrated by Sato, 1935b. His three specimens came from Palau, West Carolina Is. Sato stated the species is closely related to *S. cumanense*. However, it possesses about 80 filamentous tentacles which places it near *S. carolinense*. The chief differences between *S. carolinense* and *S. hataii* are that the longitudinal muscles of the former (18–21) anastomose 'freely' (?) while those of the latter (20–21) do not and that the nephridia of the former are free for their whole length while those of the latter are free for the posterior two thirds of their length. These two '*cumanense*'-like sipunculans with 60–80 tentacles and collected from the Caroline Islands we are regarding as synonymous.

DISTRIBUTION. Yap Is., Carolines (Fischer, 1928) and Palau, West Carolines (Sato, 1935b).

Siphonosoma (Damosiphon) cumanense cumanense (Keferstein, 1867)
(Fig. 5A–B)

Phascolosoma cumanense Keferstein, 1867 : 53–55, pl. 6, figs 19–21.
Phascolosoma semirugosum Grübe in Selenka & de Man, 1883 : 104.
Sipunculus cumanensis: Selenka & de Man, 1883 : 104–107, pl. 12, figs 172–173; Sluiter, 1886 : 486; 1891 : 123; 1902 : 4; Fischer, 1892 : 88; 1895 : 9; 1914b : 1; Shipley, 1893 : 326–333; 1899a : 157; 1902d : 135; Augener, 1903 : 297–371; Ikeda, 1904 : 32–35; Lanchester, 1905a : 27; 1905b : 36; 1905c : 29.
Sipunculus deformis Baird, 1868; Edmonds, 1955 : 90; Rice & Stephen, 1970 : 57.
Siphonosoma cumanense: Spengel, 1912 : 263; Gerould, 1913 : 432–435; Fischer, 1926 : 107–108; Stiasny, 1930 : 208; Sato, 1934a : 246–247; 1937a : 146–148; 1939 : 369; Leroy, 1936 : 425; 1942 : 24–27, fig. 7; Shitamori, 1936 : 155–175; Stephen, 1941a : 404; 1952 : 435; Wesenberg-Lund, 1954 : 376–377, 1 fig.; 1957b : 2–4; 1959b : 58–59; 1963 : 103–104; Edmonds, 1955 : 90–92, text-figs 6–7; Cutler, 1965 : 56.
Siphonosoma formosum Sato, 1939 : 375–376, pl. 20, text-figs 14–17.
Sipunculus claviger Sluiter, 1902 : 7–8, pl. 1, figs 1–2.

TYPE LOCALITY. Cumana, Venezuela.

DESCRIPTION. Introvert about one third of the body length, with 20–25 long conical pointed tentacles; hooks absent but regular circles of fine papillae present. Trunk thin and elongate. Skin opaque and variable in colour, appearing smooth to the naked eye but under magnification seen to carry elliptical bodies, largest at the base of the introvert and at the posterior end of the trunk. Longitudinal muscles gathered into 18–21 bands, usually 20, but 23 and 24 have been recorded. Circular muscles gathered into numerous bands. Two pairs of short retractors, the ventral pair arising from muscle bands 2–3 and the dorsal from band 8. Intestinal coils, about 20, fixed by mesenteries to the body wall; traversed by the spindle muscle which has three anterior roots and one posterior root. A single intestinal fixing mesentary with two roots. Rectal caecum and wing muscles present. Nephridia short and opening well in front of the anus. Numerous internal crescentic dissepiments on the posterior portion of the body wall. Skin bodies present with plates some of which are shaped like hooks. Small oval shaped bodies, the so called 'Keferstein bodies', often present on the coelomic surface of the body wall. Contractile vessel with small villi.

REMARKS. S. cumanense is widely distributed in warmer waters and is almost circumtropical. The species appears to be a variable one especially with respect to the colour and texture of its skin and six subspecies have been described: S. cumanense cumanense (Keferstein, 1867), S. cumanense koreae Sato, 1939, S. cumanense opacum (Selenka, 1883), S. cumanense semirugosum (Selenka, 1883), S. cumanense vitreum (Selenka, 1883) and S. cumanense yapense Sato, 1935.

S. cumanense is very close to and possibly synonymous with S. edule (Pallas). The main difference between the two is that the length of the introvert of the former is about one third of the length of the trunk while that of the latter is about one tenth. Just how valid a character is this ratio is uncertain. Recently one of us determined the ratio for 11 specimens of S. cumanense collected from the same locality in Madagascar by Dr E. Cutler. All of the specimens had been fixed at the same time and the introverts of all were completely everted. The following results were obtained:

length of introvert (in mm)	length of trunk (in mm)	ratio
2	14	1/7 = 0·14
2	9	1/4·5 = 0.22
2	9	1/4·5 = 0·22
5·5	18	1/3·3 = 0·30
2·7	10	1/3·7 = 0·27
2·2	13·5	1/6·1 = 0·16
3	13	1/4·3 = 0·23
2	13	1/6·5 = 0·15
1·8	4·5	1/2·5 = 0·40
3	10·5	1/3·5 = 0·29
2·5	7	1/2·8 = 0·36
2·4	10	1/4·2 = 0·24

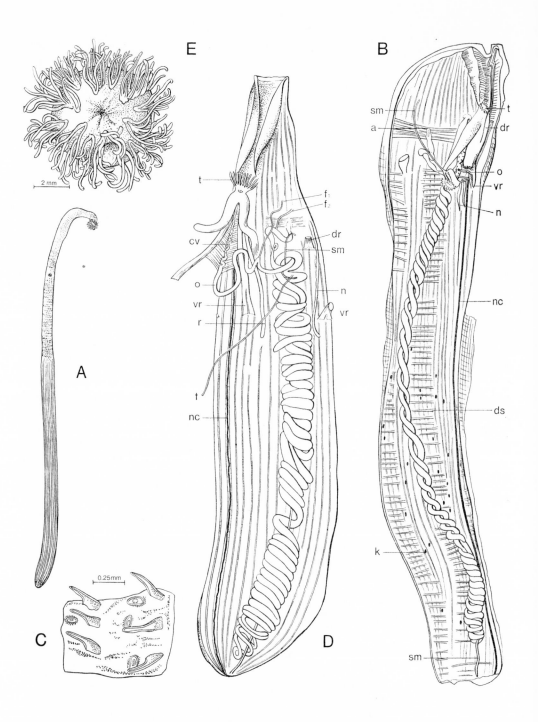

The results show that for a small sample of a given population which was fixed by the same method the ratio of the two lengths varies from 0·14 to 0·40. How careful and trustworthy the character becomes when used with specimens fixed at different times and possibly with different fixatives is problematical.

S. formosum, Sato 1939 : 373 was described from a single specimen found at Hattosi, Formosa. Sato was led to consider it a new species allied to *S. cumanense* because it possessed 18 longitudinal muscles which seldom anastomose. We consider that specimens of *S. cumanense* may have 18–21 muscles and that Sato's specimen can reasonably be classified as *S. cumanense* or a variation of it. The length of its introvert is about a quarter that of the trunk.

A re-examination of the type species has shown that *Sipunculus claviger* Sluiter, 1902 from Waingapu, Sumba, Indonesia is also *Siphonosoma cumanense*. The specimen lacks hooks and possesses 20 longitudinal muscles which anastomose only slightly, has transverse body dissepiments, two ventral retractors which arise from muscles 2–4 and two dorsal arising from muscles 8–9. The spindle muscles arise anteriorly from three roots, the ratio of the length of the introvert to that of the trunk is about 0·25, villi or tubules arise from the contractile vessel and there is an intestinal caecum.

DISTRIBUTION. East coast of America. Venezuela (Selenka & de Man, 1883); Florida (Gerould, 1913); Red Sea and Arabian Sea (Leroy, 1936; Stephen, 1941a; Wesenberg-Lund, 1957b); Madagascar (Cutler, 1965); Zanzibar (Lanchester, 1905c); Malaya, Singapore (Lanchester, 1905a); Penang (Lanchester, 1905a; Sluiter, 1891); Amboina (Augener, 1903); Laccadive and Maldive Islands (Shipley, 1902d); Pacific, New Guinea (Leroy, 1936); Loyalty Islands (Shipley, 1899); New Britain (Fischer, 1926a); Tahiti (Wesenberg-Lund, 1954b); Philippines (Selenka & de Man, 1884); Australia (Baird, 1868; Monro, 1931; Edmonds, 1955); Japan (Ikeda, 1904; Sato, 1934a, 1937a, 1939); Indo-China (Leroy, 1942).

The six subspecies of *S. cumanense* differ chiefly in the colour, thickness and texture of the skin. We have followed the lead of Wesenberg-Lund (1957b) in regarding *S. koreae* Sato, 1939 as a subspecies of *S. cumanense*.

Siphonosoma (Damosiphon) cumanense koreae Sato, 1939
(Fig. 6F)

Siphonosoma koreae Sato, 1939 : 379–381, pl. 23, text-figs 23–26; Stephen, 1952 : 181–182.
Siphonosoma cumanense var. *koreae* Wesenberg-Lund, 1957b : 4; 1959b : 59.

TYPE LOCALITY. Gunzan, Korea.

DESCRIPTION. Resembling *S. cumanense cumanense* in anatomy, but differing in colour, the posterior end being light yellow. The papillae at the base of the introvert are crowded and arranged in longitudinal rows.

DISTRIBUTION. Korea (Sato, 1939), Gulf of Aquaba (Stephen, 1952).

FIG. 5 (A–B) *Siphonosoma cumanense*. (A) Entire animal, about half natural size. (B) Dissected specimen (after Keferstein). (C–D) *Siphonosoma australe*. (c) Hooks from the introvert (after Selenka). (D) Dissected specimen (after Selenka). (E) *Siphonosoma novaepommeraniae*. Tentacular crown (after Wesenberg-Lund). KEY: *See* Fig. 2, p. 23.

Siphonosoma (Damosiphon) cumanense opacum (Selenka & Bülow, 1883)

Sipunculus cumanensis opacus Selenka & Bülow, 1883 : 106; Sluiter, 1882b : 16; Fischer, 1892 : 88; 1895 : 9; 1914a : 59–61.
Siphonosoma cumanense opaca Sato, 1935b : 304–305, pl. 3, fig. 5.

TYPE LOCALITY. Mauritius.

DESCRIPTION. Similar in anatomy to S. cumanense cumanense but differing in the following particulars. The trunk is light yellow to grey, the skin is not translucent and the musculature is well developed. The skin bodies at the anterior and posterior ends are similar in structure to those of vitrea, but larger. The dorsal retractors arise from the fourth and eighth muscle bands.

DISTRIBUTION. Mauritius (Selenka & Bülow, 1883; Fischer, 1895); Ascension (Selenka & Bülow, 1883; Sluiter, 1882b); East Africa: Madagascar (Fischer, 1895); Zanzibar (Fischer, 1892); Red Sea (Hérubel, 1904); West Caroline Islands (Sato, 1935b).

Siphonosoma (Damosiphon) cumanense semirugosum (Selenka & de Man, 1883)

Sipunculus cumanensis var. semirugosus Selenka & de Man, 1883 : 106–107; Hérubel, 1904a : 563; Lanchester, 1905a : 29; Wesenberg-Lund, 1957b : 3–4; 1959 : 59.
Siphonosoma cumanense var. semirugosa Stephen & Robertson, 1952 : 435.

TYPE LOCALITY. Red Sea.

DESCRIPTION. This subspecies differs from S. cumanense cumanense in that the trunk is thick and opaque with a more or less intensive red-brown colour, and the strong circular and longitudinal muscles are divided into rectangles. Only at the posterior end and at the base of the introvert is the skin greyer and covered with the usual large skin bodies. In these areas the muscle bands are not strong. Apparently no fastening mesentery to the intestine.

DISTRIBUTION. Red Sea (Selenka & de Man, 1883); Zanzibar (Lanchester, 1905a; Stephen & Robertson, 1952).

Siphonosoma (Damosiphon) cumanense vitreum (Selenka & Bülow, 1883)

Sipunculus cumanensis var. vitreus Selenka & Bülow, 1883 : 106–107; Fischer, 1895 : 9; Gerould, 1913 : 432–435.
Siphonosoma cumanense var. vitrea Fischer, 1921b : 3–4; 1922b : 4–5; 1925 : 4–5; Sato, 1935b : 303–304, pl. 3, figs 3–4; Stephen & Robertson, 1952 : 435.

TYPE LOCALITY. Cumana, Venezuela.

DESCRIPTION. This subspecies differs from the nominate form in that the skin is shining and transparent, so that the longitudinal and circular muscle bands are visible through it.

DISTRIBUTION. Venezuela (Selenka & Bülow, 1883); Florida (Gerould, 1913); Zanzibar (Stephen & Robertson, 1952); Philippines (Selenka & Bülow, 1883); West Caroline Islands (Sato, 1935b); Australia (Fischer, 1921b).

Siphonosoma (Damosiphon) cumanense yapense Sato, 1935

Siphonosoma cumanense var. *yapense* Sato, 1935b : 305, pl. 3, fig. 6.

TYPE LOCALITY. Mappu, Yap Island, West Caroline Islands.

DESCRIPTION. Animals rather small, 50–70 mm in length, 5–6 mm in diameter. On the posterior portion of the trunk the skin is very thin and transparent, but at the base of the introvert it is extremely thick and opaque and yellowish brown in colour.

REMARKS. Described originally from numerous specimens. Distinguished from the nominate subspecies by the size and form of the body, as well as by the different thicknesses of the skin and its colouration.

DISTRIBUTION. As for the type locality.

Siphonosoma (Damosiphon) edule (Pallas, 1774)

Lumbricus edulis Pallas, 1774 : 10–12.
Sipunculus edulis: Lamarck, 1816 : 79; de Blainville, 1827 : 310; Diesing, 1851 : 61; Quatre-
    fages, 1865 : 615; Sluiter, 1882 : 148–150, pl. 1, figs 1 & 10; pl. 2, fig. 4; pl. 3, fig. 1; 1886 :
    484; 1891 : 122; 1902 : 5; Selenka & de Man, 1883 : 107–108; Shipley, 1899a : 157–158;
    Lanchester, 1905c : 29.
Siphonosoma edule: Spengel, 1912 : 263; Gerould, 1913 : 432; Fischer, 1926 : 106; Sato, 1939 :
    371–373, pl. 20, fig. 6.
Sipunculus billitonensis Sluiter, 1886 : 487–488, pl. 3, figs 1–2; 1891 : 123; 1902 : 4–5; Shipley,
    1899a : 157, pl. 18, figs 6–7; 1902d : 135; Lanchester, 1905c : 30.
Siphonosoma billitonense: Stephen, 1941 : 402.

TYPE LOCALITY. Batavia; no locality specified. According to Pallas (1774) 'Abundant Lumbrici edules, qui a Javanis "Porut-ajang" a Chinensibus vero "Soa-see" appellantur, in littore sabuloso meridionali portus Bataviae, iis etiam in locis quae recedente aestu mare derelinquit.' The specimen from which Sluiter (1882 : 149) redescribed the species was collected at Reed, Batavia in Tandjong Priok.

DESCRIPTION (based on Sluiter, 1882 : 149 and 1886 : 484). Introvert short, an eighth to a tenth of the body-length, 24–30 large and small tentacles. Trunk elongate, cylindrical, up to 180 mm in length; posterior end drawn out to a smooth point where the longitudinal muscle bands show only as fibres. Skin smooth. Longitudinal muscles gathered into 20–21 bands which do not anastomose. Two pairs of short retractors, arising from about the same level, the ventrals from bands 1–3 and the dorsals from bands 7–8. About 30 intestinal coils fastened to the body wall by numerous fine mesenteries. A stout spindle muscle arises in front of the anus, traverses the intestinal coils and is attached to the posterior end of the trunk. A number of transverse dissepiments present on the posterior section of the body wall. A contractile vessel runs along the dorsal side of the oesophagus and bears numerous short villi. The rectum is fastened by several wing muscles. Rectal caecum present. Two pairs of fairly short nephridia, swollen anteriorly and opening just in front of the anus.

REMARKS. Pallas' account describes the general appearance of the animal and relates how it was used as food by the Batavians. Lamarck (1816), de Blainville (1827), Diesing (1851) and Quatrefages (1865) merely repeated Pallas' brief description. Sluiter (1882 : 148–150) redescribed what he believed to be *S. edule* from specimens collected at Reed, Batavia. Sluiter identified the species from the native name which Pallas mentioned in his description. In a second article Sluiter (1886 : 484) added slightly to his first description of the species.

In this second article Sluiter (1886 : 487) also described *Siphonosoma billitonense*, a second 'edulis'-like specimen from Billiton, Indonesia. *S. billitonense* differed from *S. edule* in that (1) the length of its introvert was only one fourteenth that of its body while that of *S. edule* was one eighth to one tenth and (2) its nephridia were long while those of *S. edule* were short. The following is a summary of Sluiter's description of *S. billitonense*:

Introvert short, about one fourteenth of the length of the body. Trunk slender, 250–300 mm in length; skin light yellowish and transparent in young animals, the longitudinal muscles showing up clearly. Circular muscles noticeable only in young animals. In the middle of the trunk the skin bodies or epidermal glands are elliptical and contain a few large plates arranged like hooks, and clearly distinguished from their surroundings. They are arranged in longitudinal rows so that there is almost a double row to each longitudinal muscle bundle. In the anterior and posterior regions they are of a different form with numerous small plates not clearly marked off from their surroundings and arranged irregularly; also, some larger plates are scattered amongst the smaller ones, as in *S. cumanense*. The longitudinal muscles are gathered into 19–20 bands which do not anastomose. Two pairs of retractors which join only near the base of the introvert; the ventral pair arises from muscles bands 2 and 3 and the dorsal from band 8 at some distance in front of the ventral pair. Oesophagus fairly long so that the first intestinal coil appears only behind the base of the ventral retractor. The spindle muscle emerges from the last coil and is attached to the posterior end of the body. A large rectal caecum is present. The spindle muscle splits into three branches at the level of the first coil; two short branches join the longitudinal muscles about the base of the ventral retractors and the third is attached to the body wall at a considerable distance in front of the anus. The rectum is fixed by wing muscles. The two nephridia open in front of the anus between the second and third bundles; they are fairly long and reach to the second intestinal coil. Nephrostomes with a ciliated opening. Contractile vessel present on the foregut. Semi-circular dissepiments present on the posterior wall of the trunk.

What is remarkable is that Sluiter does not seem to have considered the possibility of *S. edule* and *S. billitonense* being the same species. Although Sluiter gave no information about the number of tentacles of *S. billitonense* it seems to us that the similarity of the two descriptions justifies the conclusion that the two species are the same. The difference between the length of such a muscular organ as the introvert seems to fall within the limits of variation normally found in a species and the size of nephridia depends to some extent on the reproductive and possibly osmotic condition of the specimens examined. In addition we have examined a number of specimens from Indonesia that are now in the collection at the British Museum (Natural History) and which have been named *S. edule* and *S. billitonense* by different workers. We have been unable to distinguish between the specimens and consider the two species to be synonymous, *S. edule* being the older name.

Another important question and one that seems to have exercised Sluiter's mind is whether *S. edule* and *S. cumanense* (Keferstein)—type locality, Venezuela—are the same. They are certainly very close species. In addition *S. cumanese* appears to be a variable species because six subspecies, which differ in the colour and texture of the skin, have been described. The chief difference between the two is that the introvert of *S. cumanense* is relatively a longer structure than that of *S. edule*. Sluiter (1886 : 484) says, 'Es ist namentlich der *S. edulis* dem *S. cumanensis* Kef. sehr ähnlich. Der Unterschiede zwischen beiden Arten wäre also hauptsächlid dass der Rüssel bei *S. edulis* viel kürzer ist als bei *S. cumanensis* wo er noch immer $\frac{1}{3}$ der Körperlänge beträgt, indem er bei *S. edulis* nur $\frac{1}{10}$ der Körperlange beträgt.'

Although it is possible that the two species are the same we have hesitated to regard them as such at present. The reason is that we have seen a number of specimens of *S. cumanense* in which the introvert is a relatively longer structure than that in *S. edule*. What we have not been able to do is to examine a reasonably large sample of specimens from one locality which would enable one to decide whether the differences of length of the introvert are inter- or intra-specific. If *S. edule* and *S. cumanense* are considered synonymous the former is the older name.

DISTRIBUTION. Indonesia (Sluiter, 1882, 1886, 1891, 1902; Pallas, 1774). Christmas Is., Indian Ocean (Shipley, 1899a), Loyalty Is. (Shipley, 1899a), Laccadive and Maldive Is. (Shipley, 1902; Stephen, 1941). Japan (Sato, 1939).

Subgenus *HESPEROSIPHON* Fisher, 1950

Hesperosiphon Fisher, 1950b : 805.

DESCRIPTION. No transverse dissepiments attached to the coelomic surface of the body cavity; rectum without numerous caeca.

TYPE SPECIES. *Siphonosoma vastum* (Selenka & Bülow).

REMARKS. The species of this subgenus fall into two groups, those with spines or spinelets on the introvert, *S. vastum* (Selenka & Bülow, 1883) and *S. parvum* Fischer, 1928a and those without spines, *S. marchadi* Stephen, 1960. A re-examination of the type specimen of *S. vastum* has shown that spines are present, a fact not stated by Selenka & Bülow in their original description. *S. crassum* Spengel in Fischer, 1919a has been placed in the synonymy of *S. vastum*. *S. parvum* is very close to *S. vastum* and is said to possess fewer but larger rectal villi, very difficult characters to judge in the absence of measurements. Spengel, according to Fischer (1928a : 143) intended to divide his collection of *S. vastum* into 8–9 new species. *S. parvum* appears to have been one of them. *S. marchadi* Stephen lacks spines.

DISTRIBUTION. The warmer waters of the Indian and Pacific Oceans.

Siphonosoma (Hesperosiphon) marchadi Stephen, 1960

Siphonosoma marchadi Stephen, 1960 : 515–516.

TYPE LOCALITY.   Port of Dakar, Senegal.   *Type.*   Mus. Nat. d'Hist. Nat., Paris.

DESCRIPTION.   Introvert smooth and without spines, 35 mm long.   Trunk, anterior portion 195 mm, posterior portion missing.   Body rugose, marked in small squares each with a small reddish-brown flat papilla in the centre.   Longitudinal muscles gathered into about 23 bands with much anastomosing.   Retractors are deeply ridged and surround the anterior part of the alimentary canal like a sheath. Nephridia long, thin, brown tubes about one third as long as the body and opening in front of the anus.   Rectum with numerous long villi.   A strong spindle muscle. The ventral retractors arise from bands 2–3 and the dorsals from bands 6–7.

REMARKS.   Described originally from two incomplete specimens.   The species is not well known.   Stephen (1960 : 516) says that the 'anterior part of the oesophagus bears a large diverticulum'.   This is very unusual.   The type specimen has not been available for re-examination.

DISTRIBUTION.   As for the type locality.

Siphonosoma (Hesperosiphon) parvum (Fischer, 1928)

(Fig. 6D–E)

Sipunculus parvum Fischer, 1928a : 141–143, figs 1–2.

TYPE LOCALITY.   Marshall Islands.

DESCRIPTION.   Introvert 6 mm in length; 60–80 tentacles, yellowish grey in colour, arranged in five bundles, 20–25 in the larger and 6–8 in the smaller.   Twenty-five to thirty rows of hooks.   The points of the hooks are stumpy and bent at an angle of 45°.   Trunk 25 mm in length.   Longitudinal muscles gathered into 27 bands.   Two pairs of retractors; the ventral pair arises at the middle of the body from bands 2–6 and the dorsal somewhat more anteriorly from bands 8–9.   Both pairs are united for their anterior half to form a simple muscle.   Seventeen intestinal coils traversed by a spindle muscle which is fixed near the anus between muscle bands 12 and 13.   Rectum with a large ball-shaped intestinal caecum and numerous large diverticula between the intestinal caecum and anus.   The rectum is fixed by a broad wing muscle; another fixing muscle runs from the beginning of the blind sacs and a third from the second intestinal convolution.   The red-brown nephridia open between bands 2 and 3 on a level with the anus and the anterior half of each is fixed.

REMARKS. Known only from the holotype. Fischer gives no information about the size of the spines.

DISTRIBUTION. As for the type locality.

Siphonosoma (Hesperosiphon) vastum vastum (Selenka & Bülow, 1883)

(Fig. 6A–C)

Sipunculus vastus Selenka & Bülow, 1883 : 103–104, pl. 12, fig. 171, pl. 13, fig. 179; Shipley, 1898 : 469; 1899a : 158; 1902d : 136; Augener, 1903 : 315–317; Fischer, 1919a : 279; 1927 : 200.
Siphonosoma vastus: Wesenberg-Lund, 1937c : 2–5, figs 1, 2.
Siphonosoma vastum: Edmonds, 1955 : 92–95, figs 8–9.
Siphonosoma crassum Spengel in Fischer, 1919a : 279; 1927 : 199.

TYPE LOCALITY. Jaluit (Marshall Is.). Type. Zoological Museum of Humboldt University of Berlin.

DESCRIPTION. Introvert 25–30 mm long and trunk up to 95 mm. Colour light yellow-grey. Anterior to the anus the trunk is darker and is covered with dark grey-brown papillae; the middle of the trunk is lighter in colour. The posterior region is grey-white and carries large, dark skin bodies. Introvert bears numerous, large conical tentacles and numerous rings of dark brown, claw-like spines about 0·25–0·33 mm long. Anus conspicuous and speckled with brown. Longitudinal muscles split into 27 strong, widely separated bands which anastomose only slightly. Circular musculature forms anastomosing bands. Two pairs of retractor muscles, the stronger ventral pair arising from bands 2–5 or 2–6 and the dorsal more anteriorly from muscle 8 or 8–9. Spindle muscle arises anteriorly from three roots but only one posteriorly. Rectum short, bearing numerous villi or caeca, 2–3 mm high, along its whole length. Contractile vessel reaches as far as the first intestinal coil. Nephridia open just in front of the anus and are fixed to the body wall for some of their length. Coelomic papillae present on the coelomic surface of the body wall near the fan-shaped nephrostome.

REMARKS. Selenka's omission to mention the presence of spines on the introvert of the type species has caused some confusion about the species. Fischer (1919) gave the name S. crassum to a 'vastus-like' specimen from Western Australia which possessed spines and Edmonds (1955) and Wesenberg-Lund (1937) reported sipunculans very close to S. vastum but possessing spines. Both Edmonds and Wesenberg-Lund thought that S. vastum probably possessed spines. Fischer apparently thought so too, because his S. crassum of 1919 became in Fischer, 1926 S. vastum. The problem about the spines has been solved by a re-examination of the type specimen (cat. no. 918) in the Berlin Museum. The locality of the specimen is Jaluit and the trunk of the animal about 90 mm long. The specimen, however, is not in a good state of preservation. Nevertheless an examination of a small section of the anterior region of the introvert reveals that numerous rings of yellow-brown, claw-like hooks are present.

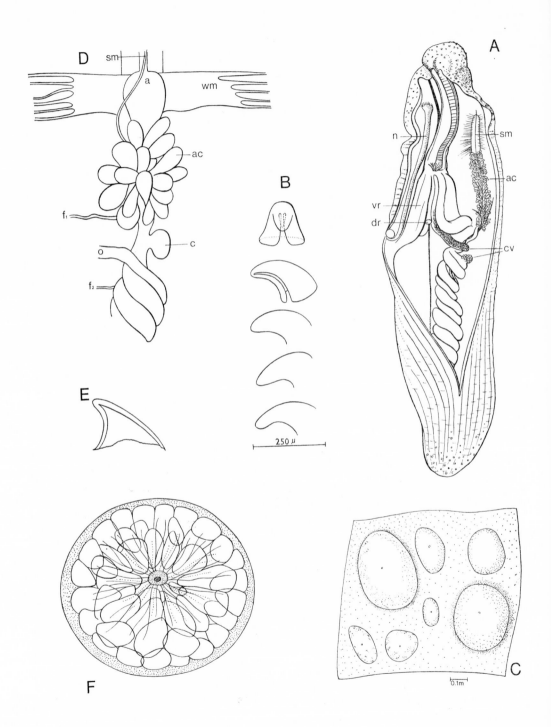

Edmonds (1955) reported that his specimen from the Barrier Reef possessed 23–26 longitudinal muscles, retractors that arose from muscles 2–6 and 9 or 10, a contractile vessel with small tubules, a globular, sac-like intestinal caecum and two fastening muscles which were attached to the last whorl of the intestine.

S. parvum Fischer is very close to *S. vastum*, especially now that it is known that the introvert of the latter is armed with spines. Wesenberg-Lund's figure of *S. vastum* (Wesenberg-Lund, 1937c, fig. 1) especially in the number and size of the rectal caeca, almost matches Fischer's figure of *S. parvum*.

Two additional subspecies have been described.

DISTRIBUTION. *Indian Ocean*: Mauritius (Selenka & Bülow, 1883); Laccadive and Maldive Islands (Shipley, 1902d); Indonesia (Wesenberg-Lund, 1937c); Western Australia (Fischer, 1927).

Pacific Ocean: Amboina (Augener, 1903); Funafuti, Rotuma (Shipley, 1898); New Britain, Loyalty Islands, New Caledonia (Shipley, 1899); Queensland (Edmonds, 1955).

Siphonosoma (Hesperosiphon) vastum album (Shipley, 1899)

Sipunculus vastus albus Shipley, 1899a : 158; 1902d : 137.

DESCRIPTION. In this subspecies the skin is pearly white and fairly translucent.

REMARKS. See *S. vastum obscurum* below.

DISTRIBUTION. New Britain, New Caledonia, Loyalty Islands (Shipley, 1899a); Laccadive and Maldive Islands (Shipley, 1902d).

Siphonosoma (Hesperosiphon) vastum obscurum (Shipley, 1899)

Sipunculus vastus obscurus Shipley, 1899a : 158.

DESCRIPTION. In this variety the skin is dark purplish brown and quite opaque.

REMARKS. These two subspecies seem to occur together when the species is taken in numbers. Whether they are true subspecies or merely colour phases is unknown.

DISTRIBUTION. As for *S. vastum album*.

FIG. 6. (A–C) *Siphonosoma vastum*. (A) Internal anatomy of type specimen (after Selenka). (B) Hooks from the introvert of the type specimen. (C) Skin from the posterior region of the body (after Selenka). (D–E) *Siphonosoma parvum*. (D) Posterior region of the alimentary canal. (E) Introvert spine. (D–E after Fischer.) (F) *Siphonosoma cumanense koreae*. Papillae from the middle region of the trunk (after Sato). KEY: *See* Fig. 2, p. 23.

E

Subgenus *SIPHONOSOMA* (sensu stricto) Fisher, 1950

Siphonosoma (s.s.) Fisher, 1950b : 808.

DESCRIPTION.   No transverse dissepiments in the body cavity; rectum without numerous caeca.

TYPE SPECIES.   *Siphonosoma australe* (Keferstein).

REMARKS.   The species of this subgenus fall into two groups, one that possesses spines or spine-like papillae and another that lacks spines on the introvert.

Species with spines or blunt spine-like papillae on the introvert	Species without introvert spines
S. arcassonense (Cuénot)	*S. amamiense* (Ikeda)
S. australe (Keferstein)	*S. boholense* (Selenka & de Man)
S. eniwetoki Fisher	*S. bonhourei* (Hérubel)
S. pescadolense (Sato)	*S. dayi* Stephen
S. rotumanum (Shipley)	*S. funafuti* (Shipley)
S. takatsukii Sato	*S. ingens* Fisher
	S. joubini (Hérubel)
	S. mourense Sato
	S. novaepommeraniae (Fischer)
	S. pellucidum (Sluiter)

Five of the species, *S. bonhourei*, *S. eniwetoki*, *S. joubini*, *S. pescadolense* and *S. takatsukii* are known only from the holotype specimens.   An examination of the type specimen of *S. rotumanum* (Shipley) shows that almost regular rings of blunt, spine-like papillae are present on its introvert.   This fact brings *S. hawaiense* Edmonds into the synonymy of *S. rotumanum*.

SUBGENUS SIPHONOSOMA—KEY TO SPECIES

1   Introvert with hooks, spines or blunt spine-like papillae   2
–   Introvert without hooks, spines or spine-like papillae   7
2   Rectal caecum present   3
–   Rectal caecum absent   5
3   Blunt-spines or spine-like papillae present in rings on the introvert (longitudinal muscles 14–17, two kinds of papillae present on the surface of trunk, spindle muscle with two lateral wing-like roots) . . . .   **S. rotumanum** (p. 71)
–   Pointed spines present   4
4   Prominent skin glands in anal and posterior regions of trunk (oesophageal fixing muscle attached in a mid-ventral line) . . . .   **S. eniwetoki** (p. 65)
–   Skin glands not prominent in anal region (no eosophageal fixing muscle attached mid-ventrally) . . . .   **S. australe** (p. 61)
5   Four yellow, tubular bodies attached at the posterior extremity of the coelom (numerous tentacles arranged rather complexly in double meridional series, 23–24 anastomosing longitudinal muscles) . . .   **S. arcassonense** (p. 60)
–   No yellow, tubular bodies attached at the posterior extremity of the coelom .   6
6   Two kinds of papillae on body surface (introvert about one fifth as long as the trunk, 14–18 longitudinal muscles, ventral retractors arise from muscles 2–3 and dorsals from 5–7) . . . .   **S. takatsukii** (p. 73)

- One kind of papillae on body surface (introvert about half as long as the trunk, 15 longitudinal muscles, ventral retractors from muscles 2–3 and dorsals from 3–4) ***S. pescadolense*** (p. 70)

7 Retractor muscles arise at the same level 8
- Retractor muscles arise at different levels 9
8 Rectal caecum present (two types of papillae on the surface of the body, longitudinal muscles 20, two intestinal fasteners; wart-like papillae in front of the anus; ventral retractors arise from bands 1–3 and dorsal from 6–7)   ***S. novaepommeraniae*** (p. 69)
- Rectal caecum absent (longitudinal muscles 28, ventral retractors arise from 3–4 and dorsal from 9–10)   .   .   .   .   .   .   ***S. pellucidum*** (p. 69)
9 Longitudinal muscle bands 30 or more (large species) .   .   ***S. boholense*** (p. 63)
- Longitudinal muscle bands less than 30   10
10 Longitudinal muscle bands 20 or more   11
- Longitudinal muscle bands less than 20   13
11 Small scale-like papillae on the introvert (longitudinal muscles 21, circular musculature of introvert arranged in rings, ventral retractors from muscles 3–4, dorsal retractors more anteriorly from 7–8)   .   .   .   .   ***S. dayi*** (p. 64)
- No scale-like papillae on the introvert   12
12 Four or five slender fusiform bodies at posterior extremity of the body cavity (tentacles numerous, arranged in 12 meridional rows, longitudinal muscles 20–25, with little anastomosation, ventral retractor muscles from bands 3–5 and dorsal retractors from 7–8, no caecum) .   .   .   .   ***S. ingens*** (p. 66)
- No fusiform bodies present (tentacles arranged in 12 radial rows each of about 20, longitudinal muscles 22, ventral retractors from bands 3–4 and dorsal from 8–10, no caecum, circular muscles not divided into fascicles)   .   ***S. mourense*** (p. 67)
13 Dorsal retractors well developed   14
- Dorsal retractors poorly developed (ventral retractors arise in posterior third of the trunk from a single longitudinal muscle, longitudinal muscles 18, no rectal caecum) ***S. bonhourei*** (p. 64)
14 Longitudinal muscle bands 18 (no rectal caecum)   .   .   ***S. joubini*** (p. 66)
- Longitudinal muscle bands less than 18   15
15 Two stout fastening muscles other than the spindle muscle (about 80 filamentous tentacles arranged in 12 rows, 15 broad longitudinal muscles, ventral retractors arise from muscles 2–3 and dorsal more anteriorly from muscle 4, no rectal caecum) ***S. amamiense*** (p. 59)
- No fastening muscles present other than the spindle muscle   ***S. funafuti*** (p. 65)

Siphonosoma (Siphonosoma) amamiense (Ikeda, 1904)

Sipunculus amamiensis Ikeda, 1904 : 36–38, figs 64–65; 1924 : 31.
Siphonosoma amamiense: Sato, 1939 : 371.

TYPE LOCALITY. Koniya, Japan.

DESCRIPTION. Introvert a quarter of the length of the trunk, deep yellowish-brown in colour and without hooks or spines; tentacles filamentous, about 80 in number and arranged in 16 rows. Trunk 100 to 120 mm in length, 10–15 mm in breadth; yellowish brown in colour. Skin covered with papillae which are largest at the base of the introvert and at the posterior end of the trunk; in the middle of the trunk, they are nearly flat and circular. Irregular wrinkle-like folds occur between the papillae and divide the surface into an irregular meshwork. Longitudinal muscles gathered into 15 broad bands which rarely anastomose. Two slender pairs of retractors; the ventral pair is the larger and springs from muscle bands 2–3 in the middle of the trunk and the dorsal arises far more anteriorly from the fourth muscle band. Contractile vessel runs along the whole dorsal side of the oesophagus and gives off very numerous contractile villi. The spindle muscle is attached anteriorly and posteriorly and gives off two lateral branches at the beginning of the intestinal convolutions. These branches end on the sixth longitudinal muscle band nearly at the same level as the roots of the dorsal retractors. Two stout fixing muscles, one arises from the fourth longitudinal muscle band close to the roots of the right dorsal retractor and is attached to the beginning of the rectum. The other springs from the first longitudinal muscle band nearly midway between the roots of the retractors and is attached to the oesophagus near the intestinal convolutions. Nephridia deep reddish-brown, opening about the level of the anus, and free for their whole length. No rectal caecum or eye-spots.

REMARKS. Known from numerous specimens.

DISTRIBUTION. Japan (Ikeda, 1904, 1924; Sato, 1939).

Siphonosoma (Siphonosoma) arcassonense (Cuénot, 1902)

(Fig. 7D)

Sipunculus arcassonense Cuénot, 1902a : 15, pl. 1, figs 1–5; 1922 : 13–14, figs 7a & b.

TYPE LOCALITY. Bay of Arcachon, western France.

DESCRIPTION. Introvert less than one third of the body length; regular, annular folds of skin present at the base which encloses a single or double row of papillae. About 216 tentacles present. Anteriorly 130–155 circles of spines, posteriorly the circles are incomplete. Total length up to 540 mm. When contracted it is nearly always in the form of a strongly bent arc. The colour when first taken is matt-white but on exposure to the air it becomes rose lilac. Four pairs retractors; the ventral pair arises from muscle bands 3 and 4, or 3, 4 and 5; the thinner dorsal pair arises from muscle bands 7 and 8. Contractile vessel with villi. Spindle muscle attached near to the posterior end of the body. Nephridia free. Four yellow tubular glands present internally at the posterior base of the trunk.

REMARKS. Description based originally on a number of specimens. One of us collected a living specimen of this species while digging for *Sipunculus nudus* near Cape Ferrat in the Bay of Arcachon, France in June, 1967. The trunk was about 150 mm long and the introvert about 60 mm. The skin is smooth and the organization and structure of the tentacles very much like those of *S. ingens* (Fisher, 1952, pl. 20, fig. 1). About 23–24 anastomosing longitudinal muscles were present and the dorsal retractors arise more anteriorly than the ventral. The spindle muscle arises anteriorly from three roots. Four yellow tubular glands like those described by Cuénot (1902) were found at the posterior end of the body cavity. Similar structure have also been found in *S. ingens*. The introvert of *S. arcassonense*, however, is definitely armed with numerous rows of spines. The living animal burrows into the sand very much in the manner of a glycerid worm.

DISTRIBUTION. Bay of Arcachon, France.

Siphonosoma (Siphonosoma) australe (Keferstein, 1865)

(Fig. 5C–D)

Phascolosoma australe Keferstein, 1865a : 422–423, pl. 32, figs 12, 13.
Sipunculus australis: Selenka & de Man, 1883 : 90, pl. 13, figs 180–183; Sluiter, 1902 : 5; Fischer, 1895 : 8, fig. 5; Shipley, 1899a : 156–157, pl. 18, figs 4–5; Lanchester, 1905c : 30; Ikeda, 1905a : 169; Graveley, 1927 : 87.
Sipunculus aeneus Baird, 1868 : 76; Edmonds, 1961 : 217–220; Rice & Stephen, 1970 : 57.
Siphonosoma australe: Augener, 1903 : 346; Prashad, 1936 : 237–238, pl. 9, figs 4–6; Fischer, 1922b : 2–4; 1926 : 106, pl. 3, fig. 1; Fisher, 1950b : 807; Stephen & Robertson, 1952 : 435–436; Edmonds, 1955 : 95; 1962 : 217–220, figs 1–2; Cutler, 1965 : 56.

Type Locality. Sydney, New South Wales, Australia.

Description. Papillae on the introvert twice as large as those on the body but smaller than those at the posterior region of the trunk. Fifty-five to sixty rows of simple, large, long, very slightly bent hooks, brownish-black in colour lie behind the tentacles. Trunk long, worm-like, up to 230 mm, 10–15 times as long as thick. The skin is thin so that the longitudinal bands are visible; strongly iridescent, yellowish or bluish-grey, reddish-yellow at the posterior end and at the introvert base. Smooth round papillae sparingly scattered over the whole body; those posteriorly being large and visible to the eye. Longitudinal muscles split into 15–20 broad irregularly anastomosing bands. Circular muscles also clearly split into bands in the middle of the body. Two pairs of retractor muscles which fuse; the broader ventral pair arises in the hinder part of the anterior third of the body from four or five muscles, the weaker dorsal pair near the anus. Very numerous intestinal convolutions traversed by a strong spindle muscle which is attached to the posterior end of the body. Three fixing muscles which arise from the forward coils: two are attached near the anus while the third, usually with two roots, is attached near the nerve cord at the level of the roots of the dorsal retractors. Contractile vessel simple. Two thin nephridia, free and about one third as long as the trunk; nephridiopore just in front of the anus.

Remarks. Both Fisher (1950b) and Edmonds (1962) have redescribed specimens of *S. australe* from the Pacific Region. Both report that the ventral retractors arise from muscles 1–3 and the dorsals more anteriorly from 3–6 (Fisher) and 4–6 (Edmonds). Both report the presence of an intestinal caecum. *S. eniwetoki* Fisher, 1950 is a very closely related species; it is very difficult to distinguish between the two.

Distribution. Zanzibar (Lanchester, 1905c). Madagascar (Cutler, 1965). Gulf of Manaar (Graveley, 1927; Prashad, 1936). Indonesia (Lanchester, 1905a). Pacific Ocean: Philippines (Ikeda, 1905a); Loyalty Islands (Shipley, 1899); Samoa and Fiji (Fischer, 1922b); New Britain (Fischer, 1922b). Australia: Sydney, New South Wales (Keferstein, 1865; Augener, 1903). Society Islands (Augener, 1903). New Zealand (Edmonds, 1961).

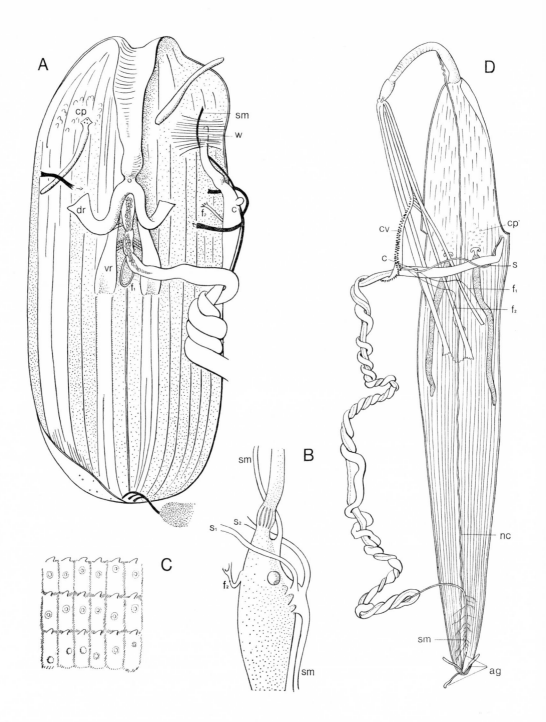

Siphonosoma (Siphonosoma) boholense (Selenka & de Man, 1883)

Sipunculus boholensis Selenka & de Man, 1883 : 109–111, pl. 12, figs 175–177; Fischer, 1895 : 5–6; Lanchester, 1905a : 27.

TYPE LOCALITY. Bohol.

DESCRIPTION. Introvert 120–140 mm in length, with small papillae. Body 80 mm, grey-brown with many dark-coloured skin bodies. Longitudinal muscles in 30 bands in the region of the retractor muscles. Two pairs of retractors which usually span three bundles, usually 4–6, but seldom two; the dorsal pair arises more anteriorly than the ventral. The intestinal convolutions are bound throughout to the spindle muscle by fine roots, thicker and more numerous posteriorly. Rectum with a caecum bound to the spindle muscle. The spindle muscle has three roots; two of about equal size arise from the twelfth band posteriorly to the base of the dorsal retractor and are attached to the beginning of the intestinal convolutions. The third unpaired root arises near the anus and is also attached to the beginning of the intestinal convolutions. The spindle muscle is attached to the posterior extremity of the body and a small intestinal fastening muscle with two roots arises anteriorly from the first muscle band. Contractile vessel with many tubules lies on the oesophagus. Two nephridia which reach to about the base of the dorsal retractors; they are red-brown in colour and are free posteriorly. Two eye-spots.

REMARKS. Described by Selenka & de Man from a manuscript by Semper. Fischer (1895) reported on two specimens in the Hamburg Museum.

One of us has re-examined in the Natural History Museum, London, two specimens of the species from Saya Is., North Borneo (reg. no. 1904.9.24.6–7). They are both very stout and robust specimens. The length of the trunk of the dissected specimen was 200 mm and of the introvert 50 mm and the width of the trunk about 15 mm. The anterior region of the trunk of both and the posterior surface of the trunk of one are pigmented dark brown in contrast to the rest of the body which is pale grey-brown. The dissected specimen shows 32 longitudinal muscles with some anastomosing. The ventral retractors arise from muscles 5–6 or 4–6 and the dorsal more anteriorly from 10–13; both pairs are very strong. On the introvert are numerous rings of small dark papillae which increase in size towards its base; similar dark but larger papillae are present on the trunk. Introvert without spines. A rectal caecum is present. The spindle muscle and the fasteners are arranged as described by Selenka (1883). The nephridia are free for about three quarters of their length and open at about the same level as, possibly just in front of, the anus.

DISTRIBUTION. Bohol (Selenka & de Man, 1883; Fischer, 1895); Sabah=North Borneo (Lanchester, 1905a); Mazatlan (Fischer, 1895).

FIG. 7 (A–C) *Siphonosoma eniwetoki.* (A) Dissection of the type specimen, × about 1·3 (after Fisher). (B) Enlargement of the region of the intestinal caecum and rectum to show the attachment of the spindle muscle (*sm*, s_1, s_2) and fixing muscle f_2 (after Fisher). (c) Three rows of introvert spines and intervening folds of the skin with their glands, × about 20 (after Fisher). (D) *Siphonosoma arcassonense.* Dissected specimen (after Cuénot). KEY: *See* Fig. 2, p. 23.

Siphonosoma (Siphonosoma) bonhourei (Hérubel, 1904)

Sipunculus bonhourei Hérubel, 1904a : 479–480; 1907 : 137–141, figs 30–34.

TYPE LOCALITY.   Gulf of Tadjourah.

DESCRIPTION.   Introvert 80 mm and shorter than the body; hooks absent.
Numerous long filiform tentacles.   Body 140 mm in length and skin thin; a few
papillae present.   Four retractor muscles, but only the long ventral ones are functional and are inserted at the beginning of the posterior third of the body; they
arise from a single longitudinal muscle band.   The feeble dorsal retractors arise
more anteriorly than the ventral.   Contractile vessel present and bearing short
lateral ramifications.   Eighteen longitudinal muscle bands with numerous anastomoses.   Longitudinal and circular muscles thicker at the insertion of the retractors.   Spindle muscle arises anteriorly from three roots.   Rectal caecum
absent.   Two long nephridia, which open just anterior to the anus, are fixed to the
body wall for the anterior third of their length.

REMARKS.   Known only from the holotype.   Hérubel, 1904a : 480, says that the
species is allied to *S. edule*.   It has the same number of longitudinal muscle bundles
but lacks transverse coelomic dissepiments.

DISTRIBUTION.   As for the type locality.

Siphonosoma (Siphonosoma) dayi Stephen, 1942

Siphonosoma dayi Stephen, 1942 : 246–247, pl. 11, figs 1–2; Wesenberg-Lund, 1963 : 103,
fig. 1.

TYPE LOCALITY.   Knysna Harbour, Cape Province, South Africa.   *Type*.   Royal
Scottish Museum.

DESCRIPTION.   Introvert with numerous circular muscle bands which bear rows
of dark-rimmed, scale-like bodies which have radiating lines in their upper parts
and small spherical granules on their lower parts.   The total length of the partially
contracted specimen is 195 mm; breadth 11 mm.   Colour uniform blue-grey externally, rose-red internally.   The outer surface is covered with elliptical papillae
which, near the introvert, are arranged in rows.   Longitudinal muscles split into
21 bands which anastomose in the anterior part of the trunk but form a continuous
sheet in the introvert.   Circular muscles also arranged in rings.   No dissepiments.
Two pairs of retractors; the stronger ventral pair arises in middle region of the trunk
from longitudinal muscle bands 3–4.   The dorsal pair arises some distance in front
from muscle bands 7–8.   The spindle muscle is attached to the posterior end of the
body by a series of lateral branches occupying a length of 1·5 mm.   Two fixing
muscles arise from just before the beginning of the intestinal coil where they split
into three branches.   One branch is attached near the anus, the other two are close
together and are attached to the tenth longitudinal muscle band at the level of the
base of the dorsal retractors.   Rectum fixed by broad wing muscles.   No rectal
caecum.   Numerous Keferstein bodies in front of the aperture of the nephridia.
Oesophagus long and accompanied by a contractile vessel.   Nephridia thin, moder-

ately long, 32 mm, free for their whole length and brown and granular in appearance.

REMARKS. Based originally on the holotype. Wesenberg-Lund records other specimens without comment.

DISTRIBUTION. Knysna Harbour (Stephen, 1942; Wesenberg-Lund, 1963).

Siphonosoma (Siphonosoma) eniwetoki Fisher, 1950
(Fig. 7A–C)

Siphonosoma eniwetoki Fisher, 1950b : 805–808, pl. 1.

TYPE LOCALITY. Bergen Island, Eniwetoki Lagoon; intertidal. *Type.* U.S.N.M. No. 21128.

DESCRIPTION. Introvert 35 mm with numerous transverse rows of inconspicuous spines. Total length 105 mm; posterior end blunt. Rosy-grey in colour. Body wall stout and slightly translucent. Skin covered with scattered conical elliptical papillae. Longitudinal muscles thick, split into 16–18 rather broad muscles which occasionally anastomose. Ventral retractors arise from bands 2 or 2–3, about the middle of the trunk; dorsal retractors arise from bands 3–4, considerably anteriorly to the ventrals. They unite about midway along their length. Two fixing muscles, one to the rectum and one to the oesophagus. Caecum present on the intestine. The spindle muscle arises in front of the anus and is free until it reaches the caecum where it is attached to the intestine; two anterior lateral roots are attached to the seventh longitudinal muscle band. Dorsal contractile vessel has numerous club-shaped villi. Intestinal coils, 28–30, fixed posteriorly by three branches of the spindle muscles. Nephridia short, free, opening on the same level as the anus.

REMARKS. Known only from the holotype. This species is very close to and hard to distinguish from *S. australe*. Fisher, 1952 : 381 states some differences.

DISTRIBUTION. As for the type locality.

Siphonosoma (Siphonosoma) funafuti (Shipley, 1898)

Sipunculus funafuti Shipley, 1898 : 469, pl. 37, figs 4–5.

TYPE LOCALITY. Funafuti. *Type.* British Mus. (Nat. Hist.) 1899.2.11.4–5.

DESCRIPTION. On the introvert there are no hooks but the papillae tend to be arranged in circular rows round the mouth. Body 50 to 80 mm in length, tapering to a sharp tail; silvery-white in colour and somewhat transparent, with numerous scattered papillae. Longitudinal muscles split into 14–15 bands, with few anastomoses. The ventral retractors arise from two muscle bands and the dorsals, which arise more anteriorly, from a single muscle band. Intestinal convolutions 8–12, free except for the spindle muscle which is attached anteriorly and posteriorly. Rectal caecum absent. Nephridia small, free, opening on the level of the anus.

REMARKS. A paratype specimen in the British Museum has 14–17 longitudinal muscles which anastomose to some extent. The circular muscles form well-developed fascicles. The body wall is thin and the internal structures very fragile. The ventral retractors arise from muscles 2–3 in the posterior third of the trunk and the dorsal much more anteriorly from muscles 4–5. The contractile vessel bears very fine villi and there appears to be no caecum. No hooks are present on the introvert and numerous filiform tentacles were dissected out. The gut was full of coarse particles of coral. No fastening muscles were observed. Prominent, rather large hemispherical papillae are present on the anterior surface of the trunk. The nephridia open between muscles 2–3 at about the level of the anus.

The species is close to S. *rotumanum* but does not possess a rectal caecum and seems to have a less convoluted alimentary tract.

DISTRIBUTION. Funafuti.

Siphonosoma (Siphonosoma) ingens (Fisher, 1947)
(Fig. 8C–F)

Siphonomecus ingens Fisher, 1947 : 365–368, pls 14, 15.
Siphonosoma ingens Fisher, 1952 : 382–385, pls 20, 21.

TYPE LOCALITY. Morro Bay, California; intertidal. *Type.* U.S.N.M. no. 20910.

DESCRIPTION. Introvert long, up to 90 mm; tentacles in 12 double meridional rows. Hooks absent. Trunk very long, over 400 mm; posterior end pointed. Skin smooth. The longitudinal muscles in the posterior region of the introvert are split into 20–25 bands which rarely anastomose. Two pairs of retractor muscles present; the dorsal pair arises well in front of the ventral, the latter arising about the middle of the body. A strong spindle muscle is attached near the anus by the roots and at the posterior end of the body. Intestinal spiral long with 60–62 convolutions. No rectal caecum. The contractile vessel bears numerous villi. Nephridia free and open a little in front of the anus. Four or five slender, fusiform bodies which open close together (around the end of the spindle muscle) are present at the extreme posterior end of the body.

REMARKS. Based originally on eight specimens. Fisher (1952) gave a very complete description, based on a further eight specimens.

This species resembles S. *arcassonense* (Cuénot) in the shape and arrangement of the tentacles and in possessing four fusiform bodies in the body cavity at the posterior extremity of the trunk. S. *arcassonense* also has about 23–24 longitudinal muscles. The introvert of the latter, however, is armed with hooks or spines. Fisher (1952 : 385) points out that S. *ingens* is also closely related to S. *mourense* Sato.

DISTRIBUTION. California (Fisher, 1947; 1952).

Siphonosoma (Siphonosoma) joubini (Hérubel, 1905)

Sipunculus joubini Hérubel, 1905a : 51–54, 3 figs; 1907 : 141–145, figs 35–37.

TYPE LOCALITY. New Caledonia.

DESCRIPTION. Introvert short, 45 mm in length and uniform whitish in colour; about 18 tentacles present. Trunk 228 mm in length and whitish in colour. Skin thin with ovoid and slightly bomb-shaped papillae which stand out because of their dark colour. Circular muscles divided into very numerous slim, anastomosing bands. The longitudinal muscles are gathered into 18 bands of uniform size showing little anastomosis. Two pairs of slim retractors; the ventral pair is inserted about 65 mm from the posterior end and is about 150 mm in length. The right root arises from muscle bands 2–3, the left from muscle bands 3–4. The dorsal pair is much weaker and measures about 100 mm in length. The right root arises from muscle bands 4–5 and the left root from muscle bands 3–5. The retractors join near the mouth. Intestinal coils 22. The contractile vessel is single and possesses small villi on its dorsal surface. Spindle muscle with three anterior roots. Wing muscles present but no intestinal caecum. Nephridia are short and free for their whole length.

REMARKS. Known only from the holotype. According to Hérubel, the species is intermediate between *S. bonhourei* and *S. cumanense vitreum*.

DISTRIBUTION. As for the type locality.

Siphonosoma (Siphonosoma) mourense Sato, 1930

Siphonosoma mourense Sato, 1930b : 6–8, pl. 1, figs 2–4; 1937 : 148–149, pl. 3, fig. 9; 1939 : 370–371; Leroy, 1936 : 425.

TYPE LOCALITY. Moura, Mutsu Bay, Japan.

DESCRIPTION. Introvert about one fifth of the length of the trunk and without hooks and spines; numerous finger-shaped tentacles arranged in 12 regular radial rows, each row with about 20 tentacles. Trunk about 350 mm in length and 10 mm in width, light yellowish-brown in colour and beset with flat elliptical papillae. Longitudinal muscles gathered into 22 bands; in the anterior part of the trunk they anastomose but form a continuous sheet in the introvert. Two pairs of slender retractor muscles. The ventral pair is larger and springs from longitudinal muscle bands 3–4 in the middle of the body; the dorsal pair arises more anteriorly from muscle bands 8–10. The spindle muscle is fixed both anteriorly and posteriorly and gives off two lateral branches at the level of the beginning of the intestinal coils; each branch is attached to the eighth longitudinal muscle band at a point about 5 mm anteriorly from the roots of the dorsal retractors. The posterior end of the muscle is divided into several long branches which are fixed separately to the body wall at the posterior end of the body. A fixing muscle which springs from the rectum close to the intestinal convolutions is attached to the first longitudinal muscle band on either side by two roots. Broad wing muscles are attached to the rectum near the anus. No crescentic dissepiments present. Many Keferstein bodies along the longitudinal muscle bands. There are some small soft, elongate blind tubules arranged in several regular, longitudinal rows lying in front of the apertures of the nephridia. The long oesophagus carries the contractile vessel from which numerous short tubules arise. About 30 intestinal convolutions fixed posteriorly by the spindle muscle. No caecum on the rectum. The anus opens between muscle bands 10–11. The two nephridia are long slender tubes of a reddish-

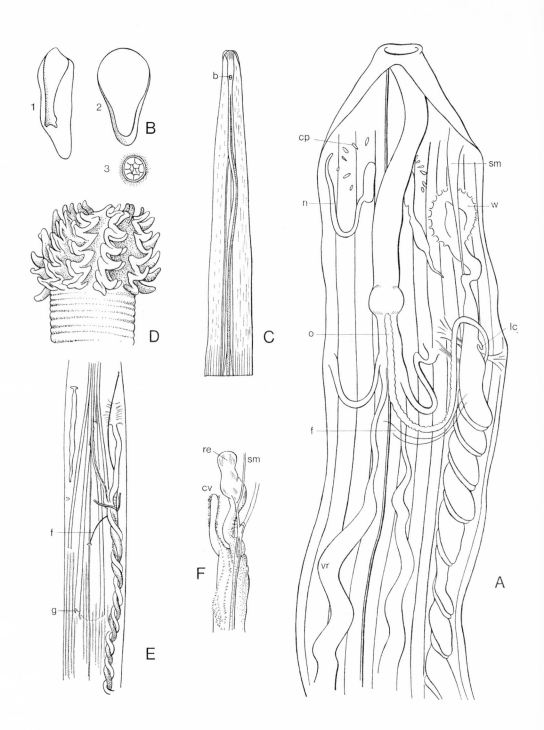

brown colour; they are free for their whole length and open between longitudinal muscle bands 3–4 almost on a level with the anus. No eyespots noticed.

REMARKS. Known from numerous specimens.

DISTRIBUTION. Mutsu Bay, Japan (Sato, 1930b, 1937, 1939).

Siphonosoma (Siphonosoma) novaepommeraniae (Fischer, 1926)

(Fig. 5E)

Sipunculus novaepommeraniae Fischer, 1926 : 104–106, pl. 3, figs. 2–4, 6.
Siphonosoma novaepommeraniae Wesenberg-Lund, 1959b : 55–58, text-figs 1–3.

TYPE LOCALITY. New Britain.

DESCRIPTION. Length of introvert one third that of the body; papillae arranged in rows. Trunk 85 mm long, blue-grey anteriorly, whitish-grey posteriorly. The musculature is visible through the skin, but is not clearly cut into rectangles. The papillae are not prominent but appear as dark brown points visible to the naked eye; they are more crowded anteriorly and more sparsely distributed posteriorly. In front of the anus they are wart-like. Two types of papillae are present, the larger are oval to roundish, the smaller are roundish only. Two pairs of retractors arise about the same level, the ventral pair from a point 20 mm behind the anus from muscle bands 1–3 in the anterior third of the body, the dorsal pair 4–5 mm behind them, from muscle bands 6–7. There is a long, brown contractile vessel with numerous villi. Intestinal convolutions 14–15, traversed by a strong spindle muscle which is attached about 3 mm in front of the anus. The rectum is short and is fastened at the level of the first coil by a mesentery to the dorsal retractor. Rectal caecum present. There are two other fixing muscles.

REMARKS. Wesenberg-Lund describes 20 longitudinal muscle bands for the species.

DISTRIBUTION. New Britain (Fischer, 1926); Mauritius (Wesenberg-Lund, 1959b).

Siphonosoma (Siphonosoma) pellucidum (Sluiter, 1902)

Sipunculus pellucidus Sluiter, 1902 : 9–10, pl. 1, fig. 3.

TYPE LOCALITY. Bay of Bima, Indonesia, 2°28′30″S, 131°3′E, at 55–118 m. (Siboga stations 47, 166).

DESCRIPTION. Introvert 6 mm in length and densely covered with conical unpigmented papillae which are not directed posteriorly. Trunk 28 mm in length

---

FIG. 8. (A–B) *Siphonosoma rotumanum*. (A) Dissected specimen (after Edmonds). (B) Blunt, spine-like structures which emerge from anterior rings of papillae (after Edmonds). (C–F) *Siphonosoma ingens*. (C) Anterior-most region of a small specimen (after Fischer). (D) Tentacular crown (after Fischer). (E) Anterior region (after Fischer). (F) Part of (E) enlarged (after Fischer). KEY: *See* Fig. 2, p. 23.

and 5 mm broad. Body wall transparent, so that longitudinal muscle bands and internal organs are visible. The body is sharply cut off from the introvert. Longitudinal muscle bands 28 (?) with broad free spaces between them; at the extreme posterior end the longitudinal muscles are continuous, forming a cap. Two pairs retractor muscles arise at the same level and from two longitudinal bundles; the ventral pair from the muscles 3 and 4, the dorsal from the muscles 9 and 10. Oesophagus short; about 8–9 intestinal convolutions which are not fixed posteriorly. Spindle muscle a broad band fixed in front of the anus. No rectal caecum. The two nephridia are short and swollen and open in front of the anus between bands 4 and 5. A small nephrostome clearly visible. The nerve cord is a conspicuous band and is enlarged into a thin oval swelling posteriorly.

REMARKS. A re-examination of one of Sluiter's specimens (not marked as the type) shows that the species is a *Siphonosoma*. The specimen is small, transparent, dissected and damaged to some extent. The introvert is not strongly marked off from the trunk, it lacks the triangular, squamiform papillae of a *Sipunculus* and there are no hooks or spines. The circular muscles are not grouped into bands although there is a tendency to form fascicles. The longitudinal muscles in the anterior region of the trunk where the specimen is less damaged appear to be grouped into about 20 bundles, although Sluiter gives 28 as the number for the species. There are no transverse dissepiments. It is clear that the spindle muscle is fixed posteriorly. We have not been able to carry the identification any further.

DISTRIBUTION. As for the type locality.

Siphonosoma (Siphonosoma) pescadolense Sato, 1939

Siphonosoma pescadolense Sato, 1939 : 376–379, pl. 20, fig. 8, text-figs 18–22.

TYPE LOCALITY. Hattosi, Formosa.

DESCRIPTION. Introvert about half the length of the body and covered with very small papillae of uniform size arranged in many rows. The anterior portion bears many spines and numerous filamentous tentacles. Trunk about 70 mm in length and 3–5 mm in diameter; yellowish-white in life, yellowish-grey in alcohol. Body wall thin, somewhat translucent and bearing numerous papillae, which are largest at the base of the introvert. Longitudinal muscles split into about 15 bands which rarely anastomose. Two pairs of retractor muscles arising at different levels; the ventral pair arises from muscle bands 2–3 and the dorsal from muscle bands 3–4. About 12 intestinal coils attached anteriorly and posteriorly by the spindle muscle. The anterior portion of the intestine is fixed to the body wall by three fixing muscles. The nephridia are free except for their anterior extremity and open almost at the level of the anus. There is no rectal caecum.

REMARKS. Described from a single specimen and not a well known species.

DISTRIBUTION. As for the type locality.

Siphonosoma (Siphonosoma) rotumanum (Shipley, 1898)
(Fig. 8A–B)

Sipunculus rotumanus Shipley, 1898 : 469–470, pl. 37, figs 1–3.
Siphonosoma hawaiense Edmonds, 1966 : 386–388, figs 1–4.

TYPE LOCALITY. Rotuma.

DESCRIPTION. Introvert one eighth of the total length and with 40–60 pointed tentacles. Body long and slender; trunk and introvert together 210–220 mm long. Skin glistening white with some dark papillae scattered over its surface; papillae closely and regularly arranged in rows on the introvert. Circular muscles arranged in rings, with numerous anastomoses. External opening of the anus conspicuous and rectum attached by numerous strands to the body wall. Intestinal coils, 30–40, unattached except by the spindle muscle which is attached posteriorly. Longitudinal muscles split into 14 bands. Two pairs of retractor muscles; the ventral pair, half as long as the body, arise from muscle bands 2–3 but the dorsal pair are shorter and arise some distance in front of them.

REMARKS. Three specimens of *S. rotumanum*, identified by Shipley, are in the collection of the Natural History Museum, London (reg. no. 99.2.11.1–3) and it seems most likely that they are paratypes. A re-examination of the species shows that Shipley described the species without mentioning the presence of spines on the introvert. At first sight the spines are not noticeable but a closer examination shows that numerous transverse rings of papillae with blunt, posteriorly directed points are present. Associated with each papilla at its base is a very small glandular opening. These papillae are puzzling structures because they are not as hard as spines usually are. They are clear in colour and lack the usual yellow-brown colour of spines. Perhaps they have deteriorated during storage. We are convinced, however, that they resemble in all other respects the yellow slipper-shaped spines described for *Siphonosoma hawaiense* by Edmonds (1966).

One of Shipley's specimens when dissected showed the presence of 15 longitudinal muscles which anastomose to some extent and that the circular muscles form numerous anastomosing fascicles. The ventral retractors arise in about the middle of the trunk from muscles 2–3 and the dorsal retractors more anteriorly from muscles 4–6. A very strong spindle muscle is attached in front of the anus and two very strong wing-like roots are given off anteriorly just like those described for *S. hawaiense* by Edmonds (1966, fig. 2). A strong fastening muscle that arises from longitudinal muscle 1 about mid-way between the dorsal and ventral retractors, probably corresponds with the two fasteners shown in a similar position in *S. hawaiense*. No other intestinal fasteners were found. The anus is held by a strong wing-muscle and a rectal caecum is present. The nephridiopores lie between muscles 2–3 at about the same level as the anus. The nephridia are free and the nephrostomes large and semilunar. The contractile vessel bear numerous, minute villi. Prominent hemispherical papillae are present on the anterior and posterior surfaces of the trunk. They correspond in size and structure with those described for *S. hawaiense*. In two specimens they are brownish-black in colour.

DISTRIBUTION. Rotuma (Shipley, 1899); Hawaii (Edmonds, 1966).

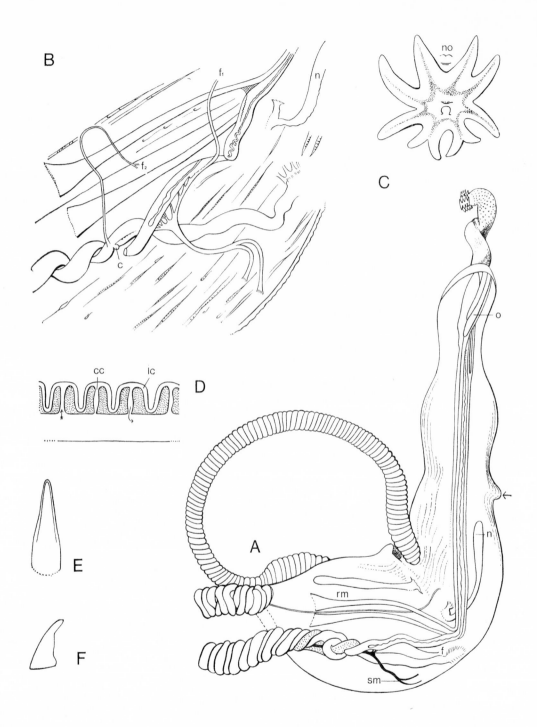

Siphonosoma (Siphonosoma) takatsukii Sato, 1935

Siphonosoma takatsukii Sato, 1935b : 308–310, pl. 3, fig. 8, text-figs 8–10; 1939 : 373.

TYPE LOCALITY. Mappu, Yap Island, West Caroline Islands.

DESCRIPTION. Introvert very short, 10 mm in length; at the anterior end are numerous spines which are slightly curved and slightly blunted at the tip and about 0·13 mm in height and 0·06 mm wide at the base. Tentacles numerous. Trunk 47 mm in length, 5–8 mm in diameter; yellowish brown in colour. Skin thick and entirely opaque. Papillae numerous and of two types: the first which is the larger being flat and elliptical 0·06–0·1 mm along the major axis and 0·04–0·07 along the minor axis, the second is much the smaller being nearly circular in surface view and 0·05 mm in diameter. The papillae in the middle of the body are of the first type but somewhat smaller than those found on the rest of the trunk. Longitudinal muscles in 14–18 bundles. Inner circular muscle layer split into numerous strands. Two pairs of broad retractor muscles; the ventral pair arises from 2–3 muscle bands at the level of about one third of the body from the posterior end and the dorsal pair, which are somewhat narrower, arises from 5–7 muscle bands at a point about 6 mm in front of the roots of the ventral pair. The spindle muscle is fixed in front of the anus and also to the posterior end of the body. Two fixing muscles run from the body wall to the anterior portion of the intestinal convolutions. The rectum is fixed by wing muscles. No dissepiments on the body wall. About 14 intestinal convolutions. Contractile vessel without villi. No caecum on the rectum. Nephridia about 10 mm in length, brown in colour and free for their whole length. Nephridiopores at about the level of the anus.

REMARKS. Known only from the holotype.

DISTRIBUTION. As for the type locality.

GENUS *SIPHONOMECUS* Fisher, 1947

Siphonomecus Fisher, 1947 : 363.

DESCRIPTION. Large animals. Introvert without scale-like papillae but with rings of simple spines; tentacular crown voluminous. Longitudinal muscles gathered into anastomosing bundles. Circular musculature strongly banded; discontinuous, transverse coelomic lacunae lie between the bands and connect with subcutaneous pockets. One pair of retractor muscles. Nephridia slender and free. Strong spindle muscle, fastened posteriorly. Contractile vessel without villi.

FIG. 9. (A–F) *Siphonomecus multicinctus*. (A) Anterior region of the body; the posterior limit of the introvert is marked by the arrow on the right. (B) Region of the origin of the retractors. (C) Tentacles, showing the grooves. (D) Longitudinal section of the body wall, showing the coelomic canals. (E) and (F) Introvert spines. (A–F after Fisher). KEY: *See* Fig. 2, p. 23.

F

REMARKS.   The genus contains only one species.   Fisher (1947) described the
genus to contain *S. multicinctus* and *S. ingens*.   At a later date Fisher (1952) transferred the latter species to the genus *Siphonosoma*.

TYPE SPECIES.   *Siphonomecus multicinctus* Fisher, 1947.

DISTRIBUTION.   Florida.

Siphonomecus multicinctus Fisher, 1947

(Fig. 9A–F)

Siphonomecus multicinctus Fisher, 1947 : 363–365, pl. 13.

TYPE LOCALITY.   Key West, Florida.   *Type.*   U.S.N.M. no. 20911.

DESCRIPTION.   Very large species.   Introvert about a third of the length of the
body.   The anterior end is thin-walled and bears 28 circles of fine spines; the
tentacular crown has eight primary divisions and numerous sub-divisions.   Trunk
very long; total length 510 mm, pale brownish with low, brown papillae.   Strongly
annulated; posterior end swollen and remainder of the trunk constricted.   Just
behind the introvert the longitudinal muscles are split into unequal, flat irregularly
anastomosing bundles; in the constricted portion they number 18–22.   One pair
of retractor muscles which arises anteriorly to the post-introvert region and spans
3–4 bands.   Contractile vessel bears no villi.   Spindle muscle attached anteriorly
to body wall by two roots and to the oesophagus by a third; attached posteriorly
to body wall.   Nephridia free, slender and opening between the base of the retractors and the posterior margin of the introvert.   Small rectal caecum present.

REMARKS.   Known only from the holotype.

DISTRIBUTION.   As for the type locality.

Genus *PHASCOLOPSIS* Fisher, 1950

Golfingia (*Phascolopsis*) Fisher, 1950a : 550.
Phascolopsis Stephen, 1965 : 459.

DESCRIPTION.   Trunk rather long and cylindrical and with the longitudinal
musculature gathered into separate, anastomosing bands.   A number of finger-like
tentacles surround the mouth.   Small skin-bodies present on the trunk.   No
coelomic canals in the trunk wall (differing in this respect from other genera of the
Sipunculidae).   Spindle muscle not attached posteriorly.

TYPE SPECIES.   *Sipunculus gouldii* Pourtalès, 1851.

REMARKS.   The type species, the only one in the genus, is well known along
the eastern coast of North America from Newhaven to Florida.   Because it resembles
species of both the genera *Sipunculus* and *Golfingia* its systematic position has always
been uncertain.   Earlier workers (Pourtalès, Quatrefages and Selenka) regarded
it as a *Sipunculus* and later workers (Andrews, Fischer and Gerould) as a *Golfingia*.
Fisher (1950) when he subdivided the genus *Golfingia* recognized the unique position

of the species and placed it in a subgenus (*Phascolopsis*) of its own. Stephen (1965) in his revision of the phylum raised the subgenus to the rank of a genus.

The genus differs from *Siphonosoma* because (1) its body wall lacks integumental canals, which are present in the larger species of *Siphonosoma,* and (2) the method of attachment of the spindle muscle. It differs from *Golfingia* (1) in its general shape and appearance and (2) in that its longitudinal musculature is grouped into bundles. We have placed the genus in the family Sipunculidae on account of its resemblance to the genus *Siphonosoma.*

DISTRIBUTION. Eastern coast of North America.

Phascolopsis gouldii (Pourtalès, 1851)

(Fig. 10A–C)

Sipunculus gouldii Pourtalès, 1851 : 40–41; Quatrefages, 1865b : 618, 674; Selenka & de Man, 1883 : 101–102, pl. 13, fig. 178.
Phascolosomum gouldii: Diesing, 1859 : 764–765.
Phascolosoma gouldii: Keferstein, 1865a : 434, pl. 33, fig. 32; 1865b : 205; 1867 : 54; Verrill, 1873b : 353, 428, 521, 627, pl. 18, fig. 93; Andrews, 1890a : 65; 1890b : 389–420, pls 44–47; Fischer, 1895 : 9; Nickerson, 1899a : 190; 1901 : 381; Gerould, 1913 : 380; MacGinitie, 1935b : 682.
Golfingia (Phascolopsis) gouldii: Fisher, 1950 : 550.
Phascolopsis gouldii: Stephen, 1965 : 459.

TYPE LOCALITY. Massachusetts, U.S.A.

DESCRIPTION. Introvert which is up to about 35 mm in length bears numerous tentacles but no hooks; covered with rounded microscopic papillae. Trunk up to 130 mm in length, covered with microscopic oval skin bodies. Longitudinal musculature gathered into 30–40 anastomosing bands. Two pairs of retractor muscles; the ventral pair arises in the anterior region of the middle third of the trunk, the dorsal pair more anteriorly. The intestinal convolutions are very numerous numbering from 35–40. The spindle muscle arises in front of the anus and is not attached to the posterior end of the trunk. Contractile vessel single and without numerous villi. Numerous fixing muscles arise from the first intestinal coil; rectal caecum present. Nephridia are short and free and open in front of the anus. The nerve cord is a single strand for most of its length; anteriorly, however, it is attached by two roots.

REMARKS. The genus is similar to *Golfingia* in having the same arrangement of tentacles but the longitudinal muscles are gathered into bands.

The structure and anatomy of the species has been described in detail by Andrews (1890b) and its development by Gerould (1906). Gerould (1913 : 380) considered that the species in structure and development resembled *Golfingia vulgaris* (de Blainville) a common littoral species of Europe.

The intact animal, nerve-muscle preparations of its retractor muscles and its eggs have often been used in physiological investigations.

DISTRIBUTION. East coast of North America from Newhaven to Florida, and possibly further south. ? California (MacGinitie, 1935).

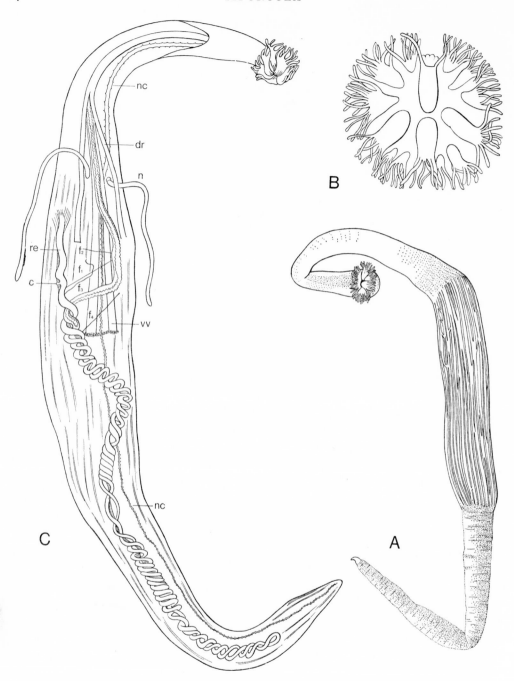

FIG. 10.   (A–C) *Phascolopsis gouldii*.   (A) Entire specimen, natural size.   (B) Surface view of the expanded tentacles (after Andrews).   (C) Internal anatomy (after Andrews). KEY: *See* Fig. 2, p. 23.

(4). Family **GOLFINGIIDAE** nov. fam.

Sipunculidae Baird, 1868 (in part).

DESCRIPTION. Tentacles basically surround the mouth; they may be digitiform, filiform, leaflike, dichotomously branched or dendritic. They may be reduced to a few lobes or even absent. Ring of tentacles usually interrupted on the mid-dorsal side by the nuchal organ. Integumentary or coelomic sacs absent. Longitudinal musculature of body wall continuous. Anterior cap or shield absent.

TYPE GENUS. *Golfingia* Lankester, 1885.

REMARKS. The family contains five genera, *Golfingia* Lankester, *Onchnesoma* Koren & Danielssen, *Nephasoma* Pergament, *Phascolion* Théel and *Themiste* Gray. In number of species it is the largest family of the phylum.

FAMILY GOLFINGIIDAE—KEY TO GENERA

1 Nephridium single 2
– Nephridia two 3
2 Anal aperture lies on the introvert near the mouth and not on the trunk; tentacles few (10) or absent; retractor single . . . . . ***ONCHNESOMA*** (p. 161)
– Anal aperture lies on the trunk and not on the introvert; trunk usually spirally coiled; species usually inhabit the empty shells of molluscs . . ***PHASCOLION*** (p. 164)
3 Anal aperture lies on the introvert and not on the trunk . ***NEPHASOMA*** (p. 214)
– Anal aperture lies on the trunk and not the introvert 4
4 Tentacles always present, dichotomously branched or dendritic ***THEMISTE*** (p. 193)
– Tentacles usually present, digitiform or filiform: may be reduced to a few lobes in some species . . . . ***GOLFINGIA*** (p. 77)

Genus *GOLFINGIA* Lankester, 1885

Sipunculus authors, in part.
Phascolosoma authors, but not F.S. Leuckart, 1828.
Phascolosomum: Diesing, 1851 : 63, in part; 1859 : 758, in part.
Phascolosoma: Keferstein, 1862 : 39, in part; 1865b : 422, in part.
Homalosoma Keferstein, 1865b : 436 (non *Homalosoma* Wagler, 1830).
Petalostoma Keferstein, 1865b : 438 (non *Petalostoma* Lidth de Jeude, 1829).
Phascolosomum: Quatrefages, 1865b : 616.
Stephanostoma Danielssen & Koren, 1880 : 464 (non *Stephanostoma* Lenz, 1794).
Phascolosoma: Selenka & de Man, 1883 : 15.
Golfingia Lankester, 1885 : 469, pls 55–56 (Type, *G. macintoshii* Lankester = *Phascolosoma vulgare* (de Blainville) according to Stephen, 1934 : 169); Fisher, 1950a : 548; 1952 : 388–389.
Apionsoma Sluiter, 1902 : 42–44 (Type, *A. trichocephalus* Sluiter); Wesenberg-Lund, 1959a : 189–190.

DESCRIPTION. Small to moderate-sized sipunculans in which the layers of longitudinal and circular muscles are continuous. The skin is often smooth but small glandular openings and papillae are sometimes present on the surface of the trunk and introvert. The mouth is surrounded by one or more rows or a series of longitudinal double rows of tentacles which are usually finger- or thread-like. In a few species the tentacles are reduced to a pair of lobes or to a fold that surrounds the mouth. The tentacular ring is interrupted in the mid-dorsal line by the nuchal

organ.   Introvert hooks, if present, are simple except in one subgenus.   One or
two pairs of retractor muscles.   The intestinal tract forms a double coil of few
to many whorls.   A spindle muscle arises anteriorly near the anus and is usually
not attached to the body wall posteriorly.   The contractile vessel is usually simple
but in one subgenus it bears numerous branched or unbranched tubules; it is very
much reduced and is reported to be absent in a few species.   The nephridia are usually
free for their whole length; in a few species they are bilobed structures.   A pair
of photic tubes leads back from the cerebral sense organ into the substance of the
cerebral ganglion.

TYPE SPECIES.   *Sipunculus vulgaris* de Blainville, 1827.

REMARKS.   Fisher (1950a, 1952) having pointed out that the long established
name of the genus, *Phascolosoma*, was preoccupied gave it the name *Golfingia*,
thus reverting to a name used by Lankester in 1885.   Fisher considered that the
genus was so large that it warranted subdivision and accordingly erected the subgenera *Golfingia* (*sensu stricto*), *Mitosiphon*, *Phascoloides*, *Thysanocardia* and *Phascolopsis*.   The subgenus *Phascolopsis* was raised to the rank of a genus by Stephen
(1965 : 459).   Fisher's revision of the phylum, however, was incomplete and a
number of species did not fall readily into his subgenera.   Subsequently Wesenberg-
Lund (1959 : 189) erected the subgenus *Phascolana*, Stephen (1965 : 457) the subgenus *Golfingiella* and Murina (1967 : 1334) the subgenus *Siphonoides*.   The genus
therefore at the present time consists of seven subgenera of which *Golfingia* (*sensu
stricto*) with 34 species, *Phascoloides* with 37 and *Thysanocardia* with 15 species
are the largest.

The chief characters on which the establishment of the subgenera depends are
(1) the number of retractor muscles, (2) the structure of the introvert hooks, (3) the
method of attachment of the spindle muscle, (4) the structure of the nephridia
and (5) the presence of tubules or villi on the contractile vessel.

Five species formerly regarded as belonging to this genus were removed by
Stephen (1965 : 457) and grouped into a new genus *Fisherana*.   Of these *Phascolosoma capitatum* Gerould is the best known.   The reasons for this action are
explained in the remarks-section under the genus *Fisherana* (p. 329).

We have considered the possibility of expanding the subgenus *Mitosiphon* Fisher
so as to include *Phascolana* Wesenberg-Lund.   In both subgenera the nephridia
are bilobed and the spindle muscle is fastened to the body wall posteriorly.   We
have refrained from amalgamating the two because the unusual structure of the
hooks of *Mitosiphon* seems to separate the group from other subgenera.

Many species of *Golfingia* are poorly known and at least 27 are known only from
their holotypes.   A number are inadequately described and it seems likely that some
of the species that now have different names will eventually prove to be synonymous.

Two golfingiids are of especial interest, *Golfingia minuta* (Kef.) and *Golfingia
procera* (Möbius).   *G. minuta*, in spite of the reports to the contrary of Gerould
(1913 : 394) and Wesenberg-Lund (1939 : 27), is capable of acting as a protrandrous
hermaphrodite, something unique in the phylum.   Paul (1910 : 24) first described
the presence of eggs and sperms in the body and Akesson (1958 : 33–41) verified

the report. Akesson also found that the eggs are rich in yolk and that development is direct, the embryo not passing through the usual pelagic stage. The large content of yolk and the loss of the pelagic stage in its development he found are connected with a primitive form of 'brood protection' (Akesson, 1958 : 41–42). Thorson (1957) has observed on a number of different occasions that *Golfingia procera* is able to introduce its introvert into the body cavity of the polychaet *Aphrodite aculeata* Linn., almost at any point. He considers that the sipunculan is able to act as a temporary parasite on the annelid. Whether organic material passes from the polychaet to the sipunculan has not yet been shown.

DISTRIBUTION. The genus is widely distributed and is known from tropical to polar waters, particularly the latter, and from the intertidal zone to the ocean depths. The following is a list of some golfingiids that have been reported from considerable depths (Wesenberg-Lund, 1955a and Murina, 1964a, 1968 and 1957 also give records of sipunculans found in very deep water).

Species	Depth	Reference
Golfingia anderssoni (Théel)	3350 m	Murina, 1964a
Golfingia appendiculata (Sato)	4811 m	Murina, 1964a
Golfingia catharinae (Mueller)	3447 m	Selenka, 1885
Golfingia depressa (Sluiter)	4100 m	Murina, 1964a
Golfingia flagrifera (Selenka) (1)	4209 m	Selenka, 1885
(2)	5000 m	Sluiter, 1912
Golfingia improvisa (Théel)	5390 m	Murina, 1958
Golfingia margaritacea (Sars)	4600 m	Wesenberg-Lund, 1955a
Golfingia minuta (Kef.)	5390 m	Murina, 1958
Golfingia muricaudata (Southern)	6860 m	Murina, 1964a
Golfingia profunda (Roule)	4255 m	Roule, 1907
Golfingia schuttei (Augener)	5397 m	Murina, 1964a
Golfingia vitjazi Murina	4150 m	Murina, 1964a

KEY TO THE SUBGENERA OF GOLFINGIA

1 One pair of retractor muscles 2
– Two pairs of retractor muscles 4
2 Contractile vessel with numerous branched or unbranched tubules (introvert without
   hooks, spindle muscle not attached posteriorly) . . ***THYSANOCARDIA*** (p. 120)
– Contractile vessel simple and without tubules 3
3 Spindle muscle attached to body wall posteriorly . . ***SIPHONOIDES*** (p. 159)
– Spindle muscle not attached to body wall posteriorly . ***PHASCOLOIDES*** (p. 131)
4 Nephridia bilobed 5
– Nephridia with single lobes 6
5 Introvert bears hooks with accessory spinelets at their base . ***MITOSIPHON*** (p. 113)
– Introvert without hooks . . . . ***PHASCOLANA*** (p. 116)
6 Spindle muscle attached to body wall posteriorly, hooks absent
   GOLFINGIELLA (p. 118)
– Spindle muscle not attached to body wall posteriorly, hooks present or absent
   GOLFINGIA (s.s.) (p. 81)

TABLE 8

Subgenera of *Golfingia*

Subgenus	Author & reference	Pairs of retractors	Introvert hooks	Spindle muscle	Nephridia	Contractile vessel	Type species	Species
1. *Golfingia* (s.s.)	Fisher, 1950a	two	present or absent	if present, not attached posteriorly	single lobed	without tubules (except *G. capensis*)	*G. vulgaris* (de Blain.)	34
2. *Mitosiphon*	Fischer, 1950a	two	hooks bear accessory spinelets	attached posteriorly	bilobed	reduced or absent and without tubules	*G. hespera* (Chamb.)	2
3. *Golfingiella*	Stephen, 1965	two	absent	attached posteriorly	single lobed	without tubules	*G. approximata* (Roule)	4
4. *Phascolana*	Wesenberg-Lund, 1959	two	without hooks and without tentacles	attached posteriorly	bilobed	absent	*G. tenuissima* (Wesenb.-Lund)	2
5. *Phascoloides*	Fisher, 1950a	one	present or absent	if present, not attached posteriorly	single lobed	without tubules (except *G. coriacea*)	*G. eremita* (Sars)	37
6. *Thysanocardia*	Fisher, 1950a	one	absent	not attached posteriorly (condition not known in *G. martensi*)	single lobed; open anterior to anus	with numerous branched or unbranched tubules	*G. procera* (Möbius)	15
7. *Siphonoides*	Murina, 1967a	one	present or absent	attached posteriorly	single lobed	without tubules	*G. immunita* (Sluiter)	3

Subgenus *GOLFINGIA* (sensu stricto) Fisher, 1950

Golfingia (sensu stricto) Fisher, 1950a : 549–550; 1952 : 390.

DESCRIPTION. Two pairs of retractor muscles. Hooks may or may not be present on the introvert. Contractile vessel simple and without villi (except in *G. capensis*). Spindle muscle not attached posteriorly to the body wall.

TYPE SPECIES. *Sipunculus vulgaris* de Blainville.

REMARKS. The subgenus contains species like *G. margaritacea* and *G. vulgaris* which are capable of considerable variation especially in the structure of the skin and in the number of tentacles. Théel (1905 : 63–65) claims that the number of tentacles of one 'form' of *G. margaritacea* increases from 8 to 104 when the length of the trunk increases from 7·5–75 mm (see the table on p. 98). A similar variation is described for two other forms of *G. margaritacea* and for *G. vulgaris* (Théel, 1905 : 60, 65, 68). Whether the number of tentacles of other sipunculans increases with the size of the specimens is important information which is not known.

The subgenus contains about 34 species of which nine are known only from the holotypes. The species are distributed in all seas. The subgenus is divisible into two groups, one with hooks and one without. Because some descriptions are inadequate we have been unable to distinguish satisfactorily between a few species. Consequently our key to the subgenus is not complete.

Three species listed in the subgenus by Fisher (1952 : 390) have been placed in the synonymy of other species; *G. trybomi* (Théel) we consider is *G. margaritacea* (Sars), *G. cluthenis* (Stephen) is *G. elongata* (Kef.) and *G. sanderi* (Collin) is *G. vulgaris* (de Blainv.).

Species without hooks

G. *anderssoni* (Théel)
G. *anguinea* (Sluiter)
G. *appendiculata* (Sato)
G. *cantabriensis* Edmonds
G. *capensis* (Teuscher)
G. *charcoti* (Hérubel)
G. *glossipapillosa* (Sato)
G. *hudsoniana* (Chamberlain)
G. *ikedai* Fisher
G. *iniqua* (Sluiter)
G. *lagensis* (Fischer)
G. *mawsoni* (Benham)
G. *margaritacea* (Sars)
G. *nota* (Sato)
G. *okinoseana* (Ikeda)
G. *profunda* (Roule)
G. *signa* (Sato)
G. *solitaria* (Sluiter)
G. *soya* (Sato)
G. *trichocephala* (Sluiter)

Species with hooks

G. *cylindrata* (Keferstein)
G. *derjugini* (Gadd)
G. *elongata* (Keferstein)
G. *kolensis* (Gadd)
G. *muricaudata* (Southern)
G. *mutabilis* (Southern)
G. *nordenskjoldi* (Théel)
G. *ohlini* (Théel)
G. *owstoni* (Ikeda)
G. *pudica* (Selenka)
G. *recondita* (Sluiter)
G. *reticulata* (Hérubel)
G. *rugosa* (Southern)
G. *vulgaris* (de Blainville)

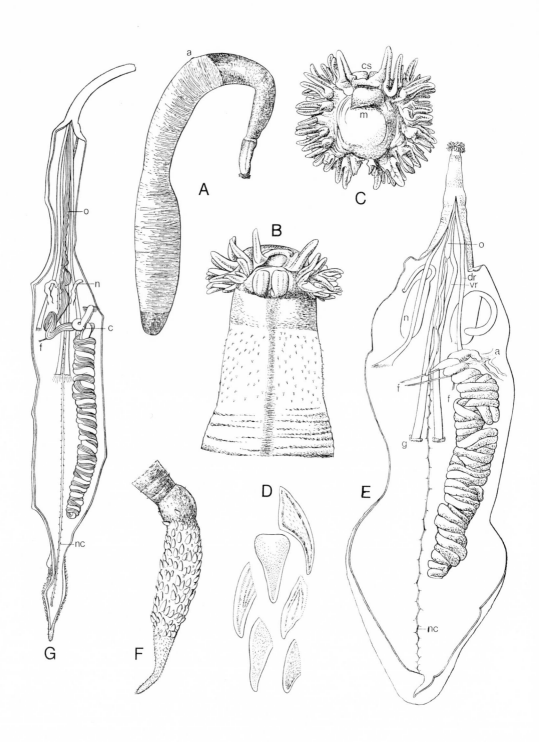

Subgenus Golfingia—Key to Species

1 Introvert with hooks 2
- Introvert without hooks 13
2 Tentacles either absent or reduced to two lobes . . . *G. nordenskjoldi* (p. 101)
- Tentacles either finger- or thread-like 3
3 Spindle muscle present 4
- Spindle muscle absent (introvert with eight rows of very small hooks, several fixing
    muscles present) . . . . *G. recondita* (p. 105)
4 Posterior region of trunk drawn out into a thread-like appendix, about one-fifth as
    long as the trunk (nephridia open in front of the anus, introvert with 25–30
    tentacles) . . . . *G. muricaudata* (p. 100)
- Posterior region of trunk not drawn out into a thread-like appendix . . . 5
5 Nephridia open anterior to the anus 6
- Nephridia open at about the same level as or just posterior to the anus . . 7
6 Introvert about twice as long as the trunk (sharply pointed hooks with a broad
    base scattered on introvert; papillae on trunk few and inconspicuous)
                                                                    G. rugosa (p. 107)
- Introvert about as long as the trunk (hooks slim and pointed and deeply grooved in
    front view; with about 52 well developed tentacles). . . *G. mutabilis* (p. 101)
7 Anus set in the middle of the trunk (nephridia open on same level as the anus; about
    16 tentacles) . . . . *G. ohlini* (p. 102)
- Anus not set in the middle of the trunk but more anteriorly 8
8 Rectal caecum present . . . . *G. owstoni* (p. 103)
- Rectal caecum absent 9
9 Introvert hooks not arranged in rows but scattered irregularly (skin at base of
    introvert and posterior region of the body bears spine-like papillae)
                                                            { *G. vulgaris* (p. 110)
                                                            { *G. kolensis* (p. 93)
- Introvert hooks arranged in rows 10
10 Hooks arranged in numerous (80–100) rows (nephridia open just posterior to the
    anus) . . . . *G. reticulata* (p. 105)
- Hooks arranged in fewer (less than 20) rows 11
11 Surface of trunk very smooth and without papillae 12
- Surface of trunk bears papillae . . . . . { *G. pudica* (p. 104)
                                                     { *G. derjugini* (p. 90)
12 Hooks in 10–15 rows (height of hook 0·032 mm; tentacles 20)   *G. cylindrata* (p. 89)
- Hooks slender and in 8–10 rows (length of hook 0·10 mm; tentacles 16)
                                                                    G. elongata (p. 90)
13 Tentacles reduced to two flaps of skin dorsally and six raised points of skin ventrally
    (nephridia, with a prominent nephrostome, open in front of the anus)
                                                            G. trichocephala (p. 109)

Fig. 11. (A–E) *Golfingia vulgaris*. (A) Entire animal, about natural size. (B) Anterior
  region of the introvert, × about 10. (C) Front view of the tentacular crown, × 10.
  (D) Hooks from the introvert. (E) Specimen dissected from the dorsal surface. (A–E
  after Théel.) (F–G) *Golfingia anderssoni*. (F) Posterior part of the body, × about 4.
  (G) Specimen dissected from the dorsal side. (F–G after Théel.) *a*, anus; *ap*, anal
  aperture; *b*, brain; *c*, caecum; *cs*, nuchal organ; *cv*, contractile vessel; *dr*, dorsal retractor;
  ds, dissepiments; *e*, eye-spot; *f*, *f*₁, etc., fastening muscles; *g*, gonad; *h*, hooks; *i*, introvert;
  in, intestine; *m*, mouth; *ms*, mesentery; *n*, nephridium; *nc*, nerve cord; *no*, nuchal organ;
  np, nephridiopore; *ns*, nephrostome; *o*, oesophagus; *om*, oblique muscles; *ph*, pharynx;
  pt, polian or contractile tubules; *re*, rectum; *rm*, retractor muscle; *sm*, spindle muscle;
  t, tentacles; *vr*, ventral retractor; *w*, wing muscle.

–   Tentacles finger- or thread-like.   14
14   Posterior region of trunk drawn out into a prominent appendix-like structure   .   15
–   Posterior region of trunk not drawn out into a prominent appendix-like structure   17
15   Appendix long and posterior region of trunk bears numerous, prominent, bladder-like
        vesicles or papillae with anteriorly directed tips; rectal caecum present
                                                               G. anderssoni (p. 84)
–   Appendix short (less than 10 mm long) and without prominent vesicles; rectal
        caecum absent   16
16   Ventral retractors arise in the anterior seventh of the trunk   *G. appendiculata* (p. 86)
–   Ventral retractors arise in the mid-region of the trunk   .   *G. hudsoniana* (p. 91)
17   No spindle muscle present   .   .   .   .   *G. lagensis* (p. 93)
–   Spindle muscle present   18
18   Contractile vessel with villi or vesicles   .   .   .   .   .   *G. capensis* (p. 87)
–   Contractile vessel without villi or vesicles   19
19   Nephridia open in front of the anus   20
–   Nephridia open at the level of the anus or just posterior to it   .   .   .   24
20   Rectal caecum present   .   .   .   .   .   .   ⎰   *G. margaritacea* (p. 94)
                                                      ⎱   *G. ikedai* (p. 92)
–   Rectal caecum absent   21
21   Nephridia with a small branch or diverticulum posteriorly (bilobed?), introvert
        about four times as long as the trunk   .   .   .   .   .   *G. anguinea* (p. 85)
–   Nephridia without secondary branches or lobes, introvert about as long as the trunk .   22
22   Two intestinal fastening muscles   23
–   Three intestinal fastening muscles   .   .   .   .   .   ⎰   *G. charcoti* (p. 89)
                                                               ⎱   *G. mawsoni* (p. 99)
23   Trunk with at least two kinds of papillae; those on the introvert are conical or pear
        shaped   .   .   .   .   ⎰   *G. soya* (p. 109)
                                                        ⎱   *G. nota* (p. 102)
–   Trunk and introvert with flat, circular to elliptical papillae only
                                                          G. cantabriensis (p. 86)
24   Rectal caecum present   .   .   .   .   *G. okinoseana* (p. 103)
–   Rectal caecum absent   25
25   Papillae on trunk tongue-like in shape (single intestinal fastening muscle)
                                                          G. glossipapillosa (p. 91)
–   Papillae on trunk not tongue-like in shape   26
26   Prominent papillae surround the anus   .   .   .   .   .   *G. solitaria* (p. 108)
–   Prominent papillae do not surround the anus   27
27   Three intestinal fastening muscles   .   .   .   .   .   .   *G. iniqua* (p. 93)
–   Less than three intestinal fastening muscles   .   .   .   ⎰   *G. signa* (p. 108)
                                                                 ⎱   *G. profunda* (p. 104)

Golfingia (Golfingia) anderssoni (Théel, 1911)

(Fig. 11F–G)

Phascolosoma anderssoni Théel, 1911 : 28–29, pl. 2, figs 28–34, pl. 5, figs 71–74; Fischer, 1928b :
    481; Stephen, 1941b : 250–251, pl. 8, fig. 2; 1948 : 216, pl. 1, fig. 1; Murina, 1957b : 992–993;
    1964a : 222–224; Edmonds, 1965 : 30, pl. 2.

TYPE LOCALITY.   Antarctica.

DESCRIPTION.   Introvert about as long as the trunk with about 21 short tentacles
but no hooks.   Trunk slender, elongate, tapering and up to 110 mm in length.
The skin is thin, shining and semitransparent.   It is covered with small cylindrical

papillae and at the posterior end there is a broad circle of rather large conical bladders or papillae which have their tips directed forwards. Two pairs of retractors; the ventral pair arises at about the middle of the trunk and the dorsal pair more anteriorly. Alimentary tract with about 24 convolutions. The spindle muscle is not attached posteriorly. The rectum is fixed by strong wing muscles and carries a caecum. The nephridia are free from the trunk wall for their whole length.

REMARKS. Characteristic of this species is the form of the posterior extremity which usually tapers to a sharp point and in some specimens is extended into an appendix-like structure. The species has been reported on a number of occasions from the Antarctic and sub-Antarctic. Murina's record (1964a) is from the North Pacific Ocean.

DISTRIBUTION. Antarctic (Théel, 1911; Fischer, 1928b; Stephen, 1941b, 1948; Murina, 1957b; Edmonds, 1965). North Pacific (Murina, 1964a).

Golfingia (Golfingia) anguinea (Sluiter, 1902)

Phascolosoma anguineum Sluiter, 1902 : 36–37, pl. 3, figs 13–16.

TYPE LOCALITY. Malaya. Siboga Stn. 295. 10°36′36″S, 124°11′42″E; at 2090 m.

DESCRIPTION. Introvert about four times as long as the trunk and sharply differentiated from it. Although it is damaged to some extent anteriorly it bears numerous threadlike 'feelers' (?) (Fühlern) but no hooks. Trunk 9 mm long, 2 mm broad, dark brown in colour and irregularly furrowed, with two large papillae at the base of the introvert which mark the openings of the nephridia. The prominent anus opens on the trunk about a third of its length behind the introvert. The papillae at the base of the introvert are large and resemble small warts and in the middle of the trunk they are flat, almost invisible and lack crowns of chitinous plates. At the posterior end of the trunk they are dome-shaped, no darker than the skin and have a flattened point with a crown of small chitinous plates that surround the central opening. The longitudinal musculature is weakly continuous, but faint bands appear on the introvert. Two pairs of retractors arise close together in the anterior quarter of the trunk. They arise as separate muscles but fuse into two bands in the middle of the trunk. About 30 intestinal convolutions present. The spindle muscle does not reach the end of the intestinal coil which is, therefore, free except for an anterior fixing muscle. The two nephridia are small and bladder-shaped, each opening on a prominent papilla anterior to the anus. They possess a large nephrostome anteriorly and a small 'caecum' or branch posteriorly.

REMARKS. Known only from the holotype. This species possesses two unusual characters, 'fadenförmigen Fühlern' and nephridia each with a small posteriorly placed tube (Sluiter, 1902, pl. 3, fig. 16). If the nephridia are bilobed then the species should be placed in another subgenus.

DISTRIBUTION. As for the type locality.

Golfingia (Golfingia) appendiculata (Sato, 1934)

(Fig. 12A–B)

Phascolosoma appendiculatum Sato, 1934b : 7–10, pl. 1, fig. 4, text-figs 7–10.
Phascolosoma appendiculata : Murina, 1964a : 224–227, figs 4a and b.

TYPE LOCALITY. Japan. Tosa Bay. Soyo-Maru Exped. stn. 342. 33°15′20″N, 133°48′40″E, at 288–527 m.

DESCRIPTION. Introvert up to 70 mm in length, much narrower than the trunk; tentacles fairly numerous, without hooks, covered with conical papillae which are larger and more densely distributed than on the trunk. Trunk up to 120 mm in length, 13 mm in width, with the posterior end drawn out into a tail-like appendage, about 10 mm in length and 1 mm in breadth. Skin thin, smooth and dirty-yellow in colour in the middle region of the trunk, rougher and dark-brown at either extremity. Under magnification the whole surface is seen to be covered with well-developed papillae which are comparatively tall at the anterior and posterior ends, low and nearly circular in the middle. Each papilla is composed of several gland-cells covered by a great number of chitinous plates. Two pairs of retractors. The ventral pair is the larger and arises at the level of the anterior seventh of the trunk; anteriorly the muscles are connected by mesenteries. The dorsal arises in front of the ventral pair. The intestine is fixed by two attaching muscles which arise near the root of the left dorsal retractor and are attached to the first coil. The rectum is attached to the trunk-wall by strong wing muscles; caecum absent. The strong spindle muscle is not attached posteriorly. The dark reddish-brown nephridia are free from the trunk-wall for all but the first 2 mm and open about the level of the anus. The nerve cord divides into two branches at its posterior end.

REMARKS. Described from three specimens, two of which were imperfect. The species is allied to *G. hudsoniana* but differs in the form of the caudal appendage.

DISTRIBUTION. Japan (Sato, 1934; Murina, 1964a), North Africa (Murina, 1964a).

Golfingia (Golfingia) cantabriensis Edmonds, 1960

Golfingia cantabriensis Edmonds, 1960 : 163–164, text-fig. 4.

TYPE LOCALITY. New Zealand. Heathcote Estuary, Banks Peninsula. *Type.* Canterbury Museum, New Zealand.

DESCRIPTION. Introvert fully retracted, 25 mm in length; hooks absent. A number of short finger-like tentacles present. Trunk cylindrical, 80 mm in length and 10 mm in width, musculature rather thick. The skin is superficially smooth but, under magnification, small dark elliptical papillae are seen to be scattered over the surface. Two pairs of retractor muscles arise at different levels; the stout ventrals in the mid-trunk region, the slenderer dorsals anteriorly. The alimentary canal is very long and consists of about 90 double coils. There are two fastening muscles, one arises near the left dorsal retractor and ends on the oesophagus, the other arises near the right dorsal retractor and ends near the last whorl of the intestine. Contractile vessel well-developed but without villi. The rectum is short and fastened by wing muscles; rectal caecum absent. The two nephridia arise just anteriorly to the anus and are free throughout their whole length.

REMARKS. Known only from the holotype. The species is similar to *G. margaritacea* but lacks a caecum.

DISTRIBUTION. As for the type locality.

Golfingia (Golfingia) capensis (Teuscher, 1874)

(Fig. 12C)

Phascolosoma capense Teuscher, 1874 : 488–489, pl. 19, figs 4, 5, 12, 14; Selenka & de Man, 1883 : 29–30, pl. 4, figs 40–43; Sluiter, 1889b : 443; Fischer, 1922a : 414; 1922b : 16; 1922c : 9–10; Leroy, 1936 : 425; Stephen, 1942 : 251; Wesenberg-Lund, 1959a : 181–182, fig. 1; 1963 : 108–110.

TYPE LOCALITY. Cape of Good Hope, South Africa.

DESCRIPTION. Introvert up to 20 mm in length with very numerous triangular, filamentous tentacles. Papillae extend over most of the surface. There are no hooks in adult animals but a few may be found in some very small specimens. Two eye-spots present. Trunk up to 30 mm in length, skin strong, iridescent, dirty-grey in colour in the middle, reddish at the introvert base and at the posterior end. It is covered with numerous short dark papillae, visible to the naked eye, which change in form as the animal grows. In young animals they appear as flattish oval humps which do not rise much above the surface; in old animals they may reach a height of 0·1 mm. The papillae are somewhat higher at the introvert base and on the posterior end of the trunk than in the middle. Two pairs of retractors present joining anteriorly; the ventral pair arises in the middle third of the trunk, the dorsal in the anterior third. The intestinal tract has about 20 coils. Three fastening mesenteries run from the first coil to the rectum. The contractile vessel runs the full length of the oesophagus and carries villi. The spindle muscle is short and not attached posteriorly. The two nephridia are free from the trunk wall for their whole length.

REMARKS. Both Stephen (1942) and Wesenberg-Lund (1963) have examined large collections of this species. Wesenberg-Lund (1963 : 110) says that it is the 'commonest intertidal sipunculid in the South African region. On the west coast it seems to extend as far north as latitude 29°S. The eastern limit of its distribution is near Durban in Natal.'

Wesenberg-Lund (1959a : 182 & 1963 : 108) points out that the structures borne on the contractile vessel are 'vesicles and not true villi' and that the use of the term 'villi' for this species is misleading. According to Wesenberg-Lund (1963 : 110) very young specimens may possess hooks.

DISTRIBUTION. Cape Province and Natal (Teuscher, 1874; Selenka & de Man, 1883; Sluiter, 1889b; Fischer, 1922b; Stephen, 1942; Wesenberg-Lund, 1959a, 1963). St Paul's Rocks (Leroy, 1936).

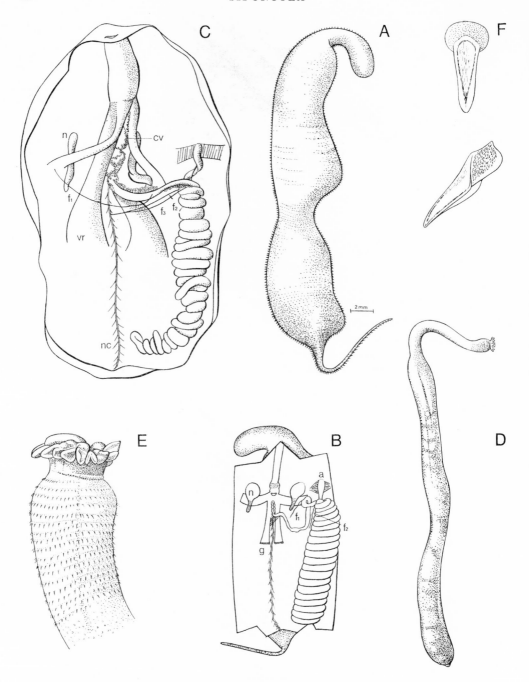

FIG. 12. (A–B) *Golfingia appendiculata*. (A) Entire animal. (B) Dissected specimen. (A and B after Murina.) (C) *Golfingia capensis*. Specimen dissected (after Selenka). (D–F) *Golfingia elongata*. (D) Entire animal, × 2·5. (E) Anterior region of the introvert, × 15. (F) Hooks from the introvert. (D–F after Théel.) KEY: *See* Fig. 11, p. 83.

Golfingia (Golfingia) charcoti (Hérubel, 1906)

Phascolosoma charcoti Hérubel, 1906a : 127–128; 1906c : 651–652; 1908 : 2–8, text-figs 1–8; Fischer, 1928b : 483.

TYPE LOCALITY. Antarctic. Port Charcot, at 40 m.

DESCRIPTION. Introvert about two-thirds the trunk length, with a crown of 20–22 tentacles, but without hooks or spines. It carries well-spaced papillae of the same type as on the trunk. Trunk cylindrical, up to 11 mm in length, whitish in colour and rounded posteriorly. There are a number of cylindrical papillae spaced over the surface. Two pairs of retractors arise in the posterior third of the trunk, the dorsals a little more anteriorly. Alimentary tract with about 14 double coils; three fastening mesenteries attach the top of the spire to the trunk wall. There is a simple contractile vessel. The spindle muscle is attached near to the anus but is free posteriorly. Rectal caecum absent. The two short nephridia open in front of the anus and are free from the trunk wall for their whole length.

REMARKS. *Golfingia mawsoni* Benham, 1922, also from the Antarctic, closely resembles this species.

DISTRIBUTION. As for the type locality.

Golfingia (Golfingia) cylindrata (Keferstein, 1865)

Phascolosoma cylindratum Keferstein, 1865a : 428, pl. 33, figs 40–41; Selenka & de Man, 1883 : 25; Verrill, 1900 : 670; Gerould, 1913 : 382–383; Leroy, 1936 : 425.

TYPE LOCALITY. Bermuda.

DESCRIPTION. Introvert about half the trunk length, with 20 long filamentous tentacles. A broad zone of some 10–15 widely-spaced rows of small, scattered, simple hooks on the anterior part. Trunk about four times as long as broad. The skin is very thick and covered with closely set and regularly-arranged, long skin-bodies which carry no papillae. Musculature thin and shiny. Two pairs of retractors which only unite near the tentacles; the ventral pair arises in the hind part of the anterior third of the trunk and the dorsal near the anus. About 25–30 intestinal coils present, a fastening muscle from the first coil and two other muscles more posteriorly join them to the trunk wall. The spindle muscle is not attached posteriorly. The oesophagus carries a simple contractile vessel. The rectum is short. The nephridia are short and open either just in front of the anus or at about the same level.

REMARKS. Gerould (1913) redescribed three specimens from Key West, Florida. The species is closely related to *G. elongata* but differs in the size and shape of the introvert hooks.

DISTRIBUTION. Bermuda (Keferstein, 1865; Verrill, 1900), Florida (Gerould, 1913), Tonkin (Leroy, 1936).

G

Golfingia (Golfingia) derjugini (Gadd, 1911)

Phascolosoma derjugini Gadd, 1911 : 82–83, 103–105, text-figs 9–14.

TYPE LOCALITY. Kola Peninsula, North Russia.

DESCRIPTION. Introvert two sevenths of the total length of animal and bears
11 tentacles with six rows of backwardly directed small hooks. Trunk cylindrical,
rounded posteriorly; numerous short, cylindrical papillae present and 12–14
irregular, longitudinal zig-zag bands of yellow colour. Two pairs of retractors
present; the ventral pair arises from the second third of the trunk. About 24
intestinal convolutions, traversed by the spindle muscle which is not attached
posteriorly. Two fixing muscles present, one from the rectum, the other from the
first convolution. Two nephridia free for their whole length.

REMARKS. Known only from the holotype.

DISTRIBUTION. As for the type locality.

Golfingia (Golfingia) elongata (Keferstein, 1863)

(Fig. 12D–F)

Syrinx forbesii McCoy, 1845 : 273, pl. 16, fig. 3.
Syrinx tenuicinctus McCoy, 1845 : 274, pl. 16, fig. 4.
Phascolosoma forbesii : Baird, 1868 : 83; Diesing, 1851 : 66.
Phascolosoma oxyurum : Baird, 1868 : 83.
Phascolosoma teres Hutton, 1903 : 29.
Phascolosoma delayei Hérubel, 1903a : 100.
Phascolosoma elongatum Keferstein, 1863 : 39, pl. 3, fig. 5; 1865a : 428, pl. 32, figs 30–31;
    Claparede, 1863 : 61–62, pl. 12, figs 21–23; Selenka & de Man, 1883 : 23–25, pl. 4, figs 35–36;
    Théel, 1905, pl. 1, figs 9–13, pl. 3, fig. 188; Sluiter, 1912 : 11; Southern, 1913b : 16–18;
    Cuénot, 1922 : 8–9; Fischer, 1922b : 6; 1925 : 16–17; Hérubel, 1924 : 109–110; Wesenberg-
    Lund, 1933 : 6–8, pl. 3, fig. 2; 1939 : 15–17; Stephen, 1934 : 165–166; 1958 : 132; Leroy,
    1936 : 425; Steuer, 1939 : 2, text-fig. 2.
Golfingia elongata Murina, 1964b : 259–261; 1967a : 1335, fig. 4 (1).
Phascolosoma elongatum quinquepunctatum Hérubel, 1913 : 105.
Phascolosoma cluthensis Stephen, 1931 : 60–61, figs 1–2.

TYPE LOCALITY. St Vaast la Hougue, France.

DESCRIPTION. Introvert about half the trunk length, with a simple crown of
tentacles arranged in a single row. On the anterior portion are 8–10 fairly closely-set
rows of thin, slightly bent hooks. Two eye-spots present. Trunk up to 90 mm in
length, thin and capable of great extension so that it may stretch to about 20 times
as long as thin. Colour dirty-flesh to light red-yellow. The leather-like skin on
the trunk and introvert is smooth and without prominent papillae but there are
numerous skin bodies which become somewhat larger at the posterior end of the
trunk, almost rising to papillae. The inner surface is lustrous. Two pairs of thin
retractors unite far forward; the ventral arise in the middle of the trunk, the dorsal
some little distance anteriorly immediately behind the anus. The intestinal spiral
with 30–35 coils, not attached to the posterior end of the trunk by the spindle
muscle. It carries a simple contractile vessel. There are two fastening mesenteries

from the spiral and rectum. The two nephridia are short, slim, and free from the trunk wall for their whole length.

REMARKS. This species is very close to *G. vulgaris* (de Blainville). The hooks on the introvert of the latter are scattered while those on *G. elongata* are arranged in rows. The illustrations of Théel (1905, pl. 1, figs 4 & 11) show this. Théel's drawing indicates about 20 rows of hooks although Keferstein gives 8–10 as the number.

We have referred *Phascolosoma elongatum quinquepunctatum* Hérubel, 1913 to *G. elongata*.

DISTRIBUTION. A widely distributed and common species from the Arctic to the Mediterranean. Spitzbergen (Sluiter, 1912); Skagerack and Kattegat (Wesenberg-Lund, 1939); North Sea (Stephen, 1934; Fischer, 1925); English Channel (Wesenberg-Lund, 1933); Eire (Southern, 1913; Farran, 1915); France (Grübe, 1869, 1872; Keferstein, 1863; Cuénot, 1922); Morocco (Hérubel, 1924, 1925); Tangier (Leroy, 1936); Egypt (Steuer, 1936, 1937); Israel (Stephen, 1958); Cuba (Murina, 1967a).

Golfingia (Golfingia) glossipapillosa (Sato, 1934)

Phascolosoma glossipapillosum Sato, 1934b : 10–12, pl. 1, fig. 5, text-figs 11–14.

TYPE LOCALITY. Sea of Japan. Soyo-Maru Exp., Stn. 489. 35°37′10″N, 131°02′00″E, at 249 m.

DESCRIPTION. Introvert 60 mm in length, 5 mm in width, with numerous finger-shaped tentacles but without hooks. Trunk up to 80 mm in length and 12 mm in diameter, tapering posteriorly to a sharply pointed end. Mostly dark brown in colour but lighter posteriorly. The whole surface is covered with tongue-shaped papillae which are covered with small chitinous plates. The papillae are largest at the base of the introvert and smallest in the middle region of the trunk. Two pairs of retractors present; the ventral pair arise from the middle of the trunk but the dorsal more anteriorly. Intestine with about 25 coils; a single fastening mesentery which arises on the left of the nerve cord, is attached to the first intestinal coil. There is a strong spindle muscle which is not attached posteriorly. The rectum is fastened by wing muscles near the anus. There is no rectal caecum. The nephridia are small yellowish tubes opening almost on a level with the anus and are free from the trunk wall for their whole length. The nerve cord is more or less free.

REMARKS. Described from several specimens, of which only one was complete. The tongue-like papillae are characteristic of this species.

DISTRIBUTION. As for the type locality.

Golfingia (Golfingia) hudsoniana (Chamberlain, 1920)

Phascolosoma hudsonianum Chamberlain, 1920 : 3d–4d, text-figs 1–4.

TYPE LOCALITY. Fort Churchill, Hudson Bay, Canada. *Type.* Victoria Memorial Museum, Ottawa, no. 101.

DESCRIPTION. Introvert about 46 mm in length, with several rows of tentacles but no hooks. It is covered with papillae which are more prominent towards the tentacles. Trunk 70 mm in length and 17 mm at its greatest diameter. It is slender, sub-pyriform and has a conspicuous caudal appendage sharply marked off from the trunk. Appendage is 7 mm in length and 3·6 mm across the base but anteriorly it is of the same width as the introvert. Musculature thin, in part translucent, the inner surface with a pearly lustre. Trunk mostly light brown in colour with a shining, pearly lustre. The papillae are visible to the naked eye and are distributed over the surface. They are sub-conical with a broad base and are densest at the caudal end and near the level and just in front of the anus. Two pairs of retractors present. The ventral pair arises about midway between the anus and the posterior end of the trunk and the dorsal pair which are much slenderer arise five twelfths of the distance from the origin of the ventral pair to the anus. Intestine with numerous convolutions which are free posteriorly. The nephridia are free, with conspicuous openings near the level of the anus.

REMARKS. Known only from the holotype.

DISTRIBUTION. As for the type locality.

Golfingia (Golfingia) ikedai Fisher, 1950

Phascolosoma japonicum Ikeda, 1904 : 5–7, figs 2, 28, 29; Chin, 1947 : 100.
Golfingia ikedai: Fisher, (nom. nov. pro *Phascolosoma japonicum* Ikeda, 1904, non *Physcosoma japonicum* Grube, 1877), 1950 : 550; 1952 : 390.

TYPE LOCALITY. Japan.

DESCRIPTION. Introvert about two thirds times the length of the trunk, into which it passes without any clear demarcation. It is without hooks or spines and numerous filamentous tentacles surround the mouth. They are arranged in 12–14 longitudinal rows, each with five tentacles; the rows are united by U-shaped elevations in sets of two. Two eye-spots on the brain. Trunk 50 mm in length, 7 mm in width, brownish-yellow in colour. The skin appears smooth to the naked eye but, under magnification, is seen to be covered with densely distributed elliptical skin bodies. These are flat, somewhat transparent and not covered with chitinous plates. They are nearly all of the same size. Two pairs of retractor muscles; the ventral pair originates near the nerve cord in the middle of the trunk and the dorsal a short distance behind the anus. About 17–23 intestinal convolutions. The oesophagus is attached to the trunk wall by numerous mesenteries. There are three fixing muscles, one on the right side and two on the left side of the nerve cord. One from each side is attached to the beginning of the rectum, the others to the terminal portion of the oesophagus. Contractile vessel simple. The spindle muscle is not attached posteriorly. Rectum fixed by wing muscles; large rectal caecum present. The nephridia which open slightly in front of the anus are about half as long as the trunk, deep brownish in colour and free.

REMARKS. Described originally from numerous specimens.

DISTRIBUTION. Japan, coasts of Tokyo Bay and Sagami Bay (Ikeda, 1904); China, Fukien (Chin, 1947).

Golfingia (Golfingia) iniqua (Sluiter, 1912)

Phascolosoma iniquum Sluiter, 1912 : 14, pl. 1, fig. 4.

TYPE LOCALITY. Princess Alice Expedition, Stn. 1450. 45°09′N, 3°18′W, at 1804 m.

DESCRIPTION. The introvert has about 30 tentacles but no hooks and is striated transversely. It carries papillae which are of the same type as those on the trunk. The trunk is barrel-shaped and narrowed anteriorly. The skin is smooth to the naked eye or only slightly striated but, under the microscope, it is seen to be covered with numerous papillae of two kinds. The first is oval in shape with chitinous plates which are characteristically few in number, the plates being smaller round the central opening than on the periphery. The second kind of papilla is very small, barrel-like, and much more numerous than the oval kind. Two pairs of retractors present; the ventral pair arises from the middle of the trunk. the dorsal pair from the anterior third of the trunk. Intestinal tract with about 20–30 convolutions. There are three fixing muscles anteriorly, but the spindle muscle is not attached posteriorly and does not reach to the end of the convolutions. The nephridia are bulky and open at the level of the anus.

REMARKS. Described originally from four specimens.

DISTRIBUTION. As for the type locality.

Golfingia (Golfingia) kolensis (Gadd, 1911)

Phascolosoma kolense Gadd, 1911 : 80–81, 102–103, text-figs 1–8.

TYPE LOCALITY. Kola Peninsula, North Russia.

DESCRIPTION. Introvert about two-thirds of the length of the trunk, carrying 16–22 tentacles; covered with papillae and small three-cornered, irregularly arranged hooks. The trunk, extended, is thin and cylindrical with a white fairly translucent, iridescent skin. It is covered with cylindrical yellow papillae which are larger and more regularly arranged posteriorly. Two pairs of retractors; the ventral pair arises in the middle third of the trunk and the dorsal pair under the anus. About 39 intestinal coils present with three fixing muscles. The first muscle arises from the first spiral and is attached to the base of the dorsal retractor; the second arises from the rectum and is attached to the right ventral retractor, while the third springs from the first intestinal coil. The spindle muscle is attached near the anus but is free posteriorly. The two nephridia, of which the right is somewhat longer, open on a level with the anus.

REMARKS. Described originally from six specimens.

DISTRIBUTION. As for the type locality.

Golfingia (Golfingia) lagensis (Fischer, 1895)

Phascolosoma lagense Fischer, 1895 : 13–14; 1914 : 76–77, pl. 2, figs 1–3.

TYPE LOCALITY. Lagos, West Africa.

DESCRIPTION. Introvert 10 mm in length, lighter in colour than the trunk and bearing large papillae. Trunk 10 mm, about 3–4 times as long as broad, drawn out to a sharp point posteriorly; under magnification it is seen to be crossed by transverse and longitudinal striae. Colour brown-black with a grey sheen, lighter coloured posteriorly. The papillae are all club-shaped but not visible to the naked eye; largest and most numerous at the posterior end. Two pairs of fairly strong retractors present; the ventral arise from the front edge of the hind third of the trunk near the nerve cord and the dorsal from the front of the middle third of the trunk. About 20 intestinal convolutions present with a fastening muscle from the first coil. Spindle muscle absent. The nephridia are about half the length of the trunk and open at about the level of the anus. They are lighter in colour than the gut and are free from the trunk wall for their whole length.

REMARKS. Known only from the holotype.

DISTRIBUTION. As for the type locality.

Golfingia (Golfingia) margaritacea margaritacea (Sars, 1851)

(Fig. 13C–E)

Sipunculus margaritaceus Sars, 1851 : 196–197.
Homalosoma laeve Oersted (in Keferstein, 1865a : 436).
Stephanostoma barentsii Horst, 1882 (in Théel, 1905 : 65); Fischer, 1922d : 233.
Stephanostoma hanseni Danielssen & Koren, 1881b : 9–13, pl. 2, figs 21–29, pl. 4, fig. 19.
Phascolosoma antarcticum Michaelsen, 1889 : 73; Sluiter, 1912 : 12.
Phascolosoma fulgens Théel, 1875b : 8, pl. 2, fig. 11; 1905 : 63.
Phascolosoma fuscum Michaelsen, 1889 : 76.
Phascolosoma georgianum Michaelsen, 1889 : 78.
Phascolosoma socium Lanchester, 1908 : 1.
Phascolosoma hanseni : Théel, 1905 : 65–69, pl. 4, figs 38–43, pl. 14, fig. 191; Gadd, 1911 : 83–88; Fischer, 1914b : 9; Wesenberg-Lund, 1925 : 89.
Phascolosoma albidum Théel, 1875 : 8, pl. 2, fig. 10; Selenka & de Man, 1883 : 26.
Phascolosoma oerstedii Keferstein, 1865a : 436, pl. 31, fig. 8, pl. 33, fig. 39; Théel, 1905 : 63.
Phascolosoma capsiforme Baird, 1868 : 83–84, pl. 11, fig. 3; Selenka & de Man, 1883 : 27–28, pl. 4, figs 38–39; Collin, 1901 : 302; Shipley, 1902a : 285; Leroy, 1936 : 425.
Phascolosoma margaritaceum var. *capsiforme :* Fischer, 1896b : 3–5; 1913 : 99; 1914b : 9; Benham, 1922 : 7–13, pl. 2, figs 1–2; Leroy, 1936 : 425.
Phascolosoma margaritaceum : Danielssen & Koren, 1877a : 135–136, pl. 15, figs 43–44; Levinsen, 1887 : 302; Gadd, 1911 : 83; Sluiter, 1912 : 7–8; J. Fischer, 1914 : 96–97; Fischer, 1914b : 9; 1922a : 409–413, text-figs 1–3; 1928b : 481; Gerould, 1913 : 381; Wesenberg-Lund, 1928 : 5, text-fig. 3; 1930 : 25–28, pl. 3, fig. 34–36, pl. 5, fig. 51; 1932 : 5–6; 1933 : 8–9; 1937a : 10–11; 1937b : 8–9; 1939b : 28; 1939c : 17–18; Stephen, 1934 : 116; 1941b : 251–253, pl. 8, figs 3–4; Gustafson, 1937 : 11; ten Broeke, 1929 : 161–162, figs 7–8; Chapman, 1955 : 351–352; Macginitie, 1956 : 126.
Golfingia margaritacea : Fisher, 1952 : 391; Wesenberg-Lund, 1955a : 197–201; 1959a : 181; 1959c : 209.
Golfingia margaritacea capsiformis : Edmonds, 1960b : 29, pl. 1.

DESCRIPTION. Introvert about half the length of the trunk, with about 50 tentacles set in several rows; smooth and without hooks. Trunk fairly stout, 4–5 times as long as thick, up to 100 mm in length. Skin thick, greyish-white in colour with a nacreous iridescence. Under magnification the surface can be seen to be reticulated by two series of fine cross lines. Numerous skin-bodies are scattered over the surface which, at the base of the introvert and the posterior end of the trunk, become low, flat, oval or rounded papillae. The musculature is strong, the colour internally also like mother-of-pearl. The pores of the nephridia are conspicuous. Two pairs of retractors present uniting far anteriorly; the ventrals arise from the middle third of the trunk, the dorsals at some distance from them in the anterior third. The oesophagus is long and carries a simple contractile vessel on its anterior half. There are numerous intestinal convolutions which are free posteriorly; three fastening mesenteries present anteriorly. Spindle muscle rudimentary. The rectum is short and bears a caecum. The two nephridia are short and free from the trunk wall for their whole length.

REMARKS. According to Wesenberg-Lund (1955a : 200), 'G. margaritacea is a widely distributed species, most probably cosmopolitan. It is at any rate bipolar; in the northern hemisphere it is circumpolar and it is fairly common in boreo-arctic and boreal areas. In the Atlantic it ranges south to Morocco and the Azores and on the western side to Philadelphia. In the Pacific it ranges from Bering Strait to Japan and along the west coast of America from Alaska to California. In the Antarctic it is reported from the Falkland Islands, Magellan's Strait, Tierra del Fuego, South Georgia, Graham Land and the Ross Sea.' Théel (1911), Stephen (1941b) and Wesenberg-Lund (1955a) all considered the species to be bipolar. If this is true of the species one would expect some flow of genes to take place between the two populations, possibly through the deeper and colder parts of the intervening oceans. Whether or not the flow does occur is not yet certain. There is, however, some evidence that G. margaritacea does inhabit deep water. Wesenberg-Lund (1930) reported the species at a depth of 3230 m (N. 60°17', W. 54°05') and in 1955a at 4540–4600 m (N. 40°33', W. 35°24').

There seems little doubt that the species possess a rectal caecum. Selenka (1883) and Théel (1905; 1911) do not mention the presence of a caecum nor does Théel show one in his carefully drawn figures. The description and illustrations of Wesenberg-Lund (1930, fig. 51), Fischer (1925, fig. 9) and Fisher (1952, pl. 23, fig. 1), however, make it clear that the structure is present.

Wesenberg-Lund (1925; 1955a) describes how the external appearance of the species may vary. She reports specimens which possess a long, tail-like appendix and others in which large, swollen vesicles appear on the posterior surface of the trunk.

DISTRIBUTION. Greenland (Wesenberg-Lund, 1925, 1928); Iceland (Wesenberg-Lund, 1937b); North Russia, Kara Sea (Levinsen, 1887); Kola Gulf (Gadd, 1911); Siberia (Théel, 1905); Norway (Sluiter, 1912; Wesenberg-Lund, 1939); Kattegat and Skagerack (Wesenberg-Lund, 1939); Scottish waters (Stephen, 1934); Azores; (Chapman, 1955; Leroy, 1936); West African coast (Wesenberg-Lund, 1959a); North America and Alaska (McGinitie, 1956); N.E. America (Gerould, 1913); Antarctic (Fischer, 1896b; Shipley, 1902; Théel, 1905; Fischer, 1926a; Stephen, 1941b); South America, Patagonia (Fischer, 1913); Chile (Wesenberg-Lund, 1955b).

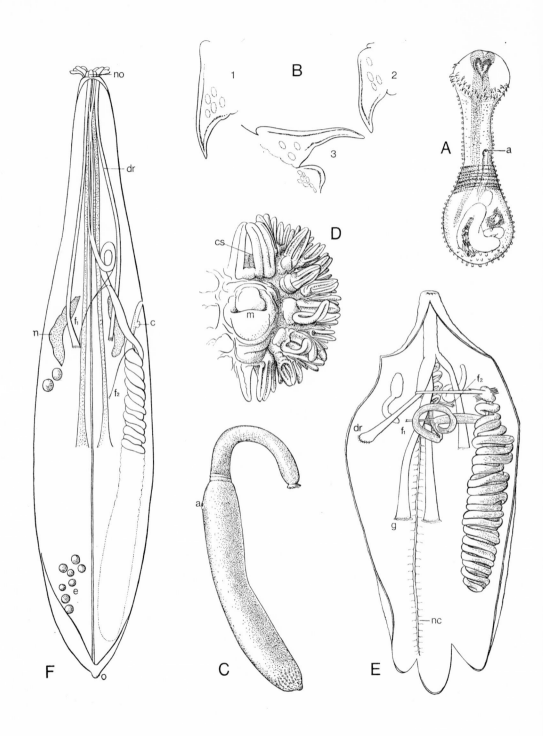

Subspecies of *G. margaritacea*

Eight subspecies in addition to the nominate form have been proposed. They are *G. margaritacea adelaidensis*, *G. m. antarctica*, *G. m. californiensis*, *G. m. finmarchica*, *G. m. hanseni*, *G. m. meridionalis*, *G. m. sibirica* and *G. m. trybomi*.

Golfingia (Golfingia) margaritacea adelaidensis Edmonds, 1956

Golfingia margaritacea adelaidensis Edmonds, 1956 : 302–303, pl. 2, fig. 2.

TYPE LOCALITY. St Vincent Gulf, South Australia.

DESCRIPTION. This species belongs to the '*margaritacea*' complex of species. It is not as stout and strong as specimens of *G. margaritacea* from Antarctica yet the two are difficult to separate anatomically. The caecum, however, does not appear to be as well developed as in forms like *G. margaritacea californiensis*; the posterior extremity of the trunk is usually pointed and sometimes it is shaped to resemble a conical cap.

DISTRIBUTION. The type locality.

Golfingia (Golfingia) margaritacea antarctica (Michaelsen, 1889)

Phascolosoma margaritaceum antarcticum Michaelsen, 1889 : 73–84, pl. 1, figs 4a–c; Fischer 1928b : 481, pl. 6, fig. 15; Sato, 1934 : 5–6, pl. 1, fig. 3, text-figs 5–6.

TYPE LOCALITY. South Georgia.

DESCRIPTION. This subspecies is closely allied to the nominate form but differs in having the surface of the trunk covered with dark papillae.

REMARKS. Described originally from three specimens. Sato recorded two more from Japanese waters.

DISTRIBUTION. Antarctic (Michaelsen, 1889; Fischer, 1928). Japan (Sato, 1934).

Golfingia (Golfingia) margaritacea californiensis Fisher, 1952
(Fig. 13F)

Golfingia margaritaceum californiensis Fisher, 1952 : 392–393, pl. 23, figs 1–2, pl. 24, figs 6–8.

TYPE LOCALITY. California, Pacific Grove, Monterey Bay. *Type*. U.S.N.M. no. 21220.

DESCRIPTION. Up to 20 mm in length. The introvert has a ring of about 16 tentacles. The trunk is slender, without papillae, and with the skin-bodies most

---

FIG. 13. (A–B) *Golfingia intermedia*. (A) Entire animal. (B) Three hooks from the introvert; all to the same scale. (A–B after Southern.) (C–E) *Golfingia margaritacea*. (C) Entire animal from the Arctic Sea, about natural size. Antarctic specimens may be twice as large. (D) Tentacular crown, × about 9. (E) Dissected specimen. (C–E after Théel.) (F) *Golfingia margaritacea californiensis*. Internal structures (after Fisher). KEY: *See* Fig. 11, p. 83.

prominent at the base of the introvert and at the posterior end of the trunk. Two fixing muscles present, a relatively larger caecum and the roots of the dorsal retractors closer together than in the nominate form.

REMARKS. Described from several specimens. Fisher considered it related to *G. margaritacea sibirica*.

DISTRIBUTION. As for the type locality.

Golfingia (Golfingia) margaritacea finmarchica (Théel, 1905)

Phascolosoma margaritacea finmarchica Théel, 1905 : 63–64.

TYPE LOCALITY. Finland.

DESCRIPTION. Body wall thick and surface reticulate. Tentacles more numerous and slightly longer than those of *G. margaritacea sibirica*.

REMARKS. Théel considered that the number of tentacles of a species increased with the age or size of the specimen. His table (Théel, 1905 : 65) supplies the evidence on which he based the conclusion. We have repeated the table for *P. margaritacea finmarchica*.

Specimen	1	2	3	4	5	6	7	8	9	10	11
Length of trunk (mm)	7·5	15	20	22	40	47	50	65	70	70	70
Number of tentacles	8	18	34	26	44	87	83	55	74	97	104

Golfingia (Golfingia) margaritacea hanseni (Danielssen & Koren, 1881)

Phascolosoma hanseni Danielssen & Koren, 1881 : 9–13, pl. 2, figs 21–29, pl. 4, fig. 19; Wesenberg-Lund, 1925 : 89.
Phascolosoma margaritaceum hanseni: Stephen, 1941b : 253.
Golfingia margaritacea hanseni: Wesenberg-Lund, 1955b : 9.

TYPE LOCALITY. Off the Arctic coast of Norway.

DESCRIPTION. The subspecies differs from the nominate form in having a leathery skin, which is very distinct from the smooth pearly skin of *G. margaritacea margaritacea*.

DISTRIBUTION. Off the Arctic coasts of Norway (Danielssen & Koren, 1881); Greenland (Wesenberg-Lund, 1925); Patagonia (Stephen, 1941; Wesenberg-Lund, 1955b).

Golfingia (Golfingia) margaritacea meridionalis (Gerould, 1913)

Phascolosoma margaritaceum var. *meridionalis* Gerould, 1913 : 382.

TYPE LOCALITY. Azores. 38°30′N, 28°40′W, shore collection. *Type*. U.S.N.M. no. 4003.

DESCRIPTION. *G. margaritacea meridionalis* is said to differ from the nominate form in three particulars: (1) the colour of the introvert which is pearly grey and not brown, (2) the extremely elongate shape of the trunk and (3) the presence of papillae on the anterior end of the trunk.

REMARKS. Based originally on six specimens.

DISTRIBUTION. As for the type locality. Off Long Island, U.S.A., 1290 m.

Golfingia (Golfingia) margaritacea sibirica (Théel, 1905)

Phascolosoma margaritaceum forma *sibirica* Théel, 1905 : 64–65.

TYPE LOCALITY. Siberia.

DESCRIPTION. Musculature thin, almost transparent, with hardly discernible reticulations on the surface of the trunk; also a more delicate development of the internal organs than in *G. margaritacea margaritacea*.

REMARKS. Described from 44 specimens.

DISTRIBUTION. Siberia; Behring Strait (Théel, 1905).

Golfingia (Golfingia) margaritacea trybomi (Théel, 1905)

Phascolosoma trybomi Théel, 1905 : 69–70, pl. 2, figs 13–18, pl. 13, fig. 189; Stephen, 1934 : 166; 1948 : 216.
Phascolosoma margaritaceum trybomi: Fischer, 1924 : 72; 1925 : 19; Lindroth, 1941 : 444–449, fig. 2.
Golfingia margaritacea trybomi: Wesenberg-Lund, 1955b : 8; Murina, 1957b : 995–996.

TYPE LOCALITY. Sweden.

DESCRIPTION. Introvert without hooks and with about 100 tentacles arranged in 10 groups. Trunk up to 100 mm in length, light brown in colour, pointed posteriorly and covered with minute granules visible under magnification. The inner surface of the trunk is lustrous and iridescent. Retractors much shorter than in the nominate form.

REMARKS. Several authors have considered *trybomi* to be a separate species but others believe it to be conspecific with *margaritacea*. Lindroth (1941) made a detailed study of several specimens and concluded that it is only subspecifically distinct.

DISTRIBUTION. Coasts of Norway and Sweden (Théel, 1905); North Sea (Stephen, 1934); Antarctic (Stephen, 1948; Murina, 1957b); Chile (Wesenberg-Lund, 1955b).

Golfingia (Golfingia) mawsoni (Benham, 1922)
(Fig. 14B)

Phascolosoma mawsoni Benham, 1922 : 13–17, pl. 2, figs 3–11; Fischer, 1928 : 482–483.
Golfingia mawsoni: Murina, 1964a : 230–233, figs 8a–b.

TYPE LOCALITY. Commonwealth Bay, Antarctica. At 46–110 m. *Type.* Australian Museum.

DESCRIPTION. The introvert is without hooks but carries about 30 short tentacles arranged in couples. The papillae are of the same type as on the trunk but are

fairly numerous and closely aggregated towards the tentacles.   Length up to about
42 mm.   The trunk ends posteriorly in a low rounded cone which is very evident
when the animal is extended but less so when contracted.   The skin is opaque,
creamy white and rather rough due partly to ridges and furrows and partly to
more or less scattered papillae.   The latter are whitish in colour and appear under
a lens as short columns about three times as high as broad; they are most numerous
posteriorly.   Two pairs of retractors; the ventral pair arises about 9 mm behind the
anus and the dorsal about 2 mm.   There are about 12–19 intestinal coils which are
loosely wound and held in place by two or three mesenteries.   The delicate spindle
muscle is not attached posteriorly.   The rectum is fixed by a broad wing muscle.
The nephridia are pale pink in colour and reach only to the base of the dorsal
retractors as a rule.

REMARKS.   Based originally on 50 specimens.

DISTRIBUTION.   Commonwealth Bay, Antarctica (Benham, 1922; Fischer, 1928).
North Pacific Ocean (Murina, 1964a).

Golfingia (Golfingia) muricaudata (Southern, 1913)

(Fig. 14A)

Phascolosoma muricaudatum Southern, 1913b : 21, pl. 4, fig. 5; Fischer, 1922c : 10–11, pl. 2,
   fig. 10; 1928 : 483; 1931 : 139.
Golfingia muricaudata: Murina, 1964a : 233–237, figs 9a–b.

TYPE LOCALITY.   Off south-west Ireland, at 475–1088 m.   Type.   National
Museum, Dublin.

DESCRIPTION.   Introvert up to 16 mm in length with 25–30 well-formed tentacles.
Hooks are lacking in adults but present in immature specimens.   Low and rounded
papillae are mingled with the hooks, but behind the hooks the papillae become
slenderer with bulbous tips; still more posteriorly they resemble those in the trunk.
Trunk up to 48 mm in length, cylindrical anteriorly, passing gradually into the introvert; posteriorly there is a filiform tail, about a fifth of the length of the trunk.
The tail may be of varying length but is always sharply separated from the trunk,
of which it must be considered as an appendage since the nerve cord does not enter
it.   The trunk is covered with slender papillae.   Skin usually very thin and transparent, pale brown in colour and delicately wrinkled.   Two pairs of retractors
present.   The dorsals are the thinner and usually arise just behind the anus; there
is some variation, however, and they sometimes arise rather more posteriorly.
The ventrals arise midway between the anus and the base of the tail.   The nephridia
open in front of the anus.

REMARKS.   Described originally from 56 specimens.

DISTRIBUTION.   Ireland (Southern, 1913b); West Africa (Fischer, 1922c); Bouvet
Is. (Fischer, 1928); Japan and North Pacific (Murina, 1964a).

Golfingia (Golfingia) mutabilis (Southern, 1913)

Phascolosoma mutabile Southern, 1913b : 19–20, pl. 3, fig. 4.

TYPE LOCALITY. South-west Ireland. 51°35′30″N, 12°26′W; at 914 m. *Type.* National Museum, Dublin.

DESCRIPTION. Introvert about 20 mm in length with about 52 well developed tentacles; behind them is a narrow band of slim, pointed hooks deeply grooved in front view. Trunk fusiform, 23 mm in length, with bluntly rounded posterior end. Skin thick and opaque, covered with fine wrinkles. Cuticle deeply coloured with dark brown pigment. Anal and nephridial pores indicated by lighter areas. Papillae scattered over the whole body and visible only under high magnification except at the posterior extremity where they are most numerous. Inner surface of the body with a pearly lustre. Two pairs of retractors of almost equal thickness; the dorsal pair arises about a quarter of the distance from the anus to the posterior end and the ventral pair about half way between the dorsal pair and the posterior end of the body. About 24 closely wound intestinal coils which are free behind. Rectum bears no caecum and is fixed with wing muscles. It is also attached to the body-wall by a slender muscle with two roots. Two other slender muscles arise in the middle of the intestine and are attached to the ventral retractors. Nephridia open some distance in front of the anus and are free except at their anterior end.

REMARKS. Described originally from four specimens. The three paratypes show some differences. Their skin is grey and unpigmented and there are no hooks.

DISTRIBUTION. South-west Ireland, at 914–1600 m. (Southern, 1913b).

Golfingia (Golfingia) nordenskjoldi (Théel, 1911)

Phascolosoma nordenskjoldi Théel, 1911 : 30–31, pl. 3, figs 35–41; Fischer, 1928 : 483; Stephen, 1941b : 253–254; 1948 : 217.
Golfingia nordenskjoldi: Wesenberg-Lund, 1955b : 9–11; Murina, 1964a : 237–238, pl. 11 (map).

TYPE LOCALITY. South Georgia.

DESCRIPTION. Tentacles absent from introvert, replaced by two lobes. A girdle of crooked hooks intermingled with papillae present on the introvert. Trunk up to 9 mm in length, subcylindrical, more or less rounded posteriorly. Skin iridescent, folded into a series of rings by numerous close-lying ridges which are broken up and wrinkled at the posterior end to form an irregular network. Small papillae are scattered over the surface and are more closely aggregated posteriorly. Two pairs of retractor muscles present; the dorsal pair arise slightly behind the openings of the nephridia and the ventral more posteriorly. About 14 intestinal convolutions, not attached to the posterior end of the trunk by the spindle muscle. The nephridia open on a level with the anus and are free from the trunk wall for their whole length.

DISTRIBUTION. Antarctic (Théel, 1911; Fischer, 1928; Stephen, 1941b, 1948); Chile (Wesenberg-Lund, 1955b); South Atlantic (Murina, 1964a).

Golfingia (Golfingia) nota (Sato, 1934)

Phascolosoma noto Sato, 1934 : 14–16, pl. 1, fig. 7, text-fig. 17.

TYPE LOCALITY. Japan, off the Noto Peninsula. Soyo-Maru Exped. stn. 559. 37°20′30″N, 136°08′45″E; at 424 m.

DESCRIPTION. Introvert about a third of the trunk length, without hooks but with only a few tentacles and a few sparse, pear-shaped papillae. Trunk up to 55 mm in length and 4 mm in width. Skin reddish-brown and carrying many papillae. At the introvert base large flat papillae, elliptical in surface view, are intermingled with pear-shaped ones. In the middle of the trunk they are small and sparse and resemble those on the introvert in size and form. At the posterior end of the trunk large hemispherical papillae are interspersed with small pear-shaped ones, like those on the introvert base. Two pairs of retractors; the ventral pair arises in the middle of the trunk and the dorsal a little way behind the anus. Two fixing muscles attach the anterior portions to the trunk wall. The spindle muscle is not attached posteriorly. The rectum is fastened by wing muscles near the anus and there is no rectal caecum. The nephridia are small sacs, about 7 mm in length, free for their whole length and opening a little way in front of the anus.

REMARKS. Described from two specimens. We have altered the specific name to agree with the generic name. Sato says that the species resembles *G. solitaria* and *G. mawsoni* but differs in the form of the papillae found on the trunk.

DISTRIBUTION. As for the type locality.

Golfingia (Golfingia) ohlini (Théel, 1911)

Phascolosoma ohlini Théel, 1911 : 29–30, pl. 2, figs 21–23, pl. 3, figs 24–27, pl. 5, figs 69–70; Fischer, 1922a : 413; 1928b : 484; Stephen, 1941b : 254–255.
Golfingia ohlini: Wesenberg-Lund, 1955b : 10; 1959b : 61; 1963 : 106–107, text-fig. 3; Edmonds, 1965 : 31, pl. 3.

TYPE LOCALITY. Antarctica. South Georgia, north of Astrolabe Island.

DESCRIPTION. Introvert with 16, sometimes only 9–10, slender tentacles arranged on each side of the median line; the dorsal tentacles are separated by ciliated pads. Behind the tentacles are wart-like bodies and posteriorly directed scattered hooks. Trunk small, up to 16–17 mm in length, elongate sub-cylindrical papillae which are scarce in the middle of the trunk but crowded posteriorly. Two pairs of retractor muscles; the dorsal pair arises in the middle of the trunk and the ventral pair more posteriorly. About 14 intestinal convolutions present. A fixing muscle is attached to the posterior part of the oesophagus. The coils are not attached posteriorly by the spindle muscle. The anus is set in the middle of the trunk. The nephridia open on a level with the anus.

REMARKS. Edmonds (1965) says that scattered hooks are present on the introvert.

DISTRIBUTION. Antarctic (Théel, 1911; Fischer, 1922, 1928; Stephen, 1941; Edmonds, 1965); Mauritius (Wesenberg-Lund, 1959); False Bay, South Africa (Wesenberg-Lund, 1963); Chile (Wesenberg-Lund, 1955b).

Golfingia (Golfingia) okinoseana (Ikeda, 1904)

Phascolosoma okinoseanum Ikeda, 1904 : 9–12, text-figs 4, 34–38.

TYPE LOCALITY.   Okinose Bank.   Sagami Sea, Japan; at 670 m.

DESCRIPTION.   Introvert as long as the trunk but much narrower, 3 mm in diameter; covered with papillae which, in the middle and anterior areas, become about as large as on the posterior part of the trunk.   There are fine striations set at right angles on the posterior part.   There are neither hooks nor eye-spots. Trunk 45 mm in length, 7 mm in diameter, with the posterior end narrowed to a small tail-like process.   The skin appears smooth but, under magnification, very numerous papillae are visible.   These are brownish-yellow in colour and consist of small closely-set granules.   They become shorter and thicker towards the base of the introvert where they are flat-bodies separated by grooves which form a mesh. Each contains one papilla made up of a yellowish-brown granular ring with a colourless transparent area in the centre containing the pore.   Large elongated sac-like bodies with a thin transparent wall and a number of parallel muscle-fibres also appear on the skin.   Two pairs of long and slender retractors; the ventral pair originates at the posterior border of the anterior third of the trunk and the dorsal arises about 7 mm in front of that border.   There are about 20 intestinal convolutions with three fixing muscles; one originates at the base of the left ventral retractor and joins the free part of the oesophagus.   The other two arise one on each side of the nerve cord and are attached to the beginning of the rectum.   A small reddish rectal caecum is present.   The nephridia are short and small, transparent and colourless, opening nearly on a level with the anus.

REMARKS.   Known only from the holotype.

DISTRIBUTION.   As for the type locality.

Golfingia (Golfingia) owstoni (Ikeda, 1904)

Phascolosoma owstoni Ikeda, 1904 : 12–15, figs 5, 39–44.

TYPE LOCALITY.   Uraga Channel, Japan; at 300 m.

DESCRIPTION.   Introvert about 20 mm in length and as thick as the narrow part of the trunk; surface opaque, closely wrinkled with the middle portion deep brown. Tentacles are fairly numerous and there are numerous rows of hooks which are slender, almost straight and yellow-brown in colour.   The papillae are more prominent on the anterior portion and, close to the hooks, become moderately tall, round-pointed and covered with small chitinous granules.   Trunk 60 mm in length, ground colour light blue suffused with pink, light brown on the posterior area. Skin relatively thin, smooth and more or less transparent with papillae sparsely distributed over it; they are largest in the posterior region and are covered with a number of small reddish granules.   Towards the base of the introvert they become progressively reduced in height and at the base of the introvert appear as round yellow discs.   Three retractors (?), the right ventral wanting; the left ventral arises at the beginning of the mid-trunk third close to the nerve cord and the dorsals arise

immediately behind the anus. About 30 intestinal convolutions. A simple contractile vessel which runs the whole length of the oesophagus. One fixing muscle
from the oesophagus to the inner side of the ventral retractor. Two other fixing
muscles run from the fourth coil to just behind the bases of the dorsal retractors.
The spindle muscle is not attached posteriorly. There is a small rectal caecum.
The nephridia are reddish-brown, moderate in size and open at the level of the anus.
The inner surface of the trunk has an irregular mesh of trabeculae in a zone between
the openings of the nephridia and a line midway between the bases of the retractors;
their function is unknown.

REMARKS. Known only from the holotype. It is most likely that the specimen
examined was defective and that the species has four retractor muscles.

DISTRIBUTION. As for the type locality.

Golfingia (Golfingia) profunda (Roule, 1898)

Phascolosoma profundum Roule, 1898a : 385; 1907 : 74–77, pl. 9, fig. 86, pl. 10, figs 106–109.

TYPE LOCALITY. Between Spain and the Azores; at 4255 m.

DESCRIPTION. Introvert about half the trunk length, with only a few short
tentacles but no hooks. Trunk oval, about 20 mm in length, greyish-yellow in
colour, lighter on the posterior part of the trunk where the musculature is thinner.
The skin has numerous scattered papillae which are larger and more numerous
towards the base of the introvert, and especially at the posterior end of the trunk.
Two pairs of relatively short retractors which are free for most of their length from
each other, the dorsal pair being shorter and thinner. They arise a little way below
the anus. The intestinal tract has 17–19 regular coils. The spindle muscle does
not appear to be attached posteriorly. The two nephridia which are brown in
colour are short and symmetrical, opening on a level with the anus.

REMARKS. Described from two specimens.

DISTRIBUTION. Between Spain and the Azores in 4255, 4253 m (Roule, 1898a,
1907).

Golfingia (Golfingia) pudica (Selenka, 1885)

(Fig. 14C)

Phascolosoma pudicum Selenka, 1885 : 11–12, pl. 3, figs 14–16; Fischer, 1928b : 484; Stephen,
    1948 : 217–218.
Golfingia pudica : Wesenberg-Lund, 1959b : 59–60, text-fig. 4

TYPE LOCALITY. Kerguelen. Type. Brit. Mus. (Nat. Hist) no. 1885.12.3.9–10.

DESCRIPTION. The species is very similar to Golfingia vulgaris and G. vulgaris
astuta but differs in three particulars, namely, (a) the hooks on the introvert are not
scattered irregularly but arranged in rows, (b) papillae are found over the whole
trunk and introvert, (c) the tentacles about 20 are fewer.

REMARKS. Wesenberg-Lund (1959b) says that the species resembles both *G. vulgaris* and *G. elongata*. The spindle muscle is attached posteriorly according to Wesenberg-Lund.

DISTRIBUTION. Antarctic (Fischer, 1928b), Kerguelen (Selenka, 1885; Stephen, 1948); Mauritius (Wesenberg-Lund, 1959b).

Golfingia (Golfingia) recondita (Sluiter, 1900)

Phascolosoma reconditum Sluiter, 1900 : 11–12, pl, 2, figs 7–8, pl. 3, figs 3–4.

TYPE LOCALITY. Off the Azores.

DESCRIPTION. Introvert about as long as the trunk, dark brown in colour, with numerous finger-like tentacles. Anteriorly there are eight rows of very small hooks with a long, sharp and only slightly bent point. Trunk 22 mm in length, 7 mm in width, yellowish-brown in colour, more deeply coloured on the anterior portion. There are two types of papillae. The first is ovoid, visible to the eye, widely scattered on the middle of the trunk but more numerous on the posterior end. Scattered amongst these are numerous small papillae, whose central opening is surrounded by only a few small chitinous plates. Two pairs of retractors; the ventral pair, which are very much the stronger, arise a little behind the middle of the trunk and the thin dorsal pair are attached to the edge of the posterior third of the trunk. About 26 intestinal coils, the anterior coil is attached by a muscle which follows the rectum and is attached to the trunk wall beside the anus. Three more thin fixing muscles arise where the oesophagus leaves the retractors and two more further down the spire. The posterior part of the spire is attached to the trunk wall by a muscle which is divided into rays and attached to the last coil. The oesophagus is attached for half its length to the ventral retractor and the fore part carries a simple contractile vessel. A spindle muscle is lacking. The nephridia are fairly short but voluminous, the left being shorter than the right. They are free for their whole length and open just posterior to the anus.

REMARKS. Described from three specimens.

DISTRIBUTION. Off the Azores. Princess Alice Exped., stns 198 & 605; at 800–1230 m.

Golfingia (Golfingia) reticulata (Hérubel, 1925)

Phascolosoma reticulatum Hérubel, 1925a : 262; 1925b : 272–277, text-figs 1–6.

TYPE LOCALITY. Morocco, north of Safi. 32°32′N, 9°35′W; at 110 m.

DESCRIPTION. Introvert 10 mm in length. About 80–100 rows of hooks of a simple type, slightly bent and irregularly arranged. A few papillae similar to those at the posterior end of the trunk scattered amongst them. Trunk 10 mm in length, dark grey and almost smooth in the middle third; grey-brown and very granular in the posterior region and at the base of the introvert. The papillae are of two types. Those at the posterior end and at the base of the introvert, seen

H

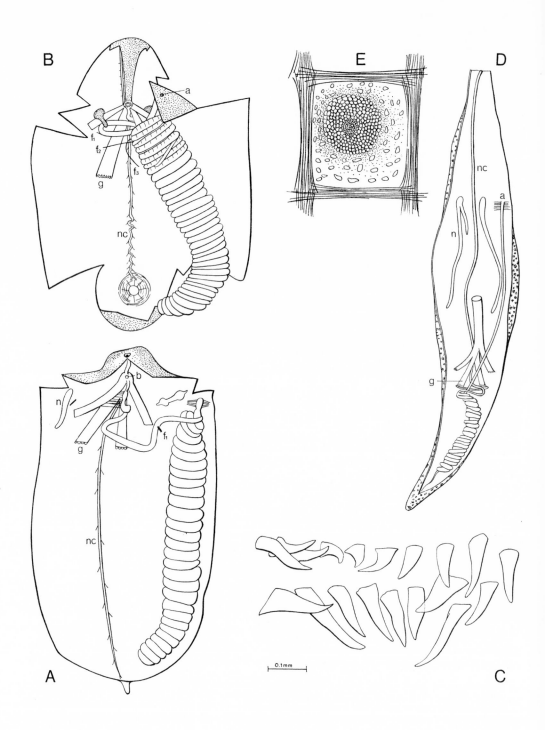

end on, show a clear central axis surrounded by a circular granular layer which, in turn, is surrounded by a less granular area; they are barrel-shaped in profile, well-spaced and arranged in more or less regular rows. The second type are lenticular and occur close together on the middle of the trunk; each has a dark central axis without surrounding plates. Two pairs of retractors probably present but the left dorsal is missing; the right dorsal arises a little below and to the left of the anus and the ventral pair arises in the posterior third of the trunk. There are 17 intestinal convolutions with a few fixing muscles at the lower end of the oesophagus; free posteriorly. The spindle muscle arises near the anus. The rectum is fastened by wing muscles. The nephridia open a little way behind the anus.

REMARKS. Known only from the holotype.

DISTRIBUTION. As for the type locality.

Golfingia (Golfingia) rugosa rugosa (Southern, 1913)

Phascolosoma rugosum Southern, 1913b : 18–19, pl. 2, fig. 2.

TYPE LOCALITY. South-west Ireland; at 1115–1242 m. *Type.* National Museum, Dublin.

DESCRIPTION. Introvert up to about 10·5 mm with sharply pointed, broad-based, small hooks scattered over it. Papillae occur amongst the hooks and flat discs with concentric striations are clustered near the tip of the introvert. Trunk up to 5 mm in length, light grey in colour. The cuticle is crossed by delicate ridges and furrows, giving it a rugose appearance. Papillae are few and inconspicuous; each arises from a large oval base and is flask-shaped in section. They vary considerably in shape; long slender papillae occur mainly on the posterior end of the trunk but a few are spread over the rest of the trunk. The anus is set very far back on the trunk. Two pairs of retractors; the ventral pair arises midway between the anus and the posterior end of the trunk and the dorsal near the anus. There are 13–16 intestinal convolutions. The spindle muscle is not attached posteriorly. The anterior part of the rectum is enveloped in a meshwork of muscle-fibres and the nephridia open in front of the anus.

REMARKS. Described originally from two specimens.

DISTRIBUTION. As for the type locality.

Golfingia (Golfingia) rugosa mauritaniensis (Hérubel, 1925)

Phascolosoma rugosum var. *mauritaniense* Hérubel, 1925 : 262.

TYPE LOCALITY. Mauritania. 33°24′N, 8°24′W; at 25 m.

DESCRIPTION. The subspecies differs from the nominate form in three characters, (a) there are no papillae scattered amongst the hooks, (b) the anus is situated

FIG. 14. (A) *Golfingia muricaudata*. Dissected specimen (after Murina). (B) *Golfingia mawsoni*. Dissected specimen (after Murina). (C) *Golfingia pudica*. Hooks from the introvert (after Selenka). (D–E) *Golfingia abnormis*. (D) Dissected specimen. (E) Papilla from body. (D–E after Sluiter.) KEY: *See* Fig. 11, p. 83.

posteriorly to the openings of the nephridia, (c) the dorsal retractors arise very anteriorly, almost at the base of the introvert.

DISTRIBUTION.   As for the type locality.

Golfingia (Golfingia) signa (Sato, 1934)

Phascolosoma signum Sato, 1934b : 16–17, pl. 1, fig. 8, text-fig. 18.

TYPE LOCALITY.   Japan.   Soyo-Maru Exped. stn. 550.   36°19′35″N, 135°34′28″E; at 658 m.

DESCRIPTION.   Introvert nearly as long as the trunk but much thinner and without hooks or spines; numerous finger-like tentacles arranged in several radial rows around the mouth.   Trunk up to 45 mm in length, 6 mm in diameter.   The surface appears smooth to the naked eye except at the posterior end, where it is rippled and pigmented.   Under magnification, numerous spherical or pear-shaped papillae are visible.   Two pairs of retractor muscles present; the ventral pair arises at the level of the anterior third of the trunk and the muscles are fused anteriorly into a single band; the dorsal retractors are very slender and arise slightly behind the anus.   About 30 intestinal convolutions present.   Two fixing muscles join the anterior portion of the convolutions to the trunk wall.   The spindle muscle is not attached posteriorly.   The nephridia open on a level with the anus.

REMARKS.   Described from three specimens.   Sato states that the species is distinguishable from other members of the genus by the presence of ripple-marks on the skin and by its extremely slender dorsal retractors.

DISTRIBUTION.   As for the type locality.

Golfingia (Golfingia) solitaria (Sluiter, 1912)

Phascolosoma solitarium Sluiter, 1912 : 15–16, pl. 1, figs 5–8.

TYPE LOCALITY.   Princess Alice Exped. stn. 1258; at 1900 m.

DESCRIPTION.   The introvert carries numerous tentacles arranged in a circle around the mouth, but has no hooks.   The papillae are rather larger and more closely set than on the rest of the trunk, giving it a velvety appearance.   Trunk 15 mm in length, 2·5 mm in diameter.   The surface is nacreous in appearance except the surroundings of the anus, where prominent papillae visible to the naked eye appear.   The anus is placed about 10 mm from the posterior end of the trunk. Two pairs of retractors present; the ventral pair is much the stronger and arises in the middle part of the trunk and the dorsal pair arises a little way in front. They do not unite until far forward.   About 26 intestinal convolutions.   The oesophagus is short and the spindle muscle is not attached posteriorly.   The two nephridia open on a level with the anus and are free from the trunk wall for their whole length.

REMARKS.   Known only from the holotype.

DISTRIBUTION.   As for the type locality.

Golfingia (Golfingia) soya (Sato, 1934)

Phascolosoma soyo Sato, 1934b : 17–20, pl. 1, fig. 9, text-figs 19–21.

TYPE LOCALITY. Sea of Japan.

DESCRIPTION. Introvert up to 60 mm in length, without hooks or spines, but carrying many finger-shaped tentacles. The papillae are mostly conical, some sharply pointed at the tip. Trunk up to 150 mm in length, reddish-brown in colour. Skin thick, opaque and nearly smooth to the naked eye, but under magnification, numerous papillae are visible. In the middle region they are flat and sparse. Two kinds occur at the posterior end, one is large and round, the other small and cylindrical. Two pairs of retractors; the ventral pair arises at the level of the anterior third of the trunk and the dorsal more anteriorly. More than 60 intestinal convolutions, with two slender fixing muscles; each arises near the roots of the dorsal retractors and terminates at the first convolution. A strong spindle muscle is attached near the anus but is not posteriorly. The nephridia are short, free from the trunk wall, and open about 10 mm in front of the anus.

REMARKS. Described originally from three specimens. It resembles *G. iniqua* in possessing two different types of papillae. We have amended the spelling of the specific name to agree in gender with the generic name.

DISTRIBUTION. Sea of Japan. Soyo-Maru Exped. stns 551, 552, 652; at 110–552 m.

Golfingia (Golfingia) trichocephala (Sluiter, 1902)

Apionsoma trichocephala Sluiter, 1902 : 42–44, pl. 4, figs 8–11; Wesenberg-Lund, 1959a : 189–190.

TYPE LOCALITY. Malaya. Siboga stn. 2°7'25"S, 113°16'E; at 56 m.

DESCRIPTION. Introvert long and thread-like, usually about 10 times longer than the trunk, and without hooks. Tentacles replaced by two flaps of skin dorsally and six small raised points of skin ventrally. The papillae are microscopic and somewhat cell-like, without a surrounding area of chitinous plates but with an opening of the skin gland in the centre. Trunk up to 8 mm in length and 2·5 mm in diameter, long and oval in shape, pointed posteriorly and tapering into the introvert. Skin yellow-grey in colour with musculature weak and transparent so that the internal organs are visible. The anus opens a little way behind the base of the introvert. Under magnification two types of papillae are visible on the trunk. On the dorsal surface of the anterior portion they are small and conical with chitinous plates; over the rest of the trunk they are seen only as round-oval bodies without chitinous plates. Two pairs of fairly thin but moderately strong retractors present. The ventrals arise about the middle of the trunk near the nerve cord. The dorsals, which are about a quarter of the trunk length, arise more anteriorly, also near the nerve cord. Both pairs join anteriorly. About 20 intestinal convolutions, with a long oesophagus. Three fastening muscles. The thin spindle muscle arises near the anus and is attached about 7 mm from the posterior end of the trunk. It does not traverse the intestinal coils, so these are free posteriorly. The rectum is short and without a caecum. The two thin nephridia arise quite near the nerve cord and open in front of the anus. The prominent nephrostome is a small frill-edge tube.

REMARKS. Described from several species. Wesenberg-Lund (1959a) considered that it should be placed in a new subgenus which she called *Apionsoma*. This seems to us to be hardly justifiable. We consider that it is best placed in the subgenus *Golfingia* (s.s.).

DISTRIBUTION. As for the type locality.

Golfingia (Golfingia) vulgaris vulgaris (de Blainville, 1827)

(Fig. 11A–E)

Sipunculus vulgaris de Blainville, 1827 : 312–313, pl. 33, fig. 3.
Sipunculus obscurus Quatrefages, 1865b : 616, pl. 16, figs 16–17; Selenka & de Man, 1883 : 21.
Sipunculus punctissimus Grosse, 1853 : 124.
Syrinx harveyii Forbes, 1841 : 249.
Phascolosoma commune Keferstein, 1863 : 39, pl. 3, fig. 3; Selenka & de Man, 1883 : 20.
Phascolosoma dubium Théel, 1875b : 6, pl. 2, fig. 8, pl. 3, fig. 19; 1905 : 60.
Phascolosoma harveyii : Diesing, 1859 : 759; 1861 : 65; Koren & Danielssen, 1877a : 136, pl. 15, figs 41–42.
Phascolosoma luteum Théel, 1875b : 5, pl. 2, fig. 7, pl. 3, fig. 17; 1905 : 60; Koren & Danielssen, 1877a : 154.
Phascolosoma margaritaceum : Keferstein, 1865a : 430, pl. 31, fig. 9, pl. 32, figs 28–29; Selenka & de Man, 1883 : 21.
Phascolosoma papillosum Thompson, 1840 : 101; Koren & Danielssen, 1877a : 138; Sluiter, 1000 : 19; Théel, 1905 : 60.
Phascolosoma sanderi Collin, 1892 : 177, pl. 11, figs 1–6; Southern, 1913 : 12.
Phascolosoma validum Théel, 1875b : 6–8, pl. 1, fig. 5, pl. 3, fig. 18, pl. 4, fig. 20; 1905 : 60.
Golfingia mackintoshii Lankester, 1885 : 469; Stephen, 1934 : 169.
Phascolosoma vulgare : Keferstein, 1863 : 39–40, pl. 3, fig. 3; 1865a : 429, pl. 31, fig. 5; Baird, 1868 : 84; Selenka & de Man, 1883 : 20–23, pl. 1, fig. 1, pl. 3, figs 25–34; Roule, 1896b : 474; 1898 : 384; Sluiter, 1900 : 13; 1912 : 7, pl. 1, fig. 1; Augener, 1903 : 335; Hérubel, 1904a : 463; 1925b : 260–261; Lanchester, 1905a : 27–28; Théel, 1905 : 60, pl. 1, figs 1–5, pl. 2, fig. 14, pl. 13, fig. 186; Southern, 1913 : 14–16; Fischer, 1914 : 94–95; 1922b : 17–18; 1925 : 21; Cuénot, 1922 : 6–8, text-fig. 2; ten Broeke, 1929 : 161–162, pl. 21, figs 17, 35; pl. 23, figs 42, 45, text-figs 4–6; Wesenberg-Lund, 1930 : 23, fig. 1; 1933 : 3–5, pl. 2, fig. 1; 1937a : 9–10; 1939a : 12–15; 1939b : 18; 1939c : 27–28; Sato, 1934b : 3–5, pl. 1, fig. 2, text-figs 1–4; 1937a : 151–153, pl. 3, fig. 10; 1939 : 402–404; Stephen, 1934 : 169–170; Stephen & Robertson, 1952 : 438; Leroy, 1936 : 425.
Golfingia vulgaris : Wesenberg-Lund, 1957b : 4; 1959a : 181; Stephen, 1958 : 131–132.

TYPE LOCALITY. Dieppe, France.

DESCRIPTION. Introvert a little shorter than the trunk and much thinner. There are about 38 tentacles, which are heart-shaped in section and arranged in several crowns round the mouth, mostly of 1–4 tentacles each. The skin behind the tentacles is smooth for a short distance and this is followed by a short zone of simple, scattered dark-coloured hooks. The papillae are smallest towards the mouth. Two eye-spots present. Trunk up to 100 mm in length, cylindrical, shiny, more or less pointed posteriorly. The colour is very variable, grey-yellow, red-yellow, pale brown, or pure white in coral habitats. Skin shiny, sometimes thin and transparent. It is covered with very numerous skin bodies, not rising above the surface and invisible to the naked eye. At the anterior and posterior ends, however, there are spine-like, often dark coloured papillae; they usually form two dark coloured zones which stand out clearly. The tropical specimens are white in colour and the papillae indistinct (Wesenberg-Lund, 1959a). The inner surface is very iridescent. Two pairs of thin retractors unite far forward in the introvert; the ventral pair arises from the front edge of the middle third of the trunk and the dorsal between them and the anus. There are three fastening muscles from the oesophagus to the first intestinal coil. Two fairly short nephridia which reach as far back as the roots of the ventral retractors and are free from the trunk wall for their whole length.

REMARKS. The nominate subspecies is well known along the Atlantic coast of Europe, Africa and parts of the Mediterranean. A number of subspecies have been described.

Watier (1932) referred to a specimen from Roscoff with only one nephridium and two more which had only three retractors.

The illustrations of Théel (1905) are excellent. According to Théel the hooks of *G. vulgaris* are scattered on the introvert while those of *G. elongata* are arranged in rows. The two species, however, are closely related.

DISTRIBUTION. Greenland (Wesenberg-Lund, 1930, 1937a); Norwegian Coast, Kattegat and Skagerack (Wesenberg-Lund, 1939); North Sea (Stephen, 1934); English Channel (Wesenberg-Lund, 1933); Eire (Southern, 1913); France (de Blainville, 1827; Keferstein, 1865; Grube, 1872; Cuénot, 1922; Leroy, 1936); Spain (Sluiter, 1900); Cape Verde Islands (Sluiter, 1912); West Africa (Wesenberg-Lund, 1959a); Morocco (Roule, 1898; Hérubel, 1925b); Israel (Stephen, 1958); Egypt (Steuer, 1936, 1939); Red Sea (Hérubel, 1904a; Wesenberg-Lund, 1957b); Zanzibar (Stephen & Robertson, 1952); Malaya, Singapore (Lanchester, 1905a); Japan (Sato, 1939).

Golfingia (Golfingia) vulgaris murinae nom. nov.

Golfingia (Golfingia) vulgaris murinae nom. nov. pro *Golfingia vulgare* var. *antarctica* Murina, 1957b : 996–997 (non *Phascolosoma margaritaceum antarcticum* Michaelsen, 1889 : 73–84).

TYPE LOCALITY. Antarctica.

DESCRIPTION. *G. vulgaris antarctica* differs from the nominate form and other subspecies in the height of its hooks and papillae.

REMARKS. The description is based on that given in the English summary by Murina (1957b).

DISTRIBUTION. As for the type locality.

Golfingia (Golfingia) vulgaris astuta (Selenka, 1885)

Phascolosoma vulgare var. *astuta* Selenka, 1885 : 11.

TYPE LOCALITY. Off south-west Norway; at 705 m.

DESCRIPTION. It differs from the nominate form in having papillae studded over the whole surface of the trunk, instead of being restricted to the anterior and posterior portions.

DISTRIBUTION. As for the type locality.

Golfingia (Golfingia) vulgaris multipapillosa (Hérubel, 1925)

Phascolosoma vulgare var. *multipapillosum* Hérubel, 1925b : 261.

TYPE LOCALITY. Morocco, Mogador.

DESCRIPTION. This is a highly papillated subspecies.

DISTRIBUTION. As for the type locality.

Golfingia (Golfingia) vulgaris queenslandensis Edmonds, 1956

Golfingia vulgaris queenslandensis Edmonds, 1956 : 303–305, text-fig. 17.

TYPE LOCALITY. Heron Island, Great Barrier Reef, Queensland. *Type.* Australian Museum, Sydney.

DESCRIPTION. Introvert about half as long as the trunk with 15–18 short stout white tentacles. A narrow area of the introvert behind the tentacles carries small yellow spines or hooks, flatter and not so tall posteriorly, arising from swellings and arranged in almost transverse rows. It is covered with numerous hemispherical to tubular papillae. Trunk covered with papillae similar to those on the introvert. Four retractors present; the ventral pair are ribbon-like and arises in the middle of the trunk, while the two even slenderer dorsals arise more anteriorly. The thin-walled intestine has about 30 convolutions and is fastened by three fine mesenteries. Two arise close together from the trunk wall just posteriorly to the left dorsal retractor, the third arises posteriorly to the right dorsal retractor. One of those from the left is fastened to the anterior region of the oesophagus, the other to the posterior portion of the intestine. The rectum is short. Two long nephridia open on about the same level as the anus and are free from the trunk wall.

REMARKS. Edmonds named this subspecies with some reservation. It is possible that this subspecies may prove to be a separate species, when more material becomes available for study.

DISTRIBUTION. As for the type locality.

Golfingia (Golfingia) vulgaris selenkae (Lanchester, 1905)

Phascolosoma vulgare selenkae Lanchester, 1905c : 31–32, pl. 1, figs 2a, b.

TYPE LOCALITY. Zanzibar, Chwaka Bay, at 18 m. *Type.* British Museum (Nat. Hist.) 1924.3.1.196.

DESCRIPTION. The subspecies differs from the nominate form in three particulars, namely : (a) the papillae on the posterior extremity are a little shorter and thicker, (b) the hooks are shorter, (c) the ventral retractors tend to be inserted more posteriorly.

REMARKS. Selenka mentioned a similar form from the Red Sea, but did not identify it.

DISTRIBUTION. Zanzibar (Lanchester, 1905c).

Golfingia (Golfingia) vulgaris tropica (Sluiter, 1902)

Phascolosoma vulgare tropicum Sluiter, 1902 : 33–34; Hérubel, 1925b : 261; Sato, 1934b : 3–5, pl. 1, fig. 2, text-figs 1–4.

TYPE LOCALITY. Malaya. Siboga Stn. 105. 6°8′S, 121°19′E; at 275 m.

DESCRIPTION. The subspecies differs in four respects from the nominate sub-species, (a) the introvert is shorter in relation to the trunk (about half the length instead of being equal to it), (b) the hooks are similar to those of the nominate subspecies but smaller, (c) the papillae are smaller and (d) the retractors arise from the same level.

REMARKS. Described from two specimens.

DISTRIBUTION. As for the type locality.

Sub-genus MITOSIPHON Fisher, 1950

Golfingia (Mitosiphon) Fisher, 1950a : 550; 1952 : 393.

DESCRIPTION. Two pairs of retractor muscles. The hooks on the introvert have an accessory comb of spinelets at the base. The spindle muscle is attached to the posterior end of the trunk and the nephridia are bilobed.

TYPE SPECIES. *Phascolosoma hespera* Chamberlain.

REMARKS. The sub-genus contains only two species.

DISTRIBUTION. Coast of Japan; California, U.S.A.; Western Australia; Aleutian Is.; Mediterranean; Cuba.

The species included are:
Golfingia hespera (Chamberlain) and *Golfingia misakiana* (Ikeda).

KEY TO SPECIES

Ventral retractors arise at about the level of the anus, introvert six to eight times as long
as the trunk . . . . **G. hespera** (p. 113)
Ventral retractors arise in the middle of the trunk, introvert about as long as the trunk
G. misakiana (p. 115)

Golfingia (Mitosiphon) hespera (Chamberlain, 1919)

(Fig. 15A–C)

Phascolosoma hespera Chamberlain, 1919 : 31.
Golfingia hespera: Fisher, 1952 : 393–395, pl. 24, figs 1–3; Murina, 1964a : 228–230, figs 7a–b; 1964c : 59–63, 5 figs; 1967a : 1335–1336.

TYPE LOCALITY. Bilbao, California. *Type.* Mus. Comp. Zool. Harvard, no. 2185.

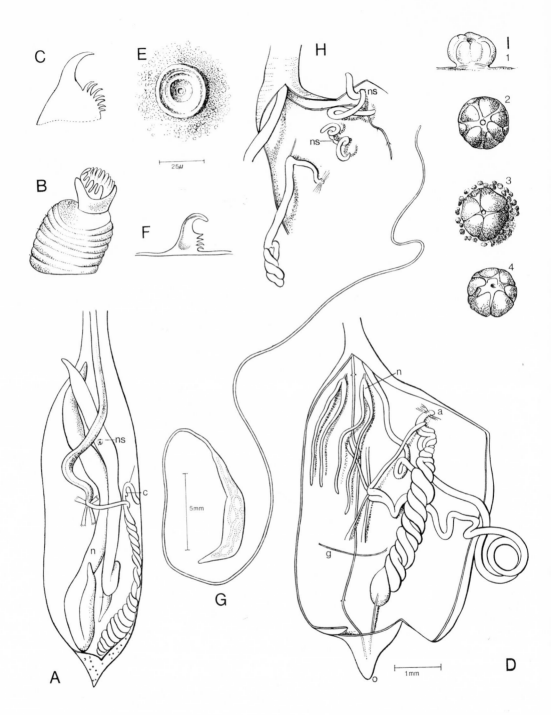

DESCRIPTION. Introvert long, filiform, 6–8 times the length of the trunk, with 30–50 rings of very small hooks set in a narrow zone, 3 mm in width. The tentacular crown is very small and consists of 12–20 tentacles. Trunk slender, fusiform and relatively short, about 20 mm in length, brown or yellow in colour. Musculature relatively weak. The posterior end of the trunk is often pointed and thickly covered with short, ovoid or cylindrical papillae. Much larger transverse, elliptical, pale brown glands extend along the introvert. Two pairs of small retractors arise at about the level of the anus, the dorsal pair in front of the ventral; they join to form a solid column. The intestinal tract has 30 convolutions and is anchored posteriorly by the spindle muscle. Contractile vessel and fixing muscles absent. The anus opens in the middle of the trunk. The nephridia are large and bilobed and open in front of the anus.

REMARKS. Described for numerous specimens. Murina (1964c) has given a very detailed redescription of the species. The species is widely distributed.

DISTRIBUTION. Bilbao and Laguna Beach (Chamberlain, 1919); Monterey Bay to Gulf Bay, California (Fisher, 1952); Aleutian Is. (Murina, 1964a); Mediterranean (Murina, 1964c); Cuba (Murina, 1967a).

Golfingia (Mitosiphon) misakiana (Ikeda, 1904)

(Fig. 15F)

Phascolosoma misakianum Ikeda, 1904 : 7–9, pl. 1, fig. 3, pl. 3, figs 30–33; Fischer, 1919a : 281; 1927 : 204.

TYPE LOCALITY. Japan. Coast of Misaki Laboratory, Tokyo Bay.

DESCRIPTION. Introvert about as long as the trunk and bearing very small, very slightly elevated papillae. About 60 rows of small hooks alternate with the papillae, five rows of hooks between two rows of papillae. The hooks are small, light yellow in colour, sharp pointed and provided with 4–5 accessory teeth which become smaller in the posterior rows and finally disappear. Specimens usually small and slender, the trunk measuring about 25 mm in length and 2 mm in diameter. Skin somewhat transparent and yellowish-pink in colour, and apparently smooth but under magnification numerous papillae are visible. These are most closely aggregated at the posterior end and are shaped like a rounded cone. The summit of each cone bears numerous small chitinous granules arranged in a ring round the aperture. In the middle region of the trunk the papillae are quite flat, elliptical and much larger than those situated posteriorly. The chitinous granules of the

FIG. 15. (A–C) *Golfingia hespera*. (A) Dissected specimen. (B) Anterior region of the introvert. (C) Hook from one of the anterior rings. (A–C after Fisher.) (D–E) *Golfingia longirostris*. (D) Dissected specimen. (E) Skin papilla. (D–E after Wesenberg-Lund.) (F) *Golfingia misakiana*. Introvert hook (after Ikeda). (G–I) *Golfingia tenuissima*. (G) Entire specimen. (H) Bilobed nephridia and the position of the nephrostome. (I) Four papillae from the posterior region of the trunk. (G–I after Wesenberg-Lund.) KEY: *See* Fig. 11, p. 83.

middle-trunk papillae are smaller than these of the posterior papillae. Two pairs of slender retractor muscles present; the ventral pair arises in the middle of the trunk, the dorsal far more anteriorly. The anus lies between the origin of the two pairs of retractors. Intestinal convolutions few, 6–10 in number. A single fixing muscle near the beginning of the convolutions joins the hind end of the oesophagus to the trunk wall on the left side of the nerve cord a short distance in front of the origin of the ventral retractors. A fine spindle muscle is attached anteriorly and posteriorly, the anterior end being fixed a considerable distance in front of the anus. The contractile vessel is only a few millimetres in length and is without villi. The rectum is fixed by wing muscles. Rectal caecum absent. The nephridia consist of two long lobes, similar in size and shape, thin-walled and reddish yellow in colour; one is directed anteriorly, the other posteriorly.

REMARKS. Described originally from several specimens.

DISTRIBUTION. Tokyo Bay, Japan (Ikeda, 1904); Shark Bay, Western Australia (Fischer, 1919a, 1927).

Sub-genus *PHASCOLANA* Wesenberg-Lund, 1959

Golfingia (Phascolana) Wesenberg-Lund, 1959a : 189.

DESCRIPTION. Two pairs of retractors. Introvert long, filiform, four to ten times the length of the trunk, without either hooks or tentacles. Trunk small, fusiform, up to about 9 mm in length. No contractile vessel or rectal caecum. The spindle muscle is attached to the posterior end of the trunk. Nephridia bi-lobed.

TYPE SPECIES. *Golfingia tenuissima* Wesenberg-Lund.

REMARKS. The genus contains two very similar species.

DISTRIBUTION. Off Angola, West Africa; St. Helen (Wesenberg-Lund, 1959); South Africa (Wesenberg-Lund, 1963).

The species included are: *Golfingia longirostris* Wesenberg-Lund and *Golfingia tenuissima* Wesenberg-Lund.

KEY TO SPECIES

Papillae on the trunk flat, circular, with two light concentric areas around the central
pore   .   .   .   .   **G. longirostris** (p. 116)
Papillae on the trunk cup-like in side view, with 4–7 large triangular plates arranged
like petals around the central opening   .   .   .   .   **G. tenuissima** (p. 117)

Golfingia (Phascolana) longirostris Wesenberg-Lund, 1959

(Fig. 15D–E)

Golfingia (Phascolana) longirostris Wesenberg-Lund, 1959a : 186–188, text-fig. 6; 1963 : 112–113, text-fig. 4.

TYPE LOCALITY. West Africa. Off Angola. 6°00′S, 12°14′E; at 25 m.

DESCRIPTION. Introvert thread-like, up to nine times the length of the trunk, and without hooks or tentacles. Trunk up to 5 mm in length, ending abruptly in a short tail-like tip. Reddish-brown in colour, finely wrinkled annularly, especially at the posterior tip. The papillae are small, scarce and uniform in size. They can only be seen under high magnification. They are flat, with two light concentric areas around the central pore. Two pairs of retractors present. The oesophagus is taut and passes straight forwards from the retractor before forming a narrow spiral of about 16–20 coils. The spiral is rather short and extends nearly to the posterior end of the trunk. The spindle muscle is fastened posteriorly and is free of the spiral for a considerable way. The rectum is fastened by delicate wing-muscles. The anus is at about the same level as the roots of the anterior retractors. Rectal caecum and fixing muscle absent; contractile vessel not found. The nephridia are bilobed and orange-coloured; each consists of two, extremely long and narrow tubes of equal length which taper slightly. They reach to the middle of the space between the roots of the two sets of retractors; free for their whole length. They have a common external opening far in front of the anus.

REMARKS. Described originally from about 25 specimens.

DISTRIBUTION. Off Angola and South Africa (Wesenberg-Lund, 1959a, 1963).

Golfingia (Phascolana) tenuissima Wesenberg-Lund, 1959

(Fig. 15G–I)

Golfingia (Phascolana) tenuissima Wesenberg-Lund, 1959a : 183–186, text-figs 2–5.

TYPE LOCALITY. St Helena.

DESCRIPTION. Introvert extremely long and thread-like, 5–9 times the length of the trunk, ending distally in a flat disc with a small ventral cushion-like expansion; without hooks or tentacles. Trunk 4–9 mm in length, only a little thicker than the introvert; white or yellowish-white in colour. Extended specimens are translucent and iridescent. The skin appears quite smooth but under high magnification fine intercrossing fibres and a few flat, scattered papillae are seen, especially at the posterior end. The papillae are cup-shaped in side view and have 4–7 large triangular plates arranged like petals round the small, circular, central pore. Some are surrounded by 2–3 irregular rings of tiny platelets. Two pairs of short, slender, retractors with narrow bases are fastened close to the nerve cord. The members of each pair are united for nearly their whole length and give the appearance of there being two pairs of ventral retractors. The free roots are of equal length and strength but one is directed straight forwards while the other is directed straight backwards. Both pairs arise in front of the anus, the posterior one at the same level as the fixing muscle which anchors the rectum, the anterior one far in front of the anus. Intestinal spiral with about 25–30 coils, tightly twisted anteriorly, becoming more loose posteriorly. Rectum long and slender, sharply bent back with a fixing muscle at the flexure. Anus lies rather far behind the bases of the retractors and rectum anchored by delicate wing-muscles. Rectal caecum and contractile vessel absent. The spindle muscle leaves the coil a considerable distance from where it is attached to the hindmost end of the trunk. Nephridia bilobed and orange-coloured. They are free for their whole length; one lobe is directed anteriorly the other posteriorly with a nephrostome at the base of the anterior lobe.

REMARKS. Described from many specimens.

DISTRIBUTION. As for the type locality.

Sub-genus *GOLFINGIELLA* Stephen, 1965

Golfingia (Golfingiella) Stephen, 1965 : 459.

DESCRIPTION. Two pairs of retractor muscles. Introvert without hooks but with tentacles or tentacular-lobes. Species usually small. Spindle muscle attached to the posterior end of the trunk. Nephridia not bi-lobed.

TYPE SPECIES. *Phascolosoma approximatum* Roule.

REMARKS. The sub-genus contains four species none of which are well known. It differs (1) from the subgenus *Golfingia* (*sensu stricto*) in that the spindle muscle is attached posteriorly to the body wall and (2) from the subgenus *Phascolana* because the nephridia are not bi-lobed. In his manuscript Stephen placed *G. trichocephala* (Sluiter) in this subgenus.

DISTRIBUTION. Off the coasts of north Africa and Malaya.

The species included are: *G. abnormis* (Sluiter), *G. approximata* (Roule), *G. innoxia* (Sluiter) and *G. pusilla* (Sluiter).

KEY TO SPECIES

1 Retractors arise in the anterior third of the trunk . . . **G. pusilla** (p. 120)
– Retractors arise in the posterior half of the trunk 2
2 Rectum very long, intestinal convolutions loosely wound . . **G. abnormis** (p. 118)
– Rectum not very long, intestinal convolutions regularly and strongly wound . . 3
3 Papillae on the trunk few and small without chitinous plates . **G. innoxia** (p. 119)
– Papillae on the trunk numerous and central pore surrounded by numerous platelets
                                                                    G. approximata (p. 119)

Golfingia (Golfingiella) abnormis (Sluiter, 1886)

(Fig. 14D–E)

Phascolosoma abnormis Sluiter, 1886 : 513–514, pl. 4, figs 3–4; 1890 : 115; 1902 : 34.

TYPE LOCALITY. Malaya.

DESCRIPTION. Introvert about as long as the trunk, but incomplete, so that no information is available about its length relative to the trunk, nor whether hooks are present. Trunk 60 mm in length and about 6 mm in breadth, covered with numerous irregularly arranged papillae, which are dark brownish on the anterior dorsal portion of the trunk. On the rest of the trunk, and posteriorly where they are more numerous, they are whitish. The central opening of each papilla is surrounded by an inner ring of several small, light-coloured plates and an outer ring of larger and darker plates. The papillae are enclosed in four-edged areas by strips of pigment but they are not clearly marked off from their surroundings since the plates of the outer ring are widely spaced. Musculature rather weak, with a tendency to split into bands in the posterior part of the trunk. Two pairs of retractors arise in the posterior third of the trunk, the ventral pair being the stronger. The intestinal spiral, which is lightly looped, lies within the posterior third of the trunk. The spindle muscle traverses the coils and is attached to the posterior end of the trunk. The rectum which is very long and fixed by wing muscles opens on the border of the anterior third of the trunk. The nephridia open on the same level as the anus and their posterior half is free. The left organ has a small secondary one, about a third of its length, arising from the swollen anterior portion, giving the appearance of a double organ. No nephrostome observed.

REMARKS. This is a difficult species to assess. One of the nephridia of the holotype, the only specimen known, is bilobed but the other is not and it is not known whether hooks are present on the introvert. If the nephridia are both bilobed then the specimen should be transferred to another genus.

DISTRIBUTION. As for the type locality.

Golfingia (Golfingiella) approximata (Roule, 1898)

Phascolosoma approximatum Roule, 1898 : 385; 1906 : 77–81, pl. 9, fig. 87, pl. 10, figs 100–101; Leroy, 1936 : 425.

TYPE LOCALITY. Moroccan coast; at 1105 m.

DESCRIPTION. Introvert about half the length of the trunk when almost completely retracted and a third of its width; hooks absent. About 20 fairly long tentacles form an incomplete ring of about three quarters of a circle around the mouth. Trunk 23 mm in length and about 8 mm in width, yellow-grey in colour. Musculature fairly thin on the ventral portion and sides, where the skin carries several large papillae. It is thicker and more opaque on the dorsal side where the papillae are more abundant. The number of papillae is in direct relation to the thickness of the musculature. Two pairs of fairly long, strong retractors are fused for about a sixth of their length anteriorly, the ventral pair are the longer and stronger. Intestinal spiral with 14–15 regular convolutions. The spindle muscle arises a little in front of the anus and is attached posteriorly. Two nephridia of unequal size, one being long and free, the other about half the size and attached to the trunk wall for most of its length. The nephrostome is at the posterior extremity.

DISTRIBUTION. As for the type locality.

Golfingia (Golfingiella) innoxia (Sluiter, 1912)

Phascolosoma innoxium Sluiter, 1912 : 13, text-fig. 3a – b.

TYPE LOCALITY. Princess Alice Exped. stn. 2210. 35°25′N, 31°22′30″W; at 1229 m.

DESCRIPTION. Introvert contracted but when fully extended probably much longer than the trunk; few papillae, hooks absent. Trunk spindle-shaped, 15 mm in length, attenuated posteriorly. Papillae few in number and without chitinous plates; somewhat smaller in the middle of the trunk. Two pairs of retractors present, arising at different levels. The ventral pair, which are much the stronger, arise at the front edge of the posterior fifth of the trunk and the much weaker dorsal pair arise from the edge of the posterior third of the trunk. The intestinal tract consists of numerous regularly-arranged convolutions which are fixed to the trunk wall by three very slender fixing muscles. The spindle muscle arises from the front of the anus, emerges from the anterior coils and is attached posteriorly. The nephridia are long and bulky and open a little way in front of the anus.

REMARKS.   Known only from the holotype.

DISTRIBUTION.   As for the type locality.

Golfingia (Golfingiella) pusilla (Sluiter, 1912)

Phascolosoma pusillum Sluiter, 1912 : 14–15; Fischer, 1914a : 77.

TYPE LOCALITY.   Off Cape Verde, Princess Alice Exped. stn. 1203.   33°59′30″N, 8°12′45″W; at 851 m.

DESCRIPTION.   Introvert up to 8 mm in length, with numerous tentacles but no hooks. Trunk small, up to 5 mm in length and 1 mm in diameter. The skin appears smooth but, under magnification, small oblong papillae are seen. They are larger at the posterior end than in the middle of the trunk. The chitinous plates which surround the central opening are very irregular in shape and differ on the various parts of the trunk. Two pairs of retractors present which join almost immediately after their origin, being separate only for a distance of 15 mm. The ventrals are rather stronger than the dorsals and arise a little way behind the anus, the dorsals a little more anteriorly. The intestinal tract is a weak spiral about 15 coils. Three fixing muscles attach the anterior portion to the rectum. The spindle muscle is fairly strong and emerges from the last coil and is attached to the posterior end of the trunk. The nephridia are long and are attached to the trunk wall for half their length. They open on a level with the anus.

REMARKS.   Described originally from three specimens.

DISTRIBUTION.   As for the type locality.

Sub-genus *THYSANOCARDIA* Fisher, 1950

Golfingia (Thysanocardia) Fisher, 1950a : 551; 1952 : 400.

DESCRIPTION.   One pair of retractor muscles. Contractile vessel with numerous branched or unbranched tubules. Nephridiopores usually open in front of the anus. Introvert without hooks (in all but one species).

TYPE SPECIES.   *Phascolosoma procerum* Möbius.

REMARKS.   In spite of the fact that it possesses introvert hooks we are placing *G. coriacea* (Keferstein) in this subgenus because its contractile vessel bears tubules. Fisher (1955 : 396) placed it in the subgenus *Phascoloides*. We have proposed a new name *G. lanchesteri* Stephen & Edmonds to replace *Phascolosoma pyriformis* Lanchester, 1905 which is preoccupied by *Phascolosoma pyriforme* Danielssen, 1859, a species now placed in the synonymy of *Golfingia procera* Möbius by Théel (1905 : 70). The subgenus contains 15 species.

DISTRIBUTION. Mainly in tropical and temperate seas.

The species included are: *G. catharinae* (F. Mueller), *G. coriacea* (Keferstein), *G. glauca* (Lanchester), *G. hozawai* (Sato), *G. hyugensis* (Sato), *G. lanchesteri* Stephen & Edmonds (to replace *G. pyriformis* Lanchester, 1905), *G. macginitiei* Fisher, *G. martensi* (Collin), *G. mokyevskii* Murina, *G. nigra* (Ikeda), *G. onagawa* (Sato), *G. procera* (Möbius), *G. pugettensis* Fisher, *G. semperi* (Selenka & de Man), *G. zenibakensis* (Ikeda).

KEY TO SPECIES—SUBGENUS THYSANOCARDIA

1	Introvert carrying hooks	*G. coriacea* (p. 122)
–	Introvert devoid of hooks	2
2	Rectum and nephridia open on the introvert (two fixing muscles, nephridia free for their whole length)	*G. lanchesteri* (p. 124)
–	Rectum and nephridia do not open on the introvert	3
3	Retractor muscles arise in the anterior third of the trunk (numerous, filiform tentacles, two fixing muscles, tubules of contractile vessel very short and numerous nephridia long and free)	*G. catharinae* (p. 122)
–	Retractor muscles arise in posterior two thirds of the trunk	4
4	Nerve cord splits into two roots posteriorly (about 20 tentacles, tubules absent from the anterior part of the contractile vessel, introvert more than twice the length of the trunk, posterior half of nephridia are free) . .	*G. procera* (p. 129)
–	Nerve cord not split into two roots posteriorly	5
5	Rectal caecum or caeca present	6
–	No rectal caecum present	10
6	Two rectal caeca present	*G. martensi* (p. 127)
–	One rectal caecum present	7
7	Tubules of contractile vessel branched	8
–	Tubules of contractile vessel not branched.	9
8	Two fixing muscles and tubules present along the entire length of the contractile vessel.	*G. macginitiei* (p. 125)
–	One fixing muscle and tubules absent from the anterior region of the contractile vessel.	*G. pugettensis* (p. 129)
9	Three fixing muscles and tubules present along the entire length of the contractile vessel.	*G. onagawa* (p. 128)
–	One fixing muscle and tubules present only on the posterior region of the contractile vessel.	*G. nigra* (p. 127)
10	Three fixing muscles (tubules present along the entire length of the contractile vessel)	*G. zenibakensis* (p. 130)
–	Less than three fixing muscles	11
11	Two fixing muscles (tubules present only on region of the contractile vessel that lies between the retractors; papillae flat and invisible to the naked eye)	*G. glauca* (p. 123)
–	Less than two fixing muscles	12
12	One fixing muscle	13
–	No fixing muscles	14
13	Nephridia attached to body wall for most of their length .	*G. moskyevskii* (p. 127)

J

- Nephridia entirely free from the trunk wall   .   .   .   .   **G. semperi** (p. 130)
14 Tentacular crown complex, consisting of many (200) tentacles   .   **G. hozawai** (p. 123)
- Tentacular crown a simple circle of tentacles   .   .   .   **G. hyugensis** (p. 124)

Golfingia (Thysanocardia) catharinae (Grübe, 1868)

Phascolosoma catharinae Grübe, 1868b : 48; Selenka & de Man, 1883 : 38–39, pl. 2, fig. 16,
pl. 5, figs 60–63; Collin, 1892 : 177; Sluiter, 1912 : 8; ten Broeke, 1925 : 83–84; Hérubel,
1925b : 261; Leroy, 1936 : 425; Sato, 1937a : 154–155; 1939 : 406–407, pl. 23, figs 36–37.
Golfingia catharinae Wesenberg-Lund, 1955b : 12; 1959a : 183.

TYPE LOCALITY. Desterro, Brazil.

DESCRIPTION. Introvert up to 53 mm in length, with numerous filiform tentacles
but no hooks; covered with papillae which are like those on the trunk but larger.
Two eye-spots present. Trunk up to 40 mm in length, nine times as long as thick
and with a conical and pointed posterior region. The skin is thin, slightly iridescent
and uniformly whitish-grey. It appears smooth but, under magnification, is seen
to be covered with very small greenish-yellow, well-scattered papillae which are
short and cylindrical or sometimes rounded and conical. Two thin retractors arise
close together from the front edge of the posterior quarter of the trunk; they unite
at the introvert. The oesophagus has a very short contractile vessel set with
tubules. There are two fastening mesenteries from the first intestinal coil; the
first is attached to the trunk wall on the right side at the posterior edge of the
anterior trunk third and the other on the mid dorsal line somewhat behind the
first. The two nephridia are rather more than half the length of the trunk. They
are free from the trunk wall for their whole length and just in front of the anus.

DISTRIBUTION. West Indies (ten Broeke, 1925); Peru (Collin, 1892); Brazil
(Grübe, 1868; Leroy, 1936); Chile (Wesenberg-Lund, 1955b); Azores (Sluiter,
1912); Cape Province (Wesenberg-Lund, 1959a); Mozambique (Leroy, 1936);
Japan (Sato, 1937a, 1939).

Golfingia (Thysanocardia) coriacea (Keferstein, 1865)

Sipunculus (Phascolosomum) coriaceus Quatrefages, 1865b : 620.
Phascolosoma coriaceum Keferstein, 1865a : 432–433, pl. 32, figs 23–24; Selenka & de Man,
1883 : 34–35, pl. 2, fig. 15, pl. 5, figs 50–53.

TYPE LOCALITY. St. Thomas, West Indies; at 3·5 m in coral.

DESCRIPTION. Introvert up to 7 mm long, about half the length of the trunk
and covered with very small red-yellow papillae. The anterior half carries scattered,
coarse hooks, which have a broad base and a slightly bent point. There are numerous long, very fine tentacles which are flecked at their base. Trunk up to 14 mm
in length, 3–4 times as long as thick. One pair of very strong retractors arises in
the middle third of the trunk. About eight intestinal convolutions, not attached
posteriorly; a fastening mesentery present from the first coil. No spindle muscle
observed. Rectum very long and longer than the intestinal coils. Contractile
vessel with very many long cylindrical tubules. The two nephridia are large and
free for their whole length.

REMARKS. Keferstein briefly described the species from two specimens. Selenka and de Man repeated the record and gave a short description. Selenka (1883 : 34) considered Quatrefage's description inadequate.

DISTRIBUTION. As for the type locality.

Golfingia (Thysanocardia) glauca (Lanchester, 1905)

Phascolosoma glaucum Lanchester, 1905a : 32, pl. 1, fig. 3.

TYPE LOCALITY. Zanzibar Channel; at 18–27 m.

DESCRIPTION. Introvert 5 mm in length, slightly darker in colour than the trunk owing to the high concentration of pigmented papillae. Papillae flat and invisible to the naked eye. Hooks absent. Trunk 13 mm in length, covered with papillae which appear as clear spots under a lens but, under magnification, appear as elongated bodies carried on a roughly oblong base with a clear apical opening. One pair of retractors arises from the anterior border of the posterior quarter of the trunk. About 16 intestinal convolutions present; two fastening mesenteries support the intestine anteriorly, while two more arise closely to each side of the nerve cord and are attached to the oesophagus where it leads forwards. The contractile vessel is thickly beset with tubules on the part lying along the oesophagus between the retractors. No rectal caecum. The two nephridia open just in front of the anus.

REMARKS. Known only from the holotype.

DISTRIBUTION. As for the type locality.

Golfingia (Thysanocardia) hozawai (Sato, 1937)

Phascolosoma hozawai Sato, 1937a : 158–160, pl. 4, fig. 15, text-figs 5–8.

TYPE LOCALITY. Miayata, Japan.

DESCRIPTION. Introvert about as long as the trunk, 45 mm, with about 20 rows of filamentous tentacles surrounding the mouth; without hooks or spines, but covered with short cylindrical papillae. Trunk 45 mm in length, 5 mm in width, conically pointed posteriorly and coiled in a spiral like the gastropod shell that it inhabits. Colour black in life, grey in preservative. The surface is covered with pear-shaped papillae, each standing on a hemispherical base. In the middle region of the trunk are interspersed large hemispherical papillae formed of a number of glandular cells. One pair of retractor muscles arises at a level of the posterior fifth of the trunk. The spindle muscle arises near the rectum but is not attached posteriorly. There are no fastening mesenteries nor rectal caecum. Contractile vessel with great number of short tubules. The two nephridia are short brown sacs, free for their whole length; they open 10 mm in front of the anus.

REMARKS. Known only from the holotype.

DISTRIBUTION. As for the type locality.

Golfingia (Thysanocardia) hyugensis (Sato, 1934)

Phascolosoma hyugensis Sato, 1934b : 12–14, pl. 1, fig. 6, text-figs 15–16.

TYPE LOCALITY.   Off Miyazaki, Japan.   Soyo-Maru Exped. stn. 309, 31°41′35″N, 131°46′40″E; at 472 m.

DESCRIPTION.   Introvert slightly longer than the trunk but much narrower; about 70 mm in length and 1–2 mm in thickness.   There are no hooks and only 7–8 tentacles.   Trunk 60 mm in length.   Skin, except at the extremities, thin and yellowish-grey in colour; nearly smooth in appearance but, under magnification, numerous papillae are seen.   They are nearly uniform in size and are most densely crowded at the base of the introvert and at the posterior end.   They are similar to those of *G. catharinae*.   Two retractor muscles arise at about the level of the posterior quarter of the trunk; they are attached to each other anteriorly by mesenteries.   The intestinal convolutions are long, reaching to the posterior end of the trunk; they are closely wound in their anterior half but the coils are much elongated in the posterior half.   The contractile vessel carries numerous, short, blind tubules. There is a strong spindle muscle which is not attached posteriorly.   No fixing mesentery or rectal caecum was found.   Nephridia greyish-brown, about 20 mm in length and free for their whole length.   They open about 10 mm in front of the anus.

REMARKS.   Known only from the holotype.

DISTRIBUTION.   As for the type locality.

Golfingia (Thysanocardia) lanchesteri nom. nov.

Golfingia lanchesteri nom. nov. pro *Phascolosoma pyriformis* Lanchester, 1905 (pre-occupied by *Phascolosoma pyriforme* Danielssen in Théel, 1875).
Phascolosoma pyriformis Lanchester, 1905 : 39, pl. 2, fig. 5; Sato, 1939 : 404–406, pl. 21, fig. 16, text-figs 44–45; Murina, 1964b : 261, fig. 6; 1967b : 43.

TYPE LOCALITY.   Palau Bidan, Penang, Malaya.   *Type*.   Museum of the Zoology Dept. of the University of Cambridge, no. W151.

DESCRIPTION.   Introvert much shorter than the trunk and carrying numerous filamentous tentacles; spines and hooks absent.   Trunk pyriform in shape, up to 15 mm in length and 9 mm in diameter; musculature strong and almost opaque. Colour reddish-brown in the Penang specimens and yellowish-orange with the posterior region greyish-white in the Japanese ones; a broad white collar present behind the tentacles with white blotches elsewhere.   The skin appears smooth but under magnification numerous small low papillae with a wide central opening can be seen.   The anus opens mid-way along the introvert.   Inner surface of the trunk wall is smooth and lustrous.   One pair of broad, short retractor muscles arises in the middle of the trunk or in its posterior third.   The intestinal convolutions number about 10–15 and coil around a stout spindle muscle which arises near the anus but is not attached posteriorly.   The contractile vessel extends over the length of the trunk and carries numerous black-tipped tubules.   Two fixing muscles present; one arises from the trunk wall near the left nephridia and is attached to the oesophagus near the beginning of the intestinal convolutions, the other arises from the trunk wall on the left side of the ventral nerve cord near the root of the left retractor and is attached to the middle portion of the oesophagus. There is a small rectal caecum (Sato, 1939 : 406). The nerve cord divides posteriorly into several branches. The nephridia are long being rather more than half of the length of the trunk and entirely free from the trunk wall; they are yellowish-grey in colour and open near the anus.

REMARKS. Described originally from numerous specimens. Sato gave a detailed description of the numerous specimens which he found. We have incorporated points from his description since the specimens differed in some ways from Lanchester's. Murina (1964b, 1967b) also redescribes some details in the anatomy of the species.

According to Lanchester 'both the anus and the nephridia open on the introvert, the anus half way between its base and the tentacles, the nephridia just in front of the base'. This means that the nephridia open behind and not anterior to the anus. Sato (1939) states that the nephridia open near the anus.

DISTRIBUTION. Malaya (Lanchester, 1905); Japan (Sato, 1939); South China Sea (Murina, 1964b); Cuba (Murina, 1967b).

Golfingia (Thysanocardia) macginitiei Fisher, 1952

(Fig. 16D–E)

Golfingia macginitiei Fisher, 1952: 402–404, pl. 26.

TYPE LOCALITY. Newport Bay, Orange County, California. *Type.* U.S.N.M. no. 21223.

DESCRIPTION. Introvert about as long as the trunk, with a purple zone behind the tentacles which is devoid of papillae; hooks absent. About 40 tentacles. Trunk 23 mm in length, musculature rather thick and opaque, with a glandular skin which appears smooth to the eye but which is beset with minute brown subclavate papillae that are slightly larger posteriorly. Two retractors arise about two-thirds of the distance from the anus to the posterior end; each has a broad emarginated base, divided into two parts by a deep notch. Intestinal spiral large with about 68 single coils. Two fixing muscles anchor the oesophagus to the trunk wall. The contractile vessel on the oesophagus has villi, arranged in a characteristic manner. At first they are short, simple, cylindrical tubules but soon they become bifid and increase in number, branching dichotomously two to four times and becoming grouped into bundles. Rectal caecum present. Nephridia short opens in front of the anus.

REMARKS. Known only from the holotype.

DISTRIBUTION. As for the type locality.

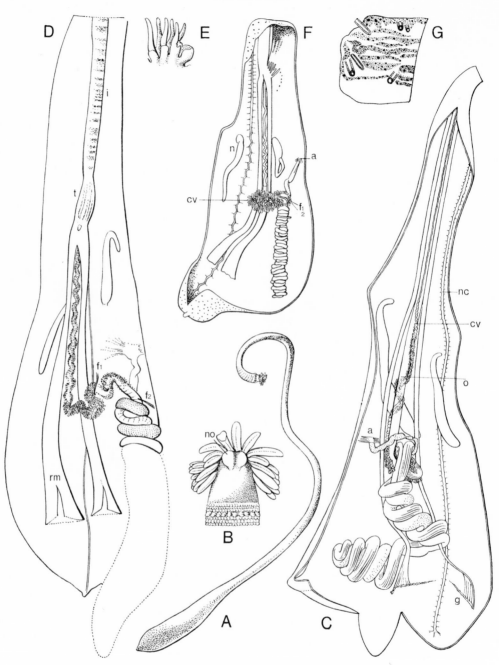

FIG. 16.   (A–C) *Golfingia procera*.   (A) Entire animal, × about 3.   (B) Tentacles and the nuchal organ; dorsal view.   (C) Dissected animal.   (A–C after Théel.)   (D–E) *Golfingia macginitiei*.   (D) Dissected specimen.   (E) Oral end of a double row of tentacles.   (D–E after Fisher.)   (F–G) *Golfingia semperi*.   (F) Dissected specimen.   (G) Skin papillae from the posterior end of the trunk.   (F–G after Selenka.)   KEY: *See* Fig. 11, p. 83.

Golfingia (Thysanocardia) martensi (Collin, 1901)

Phascolosoma martensi Collin, 1901 : 302–304.

TYPE LOCALITY. Off Liberia. 6°27′8″N, 10°20′W; at 68 m.

DESCRIPTION. Introvert grey with numerous tentacles but without hooks. Trunk rounded posteriorly, thickest at the posterior end, greyish-black. A lighter zone, 5 mm in breadth, lies behind the anus. The skin appears smooth to the naked eye, but under magnification, is seen to be covered with regularly arranged cylindrical or club-shaped papillae which are dark in colour, giving the animal a dark appearance. One pair of retractors arises in the posterior third of the trunk to meet in the middle region. About 20 intestinal convolutions present. The long oesophagus carries a contractile vessel which bears large pointed tubules near the spire. No fixing muscles; only a strong spindle muscle present which traverses the spiral. The rectum carries two round yellow caeca. The two long transparent nephridia open in front of the anus; they are free from the trunk wall for their whole length and reach to the base of the retractors.

REMARKS. Described from two specimens.

DISTRIBUTION. As for the type locality.

Golfingia (Thysanocardia) mokyevskii Murina, 1964

Golfingia mokyevskii Murina, 1964b : 256–259, figs 4, 5a–d.

TYPE LOCALITY. South China Sea.

DESCRIPTION. Introvert shorter than the trunk. Length of trunk 12–21 mm. About 50 long, white tentacles with dark red longitudinal grooves. Hooks absent. Large dome-shaped papillae on the introvert and on the anal region of the trunk. Minute, oval skin glands and amorphous small bodies in the mid-region of the trunk. Two retractors arise in the posterior part of the trunk. Spindle muscle fixed posteriorly. One fixing muscle. Two nephridia attached to the body wall for most of their length by a delicate mesentery. Contractile vessel with numerous villi.

REMARKS. Described from five specimens.

DISTRIBUTION. As for the type locality.

Golfingia (Thysanocardia) nigra (Ikeda, 1904)

Phascolosoma nigrum Ikeda, 1904 : 3–5, text-figs 1, 25–27; Sato, 1934a : 247; 1939 : 409–410; Chin, 1947 : 101.

TYPE LOCALITY. Japan.

DESCRIPTION. Introvert up to 70 mm in length, rather narrower than the trunk and of same colour, except at the base of the tentacles where it is light brown.

The tentacles are numerous, filamentous, violet in colour and arranged in 30–32 longitudinal rows. When viewed from above the tentacular rows are arranged in pairs joined by a U-shaped ridge. Thus the mouth is surrounded by 15–16 ridges. Small skin-bodies are scattered over the surface of the introvert but no hooks. Trunk up to 30 mm in length, the posterior end being drawn out to a conical point. In life the trunk is coiled into a rough spiral, dark grey or bluish-black in colour with small skin bodies scattered over the surface. These are largest at the anterior and posterior ends where they appear as low papillae. Each is elliptical, granular, brownish-black in colour. In their centre is a yellowish radially striated area surrounding the pore. One pair of retractors arises close to the nerve cord at the beginning of the posterior third of the trunk. There are 20–25 intestinal convolutions. The contractile vessel which runs along the dorsal side of the oesophagus, carries numerous short tubules on its posterior part. One fixing muscle arises from the posterior part of the oesophagus and is attached to the trunk wall a short distance in front of the origin of the left dorsal retractor. The rectum is fastened by broad wing muscles and carries a caecum. The spindle muscle is not attached posteriorly. The nephridia are deep reddish-brown in colour, very long, free for their whole length and open just anterior to the anus.

DISTRIBUTION.   Japan (Ikeda, 1904; Sato, 1934a, 1939); China (Chin, 1947).

Golfingia (Thysanocardia) onagawa (Sato, 1937)

Phascolosoma onagawa Sato, 1937a : 156–158, pl. 4, fig. 14, text-figs 3–4.

TYPE LOCALITY.   Onagawa Bay, Japan.

DESCRIPTION.   Introvert white anteriorly, otherwise brown with numerous filiform tentacles. The papillae are low anteriorly, tall posteriorly. Hooks absent. Trunk about 30 mm in length, bluntly pointed posteriorly; generally brown in colour but darker in the anal region and posteriorly. The skin appears nearly smooth but, when seen under microscope, has a rough appearance due to the presence of small papillae which are taller and more closely aggregated posteriorly and tall and club-shaped on the introvert base. One pair of slender retractors arises at the level of the posterior third of the trunk. There are 22 intestinal convolutions with a contractile vessel which carries numerous short tubules. Three fixing muscles present; one arising from the distal part of the rectum, the other two from the first coil of the spiral. The spindle muscle arises just behind the anus and is not attached posteriorly. The rectum is fixed by wing muscles and carries a small caecum. The nephridia are small sacs, deep brown in colour, free from the trunk wall, opening slightly in front of the anus.

REMARKS.   Known only from the holotype.

DISTRIBUTION.   As for the type locality.

Golfingia (Thysanocardia) procera (Möbius, 1875)

(Fig. 16A–C)

Phascolosoma procerum Möbius, 1875 : 157, pl. 3, figs 1–5; Selenka & de Man, 1883 : 39–40;
Théel, 70, pl. 2, figs 19–26, pl. 3, figs 27–28, pl. 13, fig. 190; Sluiter, 1912 : 11; Southern,
1913b : 24–25; Gerould, 1913 : 383–384; Cuénot, 1922 : 10; Fischer, 1925 : 20–21; Stephen,
1934 : 168–169; Wesenberg-Lund, 1939c : 19–20.
Phascolosoma pyriforme Danielssen in Théel, 1875 : 12; 1905 : 70.
Golfingia procera: Fisher, 1952 : 402.
Golfingia procerum: Thorson, 1957 : 128–132.

TYPE LOCALITY. Firth of Forth, Scotland.

DESCRIPTION. Introvert about two and a half times as long as the trunk and
about a third of its thickness; up to 28 mm in length. It carries about 20 cylindrical
tentacles and bears scattered papillae similar to those on the trunk. Trunk three
times as long as thick, up to 10 mm in length with the posterior end drawn out to a
point. It is grey in colour, sometimes iridescent and finely wrinkled, with papillae
scattered over its surface. They are wart-like, brown in colour, with an oval or
circular base and a rounded point. One pair of retractors arises in the posterior
part of the trunk. The oesophagus lies between their anterior ends and carries
a contractile vessel with numerous villi. The two nephridia open at about the level
or according to Théel (1905, fig. 26) in front of the anus; their posterior half, which
is narrower than the anterior half, is free.

REMARKS. Wesenberg-Lund (1939c) reports the presence of a rectal caecum on
specimens from Denmark.

Thorson (1957) reports that *G. procera* is able to act as a temporary parasite on
the tissues of the polychaete *Aphrodite aculeata*. The sipunculan introduces its
long, flexible introvert through the body wall into the coelomic cavity of the polychaete.

DISTRIBUTION. Norwegian Coast (Sluiter, 1912); Skagerack and Kattegat
(Théel, 1905; Fischer, 1925; Wesenberg-Lund, 1939c); North Sea (Möbius, 1875);
Ireland (Southern, 1913); East Coast North America (Gerould, 1913); California
(Fisher, 1952). From shallow water and up to depths of 484 m.

Golfingia (Thysanocardia) pugettensis Fisher, 1952

Golfingia pugettensis Fisher, 1952 : 401.

TYPE LOCALITY. Dogfish Bay, Puget Sound, Washington, U.S.A. *Type.*
U.S.N.M. no. 21215.

DESCRIPTION. Introvert about as long or slightly longer than the trunk but
rather less than half its diameter and carrying numerous filiform tentacles but no
hooks. Under a lens the trunk is seen to be covered with tiny papillae of varying
lengths. Skin light to dark sepia in colour and finely wrinkled. One pair of retractors arises in the posterior third of the trunk. The intestinal spiral has at least
48 single coils. The posterior end of the oesophagus is anchored by a strong fixing
muscle to the dorsal wall of the trunk. The contractile vessel carries crowded

branched villi on its free portion extending a very short distance forward between the retractors. Rectal caecum present. The nephridia are rather short and free and open in front of the anus.

REMARKS. The species is nearly related to *G. semperi*, differing mainly in the size of the papillae. The villi resemble those of *G. macginitiei*. Known from eight specimens. The original description is brief and appeared as a footnote.

DISTRIBUTION. Puget Sound and San Juan Island, Washington, U.S.A.

Golfingia (Thysanocardia) semperi (Selenka & de Man, 1883)

(Fig. 16F–G)

Phascolosoma semperi Selenka & de Man, 1883 : 37–38, pl. 5, figs 56–59; Fischer, 1895 : 13–14;
1914a : 74–76; 1921b : 5; 1922c : 17; Lanchester, 1905a : 31; Hérubel, 1904a : 563; Leroy,
1936 : 425; Stephen & Robertson, 1952 : 438.

TYPE LOCALITY. Uhoy, Philippines.

DESCRIPTION. Introvert about as long as the trunk, brown in colour but shading into grey at the base and carrying very numerous thin filament-like tentacles but no hooks. Trunk up to 28 mm in length, slim, thickest posteriorly, uniformly grey in colour; the posterior end is drawn out with a mamillate point. The body surface is covered with prominent dark papillae, which are regularly arranged and fairly uniformly distributed; they take the form of rounded cylindrical pegs. The musculature is fairly strong and iridescent internally. One pair of very strong ventral retractors arise from the anterior edge of the posterior third of the trunk and join at about the middle of the trunk. The intestinal coils form a close-set series of about 20 convolutions. A strong fastening muscle runs from the first coil to the trunk wall just posterior to the anus. A short contractile vessel with many tubules passes from where the oesophagus leaves the retractors to the first coil. The spindle muscle is present only in its anterior portion and does not traverse the intestinal coils. The rectum is fairly short. The two nephridia open some distance in front of the anus; they are brown in colour and about half the length of the trunk. They are free from the trunk wall for their whole length.

DISTRIBUTION. Fernando Po (Fischer, 1895); Red Sea (Hérubel, 1904a); Zanzibar (Lanchester, 1905c; Stephen & Robertson, 1952); Philippines (Selenka & de Man, 1883); Australia (Fischer, 1921b).

Golfingia (Thysanocardia) zenibakensis (Ikeda, 1924)

Phascolosoma zenibakense Ikeda, 1924 : 29–30, fig. 1; Sato, 1930b : 17–20, pl. 3, figs 11–12,
text-fig. 5; 1937a : 153–154; 1939 : 410.

TYPE LOCALITY. Japan. *Type.* Fisheries School, Hokkaido Imp. Univ., Sapporo.

DESCRIPTION. Introvert about as long as the trunk, but narrower, carrying over 200 filamentous tentacles arranged in about 20 regular rows; hooks absent. Trunk up to about 85 mm in length, 10 mm in width, narrowed at the posterior end but not drawn out into a tail-like process. Colour greyish-brown (preserved in formalin). The skin appears smooth to the naked eye but, under magnification is seen to be covered with small, sparsely dispersed papillae which are a little larger and more numerous at the base of the introvert. One pair of retractors arises from the middle third of the trunk and the muscles are united for much of their anterior length. About 30 intestinal convolutions present. The long foregut carries the dorsal blood-vessel which has numerous short contractile tubules on the posterior portion. There are three fixing mesenteries; one arising from the distal part of the rectum, the other two from the first spirals of the intestine. The spindle muscle is not attached posteriorly. The rectum is attached by well-developed wing muscles, but carries no caecum. The nephridia are short, free for most of their length and open nearly level with the anus.

REMARKS. Described originally from numerous specimens.

DISTRIBUTION. Japan.

Sub-genus *PHASCOLOIDES* Fisher, 1950

Golfingia (*Phascoloides*) Fisher, 1950a : 550; 1952 : 395–396.

DESCRIPTION. One pair of retractor muscles. Hooks may or may not be present on the introvert; if present they lack a comb of accessory spinelets. Contractile vessel simple and without villi. Spindle muscle, if present, is not attached posteriorly to the body wall.

TYPE SPECIES. *Sipunculus eremitus* Sars.

REMARKS. The subgenus contains 37 species of which seven are known only from the holotype. We have placed *G. abyssorum* (Koren & Danielssen) and *G. laetmophila* Fisher amongst the species of *Phascoloides* which have hooks or spinelets on the introvert. We have followed Fisher's lead (Fisher, 1952 : 396) in placing *G. intermedia* (Southern) in the subgenus. For reasons stated on p. 155 we have transferred *G. rutilofusca* (Fischer) from *Siphonoides* (Murina, 1967a : 1335) to *Phascoloides*.

The subgenus contains some golfingiids with unusual characters; *G. rutilofusca* and *G. vitjazi* each with an *Aspidosiphon*-like shield, *G. tasmaniensis* with a conical-like tip to the introvert, *G. mucida* with a felt-like covering and long filiform papillae and *G. multiaraneusa* with hair-like structures attached to the base of the introvert hooks. There is a tendency in the subgenus for the tentacles to be reduced to a few leaf-like structures or to a few lobes.

Whether *G. chuni* (Fischer) belongs to the subgenus *Phascoloides* or *Siphonoides* is uncertain; the question is discussed in this monograph on p. 137. We have left the species in the subgenus *Phascoloides* where Fisher (1952 : 396) placed it.

DISTRIBUTION. Widely distributed.

The following species are included in the subgenus:

a. without hooks or spinelets on the introvert

G. bulbosa (Southern)	*G. mucida* (Sluiter)
G. depressa (Sluiter)	*G. novaezealandiae* (Benham)
G. elachea Fisher	*G. pavlenkoi* (Ostroumov)
G. eremita (Sars)	*G. prioki* (Sluiter)
G. filiformis (Sluiter)	*G. rutilofusca* (Fischer)
G. fimbriata (Sluiter)	*G. sluiteri* (ten Broeke)
G. flagrifera (Selenka)	*G. tasmaniensis* Murina
G. lilljeborgii (Dan. & Kor.)	*G. verrillii* (Gerould)
G. macra (Sluiter)	

b. with hooks or spinelets on the introvert

G. abyssorum (Kor. & Dan.)	*G. incomposita* (Sluiter)
G. benhami (Stephen)	*G. intermedia* (Southern)
G. chuni (Fischer)	*G. laetmophila* Fisher
G. cincta (Gerould)	*G. minuta* (Keferstein)
G. cinerea (Gerould)	*G. multiaraneusa* Murina
G. confusa (Sluiter)	*G. pellucida* (Keferstein)
G. constricta (Southern)	*G. schuttei* (Augener)
G. delagei (Hérubel)	*G. subhamata* (Sluiter)
G. glacialis (Dan. & Kor.)	*G. vitjazi* Murina
G. improvisa (Théel)	*G. vitrea* (Roule)

KEY TO SPECIES—SUBGENUS PHASCOLOIDES

1   Hooks or spinelets present on the introvert 18
–   Hooks or spinelets absent from the introvert 2
2   Posterior extremity of trunk fluted and conical as in the genus *Aspidosiphon*
                                                                    G. rutilofusca (p. 153)
–   Posterior extremity without a conical shield 3
3   Posterior extremity of trunk drawn out into a tail-like appendage . . . 4
–   Posterior extremity of trunk not drawn out into a tail-like appendage . . 6
4   Nephridia open in front of the anus (no large papillae at the base of the trunk, three
    fastening muscles) . . . . ***G. bulbosa*** (p. 136)
–   Nephridia open at level of or posterior to the anus 5
5   Nephridia open at level of anus, introvert less than half the length of the trunk,
    large papillae at base of 'tail' . . . . . ***G. flagrifera*** (p. 144)
–   Nephridia open posterior to anus, introvert more than two and a half times the
    length of the trunk, no large papillae at base of 'tail' . . ***G. depressa*** (p. 140)
6   Retractor muscles arise from anterior third of trunk 7
–   Retractor muscles arise from middle or posterior third of trunk 8
7   Anterior part of introvert is conical and bears two or three slender tentacles; no
    rectal caecum . . . . ***G. tasmaniensis*** (p. 157)
–   Anterior part of introvert without conical extremity and bears numerous tentacles;
    rectal caecum present . . . . . . ***G. novaezealandiae*** (p. 151)
8   Introvert without tentacles (nephridia open posterior to anus; 3 fixing muscles)
                                                                    G. sluiteri (p. 156)
–   Tentacles present on introvert 9

9   Trunk with a felt-like covering and long filiform papillae   .   .   ***G. mucida*** (p. 150)
–   Trunk without a felt-like covering   10
10 Nephridia open well in front of anus (two fixing muscles)   .   ***G. fimbriata*** (p. 143)
–   Nephridia open at level or posterior to anus   11
11 Intestine with seven fastening muscles (rectal caecum present, introvert less than
    half the length of the trunk, nephridia open on same level as anus)
                                                              G. elachea (p. 140)
–   Intestine with three or less fastening muscles   12
12 Nephridia open just posterior to anus   13
–   Nephridia open at same level as anus   14
13 Introvert about half as long as the trunk (skin in middle of trunk transparent,
    retractors arise from posterior region of trunk, papillae on anterior and posterior
    surface of trunk are tufted like those of *G. semperi*).   .   ***G. filiformis*** (p. 143)
–   Introvert about one and a half times as long as the trunk (trunk covered with
    numerous four-sided papillae which are closely packed, flat and unequal in size,
    retractors arise from posterior region of trunk)   .   .   .   ***G. macra*** (p. 149)
14 Trunk without papillae (introvert a little larger than the trunk)   .   ***G. prioki*** (p. 153)
–   Trunk with papillae   15
15 Papillae on trunk, very small and flat   16
–   Papillae on trunk, especially at the base, shortly cylindrical, finger-like or bluntly
    conical   17
16 Tentacles 27–40, spindle muscle may or may not be present, retractors separate
                                                              G. eremita (p. 141)
–   Tentacles 8–10, spindle muscle absent, retractors tend to fuse (no rectal caecum)
                                                              G. lilljeborgii (p. 148)
17 Papillae on introvert and trunk of same size   .   .   .   .   ***G. pavlenkoi*** (p. 152)
–   Papillae at base of trunk larger than those elsewhere   .   ***G. verrillii*** (p. 158)
18 Tentacles digitiform or filiform.   25
–   Tentacles absent, reduced to a few lobes or rounded prominences or a few leaf-like
    structures   19
19 Spindle muscle absent   20
–   Spindle muscle present   23
20 Introvert without tentacles, lobes, prominences or leaf-like structures (retractors
    arise from anterior third of trunk, hooks of unequal size and largest posteriorly,
    hooks in eight rows)   .   .   .   .   ***G. vitrea*** (p. 158)
–   Introvert with lobes or prominences   21
21 Introvert bears a tentacular fold with short thick lobes (12 rows of hooks, retractors
    arise in middle of trunk, nephridia arise just behind the anus)
                                                              G. constricta (p. 139)
–   Introvert without a tentacular fold but with a few lobes   22
22 Introvert about as long as the trunk, nephridia arise posterior to anus (two indistinct
    lobes present anteriorly, hooks with long finely curved points)
                                                         ⎰ ***G. intermedia*** (p. 147)
                                                         ⎱ ***G. benhami*** (?) (p. 135)
–   Introvert twice as long as the trunk, nephridia arise at same level as anus (tentacles
    reduced to two lobes, skin hyaline and devoid of papillae, hooks in irregular rows)
                                                              G. glacialis (p. 144)
23 Nephridia arise posterior to the anus   24
–   Nephridia arise at same level as anus (anterior region of introvert club-shaped and
    bearing three lobes, retractors arise from the anterior quarter of the trunk;
    5–10 long, hair-like structures arise from the base of the hooks)
                                                              G. multiaraneusa (p. 151)
24 Tentacles reduced to a few, broad leaf-like structures, no large papillae at the base
    of the introvert or posterior region of the trunk (retractors arise from the middle

Golfingia (Phascoloides) abyssorum abyssorum (Koren & Danielssen, 1875)

Phascolosoma abyssorum Koren & Danielssen, 1875 : 129–130; 1877a : 131–132, pl. 14, figs
    25–27; Selenka & de Man, 1883 : 30–31; Fischer, 1895 : 14; 1925 : 16; 1928b : 471–472;
    Théel, 1905 : 78, pl. 5, figs 71–75, pl. 6, figs 76–81, pl. 14, fig. 206; Gadd, 1912 : 88–89;

Southern, 1913b : 27–28; J. Fischer, 1914 : 99–100; Wesenberg-Lund, 1933 : 9–11, pl. 2, fig. 3.

Golfingia abyssorum: Wesenberg-Lund, 1955a : 201; Murina, 1964a : 220–221, fig. 1; 1964c : 56–57.

not *Phascolosoma* (=*Physcosoma*) *abyssorum* (Southern, 1913b : 12).

TYPE LOCALITY. Bergensfjord, Norway.

DESCRIPTION. Introvert about a quarter the length of the trunk, with fine papillae at its base, smooth in the middle. Anterior part bullet-shaped with 10–12 rows of strongly bent hooks and a simple crown of 20–24 tentacles. Trunk cylindrical, up to 30 mm in length; light yellow in colour but with a darker coloured zone at the base of the introvert and at the posterior end. Papillae absent. Skin tough, sometimes translucent and iridescent, and is covered with numerous irregularly arranged skin-bodies. One pair of strong retractors arises about the middle of the trunk, the muscles joining in the introvert. Intestinal spiral with about 35 coils; free posteriorly. Contractile vessel present. One fastening mesentery present, spindle muscle absent. The two nephridia are free for their whole length.

REMARKS. The species shows a wide bathymetric range having been found at depths of 40 m to 4990 m. It is often associated with corals or *Cerianthus*. Hooks are present on the introvert according to Théel (1905) and Selenka & de Man (1883).

DISTRIBUTION. Kola Gulf (Gadd, 1912); Spitzbergen (Fischer, 1895); Bergensfjord (Koren & Danielssen, 1875); Heligoland Bight (Fischer, J. 1914); English Channel (Wesenberg-Lund, 1933); off south-west Ireland (Southern, 1913); Mediterranean (Murina, 1964c).

Golfingia (Phascoloides) abyssorum punctata (Hérubel, 1925)

Phascolosoma abyssorum var. *punctatum* Hérubel, 1925b : 261–262.

TYPE LOCALITY. Off Morocco. 33°42′40″N, 7°51′46″W; at 95 m.

DESCRIPTION. The subspecies differs from the nominate form in having small elliptical papillae thinly scattered over the trunk (papillae are absent in the nominate form).

DISTRIBUTION. As for the type locality.

Golfingia (Phascoloides) benhami (Stephen, 1948)

Phascolosoma benhami Stephen, 1948 : 218–219, pl. 1, figs 2–4.

TYPE LOCALITY. Antarctic. Off Kemp Land. *Type.* Brit. Mus. (Nat. Hist.) 1957.8.14.97.

DESCRIPTION. Introvert about as long as the trunk. Behind the tentacles lies a zone, about 2 mm in breadth, over which the hooks are irregularly scattered. Trunk about 16 mm in length, varying in colour from grey-green, hyaline and iridescent to brick red. Skin without visible papillae but with pores arranged in rows. The pores are most numerous on the anterior and middle regions of the trunk; scarcest, almost absent, on the posterior end.   One pair of retractors arises in the posterior third of the trunk and the muscles are united for some distance by a web.   The nephridia are small and pigmented.

REMARKS.   Described from two very different specimens.   The species closely resembles G. *minuta* of northern seas, but differs in the larger and more numerous hooks and in the number and arrangement of the pores.   Stephen remarked that the species belongs to Théel's 'abyssorum' group (Théel, 1905 : 59).

A re-examination of the holotype shows that the spindle muscle is not fixed posteriorly.   About 10 small bulbous structures which are probably retracted tentacles are present anteriorly on the introvert.   At least one fixing muscle, damaged in the holotype, is connected to the alimentary canal.   The nephridiopore is on about the same level as the anus and the nephridia are free.

DISTRIBUTION.   Antarctic.   Off Kemp Land; off Adelie Land; at 549–640 m.

Golfingia (Phascoloides) bulbosa (Southern, 1913)

Phascolosoma bulbosum Southern, 1913b : 23–24, pl. 5, fig. 6.

TYPE LOCALITY.   Off south-west Ireland.   51°48′N, 12°11′30″W; at 960 m. *Type*.   National Museum, Dublin.

DESCRIPTION.   Introvert up to 12 mm in length with 16–18 moderately long tentacles; only a few small papillae present and hooks absent.   Trunk up to 43 mm in length, thin-walled, often transparent and swollen.   Posteriorly it passes into a long, slender, thin-walled 'tail'; the last is a portion of the trunk and not an appendage since the nerve cord traverses it to the tip.   Skin buff-coloured or rusty in places, and delicately marked with granular ridges.   The small cylindrical papillae cannot be seen by the naked eye but are visible under magnification.   They are surrounded by a delicate granular ridge and are numerous on the trunk and 'tail'. There are about 20 intestinal convolutions.   A strong spindle muscle is attached by numerous fibres round the rectum, but is not attached posteriorly.   Three delicate mesenteries run from the intestine near the rectum to the muscles joining the oesophagus to the retractors.   No contractile vessel.   One pair of slender retractors arises midway between the anus and the posterior end of the trunk; the oesophagus is attached to them for most of its length.   The two nephridia are long and slender and open in front of the anus.

REMARKS.   Described from eight specimens.   It is closely allied to G. *flagrifera* (Selenka) but differs in having no large papillae on the base of the tail and in the position of the retractors.

DISTRIBUTION.   As for the type locality.

Golfingia (Phascoloides) chuni (Fischer, 1916)

Phascolosoma chuni Fischer, 1916 : 15; 1922c : 9, pl. 1, fig. 6.

TYPE LOCALITY.   Nias Nord Kanal, Bangkam.   German Deep-sea Exped. stn. 203.   1°47′N, 96°58′E; at 660 m in a shell of *Dentalium*.

DESCRIPTION. Introvert 6–7 mm in length; 15–20 fairly short tentacles present followed by a zone of irregularly arranged hooks each with a slightly bent point. Papillae which are visible to the naked eye cover the remainder of the introvert; they are generally short but elongated on the posterior portion. Trunk 25 mm in length, generally black-brown in colour but lighter in the middle region and white at the posterior end. Papillae visible to the naked eye are present. At the posterior end of the trunk there is a clearly marked zone of large pointed, dark papillae which, in side view, appear like a heap of stones; between these large papillae are smaller pointed ones covered with closely set dark chitinous plates. On the anterior half of the trunk the papillae are small and pointed. One pair of fairly broad retractors arises from the front edge of the posterior third of the trunk, and the muscles join in their anterior two-thirds to form a channel-like structure in which the oesophagus lies. About 20 intestinal coils fastened posteriorly by a 'spiral muscle'. The contractile vessel was not described. Rectum fairly long, fixed by a broad wing muscle. Nephridia short but broad, a tenth or twelfth of the length of the trunk; they open 1–2 mm in front of the anus.

REMARKS. Known only from the holotype. It is possible that the species should be assigned to the subgenus *Siphonoides*. It depends on whether or not the spindle muscle is fastened posteriorly. Fischer's description states, 'Der Darm war schlecht erhalten, er zeigte ca. 20–22 Windungen; Ein Spiramuskel schien vorhanden zu sein und ihn hinten zu befestigen'. Elsewhere in the same publication Fischer (1917 : 6, 12, 14) refers to a 'Spindelmuskel'. Fisher (1952 : 396) in placing the species in *Phascoloides* apparently considered that a spiral muscle was not the same as a spindle muscle.

DISTRIBUTION. As for the type locality.

Golfingia (Phascoloides) cincta (Gerould, 1913)

Phascolosoma cinctum Gerould, 1913 : 398–400, pl. 59, fig. 6, text-fig. 8.

TYPE LOCALITY. U.S.A. off Long Island; at 690–1290 m (in shells of *Hyalinaecia*). *Type*. U.S.N.M. no. 8328.

DESCRIPTION. Introvert 6 mm in length, cylindrical; clearly marked off from the much thicker trunk by an oblique line of junction in the region of the anus. The wall of the introvert is much thinner and more translucent than that of the trunk; it is covered with exceedingly small papillae. About three rows of delicate recurved hooks are present immediately behind the tentacles. Trunk 24 mm in length, with inconspicuous papillae scattered over much of the surface. They are largest immediately behind the base of the introvert and near the posterior extremity where they are oval. Apart from the posterior end which is yellowish-brown, the trunk is generally grey or greyish-brown in colour. At the base of the introvert there is a band of circular muscles encircling the nerve cord, oesophagus and retractors like a collar. One pair of slender, dark-brown retractors arises from the posterior portion of the trunk, slightly behind its middle. They are cylindrical but posteriorly, where they are attached to the trunk wall they become flattened

K

and fan-shaped. About 16 intestinal convolutions. Nephridia short and slipper-shaped, with a wide nephrostome, opening slightly posterior to the anus. Only one nephridium was seen.

REMARKS. The description is based on two specimens and there are no other records.

DISTRIBUTION. As for the type locality.

Golfingia (Phascoloides) cinerea (Gerould, 1913)

Phascolosoma cinereum Gerould, 1913 : 396–398, text-figs 6–7.

TYPE LOCALITY. Key West, Florida. 24°25′45″N, 81°46′45″W; at 82 m. *Type.* U.S.N.M. no. 4087.

DESCRIPTION. Introvert very short, 4–5 mm in length, slightly lighter in colour than the trunk. It is covered with fine cylindrical papillae and immediately behind the tentacles there is a narrow zone of minute, irregularly-arranged, dark-coloured hooks. Trunk 14 mm in length, 7 mm in breadth, ashen grey in colour and covered with minute brown papillae. These are bluntly conical at the anterior end of the trunk, ovate with a slight stalk in the middle portion and long and finger-like on the posterior region. Internally the trunk wall is smooth, lustrous and violet-brown in colour. One pair of strong retractors arises at about the middle of the trunk and the muscles remain free for their whole length. About 15 intestinal convolutions, fixed by a muscle-strand on each side. The spindle muscle is not attached posteriorly. The oesophagus is attached by a fine muscle strand to the retractors and carries the contractile vessel which is without villi. The rectum is short. The nephridia are free for their whole length and arise at about the level of the anus.

REMARKS. Known only from the holotype.

DISTRIBUTION. As for the type locality.

Golfingia (Phascoloides) confusa (Sluiter, 1902)

Phascolosoma confusa Sluiter, 1902 : 38–39, pl. 3, fig. 5.
Golfingia confusa: Murina, 1957b : 993–994.

TYPE LOCALITY. Malaya.

DESCRIPTION. Introvert up to 9 mm in length, marked by cross bands of colour. It carries no papillae but scattered, irregularly-arranged hooks are present at the anterior end in a band about 1 mm wide. A thickened chitinous line runs up the dorsal side of each hook, enfolds the point, and ends about a quarter of the way down the anterior side; this character is diagnostic. Trunk up to 13 mm in length, smooth, yellow-grey in colour; covered with very small ball-like papillae, each has a central opening without any surrounding chitinous plates. The papillae have the same appearance over the whole trunk but are little longer in the posterior part. One pair of long, fairly slender retractors arises in the fore part of the posterior third of the trunk and the muscles unite only just in front of the mouth. About

20 intestinal coils present reaching to the posterior end of the trunk. The contractile vessel is without villi and runs along the oesophagus. The spindle muscle is not attached posteriorly. The two nephridia are about half the length of the trunk, free for their whole length and open a little way behind the anus.

REMARKS. The description was based originally on nine specimens.

DISTRIBUTION. Malaya, Siboga stns 115 and 131 (Sluiter, 1902), Antarctica (Murina, 1957b).

Golfingia (Phascoloides) constricta (Southern, 1913)

Phascolosoma constrictum Southern, 1913b : 25–27, pl. 6, fig. 7.

TYPE LOCALITY. South-west Ireland; at 1143 m. *Type*. National Museum, Dublin.

DESCRIPTION. Introvert up to 8 mm in length, covered with narrow cylindrical papillae. A number of tentacles present and the tentacular fold carries a number of short thick lobes. About 12 rows of conical hooks with sharp or blunt points and incurved bases. Trunk up to 35 mm in length, with a deep constriction behind the anal aperture (a feature which seems to be specific). The trunk is widest at its posterior third and drawn out to a 'tail' ending in a papilla. It is a deep flesh-colour, with translucent amber skin papillae. The anterior region is somewhat rugose with the papillae concealed in the ridges of the cuticle; the posterior end is divided into rectangular areas by folds of the cuticle. The largest papillae are found on the mid-trunk area, where they are button-like with a projection in the middle. Below the anus they are cylindrical and gradually become slenderer and flattened towards the mid-trunk where a stalk begins to appear. Posteriorly the papillae increase in length but diminish in width until, on the pointed 'tail', they are like those on the introvert. About 16 intestinal convolutions are bound together and fastened to the trunk wall by several delicate mesenteries. The anterior end of the rectum is swollen and covered with transverse muscle fibres. One pair of retractors arises midway between the anus and the 'tail'. Spindle muscle is absent. Two delicate sac-like nephridia open just behind the anus. The nerve cord ends in a series of slender branches some distance from the posterior end of the trunk.

REMARKS. This species was described originally from four specimens. The three paratypes differed from the holotype in that the papillae were concentrated on the posterior third of the trunk and the retractors arose from its posterior third.

DISTRIBUTION. South-west Ireland, several localities; at 1143–1315 m (Southern, 1913).

Golfingia (Phascoloides) delagei (Hérubel, 1903)

Phascolosoma delagei Hérubel, 1903a : 100; 1907 : 115–117, pl. 9, fig. 28, text-figs. 3–5.

TYPE LOCALITY. Bay of Biscay; off Ushant. 48°14′N, 4°32′W; 48°22′N, 4°47′W.

DESCRIPTION. Introvert a little shorter in length than the trunk; musculature like that of the trunk, thin and almost transparent. A tentacular crown of about

19 tentacles joined at their base. Posterior to the tentacles lies a zone of seven circular rows of hooks, the anterior row being widely separated from the other rows which are equally spaced. The hooks are simple, each being set on a small tubercle. Trunk up to 15 mm in length, greyish-white in colour. Large skin bodies present but papillae absent. One pair of well-developed retractors present. Ten to twelve intestinal convolutions with a simple contractile vessel. The spindle muscle is not attached posteriorly. Two nephridia open above the anus.

DISTRIBUTION. Bay of Biscay.

Golfingia (Phascoloides) depressa (Sluiter, 1902)

(Fig. 17D)

Phascolosoma depressum Sluiter, 1902 : 39–40, pl. 3, figs 17–20.
Golfingia depressa: Murina, 1964a : 227–228, figs 6a–b.

TYPE LOCALITY. Malaya. Siboga stn. 223. 5°44′42″S, 126°27′18″E; at 4391 m.

DESCRIPTION. Introvert 10 mm in length, 0·5 mm in diameter. It appears smooth to the naked eye but, under magnification, small roundish papillae may be seen. Without hooks. Trunk small, only 4 mm in length and 1·5 mm in diameter, whip-like, drawn out to a long point posteriorly. Except for the posterior end the whole trunk is covered with small ball-shaped papillae, on which the chitinous plates are very poorly defined, only the central canal being visible. At the posterior end the papillae are conical, but also have no distinct chitinous plates. One pair of very long retractor muscles join to form a single muscle and are attached to the posterior end of the trunk. There are numerous intestinal convolutions. The spindle muscle is not attached to the posterior end of the trunk. The two nephridia are extremely short, barrel-shaped and with a distinct nephrostome; they open posterior to the anus.

REMARKS. Murina (1964a) has redescribed the species in considerable detail.

DISTRIBUTION. Indonesia (Sluiter, 1902); Indian Ocean (Murina, 1964a).

Golfingia (Phascoloides) elachea Fisher, 1952

Golfingia elachea Fisher, 1952 : 399–400, pl. 25, figs 1–3.

TYPE LOCALITY. Point Lobos, Espiritu Santo Island, La Paz, Baja California. *Type.* U.S.N.M. no. 21214.

DESCRIPTION. Introvert short, less than half the length of the trunk, separated from it by a shoulder. Paler in colour than the trunk, skin thin and opaque except anteriorly. Numerous filiform tentacles with a conspicuously shorter ventral cluster. The papillae are smaller than those on the trunk; hooks absent. Two large conspicuous pigment spots on the brain. Trunk up to 17·5 mm in length, pale brown in colour and covered with brown pyriform papillae of nearly uniform size. Musculature thin but opaque. One pair of retractors arises about midway between the anus and the posterior extremity. About 36 intestinal coils present;

the first has a ringed structure as if it functioned as a gizzard. Well-developed mesenteries anchor the oesophagus to the retractors. At least seven fixing mesenteries. The spindle muscle is not attached posteriorly. A small rectal caecum present. A simple contractile vessel present without villi. The short nephridia open on the same level as the anus and reach only to the origin of the retractors.

REMARKS. Described from three specimens.

DISTRIBUTION. As for the type locality.

Golfingia (Phascoloides) eremita eremita (Sars, 1851)

(Fig. 17A–C)

Sipunculus eremita Sars, 1851 : 197.
Sipunculus (Phascolosomum) borealis Quatrefages, 1865b : 620.
Chrondosoma laeve Oersted (vide Koren & Danielssen, 1877a : 134).
Phascolosoma boreale Keferstein, 1865a : 437–438, pl. 31, fig. 7, pl. 33, fig. 33; Baird, 1868 : 84;
    Diesing, 1851 : 555; 1859 : 760; Verrill, 1874 : 387, pl. 15, fig. 45; Koren & Danielssen,
    1877a : 134, pl. 15, fig. 45.
Phascolosoma digitatum Théel, 1875b : 11; 1905 : 72.
Phascolosoma eremita: Selenka & de Man, 1883 : 35–36, pl. 5, figs 54–55; Fischer, 1895 : 17;
    1914b : 10; 1922d : 245; 1928b : 463–464, pl. 6, figs 9–10; Théel, 1905 : 72–74, pl. 1, figs 6–8,
    pl. 12, fig. 173, pl. 13, fig. 187; Gadd, 1911 : 88; Sluiter, 1912 : 8; Gerould, 1913 : 385–387,
    fig. 1; J. Fischer, 1914 : 98–99; Chamberlain, 1920 : 4; Wesenberg-Lund, 1930 : 28; 1932 :
    67; 1937a : 11–12; 1937b : 9, fig. 2; Leroy, 1936 : 425.

TYPE LOCALITY. North-west coast of Norway.

DESCRIPTION. Introvert at least equal to or longer in length than the trunk. About 20 tentacles present, skin smooth, hooks absent. Trunk up to about 50 mm in length, 3–4 times as long as thick. The skin is greyish-green in colour which gives a dirty appearance but the area surrounding the anus is rather lighter in colour; papillae sometimes brownish-grey. The papillae are very small and most hardly rise above the surface but at the base of the introvert and at the posterior end of the trunk, they are slightly larger. They are more or less oval in section, and closely resemble those of *G. capensis*. One pair of retractors arise from the middle of the trunk. The intestinal coils are very numerous with a single fastening mesentery from the first coil. Spindle muscle lacking (?). A short rectum. The nephridia are short.

REMARKS. The species is very widely distributed in the Arctic and northern temperate waters and has been reported in the Antarctic. It is variable, four subspecies having been named. The spindle muscle is often lacking in the nominate form but is always present in two subspecies. The species has been collected in shallow waters and from depths down to 2000 m.

DISTRIBUTION. Arctic, Kola Gulf (Gadd, 1912); Arctic (Fischer, 1928b); Greenland (Wesenberg-Lund, 1930, 1932, 1934, 1937a); Iceland (Wesenberg-Lund, 1937b); Norway (Sluiter, 1912; Leroy, 1936); east coast North America (Gerould, 1913); north-west Canada (Chamberlain, 1920).

Golfingia (Phascoloides) eremita australis (Benham, 1922)

Phascolosoma eremita australis Benham, 1922 : 17–18, pl. 11, figs 12–15; Fischer, 1928b : 483.
Golfingia eremita var. *australe* Wesenberg-Lund, 1959a : 182–183; 1963 : 111.

TYPE LOCALITY.   Antarctica.   Commonwealth Bay.

DESCRIPTION.   This subspecies differs in three respects from the nominate form; the skin bears papillae all over the surface, there is a delicate spindle muscle and the papillae are much shorter on the introvert than on the trunk.

REMARKS.   Described originally from the holotype.   Wesenberg-Lund also recorded a single specimen.

DISTRIBUTION.   Antarctica, Commonwealth Bay (Benham, 1922; Fischer, 1928b); South Africa, Cape area (Wesenberg-Lund, 1959a).

Golfingia (Phascoloides) eremita californica Fisher, 1952

Golfingia eremita californica Fisher, 1952 : 396–397.

TYPE LOCALITY.   California, Albatross Exped. stn. 4421.   Off San Nicholas Island.   552–545 m.   *Type.*   U.S.N.M. no. 21218.

DESCRIPTION.   This subspecies differs from the nominate form mainly in having no contractile vessel.   A strong spindle muscle is present.

REMARKS.   Described originally from ten specimens.

DISTRIBUTION.   As for the type locality.

Golfingia (Phascoloides) eremita scabra (Gerould, 1913)

Phascolosoma eremita scabra Gerould, 1913 : 387–388.

TYPE LOCALITY.   Florida, Cashes Ledges.   *Type.*   U.S.N.M. no. 8396.

DESCRIPTION.   The subspecies differs from the nominate form in that the circular ridges and furrows of the external surface are nearly concealed by a loose, thick, coffee-coloured cuticle which gives it the appearance of a rough, woollen fabric.

REMARKS.   Described from several specimens.   The appearance of the cuticle is not uncommon in certain genera of sipunculans and could be an artefact caused by preservation.   This would, therefore, appear to be an uncertain character on which to base a subspecies.

DISTRIBUTION.   As for the type locality.

OTHER DEEP-WATER VARIATIONS.   Gerould (1913 : 388) also mentioned two other specimens which differed from the nominate form but gave them no subspecific name.   The first, from near Georges Bank at 2000 m had a thick greyish rough integument and was thickly covered with blunt, rounded papillae at the posterior end. The second, taken south of Martha's Vineyard at 877 m, had a smooth skin like that of *G. margaritacea*.

Golfingia (Phascoloides) filiformis (Sluiter, 1902)

Phascolosoma filiforme Sluiter, 1902 : 37–38, pl. 4, figs 1–4.

TYPE LOCALITY. Malaya. Siboga stn. 271, 5°46′42″S, 134°0′0″E; at 1788 m.

DESCRIPTION. Introvert about 30 mm in length, without hooks and carrying papillae similar to those on the trunk, but smaller. Trunk 60 mm in length with the anus about 40 mm from the posterior end. The skin is transparent in the middle region of the trunk, but not at the anterior and posterior ends where it is thicker. The whole surface is covered with papillae. Those at the anterior and posterior ends are tuft-like, very similar to those seen in *G. semperi*, but much smaller near the introvert. This type of papilla is absent in the transparent middle portion where the papillae are of a similar size but broad and conical with a darker brown base and a lighter point. The longitudinal musculature is very weak in the middle region of the trunk. One pair of weak retractors arises at the posterior end of the trunk, at the front edge of the posterior eighth of the trunk length. In the middle of the trunk they lie close together, forming a trough in which the oesophagus lies. There is a small contractile vessel where the trough ends. There are about 20 irregular intestinal coils which reach to the posterior end of the trunk. The spindle muscle is not attached posteriorly. The nephridia are small and open posterior to the anus.

REMARKS. Known only from the holotype.

DISTRIBUTION. As for the type locality.

Golfingia (Phascoloides) fimbriata (Sluiter, 1902)

Phascolosoma fimbriatum Sluiter, 1902 : 34–35.

TYPE LOCALITY. Malaya. Siboga stn. 52. 9°3′24″S, 119°42′E.

DESCRIPTION. Introvert devoid of hooks but with papillae arranged in rows; the broad base of each papilla has the usual chitinous plates. Trunk 20 mm in length, skin iridescent with only a few stumpy cylindrical papillae with a mamillate tip. The chitinous plates of the papillae are slightly darker in colour than the skin. Longitudinal musculature not very strongly developed. One pair of strong retractors arises 4 mm from the posterior end of the trunk and the muscles unite about 5 mm from the mouth. About 13 irregularly-arranged intestinal convolutions present. The spindle muscle is not attached to the posterior end of the trunk but there are two fixing mesenteries. The long nephridia are about half the length of the trunk and open on the introvert about 10 mm in front of the anus.

REMARKS. Known only from the holotype.

DISTRIBUTION. As for the type locality.

Golfingia (Phascoloides) flagrifera (Selenka, 1885)

Phascolosoma flagriferum Selenka, 1885 : 13–16, pl. 3, fig. 17; Sluiter, 1900 : 12, pl. 1, fig. 3, pl. 3, figs 7–9; 1912 : 12–13, pl. 1, fig. 2; Fischer, 1914b : 10; Gerould, 1913 : 391–392.

TYPE LOCALITY.   Pacific (Japanese Trench).   *Type.*   Brit. Mus. (Nat. Hist.) no. 1885.12.3.15.

DESCRIPTION.   Introvert studded with small papillae, but without hooks.   Trunk up to 130 mm in length, 13 mm in breadth, studded with small papillae which are wart-like, 0·5 mm in height, at the posterior end of the trunk.   Musculature thin. There is a long whip-like appendage springing from the posterior end of the trunk. One pair of retractors arises from about the middle of the trunk and the muscles soon join.   Seventy or more intestinal coils carry a simple contractile vessel, not attached to the posterior end of the trunk by the spindle muscle.   The two nephridia are free from the trunk wall and open beside the anus.

REMARKS.   Described originally from the two specimens.

DISTRIBUTION.   Pacific, Japanese Trench, 35°41′N, 157°42′E, 4230 m (Selenka, 1885); off Bermuda, 37°25′N, 71°40′W, 3110 m (Selenka, 1885); Virginia (Gerould, 1913); off Finistère (Sluiter, 1900, 4900 m; 1912, 4965–5000 m).

Golfingia (Phascoloides) glacialis (Danielssen & Koren, 1881)

Onchnesoma glaciale Danielssen & Koren, 1881a : 64; 1881b : 8–9, pl. 1, figs 15–20.
Phascolosoma glaciale: Théel, 1905 : 80–81; Fischer, 1928 : 472; Wesenberg-Lund, 1930 : 30, pl. 3, fig. 29; 1932 : 8–9, text-figs 4–5; Roule, 1896b : 473.
Golfingia glacialis: Murina, 1964c : 57–59, fig. 7.

TYPE LOCALITY.   Norwegian coast.

DESCRIPTION.   Introvert twice as long as the trunk, up to 70 mm long, thread-like.   Tentacles absent but an oral disc or a few rounded lobes present around the mouth.   The anterior quarter carries a varying number of hooks arranged in irregular rows.   Trunk up to 35 mm in length.   Skin hyaline, almost devoid of papillae. One pair of retractor muscles arises from the extreme posterior end of the trunk and the muscles are webbed together giving the appearance of a single muscle. Numerous intestinal convolutions present that are free posteriorly; spindle muscle absent.   The convolutions and the rectum are attached to the trunk wall by a few mesenteries.   Two well-developed nephridia open on the level of the anus.

REMARKS.   The accounts given by the authors listed above differ somewhat· Danielssen & Koren described the species as having a single retractor and nephridium but Théel and Wesenberg-Lund both agree that it has two retractors webbed together, giving the appearance of a single muscle, and two nephridia.   The species occurs in deep-water; one specimen was recorded from 1423 m by Théel and another from 1200 m by Wesenberg-Lund.   Théel (1905 : 80) described 17 irregular rings of hooks.

DISTRIBUTION.   Greenland (Wesenberg-Lund, 1930, 1932); Norwegian coast, several localities (Koren & Danielssen); North Atlantic, 67°56′N, 4°11′W (Théel); Gascogne (Roule, 1896); Mediterranean (Murina, 1964c).

Golfingia (Phascoloides) improvisa (Théel, 1905)

(Fig. 18D)

Phascolosoma improvisum Théel, 1905 : 82–83, pl. 5, figs 51–58, pl. 12, figs 177–182, pl. 14, figs 202–203; Gerould, 1913 : 395–396, fig. 5; Wesenberg-Lund, 1930 : 32–34, pl. 3, figs 40–41, pl. 6, fig. 64; 1939 : 22–23.
Phascolosoma minutum: Sluiter, 1912 : 10–11 (non Keferstein, 1863); Cuénot, 1922 : 9–10 (partim); Fischer, 1925 : 19–20; 1928b (partim) : 464–467.
Phascolosoma johnstoni: Southern, 1913 : 28, pl. 5, fig. 9 (partim); Lindroth, 1941 (partim) : 449–450.
Golfingia improvisa: Fisher, 1952 : 396; Wesenberg-Lund, 1955b : 11; Murina, 1958 : 1625–1628.

TYPE LOCALITY. Elleskar, West coast of Sweden.

DESCRIPTION. Introvert about half or less than half as long as the trunk. Total length of trunk and introvert is 15 mm. Trunk cylindrical but tapers posteriorly and anteriorly. Tentacles absent but replaced by irregular rounded prominences on an oval disc. Skin hyaline with papillae that are most noticeable on the introvert and on the posterior surface of the trunk. Hooks present. Two retractor muscles arise from the middle of the trunk; sometimes, however, either more anteriorly or posteriorly. Nephridia free and open posterior to the anus. About 13 intestinal spirals that are not attached posteriorly. No fixing muscles are present.

REMARKS. This species is very close to and has often been confused with *G. minuta* (Keferstein). Murina (1958) after making a careful study of the two considers that they are different species and that both are valid. She has redescribed them. *G. improvisa* differs from *G. minuta* in possessing large papillae that are thickly set on the base of the introvert and on the posterior region of the trunk. The synonymy that we have given is that stated by Murina (1958 : 1625).

G. improvisa has been collected at depths of 5390 m (Murina, 1958).

DISTRIBUTION. Sweden (Théel, 1905); Greenland (Wesenberg-Lund, 1930); east of New Jersey, U.S.A. (Gerould, 1913); Atlantic (Sluiter, 1912); France (Cuénot, 1922); British Isles (Southern, 1913); North-west Pacific (Murina, 1958).

Golfingia (Phascoloides) incomposita (Sluiter, 1912)

Phascolosoma incompositum Sluiter, 1912 : 16–17, pl. 1, figs 9–10.

TYPE LOCALITY. Princess Alice stn. 1114. 33°59′30″N, 8°12′45″W; at 851 m.

DESCRIPTION. On the anterior region of the introvert is an area of small hooks which have a single, slightly bent point; these become much smaller and less regularly arranged towards the posterior part of this area. Trunk up to 15 mm in length with the anus 13 mm from the posterior end. The skin is smooth, slightly striated anteriorly, no papillae are visible under the microscope. Anteriorly the trunk wall is more transparent than posteriorly and the intestinal coils are visible through it. One pair of retractors with broad roots which are attached 9 mm from the posterior end. About 25 intestinal convolutions present, attached to the trunk wall by three fastening mesenteries. The spindle muscle does not emerge from the

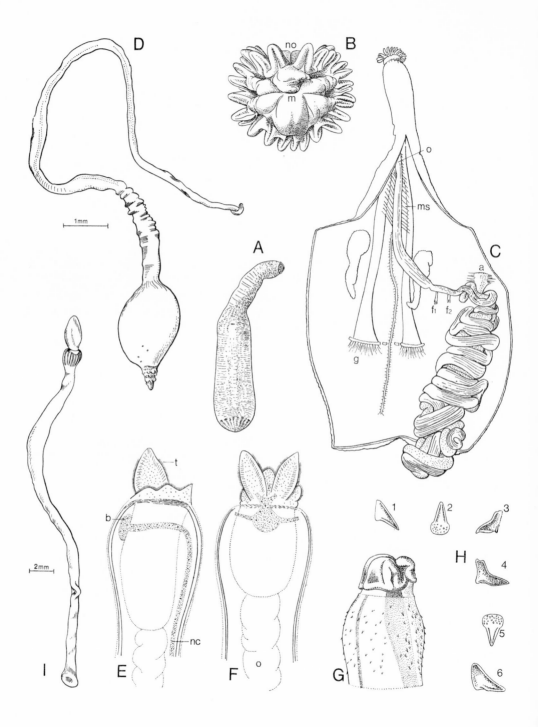

coils and so is not attached posteriorly.   The two nephridia are small, free for their whole length and open just a little way in front of the anus.

REMARKS.   Known only from the holotype.

DISTRIBUTION.   As for the type locality.

Golfingia (Phascoloides) intermedia (Southern, 1913)

(Fig. 13A–B)

Phascolosoma intermedium Southern, 1913a : 3–5, pl. 1, figs 1–8; Stephen, 1948 : 219.

TYPE LOCALITY.   Clew Bay, Clare Island, Ireland; 44 m.

DESCRIPTION.   Combined length of introvert and trunk 1·5–2·0 mm.   Introvert about as long as the trunk, cylindrical and swollen anteriorly.   Tentacles absent but two indistinct lobes present at the anterior tip.   Hooks irregularly arranged, triangular in shape and with long, finely curved points.   Trunk rounded posteriorly. Small papillae cover the whole of the body except the region of the introvert anterior to the hooks.   Two retractors (?) one of which arises from two roots near the posterior extremity of the trunk.   The intestine is not twisted into a spiral but forms a few loops.   The nephridia are small, somewhat spherical and arise at some distance posterior to the anus.   No mention is made of a spindle muscle and none is shown in the figure of a dissected specimen.   Contractile vessel not found.

REMARKS.   Southern says that 'the retractor muscles are arranged in a manner unusual in this genus and recalling the condition in *Phascolion strombi*'.   He thinks that one muscle represents a dorsal and the other, the divided one, the ventral retractor.   If such is the case it might be more correct to place the species in one of the subgenera with two pairs of retractors.   We are following the lead of Fisher, 1952 : 396 in regarding it as a member of the subgenus *Phascoloides*.

The species is closely related to *Golfingia minuta* (Kef.) and *G. improvisa* (Théel). It differs most noticeably (1) in the arrangement of the retractor muscles and (2) the irregular arrangement of the intestine without coiling.   The species was described from a number of specimens.

DISTRIBUTION.   Clare Is., Ireland (Southern, 1913); Commonwealth Bay, Antarctica (Stephen, 1948).

FIG. 17.   (A–C) *Golfingia eremita*.   (A) Entire specimen, × about 1·5.   (B) Tentacular crown, frontal view.   (C) Dissected specimen (after Théel).   (D) *Golfingia depressa*. Entire specimen (after Murina).   (E–H) *Golfingia minuta*.   (E) Anterior extremity of the introvert, lateral view.   (F) Anterior extremity of the introvert, dorsal view.   (E—F after Keferstein.)   (G) Anterior extremity of the introvert, lateral view.   (H) Six hooks from the introvert (G–H after Théel).   (I) *Golfingia vitjazi*.   Entire specimen (after Murina).   KEY: *See* Fig. 11, p. 83.

Golfingia (Phascoloides) laetmophila Fisher, 1952

Golfingia laetmophila Fisher, 1952 : 397–399, pl. 25, figs 4–6.

TYPE LOCALITY. California, off San Diego. Albatross stn. 4387, 32°32′40″N,
118°04′20″W; at 1935 m. *Type*. U.S.N.M. no. 21919.

DESCRIPTION. Introvert 17 mm in length, with 30–40 tentacles. About 2 mm
behind the tentacles there is a zone about 1–5 mm wide of irregularly scattered
dark brown, apparently flexible, spinelets. They are closely surrounded by glandular papillae. The proximal half of the introvert is covered with glandular skin,
the first 4 mm is also covered with thick glandular papillae. Brain with two large
eye-spots. Trunk 39 mm in length, skin smooth except for some minute papillae
anteriorly in a zone between the anus and the base of the introvert and posteriorly
where the skin is somewhat gelatinous and beset with filiform glands. Intestinal
coils very numerous, attached by well-developed mesenteries to the retractors, but
without mesenteries to the trunk wall. Contractile vessel functional for a short
distance only behind the head. A strong spindle muscle is attached behind the
anus and to the rectum but does not emerge from the spire. Unusually large wing
muscles present. Rectal caecum absent. One pair of retractors arises in the middle
of the trunk. The nephridia open on a level with the anus. The nephrostome is
characteristic with the dorsal lip being entire and the ventral lip thrown into five or
six marginal folds.

REMARKS. Known only from the holotype.

DISTRIBUTION. As for the type locality.

Golfingia (Phascoloides) lilljeborgii (Danielssen & Koren, 1881)

Phascolosoma lilljeborgii Danielssen & Koren, 1881a : 63–64; Selenka & de Man, 1883 : 40–41;
    Fischer, 1895 : 14; 1928b : 471–472; Sluiter, 1912 : 9; Théel, 1905 : 79–80.
Golfingia lilljeborgii: Wesenberg-Lund, 1954a : 9–10.

TYPE LOCALITY. Sweden, west coast.

DESCRIPTION. Introvert slender, equal in length to the trunk, a crown of 8–10
short broad tentacles present around the mouth; hooks absent. Trunk up to
40 mm in length, slim. Skin transparent, smooth, iridescent, nacreous in appearance.
Small papillae are scattered over the trunk; they are more numerous at the base of
the introvert and at the posterior end of the trunk, smallest anteriorly. One pair
of retractors arises in the middle of the trunk and the muscles appear as one muscle
with long roots. A long, thin oesophagus leads to a loose intestinal spiral with
10–12 coils which are free posteriorly. Spindle muscle lacking, but there is a long
contractile vessel. Two fairly long nephridia.

REMARKS. A deep-water species of the north-east Atlantic ranging from 394 m
to 1865 m. Originally described as possessing a single retractor. This was cor-
rected by Théel (1905) and Sluiter (1912).

DISTRIBUTION. Off the east coast of Iceland (Wesenberg-Lund, 1954a); off
Spitzbergen (Fischer, 1895; Sluiter, 1912); West coast of Sweden (Danielssen &
Koren, 1881).

Golfingia (Phascoloides) macra (Sluiter, 1891)

Phascolosoma macra Sluiter, 1891 : 114–115, pl. 2, figs 13–14; 1902 : 34.

TYPE LOCALITY. Bay of Batavia; at 18 m.

DESCRIPTION. Introvert about one and a half times as long as the trunk, but lighter in colour. There are numerous tentacles but neither papillae nor hooks. Trunk long, thin and uniform in breadth, ending posteriorly in a cone-shaped point such as usually seen in *Sipunculus*. The skin is slightly iridescent and yellow-brown in colour. All of the trunk is covered with numerous, four-sided papillae which are closely-packed, flat and unequal in size. A glandular opening is apparently absent from the smaller ones. In the larger papillae the central pore is situated eccentrically and is surrounded by a circular area of small plates. The small plates are still present in papillae where there is no gland opening. In addition, the whole papilla is surrounded by numerous pigmented plates, not arranged concentrically. There is a free area of skin between the papillae so that, in preserved specimens, they may be compacted. Longitudinal musculature weakly formed. One pair of retractors arises near the posterior end of the trunk and the muscles unite in the middle of the trunk. About 20 intestinal convolutions present and a fixing mesentery arises from the first coil. The spindle muscle does not emerge from the last coil, so that the intestinal coil is free posteriorly. The nephridia are whitish in colour and free for their whole length; they are about half the length of the trunk and open just posterior to the anus.

REMARKS. Known only from the holotype.

DISTRIBUTION. As for the type locality.

Golfingia (Phascoloides) minuta (Keferstein, 1863)

(Fig. 17E–H)

? Sipunculus johnstoni Forbes, 1841 : 254.
Phascolosoma minutum Keferstein, 1863 : 40, pl. 3, figs 7–10; 1865 : 438; Théel, 1911 : 31, pl. 3, figs 42–45, pl. 4, figs 46–49; Cuénot, 1922 : 9–10 (partim); Fischer, 1922b : 34 (partim); 1922d : 237 (partim); 1925 : 19–20; 1928b : 464–467, 483 (partim); ten Broeke, 1929 : 162–163; Wesenberg-Lund, 1930 : 30, pl. 3, fig. 30; 1932 : 9–10; 1937a : 12–13; 1937b : 9–10; 1939c : 20–22; Stephen, 1934 : 167–168.
Petalosoma minutum: Selenka & de Man, 1883 : 129; Southern, 1908 : 171–173, figs 1–5; Paul, 1909 : 1–50.
Phascolosoma sabellariae Théel, 1905 : 81; Gerould, 1913 : 392–395, figs 3–4.
Phascolosoma anceps Théel, 1905 : 84–86, pl. 5, figs 60–70, pl. 14, figs 204–205; Sluiter, 1912 : 10; Wesenberg-Lund, 1925 : 90.
Phascolosoma johnstoni: Southern, 1913b : 28–29; Lindroth, 1941 : 449–450 (partim).
Golfingia minuta: Wesenberg-Lund, 1955b : 11; Murina, 1957b : 994–995; 1958 : 1628–1634, 1 fig.; Akesson, 1958 : 33–46.

TYPE LOCALITY. St Vaast la Hougue, France.

DESCRIPTION. Introvert up to 8 mm long, about equal in length to the trunk, brown in colour. There are several broad leaf-like tentacles of which the two dorsal are largest. Behind the tentacles there is a broad zone of regularly-arranged pointed hooks. Two eye-spots present. Trunk up to 8 mm in length, brown in colour. The skin is covered with dome-shaped papillae; at the base of the introvert and at the posterior end they become stronger, more closely packed and almost cylindrical. One pair of slender retractors arises usually in the middle of the trunk. The alimentary tract has 7–15 convolutions. The spindle muscle is attached near the anus but is free posteriorly. Rectal caecum present. The nephridia are short and sac-like; they are free from the trunk wall for their whole length and open to the exterior posterior to the anus.

REMARKS. This species is very close to and has often been confused with *G. improvisa* (Théel). Murina (1958) after redescribing both considers them to be different. *G. minuta* lacks large papillae on the base of the introvert and on the posterior region of the trunk (Murina, 1958 : 1634). The synonymy that we have given for the species is based on the work of Murina (1958).

G. minuta has been collected at a depth of 5390 m (Murina, 1958). The development of *G. minuta* has been studied by Akesson, 1958. The species is described as being hermaphroditic (Akesson, 1958).

DISTRIBUTION. Greenland (Wesenberg-Lund, 1930, 1937a, 1937b); Iceland (Wesenberg-Lund, 1937); Norwegian coast (Théel, 1905); Skagerak and Kattegat (Wesenberg-Lund, 1939; Lindroth, 1941); North Sea (Fischer, 1925, 1928b; Stephen, 1934); Eire (Southern, 1908, 1913b); Azores (Sluiter, 1912); Chile (Wesenberg-Lund, 1955b); Falkland Islands (Fischer, 1922b; Théel, 1911); Antarctica (Murina, 1957b); North West Pacific (Murina, 1958).

Golfingia (Phascoloides) mucida (Sluiter, 1902)

Phascolosoma mucidum Sluiter, 1902 : 40.

TYPE LOCALITY. Malaya. Siboga stn. 271. 5°47′42″S, 134°0′E; at 1778 m.

DESCRIPTION. Introvert equal in length to the trunk, but only 0·5 mm in diameter. The surface is quite smooth with only small skin glands; papillae absent. Numerous small tentacles surround the mouth. Trunk 15 mm in length, 1·5 mm in diameter. The surface is covered with a felt-like layer so that the skin is not visible; this layer which is loose and easily removed, is structureless. It is apparently secreted by the skin and sand and mud grains adhere to it. On the surface of the trunk there are long thread-like papillae, embedded in the felt-like layer for half their length. Between these are small roundly elongated papillae each with a pore but without the surrounding protective, chitinous plates. Longitudinal musculature is weakly developed. One pair of moderately long retractors arises in the middle of the trunk. Intestinal convolutions well developed. The spindle muscle is not attached posteriorly. The two long nephridia are free for their whole length and open on a level with, or just posterior to, the anus.

REMARKS. Described originally from three specimens.

DISTRIBUTION. As for the type locality.

Golfingia (Phascoloides) multiaraneusa Murina, 1967

Golfingia multiaraneusa Murina, 1967a : 1332–1333, fig. 2.

TYPE LOCALITY.   Cuba; 22°35'N, 84°08'W; at 4 m.

DESCRIPTION.   Body elongate, cylindrical, flattened near anus but sharp posteri-orly; length 2 mm and maximum diameter 0·5 mm.   Introvert shorter than the body, length 1·5 mm and width 0·15 mm.   Anterior end of introvert is club-shaped and has three lobes of tentacles; a region about 0·12 mm long is armed with slightly bent, strongly chitinized, brown coloured hooks with a height of 0·015–0·030 mm and a width at the base of 0·01 mm.   At the base of each hook there are 5–10 long, thin hairs which resemble the legs of a spider and between the hooks are flat, oval skin bodies.   Two retractor muscles arise from the body wall in the upper quarter of the body.   Two bubble-like nephridia open to the exterior at the level of the anus. The contractile vessel is simple and hardly visible.   The intestinal spiral is not fastened posteriorly by the spindle muscle and hangs free.   A rectal caecum, fixing muscles and eye spots were not found.   The presence of long thin hairs at the base of the hooks is very unusual and has not been described previously in any sipunculan.

REMARKS.   Described from a single specimen.

DISTRIBUTION.   As for the type locality.

Golfingia (Phascoloides) novaezealandiae (Benham, 1904)

Phascolosoma novae-zealandiae Benham, 1904 : 301–303, pl. 15, figs 1–2, pl. 16, fig. 8.
Golfingia novae-zealandiae : Edmonds, 1960 : 162–163, pl. 3, fig. 3.

TYPE LOCALITY.   Otago, New Zealand.

DESCRIPTION.   Introvert up to half the length and darker in colour than the trunk.   Numerous simple, thread-like tentacles present, small papillae widely scattered but hooks absent.   Trunk long and subcylindrical, narrowing to a point posteriorly.   Up to 310 mm in length and 10 mm in diameter.   The skin has small papillae scattered over it.   The colour varies from pink and white to yellowish. One pair of strong retractors arises in the anterior third of the trunk and the muscles are fastened to the oesophagus by fine mesenteries.   There are about 20 double intestinal coils present and the spindle muscle is free posteriorly.   There are five fixing muscles.   The rectum is short and there is a post-intestinal caecum.   The contractile vessel runs along the dorsal surface of the oesophagus and bears no villi.   The nephridia are short and free, opening on the same level as the anus.

REMARKS.   Described originally from the holotype.   Benham (1909) recorded another specimen from near the type locality.   Edmonds (1960) recorded two more and redescribed the species.

DISTRIBUTION.   New Zealand (Benham, 1904); East Otago, Chatham Islands, 64 m (Edmonds, 1960).

Golfingia (Phascoloides) pavlenkoi (Ostroumov, 1909)

Phascolosoma pavlenkoi Ostroumov, 1909 : 323.

TYPE LOCALITY.   Northern part of the Sea of Japan.

DESCRIPTION.   Introvert about one and a half times as long as the trunk; papillae are present of the same type as those on the trunk.   Hooks absent.   Trunk slim, tapering anteriorly and posteriorly.   The surface appears smooth but, under magnification, is seen to be covered with numerous dark yellow, short cylindrical or cone-shaped papillae, all similar in size.   One pair of strong retractors arises from the edge of the posterior third of the trunk.   There is only one fastening mesentery. The two nephridia are not attached to the trunk wall.

REMARKS.   This summary is taken from a German résumé of Ostroumov's description which was in Russian.

DISTRIBUTION.   As for the type locality.

Golfingia (Phascoloides) pellucida (Keferstein, 1865)

(Fig. 18E–H)

Sipunculus (Phascolosomum) pellucidus Quatrefages, 1865b : 620.
Phascolosoma riisei Keferstein, 1865a : 437, pl. 33, fig. 38; Baird, 1868 : 96.
Phascolosoma pellucidum Keferstein, 1865a : 433, pl. 32, figs 26–27; Baird, 1868 : 86; Selenka
    & de Man, 1883 : 32–34, pl. 4, figs 44–49; Shipley, 1899a : 155; Sluiter, 1902 : 34; Augener,
    1903 : 299–300; Lanchester, 1905a : 28; Southern, 1913b : 6; Fischer, 1914b : 8; 1919a :
    281; 1922b : 17; 1923b : 23; ten Broeke, 1925 : 83; Leroy, 1936 : 425.

TYPE LOCALITY.   St Thomas, Antilles, West Indies.

DESCRIPTION.   Introvert a third to three quarters of the length of the trunk, pale reddish in colour.   A double crown of tentacles with eight in the inner row and 14–16 in the outer.   Covered with papillae which become smaller anteriorly; some in the middle may be spine-like.   A zone of irregularly-scattered awl-like, slightly bent hooks occurs anteriorly; scattered papillae often appear between the hooks. Two eye-spots on the brain.   Trunk up to 45 mm in length, pale reddish in colour, somewhat translucent and iridescent.   Small yellowish, wart-like papillae are spread in large numbers over the surface of the trunk.   They are visible to the naked eye and are larger on the introvert base than in the middle of the trunk.   At the posterior end they are more closely packed and often appear as spines.   One pair of fairly thin retractors arises in the middle or middle third of the trunk and the muscles meet far anteriorly.   Intestinal spiral with 15–20 coils.   Fastening mesenteries are attached to the oesophagus and the first coil.   The spindle muscle is not attached posteriorly.   A contractile vessel is present but without villi.   The nephridia are about half the length of the trunk and are free for their whole length.

REMARKS.   There seems to be a considerable amount of variation in specimens from different localities.   Keferstein's fig. 26 shows that the nephridia open well in front of the anus.

DISTRIBUTION. West Indies (Keferstein, 1865; ten Broeke, 1925); East Coast of South America (Selenka & de Man, 1883; Fischer, 1914b; Leroy, 1936); Malaya, Singapore (Selenka & de Man, 1883; Lanchester, 1905a); Siam (Fischer, 1923b); Amboina (Augener, 1903); Philippines (Selenka & de Man, 1883); Mergui Archipelago (Selenka, 1883); Loyalty Islands (Shipley, 1899); Australia, Torres Strait (Fischer, 1919a).

Golfingia (Phascoloides) prioki (Sluiter, 1881)

Phascolosoma prioki Sluiter, 1881a : 152–153, pl. 1, fig. 5 and fig. 9; 1891 : 115; 1902 : 34; Selenka & de Man, 1883 : 37; Selenka, 1885 : 12–13.

TYPE LOCALITY. Tandjong Priok, Djakarta, Java.

DESCRIPTION. Introvert about one and one quarter times the length of the trunk and without hooks. When retracted it forms a loop within the trunk. Trunk up to 18 mm in length, slim, dirty grey in colour. Anteriorly it is drawn out thinly and posteriorly it ends in a finger-like papilla. The skin is thin, without papillae; the musculature is weak. One pair of short retractors present, which soon join in the posterior part of the trunk. Digestive tract long, with many coils. The rectum is fastened by a weak spindle muscle, the posterior end of which is somewhat swollen and attached to the trunk wall by several radiating muscle-strands. The two nephridia are small and slightly pigmented.

REMARKS. Described originally from a single specimen found in the shell of *Dentalium*. Sluiter (1891 & 1902) merely repeated the original records, as did Selenka & de Man (1883). Selenka (1885) added one more record from Challenger station 214, Indonesia.

Sluiter's fig. 9 shows (1) that the nephridia do not open anterior to the anus and (2) that the contractile vessel, if present, lacks tubules or villi. The species, therefore, does not fall readily in the subgenus *Thysanocardia*. It appears from Sluiter's description (1882 : 153) that the weakly developed spindle muscle (not shown in fig. 9) is not attached posteriorly in the normal manner. 'Der Enddarm mit äusserst schwachen spindelmuskeln, am letzten Theil etwas blasig aufgeschwollen, und mittelst vieler radiären Muskeln an die Körperwand befestigt.' It is possibly for this reason that Fisher (1952) considered the species to fall in the subgenus *Phascoloides*.

DISTRIBUTION. As for the type locality. 4°33′N, 127°6′E; at 962 m (Selenka, 1885).

Golfingia (Phascoloides) rutilofusca (Fischer, 1916)

Aspidosiphon rutilofuscus Fischer, 1916 : 17.
Phascolosoma aspidosiphonoides Fischer, 1922c : 11–12, pl. 2, figs 8a–g.
Golfingia rutilofusca Fischer, 1952 : 395; Murina, 1967a : 1335.

TYPE LOCALITY. Off Zanzibar. German Deep-Sea Exped. stn. 258. 2°58′N, 56°5′0″E; at 1362 m.

L

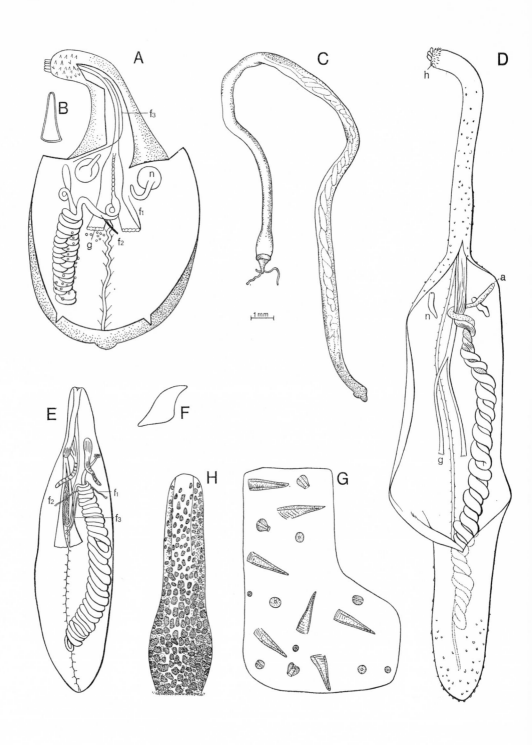

DESCRIPTION.   Introvert up to 26 mm in length, dark red-brown in colour, much thinner than the trunk and with cross-folds and points on the surface. There are 20–25 tentacles, but no hooks. Trunk up to 15 mm in length, cylindrical; posteriorly there is a pointed shield sharply marked off by a rim. The shield has 12 fairly broad anastomosing furrows which do not quite reach the tip. White, chalky bodies lie between the furrows. The general body colour is red-brown, darker at the posterior end, which is varied by longitudinal rows of lighter coloured, closely aggregated chitinous plates. The plates are rhombic with rounded edges. No distinct papillae. One pair of long thin retractors which are joined for most of their length, inserted near the posterior end of the trunk, one on each side of the nerve cord. About 28–30 intestinal coils which are attached to the trunk wall near the rectum, but not posteriorly by the spindle muscle (?). The contractile vessel is without villi. The nephridia are short and bladder-like, free from the trunk wall and open in front of the anus.

REMARKS.   Fischer first described this worm as a species of *Aspidosiphon* because it possessed a caudal shield. The introvert is, however, not extruded eccentrically and the anterior portion resembles a *Golfingia*. He recognized this fact in his second description. Although Fischer (1922c : 11) states that his specimens of *Phascolosoma aspidosiphonoides* are the same as those which he had on a former occasion called *Aspidosiphon rutilofuscus* Fischer (1916 : 17) he offers no reason for not calling his African specimens *Phascolosoma rutilofuscum*. Fisher (1952), Murina (1967a) and we have done this.

Murina (1967a : 1335) considered that the spindle muscle of the species is fastened posteriorly to the body wall and consequently placed the species in her subgenus *Siphonoides*. Her action in doing so may be correct because it is not very clear from Fischer's first description how the spindle muscle ends posteriorly. We consider, however, that it is clear from Fischer's second description that the spindle muscle is free posteriorly. Evidently Fisher (1952 : 395) thought so too because he placed the species in the subgenus *Phascoloides* where the spindle muscle is not attached posteriorly. The decision about the spindle muscle depends on the interpretation of the following statements:

(1) Fischer, 1916, 'Innerlich sehen wir . . . und eine Spira, die 28–30 enge Doppel-windungen zeigt, welche durch einen Spindelmuskel, der kurz vor dem After ansetzt und auch hinten aus der Spira heraustritt und sie dort anheftet, gestützt sind'.

and (2) Fischer, 1922c, 'Diese zeigt 28–30 enge und schmale Doppelwindungen, die hinten nicht durch den Spindelmuskel festegeheftet sind, während er vorn in den Schleifen des Rektums, deutlich sichtbar ist und die Spirale dort an die Körper-wand heftet'.

DISTRIBUTION.   As for the type locality.

FIG. 18. (A–B) *Golfingia schuttei*. (A) Dissected specimen. (B) Introvert spine. (A–B after Murina). (C) *Golfingia tasmaniensis*. Entire specimen (after Murina). (D) *Golfingia improvisa*. Dissected specimen, dorsal view (after Théel). (E–H) *Golfingia pellucida*. (E) Dissected specimen. (F) Hook from introvert. (G) Spines and papillae from the introvert. (H) Papillae from posterior region of the trunk. (E–H after Kefer-stein.) KEY: *See* Fig. 11, p. 83.

Golfingia (Phascoloides) schuttei (Augener, 1903)

(Fig. 18A–B)

Phascolosoma schuttei Augener, 1903 : 335–337, figs 17–18.
Golfingia schuttei: Murina, 1964a : 238–242, figs 12a–d.

TYPE LOCALITY.   Sydney, Australia.

DESCRIPTION.   Introvert about as long as the trunk, spotted with brown. Tentacles yellowish and set in several rows.   Behind these lies a zone of brown, depressed hooks with only slightly bent points.   Two eye-spots on the brain. Trunk 70 mm in length, about 10 mm in breadth.   Apparently smooth but, under magnification, very numerous ball-shaped papillae and points can be seen.   Longitudinal musculature continuous, except just behind the insertion of the retractors where one or two strands are visible.   One pair of retractors arises in the posterior two thirds of the trunk and the muscles are bound together by mesenteries in their anterior two thirds.   About 63 intestinal convolutions are held in position by a spindle muscle which ends in the last spiral of the intestine by breaking up into a number of fine threads.   Several fixing muscles present.   The first springs from the anterior portion of the trunk to the left of the nerve cord and retractor and is attached to the first convolution.   The second is a short strand starting just behind the anus to the left of the nerve cord and is also attached to the first convolution. A third starts from a third to a fourth of the way up the introvert and is attached to the intestine.   The contractile vessel is without villi.   The rectum bears a caecum and is attached to the trunk wall by a short mesentery and wing muscles.   The nephridia are sac-like, brown, about half the length of the trunk, free for their whole length and open a little in front of the anus.   The nerve cord splits into several strands anteriorly.

REMARKS.   The species is redescribed in detail by Murina (1964a).

DISTRIBUTION.   New South Wales (Augener, 1903); Tasmania (Murina, 1964a); Northern Pacific (Murina, 1964a).

Golfingia (Phascoloides) sluiteri (ten Broeke, 1925)

Phascolosoma sluiteri ten Broeke, 1925 : 84–86, text-figs 1–5.

TYPE LOCALITY.   Spanish Water, West Indies.

DESCRIPTION.   Introvert about equal in length to the trunk, without tentacles; hooks usually absent but were recorded in one small specimen.   Elongate papillae present, arranged in three or four longitudinal rows one behind the other in a band on the middle of the introvert.   Trunk very slim, up to 13 mm in length and 10–12 times as long as thick.   Covered with conspicuous papillae which are largest posteriorly, small in the middle of the trunk, short and thick anteriorly.   One pair of retractors arises in the posterior third of the trunk.   About 28 intestinal convolutions present terminating in a long rectum.   The contractile vessel is without villi.   The spindle muscle is not attached posteriorly.   Three fixing mesenteries are attached to the first intestinal convolution. The nephridia are short being about a quarter of the length of the trunk; they are free for their whole length and open behind the anus.

REMARKS. Described originally from 12 specimens. No other records.

DISTRIBUTION. As for the type locality.

Golfingia (Phascoloides) subhamata (Sluiter, 1902)

Phascolosoma subhamatum Sluiter, 1902 : 35–36, pl. 3, figs 10–12.

TYPE LOCALITY. Malaya.

DESCRIPTION. Introvert up to 17 mm in length, with transverse bands of colour. Long, small, slim hooks with a small hook-like point are scattered irregularly over the anterior surface. Trunk up to 18 mm in length. Most of the trunk, including the dorsal side of the introvert base, is dark coloured but the middle portion is lighter. Papillae not uniform in size and scattered over the trunk. Numerous small finger-like papillae covered with small chitinous plates are present. Anteriorly and in the middle region of the trunk the papillae are conical with a rather thicker point and a broader base. The anus is 14 mm from the posterior end of the trunk. One pair of retractor muscles arises about the middle of the trunk, and the muscles are joined for their anterior half. About 20 intestinal coils present; they are fixed anteriorly by two mesenteries but free posteriorly since the posterior end of the spindle muscle is free. The rectum is attached by broad wing muscles. The two short nephridia open a little way in front of the anus.

REMARKS. Described originally from six specimens. No other records.

DISTRIBUTION. Malaya. Siboga stns 88, 126.

Golfingia (Phascoloides) tasmaniensis Murina, 1964

(Fig. 18C)

Golfingia tasmaniensis Murina, 1964a : 242–243, figs 13a and b.

TYPE LOCALITY. Tasman Sea (37°31′S, 163°59′E); at 1330 m.

DESCRIPTION. Small, filiform animal of length 17–19 mm; length about 30 times its width. Body wall light yellow in colour, translucent, smooth, without papillae and skin glands. Anterior part of the body (the introvert?) is conical and its base is surrounded by a collar; hooks absent. At the tip of the cone are two or three slender, white tentacles. Posterior of body is sharp and slightly enlarged at its extremity. The longitudinal musculature is smooth, lustrous and undivided. Two retractors arise in the anterior fourth of the trunk. Intestinal spiral of about 25–30 single coils. No villi on the contractile vessel.

REMARKS. Described from two specimens collected at 1330 m.

DISTRIBUTION. As for the type locality.

Golfingia (Phascoloides) verrillii (Gerould, 1908)

Phascolosoma verrillii Gerould, 1908 : 488–489; 1913 : 388–391, pl. 58, fig. 5, text-fig. 2.
Golfingia verrillii: Murina, 1964a : 243–246, figs 14a and b.

TYPE LOCALITY.   Eastern North America.

DESCRIPTION.   Introvert up to 10 mm in length with one row of 24 tentacles; hooks absent.   It is covered with prominent papillae which decrease in size towards the anterior end.   There are two prominent eye-spots.   Trunk up to 15 mm in length, thick, cylindrical, tapering somewhat to the posterior end which is truncate. Dark brown or dark steel-grey in colour.   The surface is covered with prominent papillae which vary from dark brown to light yellow in colour.   They are largest at the base of the introvert and at the posterior end of the trunk; these large papillae are finger-shaped or bluntly conical and attached by a small neck.   The papillae are smallest and least numerous in a broad zone in the middle of the trunk, where small undeveloped papillae are scattered amongst large, ovate ones.   One pair of retractor muscles arises slightly in front of the middle of the trunk.   There are about 26 intestinal convolutions and a large contractile vessel without villi.   The rectum is long and straight.   The two large nephridia open almost on a level with the anus and have a prominent nephrostome.

REMARKS.   This species is closely allied to *G. eremita* (Sars).

DISTRIBUTION.   North-east America, Massachusetts to Cape Hatteras, at 7–15 m (Gerould, 1908); Japan (Murina, 1964a).

Golfingia (Phascoloides) vitjazi Murina, 1964

(Fig. 171)

Golfingia vitjazi Murina, 1964a : 246–248, figs 16a and b.

TYPE LOCALITY.   North Pacific, 28°53′5″N, 137°21′E, at 4150 m.

DESCRIPTION.   Length of body 25 mm and about 20 times its width.   Introvert short and less than one fifth the length of the trunk.   A round, chitinous, shield-like structure is present at the anterior end of the trunk.   Introvert arises on the ventral side of the anterior shield which is divided by 34–36 radial ribs.   About 10 tentacles. Posterior to the tentacles there are large, chitinous hooks 0·021–0·028 mm in height. Body wall light brown in colour, opaque and smooth.   Yellow oval glands present in the anal region.   Two retractors arise in the anterior third of the trunk.   Two long nephridia.   Intestinal spiral of about 15 single coils.

REMARKS.   Described from a single specimen collected in deep water.

DISTRIBUTION.   As for the type locality.

Golfingia (Phascoloides) vitrea (Roule, 1898)

Phascolosoma vitreum Roule, 1898a : 386; 1906 : 86–90, pl. 9, fig. 88, pl. 10, figs 102–105.

TYPE LOCALITY.   Moroccan Coast, off Mogador; at 1050 m.

DESCRIPTION. Introvert short, 5 mm in length, without tentacles but carrying eight rows of hooks just behind the mouth. Hooks are unequal in size, being longest posteriorly. They are conical, have their tips bent forwards and end in a blunt point. Trunk 12 mm in length, cylindrical with thin musculature so that, posteriorly, the viscera are visible. Numerous very small, hemispherical papillae are scattered over the surface. One pair of short, broad retractors arises at the same level a little distance posteriorly to the anus. Intestinal coils 15–16, irregularly arranged and fastened by numerous mesenteries. Rectum long and straight. Spindle muscle absent. Nephridia not described.

REMARKS. Known only from the holotype.

DISTRIBUTION. As for the type locality.

Subgenus *SIPHONOIDES* Murina, 1967

Golfingia (Siphonoides) Murina, 1967a : 1334.

DESCRIPTION. One pair of retractors. Hooks present or absent. Spindle muscle attached posteriorly to the body wall. Contractile vessel simple. Nephridia not bilobed.

TYPE SPECIES. *Phascolosoma immunita* Sluiter.

REMARKS. Murina proposed the subgenus to contain four species: *G. quadrata* (Ikeda), *G. mexicana* Murina, *G. rutilofusca* (Fischer) and *G. immunita* (Sluiter). In placing *G. rutilofusca* in the subgenus *Siphonoides* Murina considered that its spindle muscle is fixed posteriorly to the body wall. *G. rutilofusca* is a troublesome species and Murina's classification may be correct. However, for reasons given on p. 155 we have translated Fischer's descriptions of the species as showing that the spindle muscle is not fixed posteriorly and so did Fisher (1952 : 395). Consequently we have placed the species in the subgenus *Phascoloides*.

It is possible that *G. chuni* (Fischer) belongs to the subgenus *Siphonoides* and not *Phascoloides* where Fisher, 1952 : 396 placed it. Its correct position depends on whether Fischer's 'Spiramuskel' is the same as his 'Spindelmuskel'. The matter is discussed in this monograph on p. 136. We have left the species in *Phascoloides* with reservations.

KEY TO SPECIES—SUBGENUS SIPHONOIDES

1 Introvert hooks present **2**
– Introvert hooks absent . . . . *G. immunita* (p. 159)
2 Introvert about as long as the body; skin bodies rectangular in shape and nephridia
   open on the same level as the anus . . . . *G. quadrata* (p. 160)
– Introvert about three to five times as long as the body; skin bodies oval or round in
   shape and nephridia open posterior to the anus . . *G. mexicana* (p. 160)

Golfingia (Siphonoides) immunita Sluiter, 1902

Phascolosoma immunitum Sluiter, 1902 : 40–41.
Golfingia immunita: Murina, 1967a : 1334–1335.

TYPE LOCALITY. Indonesia, 6°8'N, 121°19'E at 275 m (Siboga Exped.).

DESCRIPTION. Small species with plump form. Trunk 8 mm long and 3 mm wide in the mid-region. Introvert longer than trunk. Both introvert and trunk appear smooth. Under strong magnification, however, the whole body surface is seen to be covered with small, long and round skin-bodies. They possess a central opening but the gland is not protected by a covering of chitinous plates. Hooks absent and the longitudinal musculature is continuous. Two strong retractors arise somewhat posterior to the middle of the trunk. The intestinal spirals are well developed and the spindle muscle is fixed posteriorly. Two nephridia which are usually more than half as long as the trunk open posterior to the anus.

REMARKS. The species is close to *G. prioki* (Sluiter). Known only from a single specimen.

DISTRIBUTION. As for the type locality.

Golfingia (Siphonoides) mexicana Murina, 1967

Golfingia mexicana Murina, 1967a : 1333–1334, fig. 3.

TYPE LOCALITY. Bay of Mexico; 19°26′3″N, 96°01′4″W; at 110 m.

DESCRIPTION. Body spindle-like, 10 mm long and about 1·2 mm wide and rounded posteriorly. Introvert about 3–5 times as long as the trunk; length counting the invaginated part 46 mm and width 0·2 mm. Introvert armed with more than about 50 sharp hooks with a slightly bent tip; height of hooks 0·032 mm and width at base 0·010–0·015 mm. Tentacles not found. Skin bodies at base of introvert are oval and elongate in shape; height 0·070–0·10 mm. Skin bodies on the middle of the trunk are flat, rosette shaped with a small central opening; diameter of bodies 0·020–0·025 mm. Diameter of skin bodies at posterior extremity of the trunk is 0·03–0·05 mm and height 0·025–0·030 mm. Two retractor muscles which soon fuse to form a simple muscle. Long straight post-oesophageal gut which joins the intestinal spiral. Anus lies anterior to the level of the nephridiopores. Spindle muscle fixed posteriorly. No intestinal fasteners and no rectal caecum. Contractile vessel simple and very thin. Nephridia slightly twisted, about a third as long as the trunk and (according to Murina, 1967, fig. 3) arising posterior to the anus.

REMARKS. Described from four specimens.

DISTRIBUTION. As for the type locality.

Golfingia (Siphonoides) quadrata (Ikeda, 1905)

Phascolosoma quadratum Ikeda, 1905a : 170–171, pl. 8, figs 1–4.

TYPE LOCALITY. Philippines, South Negros; sandy shore.

DESCRIPTION. Introvert about as long as the trunk but much narrower. Immediately behind the tentacles is a zone of about 30 rings of hooks. The hooks are very small, golden-yellow in colour, strongly curved with a strong point. Tubular papillae alternate with the rows of hooks. Two eye-spots. Trunk long and slender,

50 mm in length, 4 mm in width, ending posteriorly in a small conical swelling. The skin is light brown-yellow in colour and has a rough appearance, due to the presence of closely-distributed skin bodies which are fairly uniform in size and shape over the trunk. These are relatively large and rectangular. Each rectangular area is made up of numerous closely-set chitinous granules with a small clear area in the centre containing the pore. One pair of retractors arises near to the posterior extremity of the trunk. About 30 intestinal convolutions present. These are traversed by the spindle muscle which is attached posteriorly. The contractile vessel is as long as the oesophagus, villi absent. There are no fixing muscles and no rectal caecum. The nephridia are about two thirds the length of the trunk and are attached to its wall for all of their length. They open on the same level as the anus.

REMARKS. Known only from the holotype.

DISTRIBUTION. As for the type locality.

GENUS *ONCHNESOMA* Koren & Danielssen

Onchnesoma Koren & Danielssen, 1875 : 133; 1877 : 142; Selenka & de Man, 1883 : 130; Théel, 1905 : 13.

DESCRIPTION. Small, pear or club-shaped. Introvert very much longer than the trunk and lacking hooks and spines; tentacles either few (10) or absent, being replaced by a tentacular disc. Trunk small and covered with papilliform bodies or scales of irregular form and unequal size. Longitudinal musculature continuous. One retractor attached to the posterior end of the trunk. Anus lies on the introvert, especially forward, near the mouth. Nephridium single. Intestinal coils few and arranged in an irregular spiral.

TYPE SPECIES. *O. steenstrupii* Koren & Danielssen, 1875.

REMARKS. The genus *Onchnesoma* was described by Koren & Danielssen (1875) for two pear-shaped sipunculans (*onchnos* a pear, *soma* body), *O. steenstrupii* (spelt 'stenstrupii') and *O. sarsii*. *O. steenstrupii*, the first species described, seems to us to be the type of the genus. Subsequently Danielssen & Koren (1881) described another species *O. glaciale*. Théel (1905) re-examined the genus and transferred *O. sarsii* and *O. glaciale* to *Golfingia* (=*Phascolosoma*), stating that they were 'true *Phascolosoma* with highly reduced tentacular crowns'. Further, Théel transferred a species described by Koren & Danielssen, 1877 as *Phascolosoma squamatum* and by Selenka (1885) as *Phascolion squamatum* to *Onchnesoma*. We are following the lead given by Théel and regard the genus as consisting of two species, *O. steenstrupii* and *O. squamatum*. Both species are very small.

DISTRIBUTION. Known from the deeper waters of the coastal region of the north-eastern Atlantic, of north-western Africa and of the Mediterranean.

GENUS ONCHNESOMA—KEY TO SPECIES

Tentacles absent, being reduced to an oval disc . . . **O. steenstrupii** (p. 163)
Tentacles present, 8–10 in number . . . . . **O. squamatum** (p. 163)

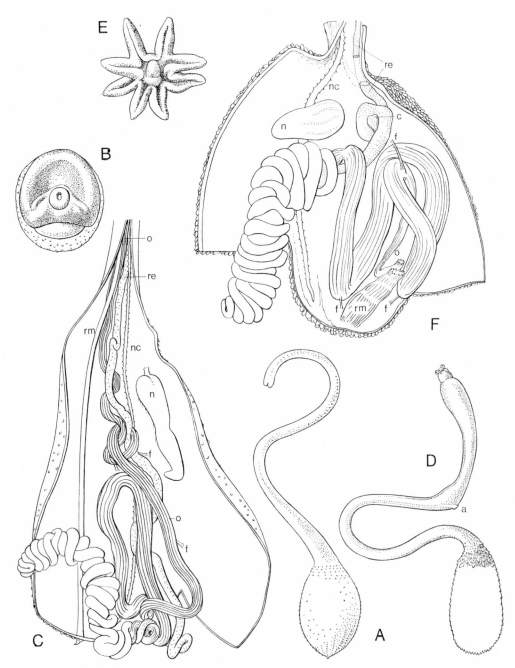

FIG. 19. (A–C) *Onchnesoma steenstrupii*. (A) Entire animal. (B) Front view of the mouth with its disc devoid of tentacles. (C) Dissected specimen. (D–F) *Onchnesoma squamatum*. (D) Entire animal. (E) Tentacular crown. (F) Dissected specimen. (A–F after Théel.) KEY: *See* Fig. 11, p. 83.

Onchnesoma squamatum (Koren & Danielssen, 1875)

(Fig. 19D–F)

Phascolosoma squamatum Koren & Danielssen, 1875 : 129; 1877 : 130–131, pl. 14, figs 11, 14, 15; Selenka & de Man, 1883 : 40; Shipley, 1892 : 235; Norman, 1894 : 151–152.
Phascolosoma olivaceum: Selenka & de Man, 1883 : 40.
Phascolion squamatum: Selenka, 1885 : 15.
Onchnesoma squamatum: Théel, 1905 : 96–98, pl. 11, figs 153–156, pl. 13, figs 183–184, pl. 15, figs 214–215; Southern, 1913b : 34; Fischer, 1914b : 15–16; 1925 : 24–25; 1928 : 473, 2 figs; Wesenberg-Lund, 1930 : 38–39, 2 pls; 1937b : 12; 1939b : 28–29; Stephen, 1934 : 172–173; 1958 : 135.

TYPE LOCALITY. Hardangerfjord, Norway; at 180–260 m.

DESCRIPTION. Introvert about two and a half times as long as the body, semi-transparent and covered with widely separated rows of fine papillae, more closely placed in the neighbourhood of the tentacles. According to Koren & Danielssen there is a single thread-like tentacle; Théel (1905 : 97), however, says that the tentacles are small, 8–9 in number and that their shape is not thread-like. Trunk, with length up to about 11 mm, covered with rust coloured papillae-like bodies or scales of irregular form and of unequal size; small normal papillae that communicate with glands are scattered among the scales. Anus placed anteriorly on the introvert near the mouth. A single retractor with four roots arises from the posterior end of the body and is fastened to the introvert near the tentacular crown. The oesophagus makes a loose loop of five coils on the right side of the body, then coils to the left to form a fairly long rectum. A thin contractile vessel present (Koren & Danielssen); Théel (1905) was unable to determine whether or not a contractile vessel was present. Nephridium single. Rectal caecum present, according to Théel.

REMARKS. Selenka (1883 : 40) refers to two 'varieties' that live side by side with the normal rust-coloured form, one is brown with green flecks and the other olive green (*Phascolosoma olivaceum*). Fischer (1928b : 473) confirmed that 8–9 tentacles are present and that they are not thread-like but of the usual form. Dredged from about 1000 m (Fischer, 1928).

DISTRIBUTION. Norway (Koren & Danielssen, 1877; Théel, 1905); Iceland (Wesenberg-Lund, 1937b); North Atlantic (Selenka, 1885; Fischer, 1914b; Stephen, 1934); West coast of Ireland (Southern, 1913b); West coast of Spain (Fischer, 1922b); Mediterranean (Stephen, 1958)

Onchnesoma steenstrupii Koren & Danielssen, 1875

(Fig. 19A–C)

Sipunculus pyriformis Danielssen, 1859 : 251.
Sipunculus aus Kilmore Müller, 1861 : 540; Selenka & de Man, 1883 : 130.
Phascolosoma pusillum Sars, 1868 : 252 (nom. nud.).
Onchnesoma steenstrupii Koren & Danielssen, 1875 : 133; 1877 : 142, pl. 15, figs 28–36; Selenka & de Man, 1883 : 130–131; Shipley, 1892 : 235; Norman, 1894 : 151; Théel, 1905 : 93–96, pl. 10, figs 151–152, pl. 11, figs 157–172, pl. 13, fig. 185; Southern, 1913b : 34; Fischer,

1922b : 22; 1925 : 24; 1928 : 473; Stephen, 1934 : 172; 1958 : 134–135; Wesenberg-Lund, 1930 : 37–38, pl. 3, figs 31 and 43, pl. 4, figs 48–49; 1939a : 28–29; 1939b : 28; 1959a : 198; Murina, 1964c : 72–73; 1968 : 198.

TYPE LOCALITY. Bergensfjord.

DESCRIPTION.   Introvert long and thin, up to 34 mm and evenly covered to about 2 mm from the mouth with small, fine papillae.   No tentacles.   Body small, up to 3 mm in length and 2 mm in thickness, barrel-like, covered everywhere with small conical papillae.   Under magnification a fine network of lines seen.   A greyish pigment present in the skin.   The retractor arises with a broad root from the posterior end of the body.   Intestinal coil made up of one or two loose windings and is fastened to the body wall by fine mesenteries.   The anus lies half way along the introvert according to Koren & Danielssen but well forward on the introvert near the mouth according to Théel (1905).   Nephridium single and elongate.

REMARKS.   There is some doubt as to whether the species should be called *O. pyriforme*.   According to Théel, 1905 : 94, both Koren & Danielssen and he agreed that the name *pyriforme* was unsatifactory.   Apparently they were not sure of the identity of *S. pyriformis*.   *Phascolosoma pusillum* was never described and is therefore a *nomen nudum*.   Théel says that the tentacular crown of *O. steenstrupii* is 'reduced to an oval disc and devoid of all traces of protrusions' and that 'no contractile vessel is present'.   In addition he claims that Koren & Danielssen incorrectly described the position of the anus.   It lies, according to Théel, 'in the neighbourhood of the mouth and the rectum traverses the length of the introvert'.   The species has been dredged at 362–564 m (Fischer, 1928).

DISTRIBUTION.   Iceland (Wesenberg-Lund, 1939); Scandinavia (Koren & Danielssen, 1875; Norman, 1894; Théel, 1905; Wesenberg-Lund, 1930, 1939); North Sea (Southern, 1913b; Fischer, 1925, 1928; Stephen, 1934; Murina, 1968); Mediterranean (Stephen, 1958; Murina, 1964c).

GENUS *PHASCOLION* Théel, 1875

Phascolion Théel, 1875b : 13; Selenka & de Man, 1883 : 41.

DESCRIPTION.   Small sipunculans that usually inhabit the shells of gastropods or scaphopods and sometimes the tubes of annelids or empty burrows in coral rock. Trunk usually spirally coiled and showing a marked asymmetry in the arrangement of the nephridial and reproductive systems.   Tentacles arranged in a single row around the mouth and a zone of small hooks or spines may be present on the introvert.   On the trunk of most species there is a zone of 'adhesive' or 'attaching' papillae with hardened, horny or chitinous (?) rims which project forward and serve to anchor the worm in its shell; the rim may be rounded, truncate or horse-shoe shaped and may possess one or more teeth.   Only one nephridium, usually the right, is present.   The gonad develops on the right side at the base of the ventral retractor. One or two retractor muscles; if two, the dorsal is usually larger than the ventral. Musculature of the body wall continuous.   Alimentary canal tends to form a number of loops rather than a series of spirals.   Rectum long and a rectal caecum may be present.   Contractile vessel usually simple.

TYPE SPECIES.   *Sipunculus strombi* Montagu, 1804.

REMARKS.   Sometimes a species which usually lives in a shell may establish itself in sand or mud and then present a slightly different appearance.   This fact may account for some of the specific and subspecific descriptions that have been made.   *P. strombi* is the best known species and has a wide geographic and bathymetric range.

We have listed 34 species for the genus.   Of these 12 are known only from single specimens.   *P. mogadorense* Sluiter, 1912 described from off Mogador, Morocco we consider to be identical with *P. hirondellei* Sluiter, 1900 described from off Gascony, France.   Because some of the species can be distinguished only by characters of slight to doubtful systematic importance we have thought it advisable to give, as well as a key, a list of the species arranged according to the number of retractor muscles that they possess and the presence or absence of adhesive papillae and introvert hooks.

GROUP 1 – Species with one retractor muscle and with introvert hooks.

Adhesive papillae present

P. collare Selenka & de Man
P. ikedai Sato
P. pacificum Murina
P. robertsoni Stephen & Robertson
P. tridens Selenka & de Man
P. valdiviae Fischer

Adhesive papillae absent

P. moskalevi Murina

GROUP 2 – Species with one retractor muscle but no introvert hooks.

Adhesive papillae present

P. murrayi Stephen
P. sumatrense Fischer

Adhesive papillae absent

P. dogieli Murina
P. hupferi Fischer
P. lutense Selenka
P. manceps Selenka & de Man
P. rectum Ikeda

GROUP 3 – Species with two retractor muscles and with introvert hooks.

Adhesive papillae present

P. abnorme Fischer
P. africanum Fischer
P. alberti Sluiter
P. brotzkajae Murina
P. convestitum Sluiter
P. dentalicolum Sato
P. hedraeum Selenka & de Man
P. heteropapillosum Wesenberg-Lund

Adhesive papillae absent

P. beklemischevi Murina
P. lucifugax Selenka & de Man
P. pallidum Koren & Danielssen
P. pharetratum Sluiter
P. tuberculosum Théel

P. hirondellei Sluiter
P. mediterraneum Fischer
P. parvum Sluiter
P. strombi (Montagu)
P. tubiculum Verrill

GROUP 4 – Species with two retractor muscles but without hooks.
Adhesive papillae present
P. artificiosum Ikeda
P. botulum Selenka

DISTRIBUTION. Species have been reported from most seas, including Arctic and Antarctic waters, and a number have been dredged at considerable depths, e.g. *P. pacificum* at 6156–6860 m (Murina, 1957) and *P. lutense* at 3506–7340 m (Murina, 1957, 1961).

GENUS PHASCOLION—KEY TO SPECIES

1   One retractor muscle   2
–   Two retractor muscles   15
2   Introvert with hooks or spines   3
–   Introvert without hooks or spines   9
3   Adhesive papillae present   4
–   Adhesive papillae absent (anterior hooks in rows, 5–10 tentacles and no papillae between hooks; trunk elongate with mamillate papillae on its anterior surface; retractor arises from two small roots in anterior quarter of trunk; rectal caecum very small, nephridium short and free)   .   .   .   .   **P. moskalevi** (p. 183)
4   Adhesive papillae with rounded, horny tips   5
–   Adhesive papillae with pointed tips   6
5   Papillae at base of introvert with chitinous tips (rectractor with single root fixed at posterior extremity of trunk)   .   .   .   .   .   **P. robertsoni** (p. 187)
–   Papillae at base of introvert without chitinous tips (retractor with a branching root arises at posterior extremity of trunk, 20–22 intestinal convolutions, large rectal caecum, nephridium arises posterior to anus)   .   .   **P. valdiviae** (p. 191)
6   Some adhesive papillae with three points or teeth (contractile vessel with short, thick 'swellings')   .   .   .   .   **P. tridens** (p. 189)
–   No adhesive papillae with three points but with only one point   7
7   Nephridiopore placed well in front of the anus   8
–   Nephridiopore placed just posterior to anus (papillae at base of introvert with horny tips, intestine coils only slightly, nephridium fixed)   .   **P. collare** (p. 173)
8   No rectal caecum present (retractor with two roots, long nephridium fixed by stout muscles, no tentacles)   .   .   .   .   **P. ikedai** (p. 179)
–   Rectal caecum present (retractor with three roots, short nephridium fixed for its whole length)   .   .   .   .   **P. pacificum** (p. 184)
9   Adhesive papillae present   10
–   Adhesive papillae absent   11
10 Adhesive papillae obliquely truncated with an untoothed chitinous rim which may be horse shoe-shaped   .   .   .   .   **P. murrayi** (p. 183)
–   Adhesive papillae large, with strong chitinous rim often with two points or teeth (anus opens in front of nephridiopore, no rectal caecum)   .   **P. sumatrense** (p. 191)

11 Nephridiopore placed just anterior to anus (retractor with single root, posterior papillae flat, squarish and arranged in longitudinal rows) . ***P. dogieli*** (p. 176)
– Nephridiopore placed posterior to anus 12
12 Introvert retractor with two or more roots 13
– Introvert retractor without roots 14
13 Nephridium fixed to body wall for its entire length (retractor arises posteriorly from several roots, up to 16 tentacles; papillae posteriorly bear 'villus-like' bodies) . . . . ***P. lutense*** (p. 180)
– Nephridium free for its entire length (retractor arises posteriorly from two short roots, about 10 filamentous tentacles) . . . . . . ***P. rectum*** (p. 186)
14 Nephridium long and free (contractile vessel long with tubules along its whole length, anus placed far forward on the introvert, papillae dome-shaped with blunted points and with numerous horny warts on the basal half)
P. manceps (p. 181)
– Nephridium short and attached posteriorly, (contractile vessel without tubules, retractor muscle arises from middle part of the trunk and anus far forward, 40 tentacles) . . . . ***P. hupferi*** (p. 179)
15 Hooks present on introvert 16
Hooks absent from introvert 32
16 Adhesive papillae present 17
– Adhesive papillae absent 29
17 Nephridiopore placed well in front of anal aperture (anus in middle of trunk, adhesive papillae dark, semicircular and chitinized; 30–35 tentacles and peg-like introvert hooks; one of retractors with two roots and nephridium fastened with six to eight strands) . . . . ***P. abnorme*** (p. 169)
– Nephridiopore placed at same level or behind the anal aperture (anus anteriorly placed on trunk) 18
18 Hardened rim of adhesive papillae bear one or more points or teeth . . 19
– Hardened rim of adhesive papillae rounded, dome-like, semi-lunar or horse shoe-shaped and lacking teeth 23
19 Papillae at base of introvert and near anus tall, thread-like and several mm long (40 tentacles; papillae dome-shaped with anteriorly directed teeth; nephridiopore well posterior to anus, nephridium free for its posterior half) ***P. hirondellei*** (p. 178)
– Papillae at base of introvert not thread like 20
20 Some adhesive papillae with two or three teeth 21
– Adhesive papillae with single anteriorly directed points 22
21 Introvert retractors arise from about the middle of the trunk (nephridium arises at about the same level as anus) . . . . . ***P. parvum*** (p. 185)
– Introvert retractors arise from posterior region of the trunk (nephridium short, fixed for its whole length and opening some distance posterior to anus)
P. tubiculum (p. 190)
22 Rectal caecum present (14–26 tentacles, hooks slender, nephridiopore placed posterior to anus) . . . . ***P. strombi*** (p. 187)
– Rectal caecum absent (hooks slender and bent, nephridiopore placed posterior to anus) . . . . ***P. alberti*** (p. 170)
23 Anterior region of trunk bears a number of papillae shaped like a four-armed cross (nephridium lies just posterior to anus; adhesive papillae with single pointed tooth) . . . . ***P. convestitum*** (p. 175)
– No papillae shaped like a four-armed cross present on trunk 24
24 Rectal caecum present 25
– Rectal caecum absent 27
25 Introvert-hooks long and sharp (introvert as long as the trunk, about 20 tentacles, two long retractors separated for most of their length, nephridium fixed)
P. dentalicolum (p. 176)

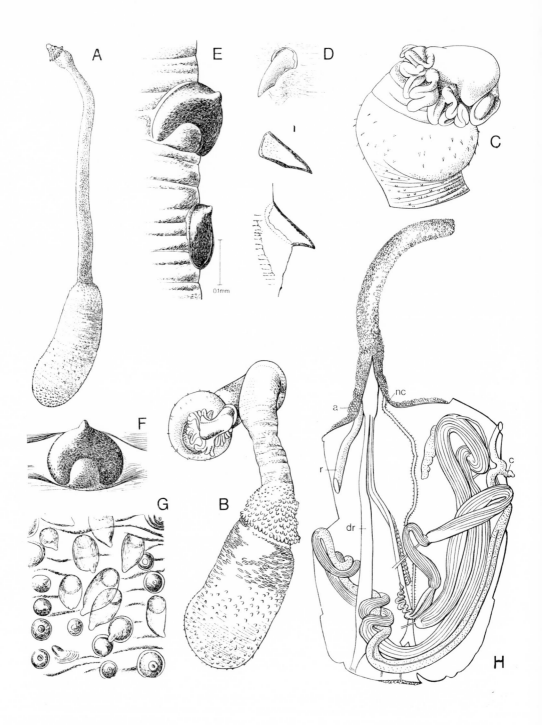

–	Introvert-hooks short and stumpy	26
26	Posterior papillae of trunk finger-like (dorsal retractor with two long roots, adhesive papillae half-moon shaped) . . . . . ***P. brotzkajae*** (p. 172)	
–	Posterior papillae of trunk flask-shaped (20 tentacles, hooks bent and nephridium free) . . . . ***P. mediterraneum*** (p. 181)	
27	Introvert-hooks blunt (25 filiform tentacles, ventral retractor arises from posterior end of trunk from a broad root that forms a semicircle about the terminal plate, no rectal caecum) . . . . . . ***P. heteropapillosum*** (p. 177)	
–	Introvert-hooks sharp	28
28	Contractile vessel simple (30 long tentacles, hooks bent, each retractor with two roots, short nephridium fixed to body wall for its whole length) ***P. hedraeum*** (p. 177)	
–	Contractile vessel wanting (21–23 short tentacles, ventral retractor with two roots) ***P. africanum*** (p. 170)	
29	Tentacles present	30
–	Tentacles absent and replaced by an oral disc . . ***P. beklemischevi*** (p. 172)	
30	Retractor muscles arise from middle of trunk (introvert-hooks with rounded extremity, retractors joined for much of their length) . . ***P. pharetratum*** (p. 186)	
–	Retractor muscles arise from posterior part of trunk	31
31	Introvert hooks sharply pointed, bent and lying in four rows . ***P. pallidum*** (p. 184)	
–	Introvert hooks blunt and not in four rows	32
32	Tentacles, 15 and stumpy; rectal caecum present . ***P. tuberculosum*** (p. 190)	
–	Tentacles, 40–45 and long; rectal caecum absent (nephridium half as long as trunk and free) . . . . ***P. lucifugax*** (p. 180)	
33	Nephridium, half as long as trunk and fixed (dorsal retractor with five roots; no hooks, few tentacles) . . . . ***P. botulum*** (p. 173)	
–	Nephridium, elongate and free (dorsal retractor with two roots; no hooks, ten tentacles) . . . . ***P. artificiosum*** (p. 171)	

Phascolion abnorme Fischer, 1895

Phascolion abnorme Fischer, 1895 : 15–16, text-fig. 12.

TYPE LOCALITY. Cape Agulhas Bank, Cape Province.

DESCRIPTION. Introvert longer than the trunk, yellow in colour; covered with irregularly spaced, peg-like hooks like those of *P. collare*. Thirty to thirty-five tentacles. Trunk 1·5 mm in length, 5 mm broad; the dorsal side is somewhat darker than the transparent ventral side. Anteriorly, there is a yellowish band about 1 mm wide which bears small closely packed papillae. This is followed by a zone about 2·5 mm wide which is sharply marked off from the first with clearly larger and more closely packed papillae. Behind this portion the papillae are the same in form and density as on the first part. On the posterior half attaching papillae are present; they are as large as the papillae in the anterior ring and their periphery is bounded by a dark, circular, chitinous ring. The last 2–3 mm bear no

FIG. 20. (A–G) *Phascolion strombi.* (A) Entire animal removed from shell. (B) Entire animal removed from shell; specimen from near South Georgia. (C) Anterior region of introvert (part of the oesophagus is protruding). (D) Different views of the introvert hooks. (E–F) Different views of the horse-shoe shaped papillae from the trunk; (E) and (F) are to the same scale. (G) Skin from the anterior region of the trunk. (H) Dissected specimen. (A–G after Théel.) KEY: *See* Fig. 11, p. 83.

M

papillae but the skin is made to appear reticulate by longitudinal and transverse ridges.   Two retractors; one is broad and springs from the posterior end of the trunk and the other arises a few mm behind the first one from near the nerve cord.   The long oesophagus is attached to the root of the smaller retractor and bears two long thin contractile vessels.   The gut is very like that of *P. lutense* and has about 20 spirals; it is fixed by the strong spindle muscle behind the root of the dorsal retractor. Another fixing muscle arises from the first coil.   The anus opens in the middle of the trunk.   The short nephridium opens well in front of the anus, is on the right side of the trunk and is fixed by six to eight mesenteries.

REMARKS.   Known only from the holotype.

DISTRIBUTION.   As for the type locality.

Phascolion africanum Fischer, 1923

Phascolion africanum Fischer, 1923a : 5; Wesenberg-Lund, 1963 : 134–135.

TYPE LOCALITY.   Cape Infante, Cape Province, 3 miles from land; at 62 m.

DESCRIPTION.   The introvert, 11 mm in length, carries 21–23 short tentacles arranged in a circle; behind these is a zone of irregularly arranged blunt hooks, like those of *P. strombi*.   Apart from the middle portion where it is lighter and more rose-brown in colour the introvert is grey to blackish-grey.   It is covered with small, darkish coloured papillae, arranged in circular bands, being most evident in the middle lighter portion.   Trunk 23 mm in length; its anterior third is also grey to dark grey, then lighter and finally yellowish-white.   In the grey part the skin is opaque, firm and thickly covered with spherical ellipsoidal papillae.   In the remaining two thirds it is transparent and the papillae are larger and more scattered. In the mid-portion there is a zone of attaching papillae.   These are light and transparent and have a semi-circular cap, visible to the naked eye.   Two retractors, a broad dorsal attached to the posterior end of the trunk and a thinner ventral one with two roots set at different levels and not close to the dorsal.   The nerve cord lies between them.   The retractors unite in the middle of the introvert.   The gonad extends from the base of the right root of the ventral retractor almost to the base of the dorsal retractor.   No contractile vessel.

REMARKS.   Described from one specimen.   Wesenberg-Lund reported three more specimens but on account of the poor state of the material she was unable to add to the description.

DISTRIBUTION.   Cape Province, Cape Infante (Fischer, 1923); Table Bay (Wesenberg-Lund, 1963).

Phascolion alberti Sluiter, 1900

Phascolion alberti Sluiter, 1900 : 9–10, pl. 1, figs 1–2, pl. 3, figs 1–2; 1912 : 17–18; Gerould, 1913 : 416; Murina, 1964c : 63–65, fig. 12.

TYPE LOCALITY.   Newfoundland, Princess Alice station 161; at 1267 m.

DESCRIPTION. Introvert about two thirds as long as the trunk; anteriorly it carries a few irregularly scattered hooks, which are long, thin and slightly bent. Trunk up to 30 mm in length and yellowish-grey in colour. The papillae on the anterior portion of the trunk, at the base of the introvert and near the anus, are never filiform like those of *P. hirondellei*. A few larger papillae with chitinous teeth are scattered over the middle of the trunk. The posterior part of the trunk has only papillae without teeth, oval in form and with small chitinous plates surrounding the central orifice. Anatomy much as in *P. hirondellei*. The gut extends to the hind end of the trunk and as usual has irregular spirals. One nephridium which opens just posterior to the anus. One pair of unequal retractors; the ventral is much weaker than the dorsal and divides just before attachment into two short roots.

REMARKS. Described originally from numerous specimens living in the shells of *Siphonorbis lachesis* and *Pleurotoma fulvocincta*. Sluiter (1912) reported two more specimens which were exactly the same as those described in his first paper. Gerould (1913) merely quoted Sluiter's record from Newfoundland. Redescribed by Murina (1964c).

DISTRIBUTION. Coasts of Newfoundland and off Cape Finistère (Sluiter, 1900); off Bear Island (Sluiter, 1912); Adriatic and Aegan Seas (Murina, 1964c).

Phascolion artificiosum Ikeda, 1904

(Fig. 21A)

Phascolion artificiosus Ikeda, 1904 : 18–20, text-figs 50–55; Sato, 1939 : 413.

TYPE LOCALITY. Sagami Bay, Japan; at 700 m.

DESCRIPTION Introvert about half as long as the trunk and 2 mm in diameter. The papillae at its base are conical and similar to those on the body; in the mid region of the trunk they are transparent and have rounded tips. Hooks and spines wanting. Tentacles about 10 and simple. Trunk, about 15 mm long and 3·5 mm in diameter, forms a spiral covered with blue-grey or blue-black papillae. Papillae are closely distributed over the whole surface and vary much in shape and size on various parts of the body. The largest, the attaching papillae, are present in a narrow zone round the middle of the posterior part of the body. Here they are low and conical. The dark coloured apical portion is more or less laterally compressed so as to be flattened. The largest are 0·1–0·2 mm across the base and 0·08–0·15 mm in height. On the remaining parts of the body and at the anterior end they are generally conical. In the middle region they do not exceed 0·05 mm in diameter and height. At the posterior end they are somewhat larger measuring about 0·1 mm in height and are pyriform. In the extreme anterior region they become digitiform processes about 0·07 mm in height and 0·04 mm in thickness. Two retractors, one very small and one very large; the large one has two roots and arises near the posterior end of the body while the small thin one, also with two small roots, arises more anteriorly. Intestinal coil consists of a few irregular spirals without muscles of any sort.   One nephridium arising on the right side of the nerve cord is an elongate sac and is free.

REMARKS   Described originally from two specimens.   Sato (1939) repeated the original record.

DISTRIBUTION.   As for the type locality.

Phascolion beklemischevi Murina, 1964

Phascolion beklemischevi Murina, 1964c : 65–68, figs 14–15.

TYPE LOCALITY.   South-west Mediterranean, off Alexandria.

DESCRIPTION.   Introvert 3 mm long and 0·2 mm wide and about the same length as the trunk; tentacles absent and mouth surrounded by an oral disc or ridge. Hooks about 0·045 mm tall and with base of 0·035 mm; tip single-pointed and slightly bent.   Two eye-spots.   Trunk short, sac-like and curved in its middle, 4 mm long and 0·5 mm wide; white, shiny and semi-transparent.   At the base of the introvert there is a region of large, transparent papillae, 0·05–0·065 mm tall and 0·035–0·04 mm wide, each bell-like in shape.   Papillae not present in the middle of the trunk and holding papillae absent.   Longitudinal musculature continuous. Two retractors arise at the posterior end of the trunk.   Intestine with two long loops and a short spiral of four twists; one loop is fixed by a short and the other a long fixing muscle.   Rectum long, extends the whole length of the body cavity and opens about 0·8 mm anterior to the nephridiopore.   Wing muscle not prominent. Contractile vessel thin and hardly distinguishable.   A single nephridium with a narrow neck.

REMARKS.   Described from a single specimen.   The species is allied to *P. lucifugux* Sel. & Bülow.

DISTRIBUTION.   As for the holotype.

Phascolion brotzkajae Murina, 1964

Phascolion brotzkajae Murina, 1964c : 68–70, figs 16a–c, fig. 17.

TYPE LOCALITY.   'Academie Kovaleskii', station 221.   Eastern Mediterranean (39°51'3"N, 25°32'5"E).

DESCRIPTION.   The specimen was stick-like in shape and tapering posteriorly. Introvert, partly invaginated, is estimated to be about 5·5 mm long and about 0·25–0·30 mm wide and longer than the trunk; light yellow in colour.   Anteriorly it is armed with randomly arranged hooks of height 0·02–0·04 mm and of width 0·005–0 030 mm, those nearer the mouth being larger.   Papillae in the mid region of the introvert are 0·01–0·015 mm high.   At the base they are conical and transparent, 0·02–0·025 mm tall and 0·025–0·02 mm in diameter.   Trunk yellow, 4·1 mm long and 0·5 mm wide; anteriorly covered with flat, round-oval skin bodies 0·01–0·015 mm in diameter.   A zone placed about 1 mm posterior to the anus bears a large number of holding papillae, half-moon or horse-shoe-shaped, of height 0·06–

0·075 mm and width 0·045–0·065 mm. Posteriorly the papillae are finger-like of height 0·02–0·025 mm and diameter 0·010 mm. Tentacles and eye-spots absent. Musculature continuous. Two retractors; the dorsal has two roots but the ventral which is narrower and fastened more anteriorly arises from only one root. The oesophagus is about one third as long as the retractor and the intestine consists of two loops, the second larger than the first. Both loops are fastened with fixing muscles. Another muscle fixes the lowest loop where it becomes the rectum and seems to correspond to a spindle muscle. A large rectal caecum present. Wing muscle absent. Contractile vessel simple. The single nephridium is shaped like a drop and opens posterior to the anus.

REMARKS. Described from a single specimen.

DISTRIBUTION. As for the type locality.

Phascolion botulum Selenka, 1885

Phascolion botulus Selenka, 1885 : 18, pl. 4, fig. 20.

TYPE LOCALITY. South-western Pacific. 4°21′S, 129°7′E; at 2606 m. *Type*. British Museum (Nat. Hist.) no. 1885.12.3.24.

DESCRIPTION. No hooks on the introvert. Tentacles few and small. Body 20 mm long. Attaching papillae on the posterior third of the body; easily distinguished by their dark colour. Two retractor muscles arise in front of the hind end of the body, one very strong, the other very weak; the base of the strong one is divided into five roots. The intestine consists of three folds, an ascending loop, a descending loop and a spiral of only two or three coils. Nephridium half the length of the body and fixed.

REMARKS. Known only from the holotype. Found in the shell of *Dentalium*.

DISTRIBUTION. As for the type locality.

Phascolion collare Selenka & de Man, 1883

(Fig. 21C)

Phascolion collare Selenka & de Man, 1883: 45–46, pl. 6, figs 71–74; Fischer, 1922c : 12.

TYPE LOCALITY. Philippines.

DESCRIPTION. Introvert about as long as the trunk, with an anterior zone of small irregularly scattered hooks, spine-like in form. Trunk about 25 mm long. Skin thin, transparent and covered with irregularly-scattered papillae which are less prominent on the middle of the trunk where they are a little lighter in colour. Between the anus and the base of the introvert there is a zone of larger, red-brown, dome-shaped papillae with rounded points; anteriorly these papillae become much smaller. On the posterior end of the trunk the papillae carry horny tips On the upper surface of the spirally coiled trunk they are larger and appear as isolated papillae. On the under side they are smaller, three-cornered, and two or three may lie close together. All the horny tips are directed backwards. A single re-

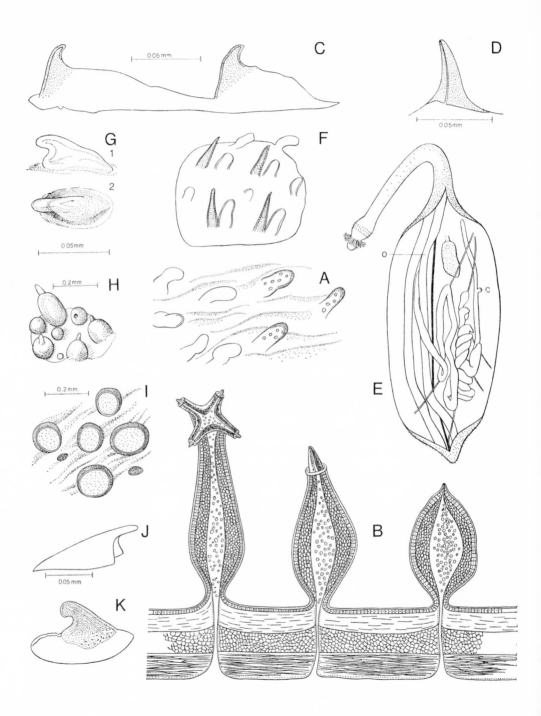

tractor is inserted at the posterior end of the trunk. Contractile vessel short. Intestine in the form of one or two loose loops which are fixed by many mesenteries. One nephridium half the length of the body, fixed for the whole of its length and opening just posterior to the anus.

REMARKS. Described from several specimens. No rectal caecum is shown in fig. 71 of Selenka (1883).

DISTRIBUTION. Philippines (Selenka & de Man, 1883); Zanzibar Channel (Fischer, 1922c).

Phascolion convestitum Sluiter, 1902

(Fig. 21B)

Phascolion convestitus Sluiter, 1902 : 32–33, text-fig. 1, pl. 3, figs 6–9.

TYPE LOCALITY. Malaya; Siboga station 105; at 275 m.

DESCRIPTION. The introvert up to about 15 mm, somewhat longer than the body, with numerous irregularly situated, broad hooks, 0·075 mm in height. Trunk up to 12 mm in length and 4 mm in thickness; sometimes strongly curved but usually spirally rolled. On the middle and posterior part of the trunk are strong attaching papillae; the other papillae are only visible under strong magnification. Anteriorly, characteristic tab-like papillae present, the largest is 1 mm in height and at its apex has a four-armed cross, which can be retracted. Single pointed papillae are also present. Between these two types ovoid papillae occur on the trunk; in the middle they are long and round with a diameter of 0·14 mm. On the hinder part of the mid-trunk are stronger papillae 0·275 mm broad, which have a strongly chitinized edge but no point. Two strong, very long retractor muscles spring from the extreme end of the trunk. The intestine is in the form of open spirals bound by numerous mesenteries; free posteriorly. A single nephridium on the left side opens several mm posterior to the anus.

REMARKS. Known only from the holotype.

DISTRIBUTION. As for the type locality.

FIG. 21.   (A) *Phascolion artificiosum*. Papillae from the posterior end of the body (after Ikeda).   (B) *Phascolion convestitum*. Papillae from the anterior region of the body (after Sluiter).   (C) *Phascolion collare*. Hooks from the introvert (after Selenka). (D–E) *Phascolion dentalicolum*.   (D) A spine from the anterior region of the introvert. (E) Dissected specimen.   (D–E after Sato.)   (F) *Phascolion hedraeum*.   Introvert spines (after Selenka).   (G–I) *Phascolion heteropapillosum*.   (G) Two views of the introvert hook. (H) Papillae from the base of the introvert.   (I) Papillae from the middle of the trunk. (G–I after Wesenberg-Lund.)   (J) *Phascolion ikedai*. A spine from the anterior region of the introvert (after Sato).   (K) *Phascolion lucifugax*. Hook from the introvert (after Selenka). KEY: *See* Fig. 11, p. 83.

Phascolion dentalicolum Sato, 1937

(Fig. 21D–E)

Phascolion dentalicola Sato, 1937a : 165–167, pl. 4, figs 20–21, text-figs 10–14; Sato, 1939 : 413.

TYPE LOCALITY. Onagawa Bay, Japan; at 23 m.

DESCRIPTION. Introvert, length about that of the trunk and width about 1 mm. Papillae, cylindrical, but very small. A group of small spines is present anteriorly. About 20 tentacles arranged in a circle. Trunk nearly straight, up to 30 mm long and about 3 mm wide; yellowish-grey in life. Introvert base deep brown, covered with numerous papillae. On the middle of the trunk the papillae are low and conical and appear like 'attaching papillae'; the dark-coloured apical part is somewhat flattened, being laterally compressed. Two long, thin retractors arise from the extreme posterior end of the trunk but do not unite till near the introvert. About 15 irregularly twisted intestinal spirals, not accompanied by a spindle muscle. The convolutions are fixed by five, fine fixing-muscles one of which is attached to the posterior end and the four others to the beginning and middle of the coils. A simple contractile vessel runs along the dorsal side of the oesophagus. A small rectal caecum present. The nephridium is a single sac placed on the right side of the nerve cord and is fixed by several stout muscle fibres; it opens posterior to the anus.

REMARKS. Based originally on numerous examples inhabiting shells of *Dentalium*. Sato (1939) merely repeated the original record. Sato (1937 : 167) points out that the species closely resemble *P. mediterraneum* Fischer, 1922.

DISTRIBUTION. As for the type locality.

Phascolion dogieli Murina, 1964

Phascolion dogieli Murina, 1964c : 70–71, figs 18–20.

TYPE LOCALITY. 'Academia Kovaleskii', station 416. Eastern Mediterranean (31°38'8"N, 32°23'7"E).

DESCRIPTION. Introvert, length 10 mm and about seven times as long as the trunk; hooks absent and no information about the tentacles was able to be given. Colour yellow but base of introvert and posterior part of trunk darker. Trunk pyriform in shape; 1·4 mm long and maximum width 1 mm. Covered with numerous, densely packed, brown papillae. Posteriorly they are flat, square, strongly chitinized plates that are arranged in longitudinal rows. Close to the posterior region of the trunk the plates are larger and more elongate. Longitudinal musculature continuous. A single retractor which arises from the posterior body wall. Intestine consists of four spirals, the last one fastened by a short, strong fixing muscle. Rectum long, thin and slightly twisted. No wing muscle and no caecum. Nephridium single, opening at about 1 mm anterior to the anus, extending to the posterior extremity of the trunk and free.

REMARKS. Described from two specimens.

DISTRIBUTION. Known from two localities in the eastern Mediterranean.

Phascolion hedraeum Selenka & de Man, 1883

(Fig. 21F)

Phascolion hedraeum Selenka & de Man, 1883 : 49–50, pl. 6, figs 87–92; Fischer, 1895 : 17, figs 19–21.

TYPE LOCALITY. Rio de Janeiro, Brazil.   In the shell of *Dentalium*.

DESCRIPTION.   Introvert half as long as or somewhat longer than the trunk. Anterior end swollen, ball-shaped, carrying a few slightly bent hooks and about 30 fairly long tentacles.   Trunk 12 mm in length, cylindrical and elongate; dusky blue-grey in colour but somewhat yellowish posteriorly.   Most of the body is covered with yellowish, broad, rounded spines.   They are absent from the posterior end and on the anterior fifth of the trunk where only skin bodies are seen.   Tall cylindrical papillae present in front of the anus becoming smaller towards the introvert.   Two retractors of equal size and both with two roots, arise from the posterior end of the trunk.   The nerve cord reaches to the roots of the ventral retractor and splits into two or three branches which are attached to the trunk wall.   Contractile vessel short and simple.   About 20 intestinal convolutions, fixed posteriorly by a fixing mesentery.   Three other fixing muscles present.   A single short nephridium, fixed to the trunk wall for its whole length by mesenteries.

REMARKS.   Based on the holotype.   Fischer (1895) gives a full description of the single specimen found in the collections of the Hamburg Museum.

DISTRIBUTION.   Brazil (Selenka & de Man, 1883); South Japan (Fischer, 1895).

Phascolion heteropapillosum Wesenberg-Lund, 1963

(Fig. 21G–I)

Phascolion heteropapillosum Wesenberg-Lund, 1963 : 135–138, text-figs 11–12.

TYPE LOCALITY.   South African coast, 33°58·5′S, 25°42·0′E; at 27 m.

DESCRIPTION.   Introvert 12 mm in length, paler than the trunk and smooth; posterior to the tentacles is a girdle of 6–7 irregular rings of minute hooks, directed backwards.   Their free end is blunt and only slightly raised above the gland to which they are attached.   About 25 long filiform tentacles.   Papillae on its base like those on the fore part of the trunk.   Trunk 9 mm in length, whitish-grey in alcohol.   On the fore part the papillae are densely crowded, vesiculous and lemon-shaped and have a rather small, blunt, erect, sharply demarcated, central tip. Behind this girdle is an area of nearly circular glandular bodies, which are capped with a slightly darker, chitinous ring.   Scattered amongst these are some smaller ones lacking the chitinous border and which may be regarded as homologous with the normal attaching papillae.   More posteriorly, the surface is densely covered with small rectangular areas formed by the intersection of deep longitudinal and circular, pigmented furrows.   Each rectangle carries one to three papillae which have a circular base and a high conical or cylindrical process.   At the posterior end of the trunk the skin is thick, tough and opaque with numerous flat, circular or ellipsoidal bodies. The whole area looks like a flat oval plate, which forms the base of the trunk. Longitudinal muscles continuous, except in the anterior portion where they tend to split into bands. Two retractors. The ventral has a broad root and arises from the extreme posterior end of the trunk, surrounding the terminal plate in a semi-circle. The dorsal is much slenderer and narrower and arises from two roots a short distance in front of the root of the ventral. No caecum. The single nephridium is short, sac-like, and opens far behind the anus.

REMARKS. Known only from the holotype.

DISTRIBUTION. As for the type locality.

Phascolion hirondellei Sluiter, 1900

Phascolion hirondellei Sluiter, 1900 : 7–9, pl. 2, figs 1–6; 1912 : 17; Leroy, 1936 : 425.
Phascolion mogadorense Sluiter, 1912 : 18–19.

TYPE LOCALITY. Gulf of Gascony.

DESCRIPTION. Introvert short, not more than a quarter as long as the trunk; no true papillae but only very small, ellipsoidal, cuticular bodies arranged in transverse rows. On the anterior portion there are a few small hooks with bent points. About 40 short tentacles. Trunk 32 mm in length, 6 mm in diameter and yellow-grey in colour. It is covered with papillae which vary in different parts. On the anterior portion, on the introvert base and near the anus they are tall and thread-like and several millimetres in length. Between these they are club-shaped and about as long as they are broad. In the middle of the trunk they become dome-like with a circular base and a free, brown point which is bent forwards. The posterior portion bears papillae which greatly resemble those on the middle of the trunk except that they are smaller. One pair of long, thin retractors, the dorsal being much the weaker. The ventral retractor divides into two short roots just before its attachment to the posterior part of the trunk. The dorsal retractors unite at about the level of the base of the introvert. The nerve cord does not extend much beyond the insertion of the ventral retractor. The gut extends to the end of the trunk; it coils irregularly and is fixed at several points by mesenteries. Spindle muscle absent. The rectum is fixed by wing muscles. The nephridium arises about 5 mm behind the anus and is free for its posterior half.

REMARKS. Described originally from several specimens. Sluiter (1912) listed all the stations at which the species was taken during the 'Monaco' investigations but added nothing to his original description.

P. mogadorense Sluiter, 1912 was described from a single specimen collected off Mogador, Morocco at a depth of 2165 m. Sluiter stated that it was closely related to and might by synonymous with *P. hirondellei* Sluiter, 1900. The differences between the two species are so slight that we are regarding them as identical.

DISTRIBUTION. Taken at a number of stations in the North Atlantic in the area of the Azores at depths from 510 m to 2100 m.

Phascolion hupferi Fischer, 1895

Phascolion hupferi Fischer, 1895 : 16–17, figs 16–18; 1914a : 77.

TYPE LOCALITY. West Africa.

DESCRIPTION. Introvert yellowish in colour and covered with closely packed papillae which are smaller than those on the trunk; no hooks. About 40 tentacles, those on the dorsal side red-brown. Trunk generally dirty white in colour, yellowish to brownish anteriorly and at the base of the introvert. The musculature of the anterior part is strong but the lighter coloured part so weak that the gut is visible. The papillae on the anterior part are dark in colour, light on the rest of the trunk, and interspersed with prominent barrel-like papillae. The oesophagus is long and the digestive tract is formed into loose coils and loops, instead of the normal spiral. It is attached to a single, strong retractor which arises from the mid-portion of the trunk. A single fastening mesentery attaches the tip of the anterior loop of the gut to the trunk wall. The spindle muscle is attached near the anus and fixes the gut near the posterior end of the trunk. The nephridium is about a quarter as long as the trunk, free in its middle part, but is attached posteriorly. Anal aperture is situated anteriorly on the introvert, as in *P. manceps*. Contractile vessel, however, lacks the long tubules that are found in the latter species.

REMARKS. Described originally from several specimens. Fischer (1914) only repeated the original record, giving a very brief summary of the specific characters.

DISTRIBUTION. Western Africa, several localities.

Phascolion ikedai Sato, 1930

(Fig. 21J)

Phascolion ikedai Sato, 1930 : 20–23, pl. 3, figs 13–17, text-figs 6–9; 1937a : 163–165, pl. 4, figs 18–19, text-fig. 9; 1939 : 413.

TYPE LOCALITY. Mutsu Bay, Japan; at 55 m.

DESCRIPTION. Introvert about two-thirds as long as the trunk; with cylindrical papillae much smaller than those on the rest of the body. A group of small spines near the anterior end; no tentacles. Trunk about 7 mm in length and covered with a great number of large flat papillae. Papillae on the anterior third of the trunk are exceedingly large being 0·05–0·1 mm in height and 0·09–0·35 mm in width; 40–80 of these papillae from the attaching papillae. The papillae on the introvert base, like those on the introvert, are the smallest, each being closely beset with numerous polygonal plates. At the base of the introvert the papillae are arranged in more or less regular rows and measure about 0·035–0·02 mm in height and 0·08–0·015 mm across the base. The papillae on the convex side of the trunk bear a large spine and those on the concave side a small spine. The papillae near the mid-ventral line are entirely devoid of spines. One retractor muscle with two short roots arises from near the posterior end of the body. The intestinal convolutions consist of a few irregular spirals. One very large nephridium on the right side of the nerve cord is fixed by several stout muscles and opens far anteriorly to the anus.

REMARKS. Described originally from numerous specimens. Sato (1937) gave a very brief description of numerous specimens collected in Onagawa Bay. In 1939 he only repeated the earlier records.

DISTRIBUTION. Mutsu and Onagawa Bay, Japan (Sato, as above).

Phascolion lucifugax Selenka & de Man, 1883

(Fig. 21K)

Phascolion lucifugax Selenka & de Man, 1883 : 43–44, pl. 5, figs 64–66; Sato, 1939 : 413.

TYPE LOCALITY. Bohol. Philippines.

DESCRIPTION. Introvert somewhat shorter than the trunk, blue-grey in colour; its surface appears smooth although thickly-crowded skin-bodies present which do not attain to the size of papillae. Anteriorly there is a short zone of scattered hooks, each of which is brown in colour, straight, stoutly built, with a thick rounded extremity. Forty to forty-five large finger-like tentacles. Trunk pale reddish-grey in colour, up to 20 mm in length. Covered with large, scattered, dome-shaped papillae, which are flattened at their apex. On the inner surface of the coiled trunk and at the hind end papillae are much scarcer or absent. Between the anus and the ntrovert they are more crowded. The musculature is stronger on the introvert than on the trunk. Two retractors arise at about the same level near the hind end of the trunk; they join far forward in the introvert. The nerve cord does not lie between the roots. A simple contractile vessel. No spindle muscle, but a fixing mesentery arises near the rectum and is attached posteriorly; branches are given off to the oesophagus at the level where it joins the intestine. The rectum is attached by numerous mesenteries. One nephridium about half as long as the trunk opens posterior to the anus and is free. In young specimens the nephridium is very short.

REMARKS. Based originally on several specimens. It is free-living at first but later occupies the shells of various species of gastropod.

DISTRIBUTION. Philippines, Japan (Selenka & de Man, 1883).

Phascolion lutense Selenka, 1885

(Fig. 22A–B)

Phascolion lutense Selenka, 1885 : 16–17, pl. 4, figs 22–23; Fischer, 1928b : 484; Murina, 1957a :
    1781–1790, figs 4a–b, figs 5a–d; 1961 : 140–142, fig. 1.

TYPE LOCALITY. South Pacific 53°55'S, 108°35'E; at 3568 m. *Type*. Brit. Mus. (Nat. Hist.) no. 1885.12.3.22.

DESCRIPTION. Introvert studded with numerous skin glands, similar to those on the trunk; tentacles few, at most 16 and no hooks. Trunk up to 30 mm long. Skin thin and studded with numerous skin glands which protrude as slight tubercles with chitinous borders. They are smallest at the base of the introvert and around the anus. No attaching papillae on the posterior part of the trunk. One retractor originates posteriorly in front of the hind end of the trunk and has several diverging roots. About 23 intestinal coils. One fixing muscle is attached to the oesophagus where it passes into the intestine; other fixing muscles attached to the three folded loops of the intestine and to the rectum. The nephridium is on the right side of the trunk and lies close behind the anus; it is fixed for its whole length.

REMARKS. Based originally on three specimens. Murina (1957a) has redescribed and illustrated the species.

DISTRIBUTION. South Pacific, at depths of 3568–3594 m (Selenka, 1885); Behring Sea, Aleutian, Kurile-Kamchatka and Japanese trenches in the north-west Pacific at depths of from 3506–7340 m (Murina, 1957a, 1961).

Phascolion manceps Selenka & de Man, 1883

Phascolion manceps Selenka & de Man, 1883 : 44–45, pl. 1, fig. 2, pl. 5, figs 67–70; Shipley, 1899a : 154.

TYPE LOCALITY. Uhoy, Philippines; in *Nassa* shell.

DESCRIPTION. Introvert very short and without hooks. Trunk drawn out into a very long thin portion projecting from the shell. The anus lies very far forward so that the introvert is very short. Anteriorly yellow-white in colour, posteriorly ochre yellow. The whole body is covered with characteristic dome-shaped papillae with a wart-like blunted point and with numerous horny warts on the basal half. At the hind end of the trunk the papillae are taller and more pointed. On the extended portion they become smaller and are finally hard to observe. One strong retractor, without roots, inserted at the posterior end of the trunk. Contractile vessel, long with fairly large and numerous tubules along its full length. Three fixing muscles present. One very long, free, nephridium stretching from the hind end of the trunk to near the anus.

REMARKS. Based originally on the holotype. Shipley (1897) records one very small animal, also living in a gastropod shell, which he considers belongs to this species.

DISTRIBUTION Philippines (Selenka & de Man, 1883); New Britain (Shipley, 1899).

Phascolion mediterraneum Fischer, 1922

(Fig. 22C)

Phascolion mediterraneum Fischer, 1922 : 20–22, text-figs 13–20.

TYPE LOCALITY. Sori, Villefranche, Mediterranean.

DESCRIPTION. Introvert up to 16–18 mm in length; grey-brown, darker at the base. Twenty tentacles; hooks short and bent. Papillae very numerous, but small. Trunk up to 16 mm in length; colour light yellow-brown. In a darker area at the base of the introvert, the papillae are very closely packed, flask-shaped and pointed. In the first third of the trunk they are more rounded and less numerous; in the last third of the trunk they are clearly attaching papillae like those of *P. hedraeum*.

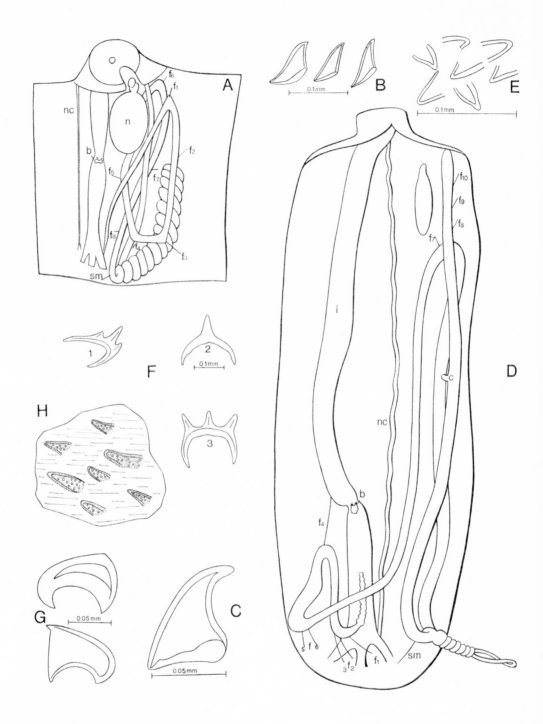

Their outer edge bears small angular plates of a dark brown colour. The posterior extremity of the trunk bears somewhat larger flask-shaped papillae. Two long, slender retractors reaching almost to the end of the trunk join in the first quarter of the trunk; the left has one root and the right two short roots. The oesophagus follows the retractors till they join. Intestine in three loops and fixed by mesenteries. The rectum has a caecum under which two of the mesenteries are fastened. The right nephridium is present and is free.

REMARKS. Based originally on several specimens.

DISTRIBUTION. As for the type locality.

Phascolion moskalevi Murina, 1964

Phascolion moskalevi Murina, 1964b : 255–256, figs 2–3.

TYPE LOCALITY. Chanzsan, Shizoto (South China Seas).

DESCRIPTION. Introvert 5 mm long and about 1 mm wide with about 5–10 yellow tentacles and numerous hooks. Anteriorly hooks arranged in about nine parallel rings but more posteriorly more irregularly; distance between rings about 0·03 mm and height of hooks 0·04 mm. No papillae between hooks. Trunk elongate, sausage-shaped and slightly curved on the ventral side; length 13 mm and maximum width 2 mm. Colour white. Papillae on the middle of the body are teat-like, 0·015–0·020 mm high and less than 0·01 mm in diameter. Fastening papillae absent. Surface of posterior region of the body appears sieve- or net-like. One retractor arising from two roots in the anterior quarter of the trunk, about 2 mm posterior to the anus. Intestinal canal consists of about 27–30 convolutions. Very small rectal caecum present but no intestinal fixing muscles. Single nephridium, short (0·5 mm), semi-transparent and free.

REMARKS. Described from a single specimen.

DISTRIBUTION. As for the type locality.

Phascolion murrayi Stephen, 1941

Phascolion murrayi Stephen, 1941a : 407, pl. 2, fig. 5.

TYPE LOCALITY. Gulf of Aden. 13°41'N, 48°17'E; at 1295 m. *Type*. Brit. Mus. (Nat. Hist.) 1952.3.25.18.

DESCRIPTION. Introvert thickly covered with small irregularly shaped papillae, scattered amongst slight cuticular ridges; hooks absent. Trunk twisted, about

---

FIG. 22. (A–B) *Phascolion lutense*. (A) Dissected specimen. (B) Spine from the introvert. (A–B after Murina.) (C) *Phascolion mediterraneum*. Hook from the introvert (after Fischer). (D–E) *Phascolion pacificum*. (D) Specimen dissected. (E) Spines from the introvert. (D–E after Murina.) (F) *Phascolion tridens*. Three holdfast papillae from the trunk; all to the same scale (after Selenka). (G) *Phascolion tuberculosum*. Hooks from the introvert (after Théel). (H) *Phascolion tubiculum*. Hooks from the introvert (after Selenka). KEY: *See* Fig. 11, p. 83.

25 to 30 mm in length; colour yellow-grey. Thickly covered with papillae, small on the anterior part, large on the posterior portion. On the anterior part they are oval in shape, of the same colour as the trunk and thickly crowded. The posterior portion is covered with attaching papillae, except for a small area at the extreme tip. These papillae have the appearance of short, stout rods, obliquely truncated at the top and having a chitinous rim of uniform thickness all round; untoothed. On some the rim is horse-shoe shaped; in others it forms a complete ring. A single retractor muscle is attached to the posterior end of the trunk.

REMARKS. Known only from the holotype.

DISTRIBUTION. As for the type locality.

Phascolion pacificum Murina, 1957

(Fig. 22D–E)

Phascolion pacificum Murina, 1957a : 1777–1781, text-figs 2a and b, 3a–e.

TYPE LOCALITY. Kurile-Kamchatka Trench.

DESCRIPTION. Introvert with small hooks and greyish-yellow in colour. Trunk small, thin, also greyish-yellow in colour. Papillae occur on the anterior and posterior eighths of the trunk, and adhesive papillae occupy the intervening area. The alimentary canal runs the full length of the trunk with only two or three coils. The spiral is small, sometimes wanting altogether. The caecum is situated a half or a third of the way from the anterior end of the trunk. A single short retractor present with three roots. The nephridium is short and fastened to the body wall for its whole length.

REMARKS. It is most closely related to *P. valdiviae* and *P. sumatrense*, especially the latter, but differs in that (1) the alimentary spiral is small, (2) the caecum is placed posteriorly and (3) the nephridium is wholly attached. Described from numerous specimens. The anal aperture is placed well in front of the nephridiopore (Murina, 1957a, fig. 3).

DISTRIBUTION. Kurile Kamchatka and Japan trenches; at 6156–6860 m (Murina, 1957).

Phascolion pallidum pallidum Koren & Danielssen, 1877

Phascolion pallidum pallidum Koren & Danielssen, 1877 : 132–134, figs 22–24; Selenka & de Man, 1883 : 42–43; Leroy, 1936 : 425.

TYPE LOCALITY. Bergensfjord, Norway; at 365 m. In a tube of *Pectinaria auricoma*.

DESCRIPTION. Introvert 9 mm in length, with a row of 16 yellowish-white tentacles and with a broad basal zone of thick, stumpy, prominent, brown-black papillae. The rest of the introvert covered with fine papillae. Four rows of strong, bent hooks. Trunk cylindrical, 28 mm in length and 4 mm broad with prominent papillae which are rounder and more brown-black in colour at the posterior end.

No attaching papillae. Skin semi-transparent. The intestine is of the usual type, except that the point of the intestinal coil lies in the middle of the trunk and not in the posterior portion. The two retractors arise from the middle of the hind third of the trunk and have two roots. Two fixing muscles anteriorly. No contractile vessel. One short, thick nephridium.

REMARKS. Based originally on the holotype. Selenka & de Man only repeated the original description and record.

DISTRIBUTION. Bergensfjord, Norway (Koren & Danielssen, 1877); Morocco at 1205 m (Leroy, 1936).

Phascolion pallidum meridionale Augener, 1906

Phascolion pallidum var. *meridionalis* Augener, 1906 : 194–196, pl. 8, figs 162–166.

TYPE LOCALITY. Barbados.

DESCRIPTION. Anteriorly and posteriorly brownish-yellow. The skin in the middle portion is darker in colour and not transparent. The introvert carries 14 tentacles. Hooks few in number, in four indistinct rows and sharply bent at the tip. The trunk carries anteriorly and posteriorly egg-shaped papillae drawn out to a point. In the middle region of the body are attaching papillae, not directed forwards.

DISTRIBUTION. As for the type locality.

Phascolion parvum Sluiter, 1902

Phascolion parvus Sluiter, 1902 : 30–31, pl. 3, figs 1–2.

TYPE LOCALITY. Malaya. Siboga station 52; at 522 m.

DESCRIPTION. Introvert about 5 mm in length. Anteriorly with scattered, single pointed hooks; only slightly bent. The thick chitinous line along the posterior side reaches the point and goes some way down the anterior side. A small species, body 8 mm. The skin is thin and soft and covered with numerous transparent papillae of the typical *Phascolion* form, longest in the middle of the trunk. The point is strongly chitinized and dark brown often ending in two or three little teeth. These papillae are seen only on the middle of the trunk. The other papillae have much the same form but are more rounded and lack the chitinized spikes. Longitudinal muscles continuous. The two retractors are weak and arise at about the middle of the trunk. Only about six intestinal convolutions, not attached posteriorly. Anteriorly there are two pairs of fixing muscles. The rounded swollen nephridium opens at about the same level as the anus.

REMARKS. Described originally from six specimens. No other records. According to Sluiter the species is closely related to *P. tridens*.

DISTRIBUTION. Malaya. Siboga stations 52, 95, 314; at 522–959 m.

N

Phascolion pharetratum Sluiter, 1902

Phascolion pharetratum Sluiter, 1902 : 31–32, pl. 3, figs 3–5.

TYPE LOCALITY. Malaya. Siboga station 51; at 9 m.

DESCRIPTION. Introvert about the same length as the trunk and smooth except anteriorly where there are about 8–10 irregularly scattered hooks. These hooks have a characteristic appearance, the broad single point being rounded, while the central part is strongly chitinized and dark brown. Trunk up to 30 mm long; skin in the middle of the trunk and at the posterior end is transparent and quite smooth to the naked eye. Anteriorly the skin becomes thicker with a zone of somewhat larger papillae behind the anus. The papillae are numerous and similar in size but always small; the largest has a diameter of 0·12 mm. They are oval in shape with an opening in the centre marked off by a strong chitinous ring but mostly covered with numerous small chitinous plates which are more or less concentrically arranged. The papillae behind the introvert are tube-like with a dome-shaped base and a mamillate opening. No attaching papillae. Two long retractors arise about the middle of the trunk and are joined for most of their length. Ten loosely coiled intestinal convolutions not fixed posteriorly but fastened by two fixing muscles anteriorly at the beginning of the intestinal convolutions. The single nephridium is rounded and small and opens 8 mm posterior to the anus.

REMARKS. Known originally from four specimens. Near *P. lucifugax* Selenka & de Man but differs in the shape of the hook and the form of the papillae.

DISTRIBUTION. Malaya. Siboga Exped. stns 41, 240; at 9–91 m (Sluiter, 1902).

Phascolion rectum Ikeda, 1904

Phascolion rectus Ikeda, 1904 : 15–18, text-figs 45–49; Sato, 1939 : 413.

TYPE LOCALITY. Sagami Bay, Japan; at 650 m.

DESCRIPTION. Introvert, half retracted, about 11 mm in length; relatively thick and about 1 mm in diameter. Papillae on the anterior region very small, transparent and oval, becoming larger, taller and less closely arranged towards the posterior end. In the middle of the introvert they resemble the papillae on the middle of the trunk. About 10 filamentous tentacles; hooks and spines absent. Trunk about 24 mm in length, straight, slightly swollen in the middle; greyish-yellow in colour, more deeply yellow in the middle portion. The skin appears smooth to the eye but, under magnification, is seen to be covered with papillae which vary in size and shape on the various parts of the trunk, where they are intermingled with irregularly-shaped patches of chitin, dark brown in colour. On the introvert base they are comparatively prominent and club-shaped, in the anal region they are short and conical with a mamillate tip and in the middle region of the trunk they are almost flat. A single slender retractor arises from two short roots in the posterior part of the trunk. About 20 irregularly twisted internal convolutions; no spindle muscle. Four fixing muscles present, two near the beginning and two near the posterior end of the intestinal convolutions. Contractile vessel short, 15 mm in length and lacking contractile villi. Nephridium single, situated immediately behind the anus, and seen as an elongate sac on the right side of the nerve cord; free for its whole length. No eye-spots.

REMARKS. Known only from the holotype from a *Dentalium* shell. According to Ikeda the species is closely related to *P. manceps*.

DISTRIBUTION. As for the type locality.

Phascolion robertsoni Stephen & Robertson, 1952

Phascolion robertsoni Stephen & Robertson, 1952 : 439–441.

TYPE LOCALITY. Zanzibar. *Type.* Royal Scottish Museum.

DESCRIPTION. Introvert several times the length of the trunk and carrying a mass of hooks behind the tentacles. The introvert is completely covered with small hemispherical papillae; in the anterior portion they are white like the trunk but in the posterior part they have chitinous tips like the adhesive papillae. In some specimens there is a zone of tall papillae at the base of the introvert. Trunk white or greyish up to 80 mm in length. The anterior eighth bears fine papillae; the rest of the trunk carries papillae arranged in rows, most compact on the middle of the trunk, large on the dorsal side, small on the ventral. On the posterior quarter the papillae are very large and arranged in widely spaced rows. The adhesive or attaching papillae with chitinous tips vary greatly in number; some have only a few, while others have a band in the middle of the trunk. The chitinous tip is rounded. One retractor inserted at the hind end of the trunk.

REMARKS. Based originally on 18 specimens. It is near *P. collare* Selenka & de Man but differs in the arrangement and size-distribution of the papillae, those on the introvert having chitinous tips and in the adhesive papillae having tips.

DISTRIBUTION. Several areas around Zanzibar; down to 16 m (Stephen & Robertson, 1952).

Phascolion strombi (Montagu, 1804)

(Fig. 20A–H)

Sipunculus strombus Montagu, 1804 : 74–76; Turton, 1807 : 74; Fleming, 1828 : 491.
Sipunculus dentalii Gray, 1828 : 8; Rice & Stephen, 1970 : 52.
Sipunculus strombus: Gray, 1828 : 8.
Sipunculus bernhardus Forbes, 1841 : 251–253; McIntosh, 1866 : 613.
Sipunculus capitatus Rathke, 1843 : 143–147, pl. 6, figs 20–23.
Sipunculus concharum Oersted, 1884 : 80.
Sipunculus (Cryptosomum) strombi Quatrefages, 1865b : 628.
Sipunculus caementarium Quatrefages, 1865b : 628.
Phascolosoma bernhardus: Pourtalès, 1851 : 41–42; Diesing, 1859 : 759; Baird, 1868 : 86.
Phascolosoma dentalii: Diesing, 1851 : 65.
Phascolosoma strombi: Diesing, 1851 : 65; Keferstein, 1865 : 431, 2 pls, 4 figs; Levinsen, 1887 : 302.
Phascolosoma hamulatum Packard, 1867 : 290.
Phascolosoma caementarium: Verrill, 1873 : 627, pl. 18, fig. 92; Théel, 1905 : 86.

Phascolion spetzbergense Théel, 1875b : 16–17, pl. 1, figs 2–3; Danielssen & Koren, 1881a : 45–46;
 Théel, 1905 : 86; Molcanov, 1909a : 69.
Phascolion strombi var. *spetzbergense:* Koren & Danielssen, 1877 : 154; Horst, 1882 : 39.
Phascolion strombi var. *verrucosum* Koren & Danielssen, 1877 : 141, 154; Selenka & de Man,
 1883 : 52.
Phascolion strombi var. *capitatum* Koren & Danielssen, 1877 : 140.
Phascolion strombi: Théel, 1875a : 1, 3 pls; 1905 : 86–89, pl. 6, figs 82–95, pl. 7, figs 109–110,
 pl. 15, figs 207–208; 1911 : 31–32, pl. 4, figs 50–66, pl. 5, fig. 75; Selenka & de Man, 1883 :
 50–51; Fischer, 1895 : 17; 1914b : 15; 1922b : 19–20; 1925 : 22–23, figs 10–12; 1928b :
 468–484; Sluiter, 1900 : 10; 1912 : 18; Cuénot, 1902a : 26–27; 1922 : 11–12, fig. 5; Augener,
 1906 : 193–194; Gadd, 1911 : 89–90; Gerould, 1913 : 403–416, figs 9–10; Southern, 1913b :
 29–31; Chamberlain, 1920 : 4–5; ten Broeke, 1928 : 163–164, figs 9–11; Wesenberg-Lund,
 1929a : 155; 1930 : 34–35, pl. 3, fig. 42, pl. 4, fig. 47; 1932 : 10–11, fig. 6; 1933 : 11, pl. 4;
 1934 : 6–7; 1937a : 14–16, fig. 5; 1937b : 10–11, fig. 3; 1939a : 23–27; 1939b : 28; 1954a :
 10; 1955b : 13; 1957b : 5; Stephen, 1934 : 170–171; Leroy, 1936 : 425; Murina, 1967a : 1339,
 fig. 6.

DESCRIPTION.   Introvert as long as or up to twice as long as the trunk; 14–26
tentacles and a zone of slender hooks lying behind them.   Trunk up to 20 mm in
length, light grey to light brown in colour.   Trunk coiled if the animal inhabits
a gastropod shell, straight if living in a *Dentalium* shell or if free; covered with small
papillae, larger and more crowded at the anterior and posterior ends.   Papillae
vary considerably according to habitat, e.g. in specimens from the Arctic the papillae
are very prominent but from the North Sea less so.   In the posterior half of the trunk
there is a broad zone of attaching papillae, readily distinguishable by their darker
colour.   Two retractors; a broad dorsal, sometimes with two roots, and a weaker
ventral which has two roots.   They are inserted at the posterior end of the trunk
posteriorly to the end of the nerve cord.   Digestive tract long, with five very
open loops and a short terminal spiral.   A simple contractile vessel and a rectal
caecum present.   Nephridiopore lies posterior to the anus.

REMARKS.   A very widely distributed and variable species.   It inhabits the
shells of gastropods and scaphopods or may live freely in the sand.   It has been
found in shallow water and in the ocean at considerable depths.   The species shows
considerable variation in colour, size and form so much so that Gerould (1913)
has described seven subspecies from the waters off the east American coast.   We
are not certain if they are all true-subspecies but we are giving his key for reference.

KEY TO SUBSPECIES OF PHASCOLION STROMBI

A.   Introvert longer than the trunk
        i Common form, orange yellow or yellowish brown, Labrador south to 40°N   *fusca*
       ii Dark-coloured with thick skin, sharp holdfasts   .   .   .   .   *tubicola*
      iii Small white form in gastropod shells, common at Wood's Hole, Mass. .   *alba*
       iv Deep sea form with short thin-walled trunk.   Large opaque ovoid eggs   *hyalina*
B.   Introvert about equal to the trunk.   In shells of *Dentalium* and *Protula*.   Off
        Cape Cod, elongate, smooth, 16 tentacles   .   .   .   .   .   *gracilis*
C.   Introvert shorter than the trunk.   Dorsal retractor in some specimens divided at
        base   .   .   .   .   *canadensis*
D.   Dorsal retractor as well as ventral probably with two roots.   Introvert longer than
        the trunk and smooth, like posterior end of trunk.   Tube has sheath for
        introvert, Mass. .   .   .   .   *laevis*

The accounts of Théel (1875, 1905), Gerould (1913) and Fischer (1925) are particularly informative. Gerould (1913 : 401) says 'P. strombi in America, as elsewhere, shows a remarkable variability in size, colour, thickness of body wall, size of the papillae and holdfasts and hence in the smoothness and roughness of its skin. The internal organization is more stable, though the eggs vary in shape, in the thickness of the yolk membrane and in the amount of yolk. In certain localities off Halifax the dorsal retractor shows a tendency to a division at the base into two roots, but this in no region is a constant character.' Further Gerould (1913 : 408) says, 'How far this diversity in external features is due to the direct action of the environment, as, for instance, the kinds of empty shells or tubes which the worms inhabit, their food supply, temperature of the water, etc. and how far it may be determined by heredity are questions which can be answered fully, of course, only by breeding and rearing the animals'. The complicated synonymy of the animal is consequently understandable.

This species has been used in a number of experimental studies, particularly by Akesson (1958) and Arvy & Gabe (1952).

DISTRIBUTION. Arctic: Kara Sea (Levinsen, 1887; Fischer, 1895; Wesenberg-Lund, 1933); Kola Gulf (Gadd, 1911); Barents Sea (Horst, 1882); Arctic localities (Fischer, 1928b); Greenland (Wesenberg-Lund, 1929a, 1930, 1932, 1933); Iceland (Wesenberg-Lund, 1937b, 1954a); Scandinavian coasts (Wesenberg-Lund, 1939b); North Sea (Stephen, 1934; Fischer, 1925); British coasts and Eire Channel (Allen & Tod, 1900; Sharp, 1908); Eire (Southern, 1913b; Farran, 1915); French coasts (Sluiter, 1900; Cuénot, 1902, 1922); Eastern coasts of North America (Pourtalès, 1851; Verrill, 1885; Kindle, 1917; Chamberlain, 1920); West Indies (ten Broeke, 1928); South America, Chile (Wesenberg-Lund, 1955b); Antarctic (Théel, 1911; Fischer, 1928b); Red Sea (Wesenberg-Lund, 1957b).

Phascolion tridens Selenka & de Man, 1883
(Fig. 22F)

Phascolion tridens Selenka & de Man, 1883 : 46–47, pl. 6, figs 75–79.

TYPE LOCALITY. Uhoy, Philippines. In Nassa shell.

DESCRIPTION. The anterior portion of the introvert is short, bulbous and whitish in colour. Hooks brown. The anterior portion of the animal is greatly extended as in P. manceps; it is pellucid, reddish in colour, iridescent and covered with large flask-shaped papillae. The papillae are of the same kind as those on the anterior and posterior parts of the trunk. In the middle of the trunk several of these papillae carry a three-pointed chitinous ring; they are not as numerous in the pointed posterior part of the body where they resemble hooks. The internal anatomy is like that of P. manceps, but the numerous thread-like contractile villi or tubules of the latter species here resemble small outgrowths.

REMARKS. Known only from the holotype. It is near P. manceps but distinguished at first sight by the presence of hooks and the shorter portion of the body extended beyond the shell.

DISTRIBUTION. As for the type locality.

Phascolion tuberculosum Théel, 1875

(Fig. 22G)

Phascolion tuberculosum Théel 1875b : 15–16 pl. 1, fig. 1, pl. 3, fig. 16; 1905 : 90–91, pl. 6,
figs 96–98, pl. 7, figs 99–108, pl. 15, figs 209; Fischer, 1925 : 23.
Phascolion strombi tuberculosum Norman, 1894 : 150.

TYPE LOCALITY.   Koster Fjord, Sweden; at 25–35 m.

DESCRIPTION.   The introvert carries about 15 stumpy tentacles; also many hooks
which are broad and curved, instead of being spine-like as in *P. strombi*.   The
general appearance and anatomy is very much the same as that of *P. strombi*.
There is no dark band of adhesive papillae, the papillae being more or less of uniform
type over the whole surface.   Another difference is that the retractors are more
or less uniform in size and are attached a little way in front of the posterior end of
the trunk.   The contractile vessel is simple.   Rectal caecum present, ventral retractor arises from two short roots and the anus lies anterior to the nephridiopore.

REMARKS.   Described from several specimens and excellently illustrated in
Théel, 1905.   Théel (1905 : 91) says that the species differs from *P. strombi* because
(1) the tentacles are obtuse, (2) the introvert hooks are different, (3) adhesive
papillae are lacking and (4) the retractor muscles are attached differently.   He
also considers the species identical with *Phascolion pallidum* (Kor. & Dan.) and
P. strombi verrucosum Selenka, 1883.   We have not followed his lead in these last
two examples.

DISTRIBUTION.   West coasts of Norway and Sweden (Théel, 1875).

Phascolion tubicolum Verrill, 1873

(Fig. 22H)

Phascolion tubicola Verrill, 1873a : 99; 1874 : 388–389; Selenka & de Man, 1883 : 47–48, pl. 6,
figs 80–86.
Phascolion strombi tubicula Gerould, 1913 : 408.

TYPE LOCALITY.   New England coast.

DESCRIPTION.   Introvert thin-walled, yellowish-red, longer than the trunk;
covered with small anterior and larger posterior papillae.   Anteriorly very small
spines or hooks present which are moderately pointed but not bent.   A single row
of about 20 tentacles.   Trunk cylindrical, elongated and covered with papillae
which are small on the posterior half of the trunk.   On the posterior third and in
a zone anteriorly lie zones of irregularly scattered three-cornered yellowish red spines
with small papillae scattered between them.   Two retractors with broad roots
arising about the same level at the posterior end of the trunk; the ventral retractor
is thin, the dorsal much stronger.   The oesophagus follows the ventral retractor.
One fastening mesentery extends from the region of the anus to the hind end of the
middle portion of the trunk.   Two fixing muscles present.   One or two intestinal
convolutions.   One short nephridium fixed all its length by mesenteries, opens some
distance behind the anus.

REMARKS. Based originally on several specimens. Selenka & de Man referred briefly to three specimens from the West Indies. Gerould (1913 : 408) considers the species to be a subspecies of *P. strombi*.

DISTRIBUTION. Eastern North America.

Phascolion sumatrense Fischer, 1922

Phascolion sumatrense Fischer, 1922c : 13–14, pl. 2, fig. 7a.
Phascolion valdiviae var. *sumatrense*: Fischer, 1916 : 17.

TYPE LOCALITY. Siberut Island, Sumatra (0°39'S, 98°52'E). Valdivia station 191.

DESCRIPTION. Introvert 24 mm in length, rust-coloured and lacking hooks; papillae and cross stripes present as in *P. valdiviae*. Trunk 35 mm in length; body wall slightly transparent, anteriorly and posteriorly matt brown, rust-coloured in the middle portion. The first third of the trunk is covered with barrel-like papillae, which do not stand out very clearly. The remaining two thirds of the trunk, even on the ventral side, carry the attaching papillae, which are large, with a strong chitinous rim, often two-pointed. Retractor arises at the extreme posterior end of the trunk. Spiral with about 20 coils fastened posteriorly by the spindle muscle and also three fine mesenteries. Apparently no caecum. The anus lies in front of the nephridium but not so far forward as in *P. valdiviae*. Nephridium very small, anteriorly ball-like, posteriorly sausage-like; anterior part free, posterior part fastened to the wall by several mesenteries.

REMARKS. Known only from the holotype. The species is very closely related to *P. valdiviae* and was at first described as a variety of that species. It differs from *P. valdiviae* mainly in lacking hooks on the introvert and in having the adhesive papillae pointed.

DISTRIBUTION. As for the type locality.

Phascolion valdiviae Fischer, 1916

Phascolion valdiviae Fischer, 1916 : 16; 1922c : 13, pl. 2, figs 7a–g.

TYPE LOCALITY. St Paul's Island, Indian Ocean (38°41'S, 77°36'E); at 158 m. In a *Dentalium* shell.

DESCRIPTION. Introvert 17 mm in length and with 6–8 thread-like tentacles. Behind these is a zone of regularly-arranged, but not closely packed, hooks. Between them, and over the rest of the introvert, are short cylindrical papillae alternating with dark cross stripes. Trunk 24 mm in length; the anterior and posterior parts transparent and whitish in colour. The centre portion has a stronger musculature and is a yellow-brown colour. A zone of elongate barrel-like papillae present on the anterior part of the trunk; the papillae are closely packed and this region appears to be tessellated. This is followed by another zone of similar size in which the papillae are more or less oval. The remaining zone bears the few attaching papillae which have a chitinous ring, as in *P. hedraeum*, that is, without points. The

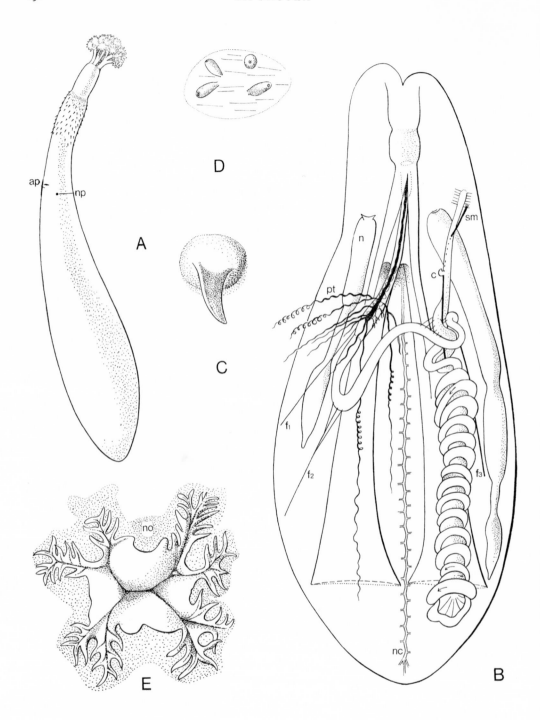

attaching papillae are larger on the dorsal side than on the ventral. At the posterior end of the trunk the smallest papillae are arranged in rows. A fairly broad retractor is attached to the extreme posterior end of the trunk by a branching root. There are three fixing muscles near the beginning of the intestinal coils. A contractile vessel is present and 20–22 intestinal convolutions are traversed by a spindle muscle which is attached posteriorly. Anus placed far forward and fixed by wing muscles. Just behind the emergence of the rectum from the spiral is a large elongate caecum. The nephridium is short and free, opening a little way behind the anus. The nerve cord is loosely bound to the trunk wall by long side roots.

REMARKS. Known only from the holotype.

DISTRIBUTION. As for the type locality.

Genus *THEMISTE* Gray, 1828

Themiste Gray, 1828 : 8, pl. 6, figs 4, 4a; Baird, 1868 : 98; Stephen, 1965 : 458; Amor, 1970 : 496; Rice & Stephen, 1970 : 66.
Dendrostomum Grübe & Oersted, 1858 : 118; Diesing, 1859 : 765; Quatrefages, 1865b : 629; Fisher, 1952 : 404.
Dendrostoma Keferstein, 1865a : 438; 1865b : 207; Selenka & de Man, 1883 : 83.

DESCRIPTION. Trunk stoutly pyriform, globose or elongate in shape. Tentacular system surrounds the mouth and consists of four to eight conspicuously (often dichotomously) branched, grooved tentacles which carry small tentacules pinnately or palmately arranged. Oral disc with four to eight primary food grooves which branch to the tentacles. Hooks or spines may be present on the introvert. Longitudinal muscle-layer continuous. Usually two, rarely four, retractor muscles. A well-developed spindle muscle attached anteriorly near the anus but not posteriorly. Two or more, usually three, intestinal fastening muscles. Two nephridia which are not attached along their length to the body wall. Contractile vessel bears few to many villi or tubules which may be short or very long. Nuchal organ and rectal caecum described for many species.

TYPE SPECIES. *Themiste hennahi* Gray (=*Dendrostomum peruvianum* Collin).

REMARKS. Stephen (1965 : 458) pointed out that *Themiste* Gray, 1828 is a senior synonym of *Dendrostomum* Grube, 1859 and that the type of the genus is *T. hennahi* Gray, 1828, a specimen in the collection of the British Museum (Natural History). The change of name is unfortunate and will probably lead to some confusion especially in the field of invertebrate physiology where *Dendrostromum zostericolum* and *D. cymodoceae* have been used as experimental animals.

FIG. 23. (A–E) *Themiste pyroides*. (A) Entire specimen, natural size. (B) Dissected specimen. The contractile vessel and tubules are shown in solid black, but not all the tubules are shown. (C) Introvert hook. (D) Skin from the introvert just anterior to the anus, showing the brown papillae. (E) Base of the four groups of tentacles, the grooves leading to the mouth and the serrate borders of the grooves. The nuchal organ lies between the dorsal tentacles. (A–E after Fisher.) KEY: *See* Fig. 11, p. 83.

We have listed 25 species in the genus, some of which may eventually be shown to be identical. The main taxonomic characters within the genus are: (1) the arrangement of the tentacles, (2) the number of retractor muscles, (3) the structure of the contractile tubules or villi and (4) the presence or absence of hooks on the introvert. Although the tentacles usually arise from four to eight primary stems it is not always easy to decide the exact number on account of a strong tendency for any or all of the stems to subdivide. It is not surprising, therefore, to find that the number of primary tentacular stems of such species as *T. blanda, T. alutacea* and *T. lageniformis* is stated to be different by different authors. Sometimes the smaller 'tentacules' are arranged either pinnately or palmately while in a few species the branching is so extensive that the tentacles become dendritic. It is usually assumed that the presence of hooks on the introvert is a specific character of a sipunculan. Specimens of *T. alutacea*, however, have been reported with and without hooks (Selenka, 1883) and according to Awati & Pradham (1935) the hooks of their specimens of *T. lageniformis* 'drop off' when they are adult. Edmonds (1960), however, considers that *T. huttoni* which is armed and *T. lageniformis* unarmed are different species. The contractile tubules or Polian villi are almost invariably either short or very long and either branched or unbranched.

Most of the known species fall into six groups some of which may contain up to seven species. The groups and species are:

1. *T. pyroides—blanda* group (hooks on introvert and contractile tubules or villi long); *T. alutacea, T. blanda, T. hexadactyla, T. pyroides, T. rosacea, T. petricola* and *T. spinifera.*

2. *T. lageniformis—huttoni* group (hooks present or absent and contractile tubules or villi short); *T. cymodoceae, T. fusca, T. huttoni, T. lageniformis* (=*D. signifer*), *T. robertsoni* and *T. tropica, T. minor.*

3. *T. zostericola—perimeces* group (hooks absent and contractile tubules long); *T. dyscrita, T. hennahi, T. perimeces* and *T. zostericola.*

4. *T. lissa—schmitti* group (nephridiopore posterior to anus, contractile tubules long and hooks absent; animals of small size); *T. lissa* and *T. schmitti.*

5. *T. dehamata—fisheri* group (nephridiopore posterior to anus, contractile tubules short, hooks absent; animals long and cylindrical); *T. dehamata, T. elliptica* and *T. fisheri.*

6. *T. pinnifolia—stephensoni* group (four retractor muscles); *T. pinnifolia* and *T. stephensoni.*

An examination of the type specimen of *Themiste lageniformis* Baird, 1868 in the collection of the British Museum (Natural History) has shown that *T. lageniformis* is a senior synonym of *D. signifer* (Selenka & de Man, 1883). It is most unfortunate that the latter, better known name has to disappear.

Gray's account gives no indication of the gender of the name '*Themiste*' which, as far as we can ascertain, is not a pure Greek word. According to our interpretation of Article 30(a) (i) of the International Code of Zoological Nomenclature (1961) the suffix 'e' makes the name feminine.

DISTRIBUTION. Mostly in tropical and temperate seas.

List of species

T. alutacea (Grübe)
T. blanda (Selenka & de Man)
T. cymodoceae (Edmonds)
T. dehamata (Kesteven)
T. dyscrita (Fisher)
T. elliptica (Sato)
T. fisheri Amor
T. fusca (Edmonds)
T. hennahi Gray
T. hexadactyla (Sato)
T. huttoni (Benham)
T. lageniformis Baird
  (=*D. signifer* Sel. & de Man)

T. lissa (Fisher)
T. minor (Ikeda)
T. perimeces (Fisher)
T. petricola Amor
T. pinnifolia (Keferstein)
T. pyroides (Chamberlain)
T. robertsoni (Stephen & Robertson)
T. rosacea Amor
T. schmitti (Fisher)
T. spinifer (Sluiter)
T. stephensoni (Stephen)
T. tropica (Sato)
T. zostericola (Chamberlain)

GENUS THEMISTE—KEY TO SPECIES

1	Two retractor muscles	2
–	Four retractor muscles	22
2	Hooks or spines on the introvert	3
–	No hooks or spines on the introvert	11
3	Contractile (Polian) tubules long (over 5 mm)	4
–	Contractile tubules short (less than 5 mm).	9
4	Tentacles arise from four to six primary stems	5
–	Tentacles arise from eight stems (each divides into two near its base, spines at base of introvert only) . . . . . . *T. spinifera* (p. 212)	
5	Tentacles arise from four stems	6
–	Tentacles arise from six stems	8
6	Contractile vessel with a network of accessory vessels and with numerous, sometimes branched, long tubules (tentacular crown dendritic) . *T. pyroides* (p. 210)	
–	Contractile vessel without a network of accessory vessels	7
7	Tentacles pinnately arranged (introvert papillae inconspicuous; tentacles arise from four stems according to Sato, Ikeda and Fischer but from 5–6 according to Selenka) . . . . *T. blanda* (p. 197)	
–	Tentacles palmately arranged (six tentacles according to Gerould but four according to Grübe) . . . . *T. alutacea* (p. 196)	
8	Hooks, more than 260 (height 0·2–0·36 mm) . . . *T. hexadactyla* (p. 203)	
–	Hooks, less than 160 and smaller . . . . . { *T. rosacea* (p. 211) / *T. petricola* (p. 209) }	
9	Contractile tubules unbranched (long rectum, rectal caecum, loosely wound intestinal spiral, nephridia open at same level as anus) . . . *T. minor* (p. 207)	
–	Contractile tubules branching, especially those placed posteriorly . . .	10
10	Species stout, body wall thick, contractile tubules densely packed, nephridia open at the level of the anus . . . . *T. huttoni* (p. 204)	
–	Species slender, body wall thin, contractile tubules less densely packed, nephridia open posterior to the anus, intestine coil loosely wound . . *T. fusca* (p. 200)	
11	Anal and nephridial apertures open at about same level	12
–	Nephridial aperture placed well posterior to the anal aperture	19
12	Contractile tubules very long	13
–	Contractile tubules very short (less than 4 mm)	16
13	Oesophagus with numerous, pointed protuberances on its wall arranged in long series (four intestinal fasteners; a small species) . . . . *T. hennahi* (p. 201)	

– Oesophagus without protuberances along its wall 14

14 Intestinal spiral of moderate length with less than 50 coils (15–16 double coils), intestinal fasteners present and contractile tubules more than 10 . . . 15

– Intestinal spiral very long with up to 100 coils, intestinal fasteners usually absent and contractile tubules 9–10 . . . . . *T. perimeces* (p. 207)

15 Intestinal fastener F_2 attached to the postoesophageal intestine, retractors attached one third to one fourth of the length of the body from the end . *T. zostericola* (p. 213)

– Intestinal fastener F_2 attached to the intestine, retractors attached one fifth to one sixth of the length of the body from the end . . . . *T. dyscrita* (p. 199)

16 Contractile tubules unbranched . . . . . . *T. tropica* (p. 213)

– Contractile tubules with some branching 17

17 Large species with trunk up to 90 mm long (yellow pigmentation on introvert) *T. cymodoceae* (p. 197)

– Smaller species with trunk up to 44 mm long (blue pigmentation on introvert) . 18

18 Tentacles, five to six (four tentacles, nuchal organ and intestinal caecum present according to Edmonds) . . . . . . *T. lageniformis* (p. 205)

– Tentacles, four . . . . *T. robertsoni* (p. 210)

19 Contractile tubules long 20

– Contractile tubules short 21

20 Small species, fastener F_2 attached to intestine only . . . *T. lissa* (p. 206)

– Large species, fastener F_2 attached to both intestine and post oesophageal gut *T. schmitti* (p. 212)

21 Tentacles arise from four primary stems . . . . { *T. dehamata* (p. 198)
{ *T. elliptica* (p. 199)

– Tentacles arise from six stems . . . . *T. fisheri* (p. 200)

22 Introvert bears hooks . . . . *T. pinnifolia* (p. 209)

– Introvert without hooks . . . . . . *T. stephensoni* (p. 212)

Themiste alutacea (Grübe, 1858)

(Fig. 24B)

Dendrostomum alutaceum Grübe, 1858 : 118; Diesing, 1859 : 765; Keferstein, 1865a : 438; Selenka & de Man, 1883 : 84–85, pl. 2, fig. 20, pl. 11, figs 156–158; Fischer, 1895 : 18; Gerould, 1913 : 417–418, figs 12, 13; Leroy, 1936 : 425.
Themiste alutacea: Baird, 1868 : 98.

TYPE LOCALITY. St Croix, Antilles.

DESCRIPTION. Introvert about one third as long as the trunk; colour brown. Four brown tentacular stems are divided into two or three sulphur coloured branches, each of which bears violet-tipped, finger-like tentacules along its edges. Midway along the introvert there are about 50 pointed, dark brown hooks lying between scattered cylindrical papillae of the same height. Hooks sometimes completely wanting. Trunk stout, up to 15 mm long, brown in colour and not narrowing anteriorly. Papillae on the middle of the trunk are oval, grain-like in shape, resembling those of *T. blanda*; at the posterior end of the body they are rounded. Two long ventral retractors arise in the middle or the posterior half of the trunk. Intestinal coils 12–15 with two or three fastening muscles attached to the first. Spindle muscle fixed anteriorly. Contractile vessel with 5–8 long villi or tubules. Two free nephridia, nearly half as long as the trunk.

REMARKS. According to Gerould (1913) the body is pearshaped, the anterior half of the introvert is smooth, the recurved hooks appear on the introvert behind the smooth area, the tentacles are grouped in six tree-shaped branches and are flecked with dark brown spots.

DISTRIBUTION. West Indies (Grübe, 1858); Argentine (Selenka & de Man, 1883); Florida (Gerould, 1913).

Themiste blanda (Selenka & de Man, 1883)

Dendrostomum blandum Selenka & de Man, 1883 : 85–86, pl. 1, fig. 9, pl. 11, figs 159–162; Ikeda, 1904 : 53–55, figs 14, 90, 91; 1924 : 30–31, fig. 2; Ostroumov, 1909 : 319–324; Fischer, 1922b : 18–19; Sato, 1930b : 24–28, pl. 4, figs 18–19, text-figs 10–12; 1937a : 162, pl. 4, fig. 16; 1939 : 412; Fisher, 1952 : 405.

TYPE LOCALITY. Japan.

DESCRIPTION. Introvert about a third as long as the trunk; numerous dark coloured hooks 0·4 mm tall are scattered in the mid-region (Sato, 1930 says that they are 0·1–0·2 mm high). Small papillae present between the hooks. There are five to six main tentacular stems (Sato says four) which in turn divide into numerous tentacules. Trunk up to 25 mm in length, stoutly built, brown or reddish-grey in colour and not narrowed posteriorly; young specimens transparent. The whole body, with the exception of the smooth dark coloured area between the hooks and the tentacles, is covered with scattered closely set papillae resembling those of other species of *Themiste*. In the middle of the body they are oval and have a clear centre but at the posterior end they are circular, larger and more crowded. Internal anatomy much like that of *T. lageniformis*.

REMARKS. Ikeda (1924) pointed out some differences from the usual specific definition in his specimens collected at Sapporo. Fisher (1952 : 409) points out that the tentacles of *T. blanda* are simpler than those of *T. pyroides* and that in the former they are pinnate and not dendritic. Ikeda (1904, fig. 91) shows that a rectal caecum is present. Sato (1930 : 27) says that a caecum is absent.

DISTRIBUTION. Japan (Selenka & de Man, 1883; Ikeda, 1904, 1924; Sato, 1930b, 1937a); ? California (Fischer, 1922b; Sato, 1939; Fisher, 1952).

Themiste cymodoceae (Edmonds, 1956)

Dendrostomum cymodoceae Edmonds, 1956 : 299–301, pl. 2, fig. 1, text-figs 15–16; Akesson, 1958 : 147–151, figs 66–67 and 219–222, fig. 102.

TYPE LOCALITY. Aldinga Beach, St Vincent's Gulf, South Australia. *Type.* Australian Museum.

DESCRIPTION. Introvert relatively short, cylindrical, without hooks or spines; pale grey in colour, usually with a light yellow or brown band round the middle. A smooth, shining area, sometimes purplish and glossy present behind the tentacles. Tentacles arise from four main stems, which usually divide into two, so that there may appear to be six to eight groups; tentacules digitiform, small and very numerous, pale straw to light brown in colour with tips always darker.   Trunk elongate, robust, pyriform, up to 90 mm in length; colour light to dark grey, sometimes light brown, usually darker and occasionally almost blue-black posteriorly.   The trunk appears smooth to the naked eye but under magnification is seen to be covered with numerous small white papillae, each with a white glandular opening in the centre.   Body wall thick, especially posteriorly.   Internal anatomy very similar to that of *T. lageniformis*, except that the system of intestinal fixing muscles is more complex and variable.   Two very long stout retractors arise in the posterior fourth of the trunk.   Intestinal tract very long, reaching to the posterior end of the trunk. A well-defined contractile vessel runs along its dorsal surface, reaching as far as the base of the retractors.   It bears numerous branching villi, densely clustered posteriorly; a single villus may be 5 mm in length.   Rectum short and with a caecum. Three to four intestinal fixing muscles present.   A strong spindle muscle arises near the anus, giving off threads to the gut.   Nephridia long, brown, thin and free, and extending as far as the middle of the trunk.   Nephridiopores just posterior to the anus.

REMARKS.   The species is well known along the coasts of the two gulfs in South Australia and the description is based on about 40 dissected specimens.   It is a very hardy animal and can be left or neglected in an aquarium for weeks without appearing to suffer any serious harm.

The species is closely allied to *T. lageniformis* (*D. signifer*).   After observing a large number of specimens Edmonds considers that it is different for the following reasons: (1) it is larger (over twice as long as *T. lageniformis*), (2) it possesses a yellow pigmented band on the introvert instead of the dark blue band, (3) its tentacules are shorter in relation to the length of its body, (4) its tentacules are always pigmented or flecked anteriorly, (5) it usually possesses one more fastening muscle than *T. lageniformis*.

Akesson (1958) has made a very careful study of the nervous system and epidermal glands of the species.

DISTRIBUTION.   St Vincent and Spencer Gulfs, South Australia (Edmonds, 1956); Port Philip Bay, Victoria.

Themiste dehamata (Kesteven, 1903)

Dendrostoma dehamatum Kesteven, 1903 : 69–73, pl. 7, fig. 7.
Dendrostomum dehamatum: Edmonds, 1956 : 296.

TYPE LOCALITY.   Balmoral, Port Jackson, New South Wales, littoral.   *Type*. Australian Museum, Sydney.

DESCRIPTION.   Introvert about one third as long as the trunk; anterior quarter quite smooth.   Papillae on the remainder of the introvert are long and slender anteriorly but stouter and more crowded posteriorly.   Hooks absent.   The tentacles arise from four main stems with two or three primary branches; false branching may give the appearance of up to eight stems.   Trunk up to 230 mm in length and of nearly uniform diameter, tapering slightly towards the posterior end.   Colour generally white.   Two retractors arising from about the posterior third of the trunk. Contractile vessel slender with many villi.   A spindle muscle present but not attached posteriorly.   Intestinal spiral is tightly wound anteriorly but loosely posteriorly. It is held by several mesenteries, two anchoring the loop of the fore-gut and two more the anterior coils of the intestinal spiral.   The two nephridia are long, slender and free and about one third as long as the trunk.

REMARKS.   This is a very long and slender species.   Edmonds (1956) re-examined three of Kesteven's specimens, 160–280 mm long and 5–8 mm wide.   He estimated the length of the introvert as 50–70 mm.   The oesophagus is very long and reaches to the posterior end of the body and the contractile vessel bears very numerous villi which gradually increase in size posteriorly.   The rectum is long and bears a small caecum.   Some variation in the number and arrangement of fixing muscles was observed.

T. fisheri (Amor, 1964) is a closely allied species.

DISTRIBUTION.   As for the type locality.

Themiste dyscrita (Fisher, 1952)

(Fig. 25A)

Dendrostomum dyscritum Fisher, 1952 : 417–419, fig. 87 B–E; pl. 30, fig. 3, pl. 34.

TYPE LOCALITY.   Monterey Bay, California.   *Type*.   U.S.N.M. no. 21221.

DESCRIPTION.   Introvert about a quarter as long as the trunk; skin glands, low and papilliform and extend as far as a smooth, red collar.   Six tentacular stems, the dorsal two being shorter than the others.   Length of trunk upwards of 170 mm. Colour dark olive green, greenish-yellow or sepia.   One pair of retractors that arise a fifth or sixth of the length of the trunk from the posterior extremity.   A strong spindle muscle is attached to the dorsal side of the anus and is united with the wall of the rectum as far as the caecum beyond which it anchors the intestinal coils by strands.   Three fixing muscles.   Intestinal spiral of about 15–16 double coils. Contractile vessel with numerous long, branching Polian tubules.   Nephridia long but shorter than those of *T. zostericola*.

REMARKS.   The species was described from 16 specimens.   It is very close to *T. zostericola*, also from California, but differs in having a shorter, thicker body, relatively longer retractors and more numerous and branching Polian tubules.

DISTRIBUTION.   California, U.S.A.

Themiste elliptica (Sato, 1934)

Dendrostoma ellipticum Sato, 1934b : 20–22, pl. 1, fig. 10, text-figs 22–25; 1939 : 411.

TYPE LOCALITY.   Suruga Bay, Japan.

DESCRIPTION.   Introvert about a fifth of the length of the trunk.   Total length of trunk 80 mm and diameter 5 mm.   Skin opaque, reddish-brown (in alcohol), covered with numerous papillae more densely distributed on the posterior end of the body. Papillae are elliptical in surface view, 0·1 to 0·17 mm along the major axis and 0·03 to 0·05 mm along the minor axis; at the posterior end they are taller than elsewhere but on the middle of the trunk smaller. On the anterior part of the trunk there are no true papillae, only numerous small processes covered with numerous small chitinous granules. One pair of retractors, long and slender and attached at the level of the posterior fifth of the trunk; they fuse into a single band in the anterior part of the introvert. Numerous short Polian tubules present on the contractile vessel which runs along the dorsal side of the oesophagus. Nephridia two long, greyish tubes, free for their whole length, opening slightly posterior to the anus.

REMARKS. Known only from the holotype, which was slightly damaged. Sato (1939) merely repeated the original record without further comments.

DISTRIBUTION. As for the type locality.

Themiste fisheri (Amor, 1964)

Dendrostomum fisheri Amor, 1964 : 467–469, pl. 3, 2 figs, pl. 4, 4 figs.

TYPE LOCALITY. Bay of Huesos (43°13′S, 64°50′W), Argentine; at 27 m in mud and stones. *Holotype*. Museum of La Plata.

DESCRIPTION. Trunk very long (100 mm long and 11 mm wide in holotype). Introvert about a quarter as long as the trunk; lacking hooks or spines. Tentacles arise from six stems with numerous dichotomous divisions. Anterior fifth of introvert is smooth; the rest of the body bears inconspicuous spiny papillae which are shorter on the trunk. Nephridiopores posterior to the anus and nephridia about one third as long as the body. Two retractor muscles arise between the middle and posterior third of the body wall and are separate for two thirds of their length. Contractile vessel long, bearing numerous, short, branching tubules. Three fastening muscles attached to the alimentary canal. Well developed spindle muscle which arises anteriorly from a position just posterior to the anus. Nuchal organ present.

REMARKS. This species is related to *T. dehamata* (Kesteven). It differs (1) in that the tentacles arise from six main stems instead of four, (2) in possessing a well defined spindle muscle—a structure poorly developed in Kesteven's material (Kesteven, 1903 : 71)—and (3) in possessing a conspicuous rectal membrane.

DISTRIBUTION. As for the holotype.

Themiste fusca (Edmonds, 1960)

(Fig. 24C–D)

Dendrostomum fuscum Edmonds, 1960 : 165–167, pl. 3, figs 7–9.

TYPE LOCALITY. Proper Bay, Port Lincoln, South Australia. *Type*. Australian Museum, Sydney.

DESCRIPTION. Introvert short, up to 3·5 mm and much narrower than the trunk; covered anteriorly with a number of scattered, almost black, blunt hooks. Tentacles arise from four primary stems, although sometimes they appear to arise from five to eight, due to the method of branching. Tentacles flecked with brown. Base of introvert and anterior part purple-brown; a prominent nuchal organ anteriorly. Trunk small and slender, up to 22 mm in length and 4 mm in breadth, light brown or straw coloured. Body wall thin. Numerous very small, circular pale-coloured papillae, largest and most prominent at the base of the introvert and on the posterior portion of the trunk. In some specimens the skin is furrowed into numerous square or rectangular areas in these regions. Two retractors arise in the posterior part of the trunk; they are slender, but have a wide base. The oesophagus runs between the retractors to near their base, and then loops up as in *T. lageniformis*. Contractile vessel present with villi well-developed but fewer and simpler than in *T. huttoni* or *T. lageniformis*. Those at the base of the oesophagus branch to some extent. The intestinal spiral is loose and irregularly wound and consists of about 6–8 double coils, the most distal loop being usually very loosely wound. The spindle muscle arises from the rectum. A small intestinal caecum is present. The two nephridia are short, free and swollen near their openings, which lie posterior to the anus. About 5–8 muscle strands run transversely just anteriorly to nephridiopores.

REMARKS. Described from a number of specimens. The species is allied to both *T. minor* (Ikeda) from Japan and *T. huttoni* from New Zealand. It differs from *T. minor* in the following respects: it is a larger species, the size of its hooks is different, it has a shorter rectum, smaller nephridia which open posteriorly to the anus and not at the same level as in *T. minor*, and contractile villi or tubules which branch to some extent. The specimens at Port Lincoln were collected from a calcareous reef.

DISTRIBUTION. South Australia and New Zealand (Edmonds, 1960).

Themiste hennahi Gray, 1828

Themiste hennahi Gray, 1828 : 8, pl. 6, figs 4, 4a; Baird, 1868 : 98; Stephen, 1965 : 458; Rice & Stephen, 1970 : 53–56, pl. 2, figs 6–8; Amor, 1970 : 496.
Dendrostoma peruvianum Collin, 1892 : 179–180, pl. 2, figs 7–13; Fischer, 1914b : 12–13, pl. 1, figs 1–3.
Dendrostomum peruvianum: Wesenberg-Lund, 1955b : 12–13.

TYPE LOCALITY. Peru. *Type*. Brit. Mus. (Nat. Hist.) No. 1963.16.1–5.

DESCRIPTION. Introvert about a third of the trunk length, devoid of hooks or spines. Four tentacle stems, two of which are large and two small; tentacles dark violet. Base and posterior portion of introvert darker than the trunk. The dorsal side of the introvert is marked by longitudinal cross stripes and skin bodies are uniformly scattered over its surface. Trunk up to 85 mm in length and 23 mm in diameter, coloured uniformly light grey. Skin bodies, which never attain the size of papillae, are scattered uniformly over the surface. One pair of retractors present arising from the edge of the posterior third of the trunk. Contractile vessel present on the anterior region of the oesophagus and a group of long moniliform villi, extending to the posterior portion of the trunk. Behind the fixing muscles

o

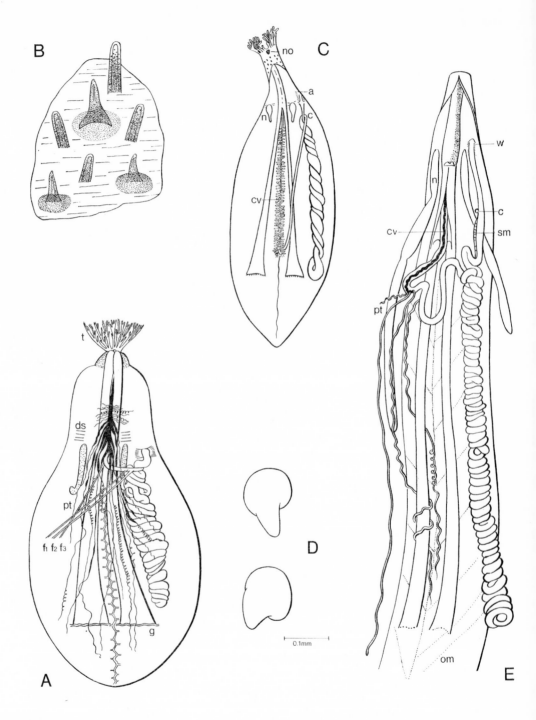

the oesophagus may carry longitudinal rows of spines (Collin) but neither Wesenberg-Lund nor Fischer have mentioned them.   Rectum fastened by a strong wing muscle. Rectal caecum present.   The nephridia open on a level with the anus, and are long, reaching nearly to the insertion of the retractors

REMARKS   The description given above differs slightly from the original by Gray due, presumably, to Gray misinterpreting certain structures (Stephen, 1965 : 458).   Both Collin and Wesenberg-Lund seem to have seen only small animals. Fischer's specimen had a trunk of length 85 mm, while Gray's specimen measured about 56 mm.   In spite of the long period of preservation Gray's specimens show very little deterioration and small structures may still be seen.   Fischer's description agrees closely with them.   The species has recently been redescribed in detail by Rice & Stephen, 1970 & Amor, 1970.

DISTRIBUTION.   Peru (Gray, 1828; Collin, 1892); Junin, Chile (Fischer, 1914b); Chile (Wesenberg-Lund, 1955; Amor, 1970).

Themiste hexadactyla (Sato, 1930)

(Fig. 24A)

Dendrostoma hexadactylum Sato, 1930b : 28–33, pl. 4, figs 20–24, text-figs 13–15; 1937a : 162–163, pl. 4, fig. 17; 1939 : 412; Okuda, 1946 : 224, pl. 29E.
Dendrostomum hexadactylum : Fisher, 1952 : 410–411, pl. 30, fig. 2.

TYPE LOCALITY.   Mutsu Bay, northern Honshu, Japan.

DESCRIPTION.   Introvert about one third of the length of the trunk.   A smooth ring, coloured light violet, occurs immediately behind the tentacles.   The introvert bears hooks and papillae; the papillae are cylindrical and of varying height in the area with hooks.   Hooks numerous, about 260 in number.   There are six main tentacular stems which subdivide again into 1–4 branches each with tentacles; the tentacles are light reddish-brown in colour.   Trunk up to 55 mm in length and 10 mm in thickness; generally yellowish-brown.   Under magnification, the surface shows numerous transverse furrows; longitudinal furrows occur in the posterior region, forming small areas each with a circular papilla in the centre.   The papillae in the middle region of the trunk are elliptical in surface view.   Longitudinal muscles continuous.   One pair of broad retractors arising at the level of the posterior third of the body.   A spindle muscle arises in front of the anus but is not attached posteriorly.   Three fixing muscles arise from the dorsal side of the body wall in the middle of the trunk; two are attached to the oesophagus and rectum respectively and the third is attached by two rootlets to both the oesophagus and rectum.   The details, however, vary from specimen to specimen.   A pair of broad wing muscles

FIG. 24.   (A) *Themiste hexadactyla*.   Dissection of type specimen, × about 1·5 (after Sato).   (B) *Themiste alutacea*.   Hooks and papillae from the introvert (after Selenka). (C–D) *Themiste fusca*.   (C) Dissected specimen.   (D) Introvert hooks.   (C–D after Edmonds.)   (E) *Themiste perimeces*.   Dissected specimen.   The nephridia are relatively short and there are no fixing muscles.   The oblique muscular bands of the body wall are shown (after Fisher).   KEY: *See* Fig. 11, p. 83, anchor the rectum near the anus. The contractile vessel passes along the dorsal side of the oesophagus and gives off a large number of blind tubules, which are often spirally twisted and entangled with the internal organs. Two nephridia are short tubes, greyish-yellow in colour opening at the same level as the anus. Several narrow dissepiments occur at the base of each organ. A small globular caecum on the rectum. No eye-spots observed.

REMARKS. This species is closely allied to *T. blanda*. According to Sato (1930 : 33) it differs from the latter (1) in the height of the papillae found in the hooked region of the introvert and (2) in possessing six main tentacular stems. Fisher (1952 : 410) says that the species closely resembles *T. pyroides* but differs in having more numerous introvert hooks, amongst which are very numerous and very small, upright, cylindrical papillae.

DISTRIBUTION. Japan (Sato, 1930b, 1937a, 1939; Okuda, 1946); California (Fisher, 1952).

Themiste huttoni (Benham, 1904)

Phascolosoma huttoni Benham, 1904 : 307.
? *Dendrostoma signifer* (partim) Selenka & de Man, 1883 : 86–87; Augener, 1903 : 337; Fischer, 1914b : 11.
Dendrostomum huttoni: Edmonds, 1960 : 164–165, pl. 3, text-figs 5–6.

TYPE LOCALITY. New Zealand.

DESCRIPTION. Introvert short, about 4–7 mm in length, with a few scattered dark brown irregularly-directed hooks on the anterior surface. Tentacles arise from four stems. Trunk up to about 45 mm in length; pear-shaped or flask-shaped, rather stout and bluntly pointed at the posterior end. Body wall thick, skin wrinkled at the posterior end otherwise apparently smooth. Under magnification the skin is seen to be covered with very small rounded papillae. Anatomy similar to that of *T. lageniformis*. Two stout retractors arise in the posterior half of the trunk and are fastened to the oesophagus by a thin sheet of tissue. Dorsal contractile vessel extending to the base of the retractors with numerous prominent branching villi. Intestinal coils tightly wound round a stout spindle muscle which is not attached posteriorly. Rectum short; post intestinal caecum present. Nephridia free, opening just posterior to the anus. Two or three fixing muscles; F_1 attaches the end of the oesophagus to the body wall, F_2 is attached near the first loop and F_3 the last loop of the intestine. F_2 was not always found.

REMARKS. Described originally from 20 specimens. Closely allied to *T. lageniformis* but differs most noticeably in the possession of prominent, stout hooks on the introvert. It is possible that the specimens from Sydney, Australia identified by Selenka (1883 : 86) as an 'armed variety of *T. signifer*' are *T. huttoni*. This needs to be checked.

DISTRIBUTION. New Zealand, several localities.

Themiste lageniformis Baird, 1868

(Fig. 25C)

Themiste lageniformis Baird, 1868 : 98–99, pl. 10, fig. 3; Rice & Stephen, 1970 : 66–67, pl. 3, figs 12–13.

Dendrostoma signifer Selenka & de Man, 1883 : 86–87, pl. ii, fig. 21, pl. 11, figs 163–169; Sluiter, 1886 : 515; 1891 : 115; 1902 : 19; Fischer, 1895 : 17; 1914a : 72–74; 1914b : 10–11; 1919a : 282–283; 1922c : 19; 1923b : 22; Augener, 1903 : 300–301; Ikeda, 1904 : 56–57, fig. 15; Hammerstein, 1915a : 2–3; Graveley, 1927 : 87; Awati & Pradham, 1935 : 102–113, 2 pls; 1936 : 114–131, 11 figs; Leroy, 1936 : 425; 1942 : 41–43, fig. 11.

Dendrostomum signifer: Edmonds, 1956 : 297, pl. 1, fig. 2; Wesenberg-Lund, 1959a : 198–199; 1959b : 213; 1963 : 129–130.

TYPE LOCALITY. ? Australia (collected by John Macgillivray). *Type*. Brit. Mus. (Nat. Hist.).

DESCRIPTION. Introvert short, brownish or yellowish-grey, with a dark band around the middle; more bluish-grey towards the tentacles; hooks absent. Tentacles numerous, arising from five to six stems. Trunk stoutly built, up to 40 mm in length, posteriorly drawn out to a point. Skin a brownish- or yellowish-red colour throughout; superficially smooth but under the microscope numerous scattered dark pigmented skin bodies, oval in shape, not raised into papillae can be seen. Two very strong retractors arise from the beginning of the hind trunk and join far forward. The oesophagus runs between the retractors, reaches the retractor roots and then as far as the intestinal coils. It carries a contractile vessel with many villi which reaches as far as the intestinal coils where it is fastened by a strong mesentery. Intestine looped into 15–20 convolutions; spindle muscle not attached posteriorly. Two long, free nephridia extend for half the length of the trunk.

REMARKS. There seems no doubt that the more usual and better known name *T. signifer* has to be abandoned for Baird's older name *T. lageniformis*. This is unfortunate and the new name will probably prove puzzling to many workers for some time.

The species is not always easy to identify. It appears that there are widely distributed populations of *Themiste* with a form and organization basically that of *T. lageniformis* but which represent a number of different species. They are:

 T. lageniformis Baird (=*T. signifer*) from the Philippines, Australia, Japan, Pacific Islands and South Africa.

 T. cymodoceae (Edmonds) from southern Australia.

 T. huttoni (Benham) from New Zealand and southern Australia—armed.

 T. fusca (Edmonds) from New Zealand and southern Australia—armed.

 T. minor (Ikeda) from Japan—armed.

 T. robertsoni (Stephen) from South Africa.

Selenka's specimens came from the Philippines, Singapore and Cape York (Queensland, Australia ?). Selenka describes the tentacles of the species as arising from 5–6 stems and makes no mention of a rectal caecum. Augener (1903 : 301) reports that a caecum is present in his specimens from Amboina, Ikeda (1904 : 56) describes specimens from Riukiu Is., Japan with four main tentacular stems and a

rectal caecum and Edmonds (1956 : 298) reports that the tentacles of some specimens from Queensland, Australia arise from four stems and that a caecum is present.
It seems likely, therefore, that the rectum does carry a caecum.

Selenka (1883) also refers to a 'variety' of *T. lageniformis* from Sydney, Australia
which is armed with posteriorly directed hooks about 0·2 mm long. A similar
'variety' is reported from New Zealand (Augener, 1903 : 337) and Tasmania (Fischer,
1914 : 10). There is little doubt that the hooked specimens from New Zealand
are *T. huttoni* (Benham, 1904). Edmonds (1960 : 164) confirmed that the internal
anatomy is like that of *T. lageniformis*. All the specimens from New Zealand that
Edmonds examined bore hooks and all the specimens of *T. lageniformis* from
Queensland lacked hooks. No specimens of the armed and unarmed forms were
found together. This leads Edmonds to conclude that the two 'varieties' are
different species. It must be pointed out, however, that Awati and Pradhan
(1935) state that the hooks present on the juveniles of their specimens of *T. lageniformis* 'fall off' when the animals are full grown. This cannot be true for the New
Zealand specimens of *T. huttoni* most of which contained developing or ripe eggs
and must have been mature specimens.

DISTRIBUTION   West Africa (Fischer, 1914a; Wesenberg-Lund, 1959a); Cape
Province (Fischer, 1914a; Wesenberg-Lund, 1959, 1963); Madagascar (Hammerstein,
1915); Red Sea (Leroy, 1936); Indonesia (Sluiter, 1902); Gulf of Manaar (Graveley,
1927); Siam (Fischer, 1923b); Indo-China (Leroy, 1936, 1942); Amboina (Augener,
1903); Riukiu Islands, Japan (Ikeda, 1904); Luzon, Philippines (Selenka & de Man,
1883); Australia (Selenka & de Man, 1883; Fischer, 1914b; Edmonds, 1956); New
Zealand (Fischer, 1914b); India (Awati & Pradhan, 1935).

Themiste lissa (Fisher, 1952)

(Fig. 25D)

Dendrostomum lissum Fisher, 1952 : 419–422, pl. 35.

TYPE LOCALITY. Point Lobos, Espiritu Santo Island, Baja California. *Type*.
U.S.N.M. no. 21222.

DESCRIPTION. Introvert short and thick, about a quarter of the length of the
body and without spines or papillae. Tentacles relatively large and profusely
branched; four main stems. Anterior third of introvert smooth, collar translucent; remainder covered with minute glands. Trunk about 24 mm long and
thick set. Colour warm sepia with darker zones particularly around the anus,
nephridiopores and at the posterior end. Skin glands minute, convex and closely
placed. One pair of large retractors arising at the beginning of the terminal fifth
of the body. Spindle muscle normal for genus. Very broad wing muscles. Three
fixing muscles as in *D. dyscrita*; 26 intestinal convolutions. Contractile tubules
very numerous, most branching near their base. Nephridia of unequal length and
opening well behind the anus.

REMARKS   Based originally on 16 specimens. No other records.

DISTRIBUTION. Known only from the intertidal zone, Gulf of California.

Themiste minor (Ikeda, 1904)

Dendrostoma minor Ikeda, 1904 : 57–59, text-figs 16, 92–95; Sato, 1939 : 411; Stephen, 1942 : 252; Chin, 1947 : 100.
Dendrostomum minor: Wesenberg-Lund, 1963 : 128–129.

TYPE LOCALITY. Japan.

DESCRIPTION. Introvert about one third as long as the trunk; anterior portion light violet. Hooks about 50, scattered over the anterior part of the introvert, with a slightly curved and bluntly pointed apex; brown in colour. In the hooked region the papillae are small, nearly the same height and appearing like hemispherical tubercles resting on a broader basal elevation. Tentacles given off from four stems, each of which splits into two branches. Each branch divides into 4–6 tentacules which are violet with bright yellow tips. Trunk small, up to 15 mm in length and 3 mm in breadth; yellowish brown in colour. The surface of the trunk is covered with papillae which are small and nearly flat in the mid region of the body. Anteriorly and posteriorly they are somewhat raised and appear as oval tubercles 0·02–0·03 mm in height and 0·10 mm along the long diameter. They are formed of numerous polygonal chitinous plates which grow larger towards the centre of the papilla. One pair of retractors originates in the middle of the trunk or slightly more posteriorly. The contractile vessel has numerous short villi. Intestinal convolutions 7–12, loosely and irregularly coiled especially in young animals. The spindle muscle is not attached posteriorly. Rectum fairly long with a caecum. Fixing muscles may be two, one or none; if two present each is attached to the first convolution and arises from the side of the nerve cord. When only one is present it is on the left side. Nephridia about a third as long as the trunk and free and opening at the level of the anus. Eye-spots present.

REMARKS. *Themiste fusca* (Edmonds) from southern Australia and New Zealand is closely allied.

DISTRIBUTION. Japan (Ikeda, 1904; Sato, 1939); Fukien, China (Chin, 1947); South Africa (Stephen, 1942; Wesenberg-Lund, 1963).

Themiste perimeces (Fisher, 1928)

(Fig. 24E)

Dendrostoma perimeces Fisher, 1928 : 196–198, pl. 6, figs 3, 3a, pl. 7, fig. 1, pl. 8, figs 2, 2a: 1952 : 415–417, pl. 27, fig. 3, pl. 28, fig. 1; pl. 30, fig. 4, pl. 33; MacGinitie, 1935b : 631–682.

TYPE LOCALITY. Elkhorn Slough, Monterey Bay, California. *Type.* U.S.N.M. no. 19615.

DESCRIPTION. A very long and slender species. Introvert cylindrical, about a sixth of the total length of animal; anterior fifth forms a glossy brown collar with fine longitudinal creases which is separated by a smooth whitish zone from the main part where the skin is sepia coloured. The sepia coloured area is scattered with tiny dark brown papillae each with a terminal pore. Hooks absent. Tentacles six, highly dendritic, branching down to the base; pale olive-green or brown. Worms

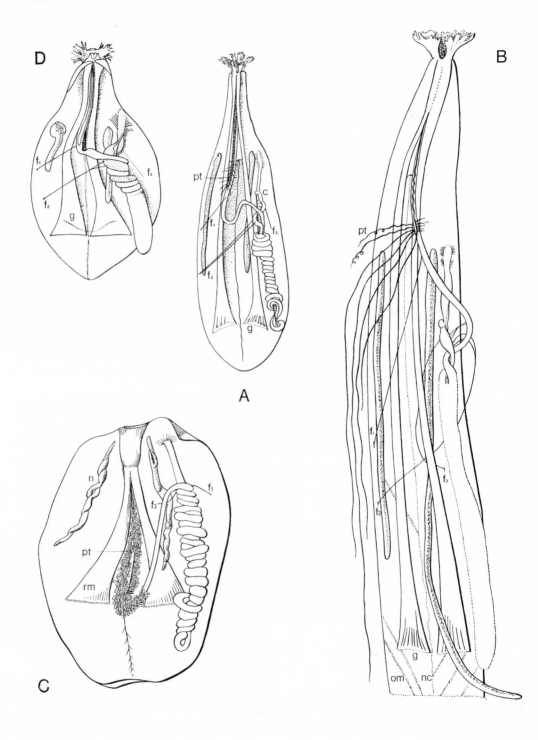

large, over 260 mm; body very slender, cylindrical, tapering gradually to the rounded or bluntly pointed posterior end. Papillae forming low brown protuberances. One pair very large, long retractors which arise from the beginning of the posterior fifth of the body. Oesophagus long and fixed by a mesentery between the retractor muscles. Contractile vessel passes along the oesophagus and has a collateral vessel on each side; posteriorly it gives off six to eight long villi. The nephridia are long and open behind anus.

REMARKS. The species is generally similar to *T. zostericola*. It is, however, longer. It differs in having more numerous papillae on the introvert, fewer Polian tubules at the end of the contractile vessel and a much longer alimentary canal.

DISTRIBUTION. Bodega Head to Venice, California. An intertidal and shallow water form.

Themiste petricola Amor, 1964

Dendrostomum petricolum Amor, 1964 : 463–467, pl. 3, 5 figs.

TYPE LOCALITY. Santa Clara de Mar, Prov. of Buenos Aires, Argentina. *Type*. Museo de La Plata, Argentina.

DESCRIPTION. Trunk subpyriform to fusiform; length 27 mm width 4 mm. Introvert 6 mm long. Zone of simple spines or hooks present in the middle of the ntrovert. Tentacles arise from six stems which branch dichotomously and become dendritic. Introvert except for the anterior quarter bears subcylindrical to pyriform papillae; trunk with elliptical papillae. Two free nephridia open on the same level as the anus. Two retractors inserted between the middle and posterior third of the trunk. Contractile vessel with large, numerous, branching tubules. Three fixing muscles.

REMARKS. Described from 12 specimens. The species is close to *T. rosacea* Amor, 1964. It differs, according to Amor, in its shape and colour and the way in which its intestinal fasteners are arranged.

DISTRIBUTION. Argentina.

Themiste pinnifolia (Keferstein, 1865)

Dendrostoma pinnifolium Keferstein, 1865a : 429, pl. 33, figs 42–43; Selenka & Bülow, 1883 : 83–84.
Themiste pinnifolia: Baird, 1868 : 98.

TYPE LOCALITY. St Thomas, West Indies.

DESCRIPTION. Introvert about a third of the length of the trunk with a zone of very irregular rows of scattered hooks present in the middle; anteriorly it is smooth

---

FIG. 25. (A) *Themiste dyscrita*. Dissected specimen, details of polian tubules have been omitted. (B) *Themiste zostericola*. Dissected specimen. Only six of the 11 polian tubules have been completed. (C) *Themiste lageniformis*. Dissected specimen (after Selenka). (D) *Themiste lissa*. Dissected specimen. The polian tubules have been omitted for simplification. (A, B and D after Fisher.) KEY: *See* Fig. 11, p. 83.

and without papillae. Six large, regularly divided broad tentacles which have
on either side 8–10 tentacules. Trunk four to five times as long as thick and up
to 12 mm in length. Skin thin and translucent, with a nacreous lustre, covered
with scattered, hemispherical papillae more densely crowded at the posterior end
and in front of the anus. Musculature thin. Two pairs of retractors arise near
each other in the middle third of the body. Contractile vessel appears in the middle
of the trunk as a cylindrical, free lying, vessel. Nephridia short.

REMARKS. Known only from the holotype.

DISTRIBUTION. As for the type locality.

Themiste pyroides (Chamberlain, 1919)

(Fig. 23A–E)

Dendrostoma pyroides Chamberlain, 1919 : 31; Fisher, 1952 : 406–409, pl. 27, figs 1, 2, pl. 28,
    fig. 2, pl. 29, 3 figs.
Dendrostoma petraeum Fisher, 1928 : 195–196, pl. 6, figs 1 1a 1b, 2; pl. 7, fig. 2, pl. 8, figs 1, 1a.
? *Dendrostoma blandum* Sato, 1930 : 27; 1939 : 411.

TYPE LOCALITY. Laguna Beach, Orange County, California. *Type.* Originally
in the Museum of Comparative Zoology.

DESCRIPTION. Introvert cylindrical and about a half to a third the length of
the body; anterior third is a red-brown to purplish glossy zone, middle third armed
with dark brown, well-spaced, curved spines and basal third smooth. Four main
branches of highly dendritic tentacles, each branch consisting of two main stems
between which is a minor branch that may sometimes become large. Trunk
large, over 120 mm long and pear-shaped; its surface peppered with minute brown
spots of two or three sizes. Two large retractor muscles arise in the middle of the
posterior third of the body. Spindle muscle attached just behind the anus. Rectal
caecum present. A contractile vessel runs along the dorsal surface of the oesophagus
and gives off numerous anastomosing branches that form a network. Two long
nephridia.

REMARKS. Fisher suggests that *T. blanda* described by Sato from California may
be synonymous with *T. pyroides*. This seems most likely. Fisher places his *T.
petraea* in the synonymy of *T. pyroides* without comment.

DISTRIBUTION. Baja California.

Themiste robertsoni (Stephen & Robertson, 1952)

Dendrostoma robertsoni Stephen & Robertson, 1952 : 438–439, pl. 1, figs 3–4.
Dendrostomum robertsoni : Wesenberg-Lund, 1963 : 130.

TYPE LOCALITY. Chwaka Bay, Zanzibar. *Type.* Royal Scottish Museum,
Edinburgh.

DESCRIPTION. The introvert with a darker shading on its upper part and a blue
area near the tentacles whatever the colour of the specimen. The tentacles arise
from four stems, each of which in turn branches into two. Total length 17–44 mm.

Body covered with scattered clear papillae, small in some specimens, more prominent in others, especially at the base of the introvert and at the posterior end. Two moderately long retractors, arising from a level about three quarters of the way along the trunk towards the posterior end. The nephridia, which open at about the level of the anus, are long and about half the length of the trunk. The intestine is not attached posteriorly by the spindle muscle. There are two fixing muscles, which hold the anterior portion of the intestine to the body wall; the first is short and stout and fixes the basal loop of the oesophagus. The second is long and thin and is inserted at the level of the first intestinal convolution. Contractile tubules of moderate length, fairly numerous, brown in colour and branched; each branch is club-shaped at the end.

REMARKS. Based originally on 28 specimens. Closely related to *T. lageniformis* Baird but differs in the arrangement of the tentacles, arrangement of the papillae on the trunk, lighter and longer retractors, length and number of the contractile tubules, and the number and arrangement of the fixing muscles.

DISTRIBUTION. Zanzibar (Stephen & Robertson, 1952); South Africa (Wesenberg-Lund, 1963).

Themiste rosacea (Amor, 1964)

Dendrostomum rosaceum Amor, 1964 : 459, pls 1, 2 and 3.

TYPE LOCALITY. North west Mar del Plata (37°55′S, 57°20′5″W), Argentine; at about 18 m. *Holotype.* Museo de La Plata, Argentina.

DESCRIPTION. Trunk pyriform to globose, about 19·2 mm long and 16 mm wide in the type specimen. Introvert about 5·8 mm long, bearing in its middle region spines about 0·117 mm tall and with a basal diameter of 0·173 mm. Anterior third of the introvert is smooth, the remaining area bearing subcylindrical to pyriform papillae of varying height. At the base of the introvert and on the trunk the papillae are elliptical and flat. Tentacles arise from six stems which divide dichotomously a number of times so that the tentacular crown is dendritic; tentacules digitiform prolongations. Two retractors arise in the middle third of the trunk and remain separate for the greater part of their length. Three fixing muscles to the alimentary canal. Contractile vessel with a few (20 in the holotype) very long tubules, some of which branch once or twice. Rectal caecum, spindle muscle and wing muscle present. Nephridia about one third as long as the trunk and free; nephridiopore and anal aperture at the same level. Nuchal organ present and two pigment spots on the cerebral ganglion.

REMARKS. Described from 24 specimens. The species is allied to *T. blanda* (Selenka, 1883) but differs in the size of the spines, the arrangement of the intestinal fasteners and the presence of an intestinal caecum.

T. petricola (Amor) and *T. rosacea* are very close species, both described from Argentine. According to Amor (1964 : 465) the two differ in the form and colour of their body, the complexity of their tentacular crown, the arrangement of their intestinal fasteners and the presence of a constriction at the end of the oesophagus.

DISTRIBUTION.   Several localities in Argentine.

Themiste schmitti (Fisher, 1952)

Dendrostomum schmitti Fisher, 1952 : 422, fig. 87F.

TYPE LOCALITY.   Independencia Bay, Peru.   *Type*.   U.S.N.M. no. 21216.

DESCRIPTION.   Introvert lacking papillae.   Trunk lacking convex papillae.   No elevations on the oesophagus.   Nephridia opening posteriorly to the anus.   Intestinal fixing muscle anchors both the descending and ascending portions of the gut and not only the post oesophageal gut.

REMARKS.   Fisher gave only a very brief description, which consists mainly in pointing out the differences between this species and *T. hennahi*.   The relationship between *T. lissa* and *T. schmitti* is also very close and according to Fisher (1952 : 422) possibly represents the extreme geographical variations of one species.

DISTRIBUTION.   As for the type locality.

Themiste spinifera (Sluiter, 1902)

Dendrostoma spinifer Sluiter, 1902 : 41, pl. 4, figs 6–7.

TYPE LOCALITY.   Siboga Stn. 105 (6°8'N, 121°19'E); at 275 m.

DESCRIPTION.   Introvert short, about a quarter of the length of the trunk; eight fairly long tentacles branching once near the base and gain towards the tip where they split into further shorter branches.   No hooks but near the base there are irregularly arranged fairly large thin spines, 0·24 mm in height.   Trunk about 10 mm in length and 4 mm in diameter.   The skin appears quite smooth under the lens but the microscope shows it to be covered with small elongate-oval papillae with a central opening but no chitinous plates.   Two broad retractors arise just posterior to the middle of the trunk.   The contractile vessel bears numerous fairly long villi.   The intestinal spiral is well developed and is not fixed posteriorly by the spindle muscle.   The two nephridia are about half the length of the trunk and open posterior to the anus.

REMARKS.   Known only from the holotype.

DISTRIBUTION.   As for the type locality.

Themiste stephensoni (Stephen, 1942)

Dendrostoma stephensoni Stephen, 1942 : 252–253, pl. 1, fig. 5.
Dendrostomum stephensoni Wesenberg-Lund, 1963 : 133–134, text-fig. 10.

TYPE LOCALITY.   Port Alfred.   Cape Province; littoral.   *Type*.   Royal Scottish Museum.

DESCRIPTION.   Introvert yellowish-brown to violet and without hooks and spines. Trunk yellowish-brown to rusty red, much ridged without visible papillae, under a lens papillae are seen to be numerous anteriorly and on the middle of the trunk, sparse posteriorly. Two pairs of retractors. A spindle muscle, not attached posteriorly; two fixing mesenteries anchor the top intestinal coil to the body wall. The dorsal contractile vessel carries a band of very short, flat, light yellow villi. Rectum anchored by wing muscles. A small rectal caecum present. The two nephridia are short, free for their whole length, and open on the same level as the anus.

REMARKS. Based originally on ten specimens. Wesenberg-Lund briefly described three and included notes on further specimens. The species is closely related to *T. pinnifolia* Keferstein, recorded from the West Indies. It differs mainly in the contractile villi, which are few and short, whereas in *T. pinnifolia* they are long and numerous and in lacking hooks on the introvert.

DISTRIBUTION. Cape Province and Natal (Stephen, 1942; Wesenberg-Lund, 1963).

Themiste tropica (Sato, 1935)

Dendrostoma tropicum Sato, 1935b : 313–315, pl. 4, fig. 15, text-fig. 11; 1939 : 411.
Dendrostomum tropicum: Wesenberg-Lund, 1963 : 131–132.

TYPE LOCALITY. Takagen, Yap Island, West Caroline Islands.

DESCRIPTION. Introvert extremely short, only 4 mm in length and 1·5 mm thick, without papillae. Trunk spindle shaped, 18 mm in total length, 6 mm in thickness. Skin opaque, dark reddish-brown in alcohol; in the posterior region the pigment forms reticulations. Numerous flat papillae on the surface of the trunk; in surface view they are roundish in the posterior region, but elongate in the middle and anterior portions of the trunk. One pair of broad retractors arises from the body wall at the level of the posterior quarter of the trunk. The spindle muscle arises near the rectum at the level of the first intestinal convolution; it is not attached posteriorly. Three fixing muscles, one short and broad the others long and narrow, attach the anterior portion of the digestive canal to the body wall. Wing muscles well developed. About 10 intestinal convolutions very irregularly arranged; a small caecum on the rectum. The contractile vessel passes along the oesophagus and carries numerous short tubules. The nephridia are tubes about 15 mm in length and 1 mm in diameter opening almost on the same level as the anus.

REMARKS. Wesenberg-Lund redescribed the species.

DISTRIBUTION. Japan (Sato, 1938); South Africa (Wesenberg-Lund, 1963).

Themiste zostericola (Chamberlain, 1919)

(Fig. 25B)

Dendrostoma zostericolum Chamberlain, 1919 : 30; Peebles & Fox, 1933 : 201, figs 1–11.
Dendrostomum zostericolum Fisher, 1952 : 411–415, pl. 30, fig. 1, text-fig. 87A, pls 31–32; Gross, 1954 : 403–423, 10 text-figs.
Dendrostoma mytheca Chamberlain, 1919 : 30.

TYPE LOCALITY. Laguna Beach, Orange County, California. *Type.* Museum of Comparative Zoology.

DESCRIPTION. Introvert relatively short, 30 mm with tiny club-shaped papillae which decrease in size towards the broad band behind the tentacles. Hooks absent. Tentacles six, branching profusely; each branching into two major stems near the base. Trunk long, slender, cylindrical up to 245 mm. Skin rather smooth, in the post-anal region with tiny brown glands, which in the anal zone, gradually lengthen into the papillae of the introvert. Three fixing muscles. Two long retractors which do not join till near the head. Dorsal contractile vessel with 10–12 very long villi. Nephridia very long, slender and free, opening close behind the anus.

REMARKS. Fisher (1952 : 415) considers that this 'species is probably the North American equivalent of *Dendrostomum peruvianum* Collin, 1892'. *D. peruvianum* Collin, 1892 is now called *Themiste hennahi* Gray, 1828.

D. mytheca Chamberlain, 1919 : 30 was based on a specimen 20 mm long from Laguna Beach which is no longer in existence. The trunk measured 12 mm and the introvert 8 mm. Fisher (1952 : 415) considers that it 'may well have been a young *D. zostericola*'. We are following his lead.

DISTRIBUTION. California, U.S.A.

GENUS *NEPHASOMA* Pergament

Nephasoma Pergament, 1940 : 55–61.

DESCRIPTION. Small animals with a cylindrical body which tapers slightly at both ends. Introvert about twice as long as the trunk. Skin smooth; glandular bodies are present near the anal aperture and on the posterior surface of the body. Introvert without hooks, without tentacles and without an oral disc. Vascular system lacking. Longitudinal muscles of the body wall continuous. Single retractor muscle, sometimes bifurcated at its base, arises in the anterior third of the trunk. Two nephridia. Intestinal spirals irregular. Anal aperture not on the trunk but on the mid-region of the introvert. No spindle muscle.

TYPE SPECIES. *Nephasoma marinki* Pergament, 1940.

REMARKS. This genus is closely allied to the genus *Onchnesoma* Koren & Daniels-ssen, especially in the position of the anus in the middle of the introvert and in the reduction of the tentacular crown. The most noticeable difference is that two nephridia are present in *Nephasoma* but only one in *Onchnesoma*. Pergament also points out that the retractor muscle of *Nephasoma* arises from the anterior region of the trunk but that of *Onchnesoma* from the posterior.

The genus also resembles *Golfingia* but differs most noticeably in possessing only one retractor and in the absence of a tentacular system, although a reduction of the tentacles to a few lobes or prominences does take place in some golfingiid species of the subgenus *Phascoloides*. The genus contains only one species.

DISTRIBUTION. Arctic.

Nephasoma marinki Pergament, 1940

Nephasoma marinki Pergament, 1940 : 55–61, 2 figs.

TYPE LOCALITY. Northern Arctic Ocean: 'Sedov' Expedition.

DESCRIPTION. Introvert twice as long as the trunk, widened in the middle and without hooks or tentacles. Trunk 15 mm long and 2·5 mm thick, semi-translucent and yellow-grey (in alcohol). Small, inconspicuous glandular bodies are present in the region of the anus and on the posterior quarter of the trunk. A single retractor arises in the anterior third or quarter of the trunk and may bifurcate slightly posteriorly. Intestine of about 15–25 coils is wound in an irregular spiral. Spindle muscle absent. Long rectum which may wind itself around the retractor once or twice before reaching the anus in the middle of the introvert. Two elongate, sac-like nephridia arise just posterior to the anal aperture or in some specimens at about the same level.

REMARKS. The species was described from several specimens. Pergament reports that the nephridial openings also lie in the mid-region of the introvert. This is very uncommon in sipunculans and certainly very different from the position of the nephridiopore in *Onchnesoma* where it is on the trunk. It must be very difficult in *Nephasoma* to decide where the introvert ends and the trunk begins.

DISTRIBUTION. As for the type locality.

(5). Family **ASPIDOSIPHONIDAE**

Aspidosiphonidae Baird, 1868 : 100 (in part).
Loxosiphonidae Baird, 1868 : 103.

DESCRIPTION. Rather small sipunculans in which a horny anal shield or calcareous cap is clearly marked off on the anterior part of the trunk and in which the tentacles surround or partly surround the mouth. A caudal shield may be present at the posterior extremity of the trunk. The introvert arises from the trunk ventrally to the anterior shield or cap in all genera except *Cloeosiphon* and *Centrosiphon;* in the last two it arises from the middle of the cap. Longitudinal musculature of the body wall either continuous or grouped into bundles, the latter often anastomosing. Two nephridia.

TYPE GENUS. *Aspidosiphon* Diesing, 1851.

REMARKS. The name Aspidosiphonidae was first given to a family of sipunculans by Baird (1868) which contained the genera *Aspidosiphon* Diesing, 1851 and *Pseudaspidosiphon* Baird, 1868. Baird gave no description of the family. The term has been used only rarely, if at all, since Baird's day. We are reintroducing it into the literature of the phylum with an amended diagnosis. The family now contains the genera *Aspidosiphon* Diesing, 1851, *Paraspidosiphon* Stephen, 1965, *Lithacrosiphon* Shipley, 1902, *Cloeosiphon* Grübe, 1867 and *Centrosiphon* Shipley, 1903. Aspidosiphonids are usually borers that live in calcareous rock or coral.

The genus *Aspidosiphon* Diesing has always been readily divisible into two according to the condition of the longitudinal musculature of the body wall (Selenka & de Man, 1883 : 14; Wesenberg-Lund, 1937c : 18–19; Sato, 1939 : 449). Because he considered the nature of the longitudinal muscles to be a character of high order in the systematics of the phylum Stephen, 1965 split the original *Aspidosiphon* into two genera, viz. *Aspidosiphon* Diesing, 1851 (*sensu stricto*) in which the longitudinal musculature is continuous and *Paraspidosiphon* a new genus, in which the longitudinal musculature is grouped into bundles. It is true that the relation between the two genera is closer than that between any other two genera of the Aspidosiphonidae. If, however, the genus *Fisherana* Stephen is to be distinguished from *Phascolosoma* Leuckart, then *Paraspidosiphon* is entitled to generic status.

The relation between the four genera is shown in Table 9.

TABLE 9

The relations between the genera of the family Aspidosiphonidae

	Anterior shield or cap	Posterior shield	Introvert arises	Longitudinal musculature
Aspidosiphon	present	present	ventral to shield	continuous
Paraspidosiphon	present	present	ventral to shield	banded
Lithacrosiphon	present	absent	ventral to cap	banded
Cloeosiphon	present	absent	middle of cap	continuous
Centrosiphon	present	present	middle of cap	continuous

FAMILY ASPIDOSIPHONIDAE—KEY TO GENERA

1 Caudal shield present 2
– Caudal shield absent 4
2 Longitudinal musculature of body wall in bundles which may anastomose (introvert arises ventral to the shield) . . . . . ***PARASPIDOSIPHON*** (p. 237)
– Longitudinal musculature of body wall continuous 3
3 Introvert arises ventral to the anal shield . . . . ***ASPIDOSIPHON*** (p. 216)
– Introvert arises from middle of anterior cap or shield . . ***CENTROSIPHON*** (p. 268)
4 Longitudinal musculature of body wall continuous (anterior cap subspherical and pineapple-like: introvert arises from the middle of the cap).
CLOEOSIPHON (p. 267)
– Longitudinal musculature of body wall in bundles which may anastomose (anterior cap has shape of truncated cone: introvert arises ventral to the anterior cap)
LITHACROSIPHON (p. 259)

Genus *ASPIDOSIPHON* Diesing, 1851

Aspidosiphon Diesing, 1851 : 67–68 (restricted).
Pseudaspidosiphon Baird, 1868 : 102 (in part).
Aspidosiphon Stephen, 1965 : 457.

DESCRIPTION. Sipunculans with prominent anal and caudal shields and with the longitudinal musculature of the body wall continuous. Introvert arises eccentrically from the ventral side of the anterior or anal shield; anteriorly it is usually armed with rows of single- or double-pointed hooks and posteriorly with spines. Hooks and spines are lacking in some species.   Tentacles usually small and finger-like; they surround or partly surround the mouth in a semi- or three quarter-circle (but never lie in a horseshoe shaped ring completely dorsal to the mouth as in the genus *Phascolosoma*).   The anal and caudal shields are usually circular, elliptical, truncate or conical in shape and darker in colour than the trunk; their surface may be furrowed, grooved, covered with calcareous, horny or chitinous granules or in some species with conical or spine-like protuberances.   Differs from the genus *Paraspidosiphon* in that the longitudinal musculature forms a continuous sheet.   One or two retractor muscles, a single retractor usually arising from two short roots which are fastened to the posterior surface of the body wall or to the caudal shield.   Two nephridia.   Contractile vessel simple.   Spindle muscle may sometimes be attached posteriorly to the caudal shield.   Simple rectal caecum present in some species.

TYPE SPECIES.   *Aspidosiphon muelleri* Diesing, 1851.

REMARKS.   We have followed the lead of Stephen (1965) in restricting the genus *Aspidosiphon* to species in which the longitudinal musculature is continuous and in placing the species in which the longitudinal musculature is banded into the genus *Paraspidosiphon*.   The matter is also discussed on p. 216.

We have not been able to group the species of *Aspidosiphon* and *Paraspidosiphon* according to the number of their retractor muscles on account of the difficulty of distinguishing between the condition of 'two retractor muscles which soon join to form one' and the condition of 'one retractor muscle which arises from two short roots'.

Aspidosiphon muelleri has during the past 50 years been regarded as the type of the genus, although Diesing (1851) did not make this clear.   Cuénot (1922), Hérubel (1924) and Leroy (1936) have regarded *A. clavatus* (de Blainville, 1827) and *A. muelleri* as synonymous with the former having priority.   They may be right.   *Sipunculus clavatus*, however, is a poorly described species nor is it clear that any of the French workers re-examined the type.   Quatrefages (1865 : 611) considered *S. clavatus* as *species incertae sedis*.   We consider it best to do the same. Records of the species other than that of the type we have placed in the synonymy of *A. muelleri*.

DISTRIBUTION.   Usually in tropical and temperate seas.

List of species

Species without hooks and spines on the introvert

A. albus Murina
A. imbellis Sluiter
A. venabulus Selenka & de Man

P

Species with hooks and spines on the introvert

All hooks with single points	All or some hooks with two points
A. cylindricus Horst.	*A. brocki* Augener
A. exhaustus Sluiter	*A. carolinus* Sato
A. inquilinus Sluiter	*A. elegans* (Cham. & Eys.)
A. jukesii Baird	*A. exilis* Sluiter
A. kovaleskii Murina	*A. gerouldi* ten Broeke
A. parvulus Gerould	*A. gracilis* Baird
A. ravus Sluiter	*A. hartmeyeri* Fischer
A. spiralis Sluiter	*A. homomyarius* Johnson
	A. misakiensis Ikeda
	A. muelleri Diesing
	A. spinalis Ikeda
	A. spinosus Sluiter
	A. tortus Selenka & de Man

GENUS ASPIDOSIPHON—KEY TO SPECIES

1 Hooks and spines present on the introvert. 4
– Hooks and spines absent from the introvert 2
2 Two retractor muscles (anal and caudal shields clearly furrowed, retractors arise from the caudal shield, spindle muscle attached posteriorly, nephridia as long as the trunk) . . . . *A. imbellis* (p. 227)
– One retractor muscle which arises from two roots 3
3 Anal shield with dark, pointed papillae around its edge (introvert about five times as long as trunk, one fixing muscle, nephridia about as long as trunk and attached for anterior two-thirds) . . . . *A. venabulus* (p. 237)
– Anal shield without dark, pointed papillae around its edge (introvert about four times as long as trunk, no fixing muscle, radial grooves on both shields indistinct, no caecum) . . . . *A. albus* (p. 219)
4 All or some hooks on introvert with double points 12
– No hooks on introvert with double points but all with single points . . . 5
5 Retractor muscle not attached to the caudal shield 6
– Retractor muscle attached to the caudal shield 7
6 Nephridia very long and attached along their anterior half (spines on introvert with 'pockets', both shields covered with horny points and show little sign of furrowing; fixing muscle and rectal caecum present) . . *A. ravus* (p. 234)
– Nephridia long but free for their whole length . . . *A. cylindricus* (p. 222)
7 Anal shield with prominent, spine-like structures 8
– Anal shield without prominent, spine-like structures 9
8 Trunk stick-like; alimentary canal with three fixing muscles . *A. kovaleskii* (p. 229)
– Trunk stumpy; alimentary canal without fixing muscles . . *A. parvulus* (p. 233)
9 Spindle muscle not attached posteriorly (anal shield coarsely papillose and with straight furrows, caudal shield clearly furrowed; nephridia about half as long as trunk and opening posteriorly to the anus) . . . *A. inquilinus* (p. 227)
– Spindle muscle attached posteriorly 10
10 Caudal shield weakly developed 11
– Caudal shield strongly developed (anal shield with 12 furrows and caudal with 10; nephridia are long, attached to trunk for most of their length and open on the same level as the anus) . . . . *A. exhaustus* (p. 224)

11 Anal shield weakly developed (nephridia free for half their length)   **A. spiralis** (p. 236)
–   Anal shield very distinct (nephridia attached for most of their length, no rectal
      caecum, one fixing muscle) . . . .   **A. jukesii** (p. 228)
12 Some hooks on introvert with single- and some with double-points (introvert about
      three times as long as trunk, anterior hooks with two points and posterior ones
      with a single point; scattered spines also present; both shields brown-black and
      incised by radial and concentric furrows to form regular patches; rectal caecum
      present, nephridia fixed for two-thirds of their length and open on same level as
      anus) . . . .   **A. muelleri** (p. 231)
–   All hooks on introvert with double points   13
13 One retractor muscle which arises from a single broad root (retractor attached
      posterior to the middle of the trunk, furrows on shields indistinct, nephridia
      very long and free along their posterior half) . . .   **A. exilis** (p. 224)
–   One retractor which arises from two roots   14
14 Retractor muscle(s) arise(s) from or just near the caudal shield   15
–   Retractor muscle(s) arise(s) well in front of the caudal shield   20
15 Rectal caecum present   18
–   Rectal caecum absent   16
16 Nephridia free for their whole length . . . .   **A. carolinus** (p. 222)
–   Nephridia not free for their whole length   17
17 Nephridia attached for their whole length . . .   **A. gerouldi** (p. 225)
–   Nephridia attached for two thirds of their length . . .   **A. tortus** (p. 236)
18 Nephridia free . . . .   **A. hartmeyeri** (p. 226)
–   Nephridia attached for all or most of their length . . .   19
19 No fixing muscle . . . .   **A. spinalis** (p. 234)
–   One fixing muscle . . . . . .   **A. misakiensis** (p. 229)
20 Rectal caecum present   21
–   Rectal caecum absent (spines sharp and with four-cornered bases; retractors
      attached to body wall one sixth of the length of the trunk anterior to caudal
      shield; nephridia long and attached along their whole length)
                                    { **A. gracilis** (p. 225)
                                    { **A. homomyarius** (p. 227)
21 Spines on the introvert strongly curved . . . . .   **A. spinosus** (p. 235)
–   Spines on the introvert not strongly curved but almost straight   22
22 Nephridia fixed to trunk for their whole length (35–100 regular rows of hooks,
      trunk long and slim, one fixing muscle, retractors arise from anterior edge of
      posterior third of trunk) . . . .   **A. elegans** (p. 223)
–   Nephridia fixed to trunk only for the anterior half of their length   **A. brocki** (p. 221)

Aspidosiphon albus Murina, 1967

Aspidosiphon albus Murina, 1967a : 1330–1331, fig. 2 (1)–(3).

TYPE LOCALITY. Cuba (22°56′N, 83°23′W); at 14 m.

DESCRIPTION. Introvert slender, about four times as long as the trunk, white in colour, lacking hooks and spines but possessing numerous lens-like skin-bodies which lie in ring-like rows; several white tentacles and two eye-spots present. Trunk 4 mm long and 1 mm wide. Body wall white, opaque and bearing brown skin papillae (height 0·01–0·15 mm) that are very thickly distributed near the two shields. Anal shield oval, 0·7 mm long and 0·6 mm wide, narrowing slightly towards the introvert and dark brown in colour. The shield is covered with a mosaic of small, polygonal plates and the radial grooves are not well developed. Caudal shield

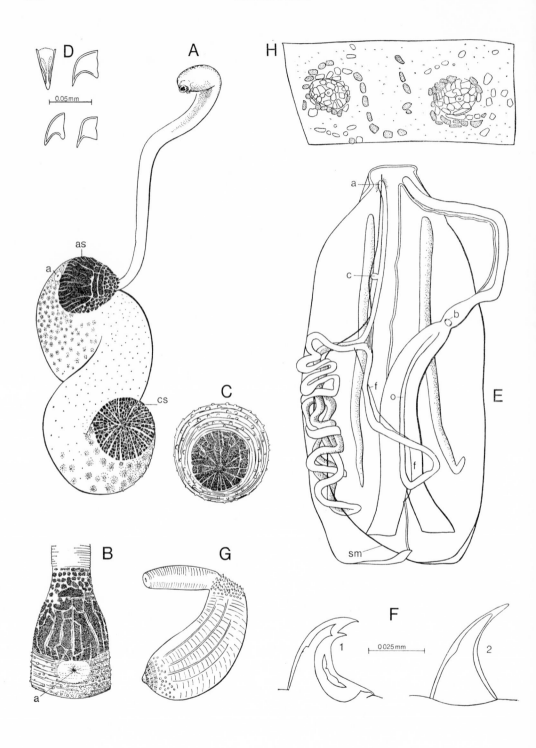

round, conical with a diameter of 0·7 mm and a height of 0·25 mm; yellow in colour and radial grooves indistinct. Longitudinal musculature continuous. A single retractor muscle arises from two short roots fastened to the body wall just in front of the caudal shield. Intestinal spirals 20, fastened posteriorly by a spindle muscle. Nephridia two, twisted and opening at about the same level as the anus. Caecum, contractile vessel and fixing muscles not found.

REMARKS. Described from a single specimen. The species is allied to *A. imbellis* Sluiter.

DISTRIBUTION. As for the holotype.

Aspidosiphon brocki Augener, 1903

(Fig. 27B)

Aspidosiphon brocki Augener, 1903 : 34–36, text-figs 9–13; Murina, 1967b : 42.

TYPE LOCALITY. Polo Ednam, Amboina, Malaya.

DESCRIPTION. Introvert about three quarters the length of the trunk, with numerous rows of double pointed hooks anteriorly and spines posteriorly. Trunk up to 40 mm in length; body wall transparent. The well-developed anal shield is darker than the mid-trunk, has furrows at its periphery and a granular centre. The more or less hemispherical caudal shield is not clearly differentiated from the trunk and is lighter in colour than the anal shield; around its periphery, it has furrows that do not reach the centre. The mid-portion of the trunk appears to be smooth, but, under magnification, is seen to bear small scattered papillae; they are arranged in rows at the introvert base and at the posterior end of the trunk. The largest papillae appear as a rim behind the anal shield and are not separated from it by furrows. One retractor with two roots, about a third to a quarter of the trunk length; 23–30 intestinal convolutions. A spindle muscle arises near the anus and is attached to the caudal shield. The rectum is fastened by strong wing muscles; a small rectal caecum present. Nephridia about two thirds as long as the trunk. Their anterior half is attached to the trunk wall and they open behind the anus.

REMARKS. Based on six specimens.

DISTRIBUTION. Malaya (Augener, 1903); Cuba (Murina, 1967b).

FIG. 26. (A–D) *Aspidosiphon muelleri*. (A) Entire specimen, showing anal and caudal shields. The introvert arises ventral to the anal shield (original). (B) Anal shield. (C) Caudal shield. (D) Hooks from the introvert. (B–D after Théel.) (E–F) *Aspidosiphon misakiensis*. (E) Dissected specimen. (F) Double-pointed hook and a spine from the introvert. (E–F after Ikeda.) (G) *Aspidosiphon parvulus*. Entire specimen (after Gerould). (H) *Aspidosiphon tortus*. Skin from the posterior region of the trunk (after Selenka). *a*, anus; *ac*, anal caeca; *as*, anal shield; *b*, brain; *c*, caecum; *cs*, caudal shield; *e*, eye-spot; *f*, fastening muscle; *g*, gonad; *h*, hooks; *i*, introvert; *in*, intestine; *n*, nephridium; *nc*, nerve cord; *o*, oesophagus; *re*, rectum; *rm*, retractor muscle; *sm*, spindle muscle.

Aspidosiphon carolinus Sato, 1935

(Fig. 27C–D)

Aspidosiphon carolinus Sato, 1935b : 318–319, pl. 4, fig. 19, text-figs 16–17.

TYPE LOCALITY. Arukoron Island, West Caroline Islands.

DESCRIPTION. Introvert much narrower than the trunk but almost as long. The anterior portion carries about 13 complete rings of hooks, each hook having two sharp teeth at the apex. Numerous spines lie scattered behind the hooks. The species is small, the trunk measuring only 4 mm in length and 1·5 mm in thickness. Over most of the surface the papillae are transversely elongate and nearly all of the same size, but are considerably larger at the anterior and posterior ends. The anal shield is oval and composed of small chitinous bodies of a deep brown colour. The caudal shield is rounded and is also composed of numerous small chitinous bodies. Two retractor muscles arise slightly in front of the caudal shield but are joined into a single band for most of their length. Several intestinal convolutions. Two long tubular nephridia free for their whole length, open slightly behind the anus.

REMARKS. Described originally from four specimens.

DISTRIBUTION. As for the type locality.

Aspidosiphon cylindricus Horst, 1899

Aspidosiphon cylindricus Horst, 1899 : 195–198, text-figs 3–4.

TYPE LOCALITY. Kisser, Malaya.

DESCRIPTION. Introvert about 8 mm in length; the anterior third is densely covered with parallel rows of small brown hooks which are shaped like a triangular pyramid with concave faces. The remaining portion of the introvert carries slightly bent conical spines which have several prominent spinelets near the base. Conical papillae are interspersed between the hooks and spines. Trunk nearly cylindrical, 26 mm in length, 3·5 mm in diameter; a few papillae are scattered over the surface. Brownish-yellow in colour with the shields dark brown or almost black. Trunk wall rather thicker and marked by annular grooves anteriorly, plain and thin posteriorly so that the nephridia and retractors are clearly visible. About 3 mm from the caudal shield the skin shows a girdle-shaped area of glistening appearance. The anal shield is elliptical and lies at an oblique angle to the trunk; in profile it is convex. It is divided into a great number of small polygonal areas of dark brown chitinous material. The caudal shield is paler in colour, circular and concave; its margin is divided by grooves into numerous polygonal areas. Two strong, broadly based retractor muscles present, attached near the caudal end of the trunk and joining near the middle of the trunk Alimentary canal with nine double coils, furnished with a spindle muscle which is attached to the middle of the caudal shield. A fastening mesentery runs from the point where the oesophagus joins the intestinal spiral between the angle of the retractors to a point on the left of the nerve cord.

No rectal caecum observed. The nephridia are slender, almost as long as the retractors and are attached to the trunk wall for most of their length.

REMARKS. Known only from the holotype.

DISTRIBUTION. As for the type locality.

Aspidosiphon elegans elegans (Chamisso & Eysenhardt, 1821)

(Fig. 27E–F)

Sternaspis elegans Chamisso & Eysenhardt, 1821 : 351–352, pl. 24, figs 5a–e.
Sipunculus elegans: de Blainville, 1827, pl. 26, fig. 2.
Loxosiphon elegans: Diesing, 1851 : 70; Quatrefages, 1865b : 605.
Phascolosoma (Aspidosiphon) elegans: Grübe, 1868a : 615–647, pl. 8, fig. 5.
Aspidosiphon elegans: Grübe, 1868b : 69; Selenka & de Man, 1883 : 124–126, pl. 1, figs 10–10a,
  pl. 14, figs 205–208; Shipley, 1898 : 471, pl. 27, fig. 8; 1899a : 153; Whitelegge 1899 : 393;
  Sluiter 1891 : 116; 1902 : 19; Hérubel, 1904a : 564; Lanchester, 1905c : 33; 1905b : 40;
  Fischer, 1914b : 14, pl. 1, fig. 7; Gravely, 1927 : 87, fig. B; Sato, 1935b : 316, pl. 4, fig. 7;
  1939 : 426–427, pl. 21, fig. 20; Wesenberg-Lund, 1954a : 10–11; 1957a : 198–199; 1959b : 68.

DESCRIPTION. Introvert of moderate length, thinner than the trunk, anteriorly carrying 35–100 regular rows of hooks. The hooks are flat, strongly bent and with two points; small cylindrical papillae occur here and there between the rows. On the posterior portion red-yellow spines present, largest at the introvert base. Trunk slim, up to 80 mm in length and about twelve times as long as thick; reddish-grey in colour, opaque in old animals, translucent and yellowish-brown in young ones. The skin appears smooth to the eye but, under magnification, is seen to bear groups of irregular polygonal plates. The anus is slit-like, placed behind the anal shield, and surrounded by large papillae. The anal shield is oval, and is divided irregularly by the numerous furrows, into dark brown or black patches which are larger in the middle than at the edge. The caudal shield is usually like a short cone but some-times it is discoid. It is of a horny consistency and is divided into a number of patches by the concentric and radial furrows; sometimes there are also small irregular plates. About 20 intestinal coils. The spindle muscle arises behind the anus and is attached posteriorly at the centre of the caudal shield. A rectal caecum present. One fastening mesentery. Two retractors, which soon join to form a single muscle, arise from the anterior edge of the posterior third of the trunk. The nephridia reach to the base of the retractors and are fastened to the trunk wall for their whole length.

DISTRIBUTION. Florida (Wesenberg-Lund, 1954a); Red Sea (Hérubel, 1904a; Fischer, 1914b; Wesenberg-Lund, 1957a); Tanganyika (Lanchester, 1905c); Mauritius (Wesenberg-Lund, 1959b); Gulf of Manaar (Gravely, 1927); Malaya (Sluiter, 1891; Lanchester, 1905a); Funafuti (Shipley, 1899a; Whitelegge, 1899); Loyalty Islands (Shipley, 1899a); West Caroline Islands (Sato, 1935b); Japan (Sato, 1939).

Aspidosiphon elegans yapensis Sato, 1935

(Fig. 27G)

Aspidosiphon elegans var. *yapense* Sato, 1935b : 316–318, pl. 4, fig. 18; text-figs 12–15.

TYPE LOCALITY.   Yap Island, West Caroline Islands.

DESCRIPTION.   This subspecies differs from the nominate form in having the two points of the hooks on the introvert sharply pointed.

REMARKS.   Sato gave a long description of several specimens.

DISTRIBUTION.   As for the type locality.

Aspidosiphon exhaustus Sluiter, 1912

Aspidosiphon exhaustum Sluiter, 1912 : 20–21, pl. 1, fig. 11.

TYPE LOCALITY.   Off Morocco (36°42′N, 8°40′30″W); at 310–749 m.

DESCRIPTION.   Introvert about as long as the trunk, thin, thread-like anteriorly and pale yellow in colour; numerous rows of very small transparent hooks with a long bent point.   Trunk 17 mm in length but only 2 mm in diameter.   The anal shield is oval, greyish-brown in colour and darker than the trunk.   There are 12 radiating furrows on its posterior edge; centrally they disintegrate into grains. The caudal shield has ten furrows radiating from the periphery; they do not reach the centre which has only a few granules.   The colour is pale, like the trunk and the skin appears smooth to the eye.   Two retractors join to form a single muscle and are attached to the caudal shield.   Numerous intestinal coils present.   The spindle muscle emerges from the last coil and is attached in the posterior end of the trunk. The two nephridia are long and are attached to the trunk wall for most of their length; they open almost on a level with the anus.

REMARKS.   Known only from the holotype.

DISTRIBUTION.   As for the type locality

Aspidosiphon exilis Sluiter, 1886

(Fig. 27H)

Aspidosiphon exilis Sluiter, 1886 : 497, pl. 3, figs 11–12; 1891 : 116; 1902 : 18; Leroy, 1942 : 39–40, fig. 10.

TYPE LOCALITY.   Tausend Island, Java.

DESCRIPTION.   Introvert somewhat longer than the trunk; the anterior portion bears numerous rows of closely packed small hooks, each with two points.   Strong, horny spines present on the posterior part of the introvert which, proximally, are conical and bent.   Trunk slender, 40 mm long but only 2·5 to 3 mm wide; colour light yellow but sometimes colourless and quite transparent.   Anal shield dark brown and covered with small irregular granules; no clear furrows.   Caudal shield light yellow with furrows at the edge which do not continue to the centre, where there is a cross of prominent horny points.   Papillae appear only as light coloured patches with an opening in the middle. One broad retractor, inserted behind the middle of the trunk; 18 intestinal convolutions. Spindle muscle not attached posteriorly, but is fastened by a band of mesenteries half-way down the gut. Rectum long, anus opening at the edge of the anal shield. Two long nephridia reach to the hind end of the trunk. They are free in their posterior half; each has a well-defined nephrostome.

REMARKS. Described from the holotype. Sluiter (1891) repeated the earlier record. In 1902 he recorded two more specimens which agreed with his original description.

DISTRIBUTION. As for the type locality. Siboga station 172, Gisser Reef, Indonesia (Sluiter, 1886); Indo-China (Leroy, 1942).

Aspidosiphon gerouldi ten Broeke, 1925

Aspidosiphon gerouldi ten Broeke, 1925 : 93, text-figs 23–25.

TYPE LOCALITY. Port de Paix, Haiti, West Indies.

DESCRIPTION. Introvert somewhat longer than the trunk with about 12 digitiform tentacles behind which are many rows of small doubly pointed hooks. Numerous small spines occur on the posterior portion of the introvert. Trunk 4 mm in length, about three times as long as thick and covered with papillae which are composed of concentrically arranged plates of uniform size. Longitudinal muscles weakly continuous; they appear to be gathered into bands but these are so weak and indistinct that they cannot be counted. Two retractors are attached to the caudal shield; they soon unite to form a single muscle. Only six intestinal coils. The rectum is long, being about half the trunk length. The polian canal on the oesophagus carries a single villus. The strong spindle muscle is attached in the posterior part of the trunk. Nephridia are about half as long as the trunk and are attached to the trunk wall for their length; they open behind the anus.

REMARKS. Known only from the holotype.

DISTRIBUTION. As for the type locality.

Aspidosiphon gracilis Baird, 1868

(Fig. 271)

Aspidosiphon gracilis Baird, 1868 : 103, pl. 10, figs 1, 1a; Selenka & de Man, 1883 : 122–123, pl. 2, fig. 22, pl. 14, figs 209–213; Sluiter, 1902 : 17; Hérubel, 1904a : 564.

TYPE LOCALITY. Philippines. *Type.* British Museum (Nat. Hist.) no. 1843.5.18.58.

DESCRIPTION. Introvert about as long as the trunk, thinner, greyer and with smaller papillae than on the trunk; behind the tentacles lie rows of closely-set flattened hooks with two points. Posterior to the hooks lie numerous sharp-pointed spines with four-cornered bases. Small papillae are scattered between the hooks and spines. Trunk long and slender, 10–15 times as long as thick; yellowish-brown in colour. The surface is cut up into small areas by the intersection of the longitudinal and circular muscles; each area carries one, seldom two papillae. Papillae have a dark ring round a clear centre, the whole surface being covered with granules which become smaller towards the edge. The yellow-brown conical caudal shield has radial furrows, together with pads carrying 8–10 small papillae. Two strong retractor muscles arise from the front edge of the posterior sixth of the trunk and soon unite to form a single muscle. Rectum fairly long; 20–25 intestinal coils with a strong spindle muscle which is attached to the caudal shield. The two nephridia are about two-thirds as long as the trunk and attached to the trunk wall for their full length.

REMARKS. Described originally from a single specimen. Selenka & de Man only repeated the description and record. Sluiter (1902) recorded single specimens from three Siboga stations but added nothing to the description. Hérubel (1904) recorded three more specimens without redescribing them.

DISTRIBUTION. Philippines (Baird, 1868); Indonesia (Sluiter, 1902); Red Sea (Hérubel, 1904a).

Aspidosiphon hartmyeri Fischer, 1919

(Fig. 27J)

Aspidosiphon hartmyeri Fischer, 1919a : 281–282, text-figs 1–3; 1927 : 204–205, pl. 2, figs 8–14; Edmonds, 1956 : 306–307, fig. 18; Wesenberg-Lund, 1957c : 7–8; 1959c : 197, 212; Murina, 1967a : 1332.

TYPE LOCALITY. Shark Bay, Western Australia.

DESCRIPTION. Introvert up to 7 mm in length, white in colour. Six tentacles present behind which is an area without hooks, followed by 33–34 rows of double pointed hooks. These are followed by very numerous irregularly arranged hooks which, in the posterior portion, change into spines covering the rest of the introvert. Trunk up to 20 mm in length, cylindrical, slightly thicker posteriorly. Skin transparent, yellowish-white in the middle, brownish anteriorly and posteriorly. It is covered with microscopic cross striations and numerous closely-set groups of chitinous plates. The shields stand out from the trunk by their darker colour; they are flat and furrowed. The anal shield is oval and shows 5–6 flat grooves and is also covered with chalky points, as in *Paraspidosiphon steenstrupii*. The caudal shield is circular and has 24–25 distinct grooves, which reach about half way to the small central area. One retractor with two long roots arises from the caudal shield. A strong spindle muscle arises from the anal shield and is fixed posteriorly. The nephridia which open just posterior to the anus are more than half as long as the trunk; they are free for most of their length and darker in colour than the gut. Two eye-spots present.

REMARKS. Edmonds (1956) redescribed five specimens from Rottnest Is., Western Australia. The trunk of his specimens was 10–14 mm long and the extended introvert 10 mm. A fixing muscle arises from the last whorl of the intestine. Rectum long and bears a caecum.

DISTRIBUTION. West Australia (Fischer, 1919a, 1927; Edmonds, 1956); Central West African coast (Wesenberg-Lund, 1957c, 1959c); Cuba (Murina, 1967a).

Aspidosiphon homomyarius Johnson

Aspidosiphon homomyarium Johnson, 1964 : 332–334, pl. 8.

TYPE LOCALITY. Okha, west coast of India (*Type*. Museum Zoology Department, Birla College, India.)

DESCRIPTION. Skin very thin and nearly transparent. Trunk 15–40 mm long, 2–4 mm wide. Introvert slightly shorter than the trunk. Two chitinous shields. Tentacles 10–11. Introvert armed with 60–70 circlets of double-pointed hooks. Two kinds of spines also present. Two retractor muscles which fuse to form a single muscle. Nephridiopore is posterior to the anus. Longitudinal muscles continuous. No intestinal caecum.

Aspidosiphon inquilinis Sluiter, 1902

Aspidosiphon inquilinus Sluiter, 1902 : 29–30, pl. 2, figs 21–22.

TYPE LOCALITY. Indonesia. Siboga stn. 282. 8°15′12″S, 127°18′24″E; at 27–34 m.

DESCRIPTION. Introvert 8 mm in length, with very numerous closely packed rows of hooks, which have only a single point. Trunk cylindrical, 21 mm in length but only 1·5 mm in diameter. The anal shield is coarsely papillose but with clearly seen straight furrows. The caudal shield is clearly furrowed at the edge but in the centre bears large irregular knobs. Both shields are clearly marked off from the trunk. Trunk appears smooth; under the microscope very small, dark brown papillae which are larger anteriorly and posteriorly can be seen. The central opening of the papillae is surrounded by several rows of very small chitinous plates. Two long retractors are attached to the posterior end of the caudal shield. The gut is free at the posterior end and the anus lies on the edge of the anal shield. The two nephridia are about half the length of the trunk and open somewhat behind the anus.

REMARKS. Known only from the holotype.

DISTRIBUTION. As for the type locality.

Aspidosiphon imbellis Sluiter, 1902

Aspidosiphon imbellis Sluiter, 1902 : 29, pl. 2, fig. 20.

TYPE LOCALITY. Siboga station 105. 6°8′N, 121°19′E; at 275 m.

DESCRIPTION. Introvert about as long as the trunk; hooks and spines wanting. Trunk 13 mm in length, 4 mm in diameter. Anal shield damaged but apparently clearly marked off from the trunk and clearly furrowed radially. There is no sharp boundary between it and the papillae at the anterior end of the trunk. The caudal shield is a little more heavily chitinized and is clearly marked with radial furrows.

The whole trunk is covered with circular papillae which are largest anteriorly. The clear centre of each papilla is surrounded by three or four rows of closely-set plates with a few rows of single lines of plates connecting them. The two retractors arise from the caudal shield. The gut has very numerous convolutions. The spindle muscle threads the gut and is attached posteriorly. The two nephridia open some-what behind the anus and are very long, reaching to the hind end of the trunk.

REMARKS. Known only from the holotype.

DISTRIBUTION. As for the type locality.

Aspidosiphon jukesii Baird, 1873

Aspidosiphon jukesii Baird, 1873 : 97; Rice & Stephen, 1970 : 68–69.
Aspidosiphon corallicola Sluiter, 1902 : 19–22, pl. 2, figs 1–5; Shipley, 1903 : 169–171, pl. 1, figs 1–3 and 11–12; Stephen & Robertson, 1952 : 441–442, pl. 1, fig. 2; Cutler, 1965 : 58, fig. 6.

TYPE LOCALITY. In coral, Lee Sandbanks (voyage of *H.M.S. Fly* to New Guinea and Torres St.). *Type.* Brit. Mus. (Nat. Hist.) 1965.25.3.

DESCRIPTION. Introvert rather more than half the trunk length; the anterior third carries about 40 rows of single-pointed hooks, with papillae between the rows. Posteriorly the introvert carries spines. Trunk up to 30 mm in length, stout and rolled in a spiral, 5 mm thick in the middle. Anal shield very distinct, dark brown in colour, with cross furrows anteriorly and longitudinal furrows posteriorly. Caudal shield weakly developed, more so in the larger animals than the smaller ones; it is not strongly chitinized, light in colour and not clearly distinguished from the trunk. It is marked with indistinct radial furrows. Trunk colour light grey, especially posteriorly where it is thin and translucent. Papillae small and very numerous; in the middle of the trunk they are oval and clearly marked off from their surround-ings. The chitinous plates are arranged irregularly round the light centre in which the opening lies. In the anterior and posterior regions the papillae are smaller and more rounded and the chitinous plates are somewhat larger and less well marked off from their surroundings, although there are some detached plates round the edge. Longitudinal muscles continuous except anteriorly where they tend to split. Two retractors with broad roots spring from the caudal shield; they join in the hind fifth of the trunk to form a single strong muscle. The oesophagus is long so that the coils begin only where the retractors join. More than 30 intestinal coils. A strong spindle muscle fixed near the anus and at the posterior end of the trunk. Two other fixing mesenteries. Most of the rectum is fixed by mesenteries. The two nephridia open at the level of the anus; they are about a quarter the length of the trunk and their posterior half is free.

REMARKS. Based originally on numerous specimens. In several specimens taken at Zanzibar, the anal shield showed some differences from Sluiter's description. Rice & Stephen, 1970 consider *A. jukesii* a senior synonym of *A. corallicola* and redescribe the species.

DISTRIBUTION. Malaysia, in coral on many reefs (Sluiter, 1902); Gulf of Manaar (Shipley, 1903); Zanzibar (Stephen & Robertson, 1952); Madagascar (Cutler, 1965).

Aspidosiphon kovaleskii Murina, 1964

Aspidosiphon kovaleskii Murina, 1964c : 51–55, figs 1–5.

TYPE LOCALITY.   Mediterranean (station 354, 'Academie Kovaleskii'); in shell of *Dentalium vulgare*.

DESCRIPTION.   Introvert, 5·6 mm long and 0·5 mm wide in the holotype, less than half the length of the trunk; armed with numerous, small single pointed hooks, 0·02–0·025 mm tall.   Spines absent and tentacles not described.   Trunk, stick-like, 17 mm long and 0·5–1·0 mm wide.   Anal shield larger than caudal and golden in colour; oval in shape, 1·5 mm long and 1·0 mm wide, and narrowing towards the introvert.   Anal shield bears more than 20 spine-like structures on the part near the introvert.   The caudal shield is grooved but not clearly marked off from the trunk.   Longitudinal musculature continuous.   A single retractor arises from two short roots which are attached to the caudal shield.   Intestinal spirals 18, fastening muscles three.   Contractile vessel simple and not well developed.   Nephridia thin, 3–4 mm long and 0·2 mm wide, fixed for most of their length and opening posterior to the anus.

REMARKS.   Described from nine specimens.   The species is allied to *A. parvulus* Gerould.

DISTRIBUTION.   Adriatic and Aegean Seas.

Aspidosiphon misakiensis Ikeda, 1904

(Fig. 26E–F)

Aspidosiphon misakiensis Ikeda, 1904 : 41–43, text-figs 9, 68–72; Sato, 1939 : 428.

TYPE LOCALITY.   Misaki, Japan (shore).

DESCRIPTION.   Introvert about three times as long as the trunk with about 35 rows of yellowish-brown hooks, each with two apical teeth; behind the hooks are numerous gently curved spines.   The papillae appear as small colourless hyaline tubes standing on a tubercle-like base.   Eight to ten short stout tentacles present. Trunk up to 20 mm in length and 5 mm in breadth; light brownish-pink in life with the introvert base and shields darker.   In the anal region the skin is covered with large and closely set papillae deep brown in colour and composed of small granules hardened by calcareous matter.   In the middle region of the trunk the papillae are nearly flat.   The papillae are covered with numerous, irregular, polygonal chitinous plates of varying sizes, light brownish-yellow or yellow in colour.   Anal shield oval and composed of minute deep brown calcareous granules.   Caudal shield conical, deep brown in colour, and also composed of small calcareous granules. Caudal shield conical, deep brown in colour and also composed of small calcareous granules; its margin is slightly folded radially.   The longitudinal muscles in young specimens are continuous but in adults partially divided into frequently anastomosing bundles.   One pair of retractors which are joined for most of their length arises very close to the caudal shield.   Contractile vessel very short, 2–3 mm long and lacking villi or tubules   Intestinal convolutions irregularly and loosely arranged.

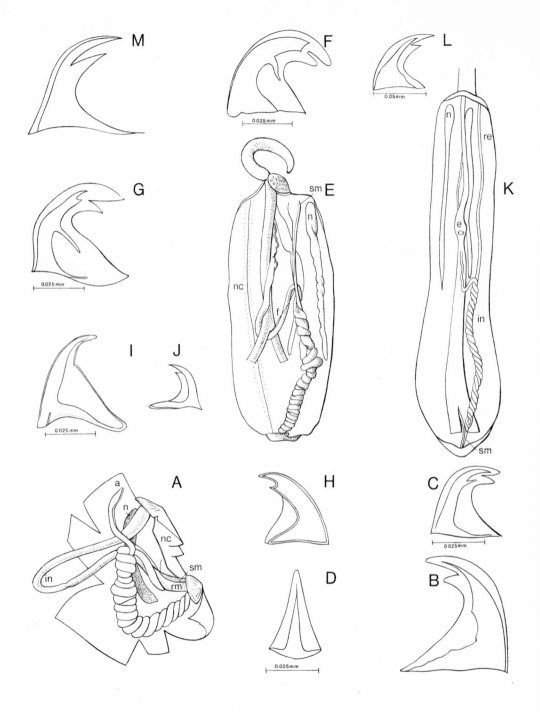

A small rectal caecum is present.   Only one slender fixing muscle attached to the first spiral and to a point on the left of the nerve cord far more anteriorly than the root of the retractor.   Nephridia remarkably long, three quarters of the body length and fixed throughout   Two eye-spots present.

REMARKS.   Ikeda's description is given in considerable detail.

DISTRIBUTION.   As for the type locality.

Aspidosiphon muelleri Diesing, 1851

(Fig. 26A–D)

Aspidosiphon muelleri Diesing, 1851 : 68; Quatrefages, 1865b : 610; Schmidt, 1865 : 56; Baird, 1868 : 101; Selenka & de Man, 1883 : 120–121, pl. 1, fig. 2; Fischer, 1895 : 18; 1914a : 69–70; 1914b : 13–14; 1922b : 22–23; 1925 : 25–26; Sluiter, 1900 : 14; 1912 : 19; Southern, 1913b : 31–34; Ikeda, 1924 : 38; Stephen, 1934 : 173; 1941b : 257; 1958 : 133–134; 1960a : 518–519; Steuer, 1936 : 5, fig. 1; 1939 : 3, fig. 2; Sato, 1939 : 428; Chapman, 1955 : 351; Wesenberg-Lund, 1957c : 4–5; 1957a : 197–198; 1959a : 194–196; 1959b : 68; Longhurst, 1958 : 1.

Sipunculus scutatus J. Müller, 1844 : 166 (not *scutatum* J. Müller, 1843).

Phascolosoma scutatum: Kröhn, 1851 : 371; Selenka & de Man, 1883 : 120.

Phascolosoma radiata Alder, 1860 : 75; Southern, 1913b : 32.

Lesinia farcimen O. Schmidt, 1854 : 2; Selenka & de Man, 1883 : 120.

Sipunculus scutatus: Keferstein, 1867 : 52; Selenka & de Man, 1883 : 120.

Aspidosiphon clavatus: Diesing, 1851 : 68; Cuénot, 1922 : 12–13, text-fig. 6; Hérubel, 1924 : 111; Leroy, 1936 : 426; Akesson, 1958 : 206.

Pseudaspidosiphon clavatus: Baird, 1868 : 103.

Aspidosiphon eremitus Diesing, 1859 : 768 (not *eremita* Sars, 1851).

Aspidosiphon armatus Danielssen & Koren, 1881 : 4–7, 2 pls; Selenka & de Man, 1883 : 124; Théel, 1905 : 91; Southern, 1913b : 31–33.

Aspidosiphon mirabilis Théel, 1875 : 17, 2 pls; Selenka & de Man, 1883 : 121; Théel, 1905 : 91, pl. 8, figs 111–119; Southern, 1913b : 31–33.

TYPE LOCALITY.   Palermo, Sicily.

DESCRIPTION.   A translation of Diesing's description reads thus (Diesing, 1851 : 68).   Trunk subcylindrical, narrowed posteriorly, golden yellow in colour and made rough with brown papillae.   Anterior shield semi-elliptical, brown-black in colour with longitudinally arranged grooves.   Caudal shield disc-like with radiating grooves.   Habitat: Mediterranean (near Panormus).

FIG. 27.   (A) *Aspidosiphon tortus*.   Dissected specimen (after Selenka).   (B) *Aspidosiphon brocki*.   Hook from the introvert (after Augener).   (C–D) *Aspidosiphon carolinus*. (C) Hook from the introvert.   (D) Spine from the middle region of the introvert.   (C–D after Sato.)   (E–F) *Aspidosiphon elegans*.   (E) Dissected specimen.   (F) Hook from the introvert.   (E–F after Selenka.)   (G) *Aspidosiphon elegans yapensis*.   Hook from the introvert (after Sato).   (H) *Aspidosiphon exilis*.   Hook from the introvert (after Sluiter). (I) *Aspidosiphon gracilis*.   Hook from the introvert (after Selenka).   (J) *Aspidosiphon hartmeyeri*.   Hook from the introvert (after Fischer).   (K–L) *Aspidosiphon spinalis*. (K) Dissected specimen.   (L) Hook from the introvert.   (K–L after Ikeda.)   (M) *Aspidosiphon spinosus*.   Hook from the introvert (after Sluiter).   KEY: *See* Fig. 26, p. 221.

According to Selenka & de Man's redescription the introvert is about three times as long as the trunk.   On its anterior third are numerous rows of hooks which are exceptional in that the anterior ones are double-pointed and the posterior ones single-pointed.   Scattered spines are spread over the posterior part of the introvert but, at the base, they disappear and a patch of papillae replaces them.   About 10 finger-like tentacles.   Trunk up to about 25 mm in length, grey to red-brown in life.   Both shields are black to black-brown in colour and incised by radial and concentric furrows to form regular patches.   The anal shield is furrowed on the dorsal half, warty on the ventral half.   The strong retractor forks in its hind third and arises by two roots from the caudal shield.   Intestine with 28–30 double coils. Rectal caecum present.   The spindle muscle arises from the middle of the caudal shield, traverses the intestinal coils, runs along the rectum and is fastened to the body wall just in front of the rectum.   The nephridia are fastened for two thirds of their length and open on the same level as the anus.   Two carmine-red eye-spots present.

REMARKS.   According to Southern (1913b), Cuénot (1922) and Wesenberg-Lund (1957, 1959) the species is widely distributed and ranges from Norway, along the Atlantic coast of Europe and Africa as far as West Africa and into the Mediterranean. Wesenberg-Lund reports it also from East Africa and Mauritius.

This is a troublesome species with a complicated and to some extent uncertain synonymy.   Cuénot (1922), Hérubel (1924) and Leroy (1935) considered that *Sipunculus clavatus* de Blainville, 1827 was a senior synonym.   Their decision may be correct because only one species of *Aspidosiphon* seems to be common along the coasts of France and the Mediterranean (*A. kovaleskii* described from the Mediterranean by Murina (1964) has spine-like structures on its anal shield and is different). Quatrefages (1865b : 611), however, considered *S. clavatus* as *species incertae sedis*. We support this view because de Blainville fails to describe an anal shield, an important character of an *Aspidosiphon*.   It does not seem certain to us that *S. clavatus* is an *Aspidosiphon* because a number of species of *Golfingia* (e.g. *G. rutilofusca* Fischer, 1916) have been described as possessing a posterior, cone-like structure.   It may be worth pointing out that the reference of Diesing (1851 : 68) to the habitat of *S. clavatus* appears to be in error.   His statement, 'in the Mediterranean Sea near Caen (Lesauvage)' seems likely to refer to de Blainville's sentence, 'Cette espèce m'a été envoyé des rivages de la basse Normandie par le lieutenant Lesauvage de Caen'.

It is not clear to us why *A. muelleri* Diesing, 1851 is preferred to *A. scutatus* J. Müller, 1844 which has priority.   Diesing (1851 : 68) placed *S. scutatus* in the synonymy of *A. muelleri* without comment.   Müller's description is clearly that of an aspidosiphonid.   His figures are excellent.   The specimen possessed furrowed anal and caudal shields, the introvert was eccentrically placed and the introvert-retractor muscle was fastened to the caudal shield.   Quatrefages (1865b : 609) and Selenka & de Man (1883 : 120) also accepted *muelleri* without comment.   Sherborn (1930) lists *Phascolosoma scutatum* J. Müller, 1843 and *Sipunculus scutatum* J. Müller, 1844.   It is possible that the two grouped species are different in which case the name *scutatus* would have been preoccupied.   We have, unfortunately, been unable to consult Müller's (1843) record. In any case *P. scutatum* Müller, 1843 seems to have dropped out of the literature of the group.

Both Selenka and Cuénot state that the hooks on the anterior-most rows of the introvert are double-pointed and that those more posteriorly placed are single-pointed. Several authors have pointed out that this is not always so. Southern (1913b : 31–32) examined specimens from Ireland, Naples, Azores, the Bay of Biscay and Accra and said 'All the species agree closely except on one point, the shape of the hooks . . . The proboscis is covered with hooks throughout its whole length. In the Mediterranean specimens the 14 distal rows of hooks are two-pointed, as figured by Schmidt (1865, pl. 1). In the 12th–14th rows the lower point is getting smaller and there are some single-pointed hooks present. Further behind, the hooks are all single-pointed. In all the Atlantic specimens I have examined I failed to find any bifid hooks.' Sluiter (1912 : 19), in describing some specimens from the Azores and from Accra, says that the kind of hook present may vary; all the hooks on some specimens were unidentate, but on others bidentate. In some specimens both kinds were present and in others no hooks at all. Wesenberg-Lund (1957 : 5) reports that her specimens from West Africa have only single points.

Southern (1913b : 32), after examining the type specimens of *A. mirabilis* Théel, 1875 and *A. armatus* Danielssen & Koren, 1881, concluded that they were identical with *A. muelleri*. We are also following his lead in placing *Phascolosoma radiata* Alder, 1860 in the synonymy of *A. muelleri*.

DISTRIBUTION. Norwegian coast (Théel, 1905); North Sea (Alder, 1860; Stephen, 1934; Fischer, 1925); Ireland (Southern, 1913b); Atlantic coast of France (Southern, 1913b; Cuénot, 1922; Hérubel, 1908); Azores (Southern, 1913b; Sluiter, 1912; Chapman, 1955); West Africa (Fischer, 1895; Stephen, 1941b, 1960; Longhurst, 1958; Wesenberg-Lund, 1959a); Mediterranean (de Blainville, 1827; Diesing, 1851; Hérubel, 1924; Steuer, 1939; Cuénot, 1922); Israel (Wesenberg Lund, 1957a; Stephen, 1958); East Africa and Mauritius (Wesenberg-Lund, 1959b); Japan (Ikeda, 1924).

Aspidosiphon parvulus Gerould, 1913

(Fig. 26G)

Aspidosiphon parvulus Gerould, 1913 : 425–426, pl. 61, fig. 17, text-fig. 15.

TYPE LOCALITY. Off Cape Hatteras, North Carolina, U.S.A. (35°21′15″N, 75°21′30″W); at 29 m.

DESCRIPTION. Introvert shorter than the trunk, covered with numerous fine slender hooks. Trunk short and thick, up to 4 mm in length; light yellowish to greyish-brown. Shields sharply marked off by their deep yellowish-brown colour. Anal shield irregularly covered with prominent spines which are conical at the edge and flat in centre. Caudal shield divided into sections by radial furrows; a knob-shaped elevation present in the centre. One retractor muscle with two roots, one being inserted on each side of the caudal shield. A fixing muscle arises at the point

Q

where the roots split off and is attached to the trunk wall.   About 10 intestinal convolutions, with a very strong spindle muscle.   The nephridia are long and slender and are fixed to the trunk wall.

REMARKS.   Described originally from two specimens.   No other records.

DISTRIBUTION.   As for the type locality.

Aspidosiphon ravus Sluiter, 1886

Aspidosiphon ravus Sluiter, 1886 : 495–496, pl. 3, figs 9–10; 1891 : 116; 1902 : 18; Shipley, 1899a : 56–153, pl. 18, figs 2–3.

TYPE LOCALITY.   Bay of Bantam, Malaya.

DESCRIPTION.   Introvert about as long as the trunk and carrying numerous rows of single-pointed hooks.   Folded horny spines present posteriorly, each with two horny plates, the space between them being free, while the base is so deeply incised as to appear to be in two halves.   Larger, anterior spines present with a semicircular base; each spine has two pockets, a larger one near the base and a smaller one further forward.   Trunk 30 mm in length and about 5·5 times as long as broad; broader posteriorly, tapering anteriorly and light yellow-grey in colour   The anal shield is only slightly inclined to the trunk axis, dark brown in colour and proportionally small.   The caudal shield is fairly large but only thin and lightly coloured. Both shields are covered with horny points.   Only in the caudal shield is there a suggestion of furrows.   The longitudinal muscles are continuous and weak; the circular muscles are stronger and show up faintly.   Papillae similar to those of *P. klunzingeri*.   One pair of broad retractor muscles which arise from the hind third of the trunk and join in the middle of the trunk.   About 18 intestinal convolutions. There is a fixing muscle on the first convolution and also a small caecum.   The anus is at the edge of the anal shield.   Two very long nephridia which are free for their posterior half; the nephrostome is anterior and tube-like.

REMARKS.   Described originally from one specimen.   Sluiter (1891) repeated the original record and in 1902 recorded another specimen from the Obi Major Riff. Shipley (1899) remarked that in several specimens from the Loyalty Islands the longitudinal muscles showed anastomoses and the nephridia were long and attached posteriorly.

DISTRIBUTION.   Malaya (Sluiter, 1886, 1902); Christmas Island, Indian Ocean (Shipley, 1899a); Loyalty Islands (Shipley, 1899a).

Aspidosiphon spinalis Ikeda, 1904
(Fig. 27K–L)

Aspidosiphon spinalis Ikeda, 1904 : 47–49, text-figs 12, 81–85; 1924 : 37; Sato, 1939 : 428.

TYPE LOCALITY.   Koniya, Amami-Osima, Japan.

DESCRIPTION.   Introvert nearly as long as the trunk, with numerous rows of dark double-pointed hooks at the extreme anterior end; numerous colourless transparent tubular papillae occur between the rows. Most of the introvert is covered with dark brown spines that are straight, sharply pointed, and formed of a thin chitinous lamella, folded like a funnel. They gradually become taller towards the introvert base and are most closely aggregated on the posterior dorsal side. Trunk up to about 28 mm in length and about 3 mm in breadth. Skin smooth, mainly light yellow-brown in colour. Anal shield elliptical and nearly flat, covered with large brown papillae composed of minute chitinous granules. Caudal shield thin and not so distinctly coloured as the anal shield; its peripheral border is marked with small chitinous brown granules. Near both shields are slightly elevated, elliptical and brownish papillae. Two retractors arise just in front of the caudal shield; 10–15 intestinal convolutions. The spindle muscle is attached at the posterior end of the trunk. No fixing muscle. The rectum is long and without a caecum. The anus is situated just behind the anal shield. The nephridia are reddish-brown, about as long as the trunk and attached for their whole length; they open a short distance behind the anus. Two eye-spots present.

REMARKS. Described originally from several specimens. Ikeda (1904) recorded several small specimens but gave no description. Sato repeated the earlier records.

DISTRIBUTION. Koniya (Ikeda, 1904); Jaluit Island (Ikeda, 1924).

Aspidosiphon spinosus Sluiter, 1902

(Fig. 27M)

Aspidosiphon spinosus Sluiter, 1902 : 28, pl. 2, figs 17–19.

TYPE LOCALITY. Damar Island, Indonesia.

DESCRIPTION. Introvert 15 mm in length with six stumpy tentacles in a half circle on the dorsal side of the mouth and with 18 complete rows of double-pointed hooks. These are followed by a zone, about 3 mm in breadth where the hooks are horn-like in shape and bent. The greater part of the introvert is covered with dark brown spikes, which reach as far back as the anal shield; they have a backwardly bent point and a basal plate with strong chitinous patches. Anal shield dark brown, sharply marked off from the trunk, and composed of patches which are not arranged radially. The caudal shield has furrows at the edge but these do not reach the centre. The skin appears smooth to the naked eye. In formalin it is mostly blue-grey with a deep rose iridescence, the posterior quarter is yellowish. Under the microscope numerous small oblong papillae can be seen. Two long and strong retractors arise from the posterior fourth of the body and soon fuse. Two long nephridia extend almost to the base of the retractors. Gut with many spirals. Spindle muscle attached to the caudal shield. In the front of the intestinal spiral is also a fixing mesentery. A contractile vessel and rectal caecum present.

REMARKS. Known only from the holotype.

DISTRIBUTION. As for the type locality.

Aspidosiphon spiralis Sluiter, 1902

Aspidosiphon spiralis Sluiter, 1902 : 25–26, pl. 2, figs 9–13; Shipley, 1903 : 171.

TYPE LOCALITY.   Indonesia.

DESCRIPTION.   Introvert about the same length as the trunk; smooth to the naked eye but under magnification the many small single-pointed hooks which are closely set over most of the introvert may be seen.   Six small tentacles.   The trunk about 40 mm long is a compactly rolled spiral which, in life, is completely encased in a shell but with the introvert protruding.   The shields are not sharply marked off so that it is difficult to know at first sight whether it is an *Aspidosiphon* or a *Phascolion*.   The anal shield is made up of regular, four-cornered patches separated by deep furrows and with the opening showing up as a dark spot.   In its fore part at the introvert base it is darker and reinforced with chitin; posteriorly it merges into the trunk.   The caudal shield forms the conical posterior end of the trunk and occupies the last chamber of the shell; its radial furrows are fairly clear but, owing to the form of the trunk, the longitudinal ones are difficult to observe.   About 40 intestinal convolutions.   Spindle muscle attached posteriorly.   Rectum fixed near the anus.   A contractile vessel on the fore part of the gut.   Two long nephridia reaching almost to the end of the trunk and opening behind the anus; free for half their length.

REMARKS.   Described originally from four specimens.   Shipley (1903) recorded three more; in two the anal shield was black, in the other pinkish.

DISTRIBUTION.   Indonesia, several localities (Sluiter, 1902); Ceylon (Shipley, 1903).

Aspidosiphon tortus Selenka & de Man, 1883

(Figs 26H, 27A)

Aspidosiphon tortus Selenka & de Man, 1883 : 119–120, pl. 11, figs 196–201; Hérubel, 1904a : 564; Fischer, 1923b : 21–22.

TYPE LOCALITY.   Philippines.

DESCRIPTION.   The anterior portion of the introvert carries regularly arranged, double-pointed hooks while the posterior portion carries regularly arranged spines. Trunk up to 25 mm in length, anterior third light brown in colour, the posterior two thirds shiny grey.   Dark papillae of two sizes are scattered over the light portion. The anal shield is dark brown in colour and oval in form; the dorsal half is furrowed and the ventral half covered with warts.   The thin caudal shield is of the same colour as the anal shield and from its centre furrows radiate to the circumference.   The longitudinal muscles in general form a continuous sheet, but on the dorsal anterior portion they tend to split.   The single retractor arises from the caudal shield with two unequal roots placed close together.   Numerous intestinal convolutions. The spindle muscle arises near the anus, traverses the coils and is attached to the centre of the caudal shield.   Only the left nephridium is present; it is fairly well developed and is attached to the trunk wall for two thirds of its length.

REMARKS. Described from a single specimen. It seems from Selenka's description that the species might be a *Cloeosiphon*. Fischer (1923) gave a short description of two specimens from Siam, pointing out (1) that there are two nephridia, (2) that the shields are brownish-yellow in colour, the anal shield being clearly furrowed and distinguished from the skin on the ventral side, (3) that the caudal shield bears 33–34 furrows, sometimes only half complete. Whether Fischer's and Selenka's specimens are conspecific is doubtful.

DISTRIBUTION. Philippines (Selenka & de Man, 1883); Siam (Fischer, 1923b); Red Sea (Hérubel, 1904a).

Aspidosiphon venabulus Selenka & de Man, 1883

Aspidosiphon venabulum Selenka & de Man, 1883 : 123, pl.14, figs 202–204; Fischer, 1895 : 18; 1914a : 68–69; Wesenberg-Lund, 1957c : 5–7, text-fig. 1; 1959a : 196–197; 1959c : 212; Longhurst, 1958 : 85; Stephen, 1960a : 519.

TYPE LOCALITY. Congo. *Type.* Berlin Museum.

DESCRIPTION. Introvert very long, at least five times as long as the trunk and completely devoid of hooks or spines. Trunk up to 10 mm in length; closely arranged flecks make it look darker in the region of the anal shield. The trunk is covered to a greater or lesser degree with microscopic, dark brown rings which are smaller, finer and somewhat lighter in the middle of the trunk. The anal shield is very dark in colour, flat or concave in shape, and is set round the edge with dark pointed papillae, which have a round or short oval base. The centre is covered with irregular chitinous plates. The caudal shield is without the pointed papillae but, under the microscope, is seen to be covered with small closely arranged plates. Longitudinal muscles continuous, except under the anal shield where they tend to split. One retractor present with two roots arises from the caudal shield. Numerous intestinal coils. The spindle muscle arises a little below the anus and is inserted in the middle of the caudal shield. One fastening mesentery. The nephridia reach almost to the posterior end of the trunk and are attached to the trunk wall for two thirds of their length.

DISTRIBUTION. West African coast (Selenka, 1883; Fischer, 1895; Wesenberg-Lund, 1957c, 1959a; Stephen, 1960a).

Genus *PARASPIDOSIPHON* Stephen, 1965

Paraspidosiphon Stephen, 1965 : 457.
Aspidosiphon Diesing, 1851 : 67 (in part).
Pseudaspidosiphon Baird, 1868 : 102 (in part).

DESCRIPTION. Sipunculans with prominent anal and caudal shields and with characters similar to those of the genus *Aspidosiphon* Diesing except that in *Paraspidosiphon* the longitudinal musculature of the body wall is not continuous but grouped into bands, which may sometimes anastomose considerably. Introvert arises eccentrically from the ventral side of the anterior or anal shield; anteriorly it is usually armed with rows of single- or double-pointed hooks and posteriorly with spines. Tentacles usually small and fingerlike; they incompletely surround the mouth in a semi- or three quarter-circle (but never lie in a horseshoe-shaped ring dorsal to mouth as in *Phascolosoma*). The surface of the shields may be furrowed, grooved and covered with horny calcareous or chitinous material. Introvert retractors one or two, a single retractor usually arising from two short roots which are fastened to the posterior surface of the body wall or the caudal shield. Nephridia two. Spindle muscle present and sometimes attached posteriorly to the caudal shield.

TYPE SPECIES. *Aspidosiphon steenstrupii* Diesing, 1859.

REMARKS. The genus is distinguished from *Aspidosiphon* by the presence of bands of longitudinal muscle. Stephen (1965) considered the condition of the longitudinal musculature of the body wall a taxonomic character of sufficiently high order to warrant the splitting of the original genus *Aspidosiphon* into two genera rather than subgenera. The relation of *Paraspidosiphon* to the other genera in the family is shown in Table 9. The genus contains 24 species.

DISTRIBUTION. Often found in burrows in calcareous rock or in coral. Inhabitants usually of tropical and temperate seas.

List of Species
Species without hooks and spines on the introvert
P. gigas (Sluiter)

Species with single-pointed hooks on the introvert

P. angulatus (Ikeda)
P. brasiliensis (Cordero & Mello-Leitao)
P. cumingii (Baird)
P. grandis (Sato)
P. klunzingeri (Selenka & de Man)
P. pachydermatus (Wesenberg-Lund)
P. schnehageni (Fischer)
P. speciosus (Gerould)
P. tenuis (Sluiter)
P. trinidensis (Cordero & Mello-Leitao)

Species with double-pointed hooks on the introvert

P. ambonensis (Augener)
P. exostomus (Johnson)
P. fischeri (ten Broeke)
P. formosanus (Sato)
P. insularis (Lanchester)
P. levis (Sluiter)
P. makoensis (Sato)
P. pygmaeus (Fischer)
P. semperi (ten Broeke)
P. speculator (Selenka)
P. spinososcutatus (Fischer)
P. steenstrupii (Diesing)
P. truncatus (Keferstein)

GENUS PARASPIDOSIPHON—KEY TO SPECIES

1 Introvert with hooks 2
- Introvert without hooks and spines (retractor arises from two short, broad roots that are fastened to the body wall well in front of the caudal shield; about 40 longitudinal muscles with few anastomoses) . . . . . **P. gigas** (p. 246)

2 Introvert-hooks with single points 3
– Introvert-hooks with double points 12
3 Numerous appendages present on rectum (single rectal caecum may also be present) 4
– Numerous appendages not present on rectum (single rectal caecum may be present) . 7
4 Single rectal caecum present 5
– Single rectal caecum absent 6
5 Nephridia open just in front of anus (anal shield 15 radial grooves, single retractor
    arises from four roots; 28 longitudinal muscles in middle of trunk; nephridia long
    and their anterior half is attached to trunk) . . . . ***P. grandis*** (p. 246)
– Nephridia do not open in front of anus (anal shield 12–13 furrows, caudal shield with
    30 furrows at edge but only 12–13 in the centre; single retractor arises from two–
    four roots which spread over 19 muscle bands; 27–38 longitudinal muscles;
    nephridia long and anterior two fifths fixed) . . . ***P. cumingii*** (p. 243)
6 Longitudinal muscle forms 38 bands in middle of trunk (single retractor arises
    from a broad base spanning 20 longitudinal muscles) . ***P. klunzingeri*** (p. 247)
– Longitudinal muscle forms 24 bands in middle of trunk (single retractor arises from
    two roots each spanning five longitudinal muscles) . ***P. pachydermatus*** (p. 250)
7 Retractor muscle(s) arise(s) well in front of the caudal shield (one third to half the
    trunk-length) 8
– Retractor muscle(s) arise(s) from or just near the caudal shield . . . 9
8 Rectal caecum present . . . . ***P. speciosus*** (p. 253)
– Rectal caecum absent . . . . ***P. angulatus*** (p. 241)
9 Longitudinal musculature in bundles over whole trunk 10
– Longitudinal musculature in bundles only anteriorly . . ***P. schnehageni*** (p. 252)
10 Rectal caecum present (28 anastomosing longitudinal muscles in middle of trunk,
    two retractors arising from muscle 2–6 fuse to form one, nephridia free for their
    whole length) . . . . ***P. tenuis*** (p. 257)
– No rectal caecum 11
11 Twenty-three anastomosing longitudinal muscles in middle of the trunk (nephridia
    fixed to body wall along their whole length) . . . ***P. trinidensis*** (p. 257)
– Forty-eight anastomosing longitudinal muscles in middle of trunk
    P. brasiliensis (p. 241)
12 One or two retractor muscle(s) 13
– Four retractor muscles 22
13 Retractor arises some distance (a quarter of the length of the trunk) in fron t of the
    caudal shield (16–25 anastomosing longitudinal muscles, strongest an teriorly;
    rectal caecum present, nephridia fixed for their anterior half)
    { ***P. steenstrupii*** (p. 254)
    { ***P. exostomus*** (p. 244)
– Retractor(s) arise(s) from or just in front of the caudal shield 14
14 Nephridia completely fastened to the body wall 15
– Nephridia not completely fastened to the body wall 16
15 Anal shield indistinctly marked off from the trunk (40 rows of hooks, 24–25 anasto-
    mosing longitudinal muscles, two retractors each arising from two roots)
    P. spinososcutatus (p. 254)
– Anal shield clearly marked off from the trunk (100 rows of hooks, 20–25 frequently
    anastomosing longitudinal muscles, two retractors) . . ***P. makoensis*** (p. 250)
16 Nephridia completely free 17
– Nephridia fixed for their anterior half 19
17 Hooks on introvert in rows 18
– Hooks on introvert scattered (second tooth or point of the hook is small, retractor
    arises from two roots attached to the caudal shield, rectal caecum present)
    P. truncatus (p. 258)
18 Intestinal coil consists of very few (4–5) spirals . . ***P. pygmaeus*** (p. 251)

Paraspidosiphon ambonensis (Augener, 1903)

(Figs 29K, 30C)

Aspidosiphon ambonensis Augener, 1903 : 325–328, figs 5–8.
Aspidosiphon steenstrupii var. *ambonensis* Fischer, 1922b : 24–26, pl. 3, figs 23–29; 1923b : 21.

TYPE LOCALITY.   Amboina, Malaya.

DESCRIPTION.   Introvert lighter in colour than the trunk and with 50–100 complete rows of hooks present becoming sparser towards the base.   Each is two-pointed, bent at 90° and has a thin, wavy line along its mid-line to the anterior point of the base; a row of platelets is present at the anterior point of the base. Trunk 25–30 mm long, cylindrical, light yellow or greyish white in colour, with a band of darker colour behind the shields.   Numerous irregularly arranged minute papillae in the middle region; each has a small central opening surrounded by small chitinous plates.   In the darker zones of the trunk the papillae are larger and lighter, those in the central area being more numerous and stronger and having many more surrounding plates.   Two prominent shields darker than the body are present.   The caudal shield has radial and concentric furrows but the central area is not furrowed and carries irregular plates.   The anal shield is parallel to the body; it is circular or oval and covered with small calcareous granules which form a row round the edge.   Longitudinal muscles split into anastomosing bands which are stronger at the posterior end; in the middle of the body there are about 25 and anteriorly 20.   One pair of retractors about one fifth or sixth the length of the trunk arises at the posterior region of the trunk from muscles 3 (4) to 6 (7).   About 20–25 intestinal convolutions, traversed by a strong spindle muscle which fastens the last coil to the caudal shield.   No fixing muscles.   Contractile vessel and a small rectal caecum present.   Two long thin, brown nephridia arise between muscles 3–4 posterior to the anus; they are fastened to the body wall for half of their length.

REMARKS.   Based originally on numerous specimens.   Fischer (1922) discussed whether it is a separate species or whether it should be regarded as a subspecies of *P. steenstrupii*. The shape of the clear areas of the hooks of *P. steenstrupii* and *P. ambonensis* seem to be different.

DISTRIBUTION. Amboina (Augener, 1903); Java Sea (Fischer, 1922b); Gulf of Siam (Fischer, 1923b).

Paraspidosiphon angulatus (Ikeda, 1904)

(Fig. 30I)

Aspidosiphon angulatus Ikeda, 1904 : 45–47, fig. 11, figs 78–80; 1924 : 37; Sato, 1939 : 428.

TYPE LOCALITY. Katsuyoki Inlet, Amami-Oshima Island, Japan, low water.

DESCRIPTION. Introvert about as long as the trunk and bearing 10 filamentous tentacles and numerous rows of hooks, with small papillae between them. The hooks have a bluntly pointed apex; no spines occur behind the hooks. Trunk 15 mm in length. Skin smooth, thin and partly transparent; light yellowish-brown, darker at the anterior end where the surface has a rough granular appearance. The anal shield is made up of a main oblique conical portion, marked with radial grooves, and a short cylindrical portion with grooves alternating with those on the conical part. The anal shield is formed of small, densely aggregated, chitinous plates. The caudal shield is in the shape of two cones juxtaposed at the base, with the radial grooves alternating. Most of the trunk is devoid of papillae, but under magnification the openings of numerous subdermal glands can be observed. Anteriorly to the caudal shield are some slightly more prominent papillae which are composed of small, light yellowish-brown, polygonal chitinous plates, smallest towards the centre. The papillae are largest around the base of the anal shield and are deep brown in colour. Two retractor muscles arising slightly posterior to the middle of the trunk fuse to form one. Longitudinal muscles incompletely divided into frequently anastomosing bundles. Oesophagus almost free from the retractors. About 15 intestinal convolutions. Spindle muscle attached anteriorly and posteriorly. No fixing muscle and no rectal caecum. Nephridium about a third as long as the trunk and attached to the trunk wall for the anterior half. A small sac-like body present on the nephrostome.

REMARKS. Ikeda (1924) recorded a specimen from Palau but gave no description.

DISTRIBUTION. Japan (Ikeda, 1904); West Caroline Islands (Ikeda, 1924).

Paraspidosiphon brasiliensis (Cordero & Mello-Leitao, 1952)

Aspidosiphon brasiliensis Cordero & Mello-Leitao, 1952 : 277–292, text-figs 1–5.

TYPE LOCALITY. Trinade Island, Brazil. *Type*. Hydrobiol. Inst. Oswaldo Crux; Rio de Janeiro; no. 2737.

DESCRIPTION. Introvert, fully retracted, 14 mm in length, 2 mm in diameter; more or less cylindrical, surface annulated, brownish-white in colour. One hundred and five transverse, equidistant, parallel rows of hooks, the first fifty more clearly separated from each other. The hooks are deeply embedded in the epidermis,

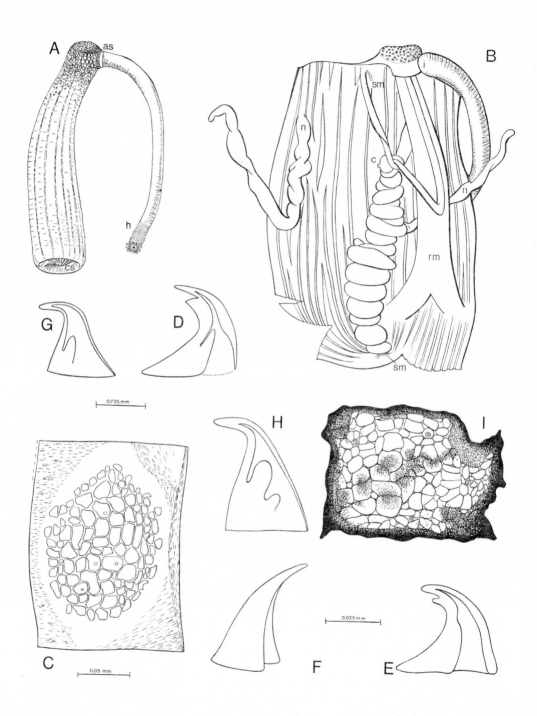

only the curved tip showing, the buried portion consists of two membranous expansions. Trunk 14 mm in length, 6 mm in diameter. The colour is the same as that of the introvert, with the extremities darker. The surface is striated, appearing as false annulations. Longitudinal muscle bands clearly visible on the posterior third of the trunk. Anal shield perpendicular to the axis of the trunk, oval-roundish in shape, dark brown in colour and surrounded by well-marked papillae. Superficial furrows which seem to originate near to the introvert base, where they are deepest, are arranged along the major axis. Four more conspicuous furrows divide the shield into five lobes. Caudal shield appears as a circular disc, coloured like the anal shield, but its deeper furrows make it seem darker. About 34 well-marked radial furrows, of which 18 reach the centre. Longitudinal muscle bands, strong, brownish-white in colour extending over the length of the trunk and anastomosing; 48 bands in the middle of the trunk and 42 at the level of the lower insertion of the retractor. One retractor inserted about 2 mm from the caudal shield. It is attached to only one muscle band near the anal shield at the level of the beginning of the introvert; but at its lower end broadens out to cover 22 muscle bands. A thin triangular mesentery, parallel to the anal shield, and about 3 mm from it, divides the body cavity into two chambers. Oesophagus long and thin with about 16 intestinal convolutions. Rectum long and dilated and without a caecum. The spindle muscle is attached posteriorly. Two nephridia open slightly below the anus; each organ has a bulbous base and a long-pointed terminal portion reaching nearly to the base of the retractors.

REMARKS. Known only from the holotype.

DISTRIBUTION. As for the type locality.

Paraspidosiphon cumingii (Baird, 1868)

(Fig. 29A–C)

Aspidosiphon cumingii Baird, 1868 : 102, pl. 11, fig. 2; Selenka & de Man, 1883 : 113–115, pl. 13, figs 183–186; Fischer, 1892 : 85, fig. 5; 1922c : 12; Collin, 1892 : 177; Sluiter, 1902 : 17; Augener, 1903 : 321–322; Hérubel, 1904a : 564; Monro, 1931 : 34; Leroy, 1936 : 426; Andrew & Andrew, 1953 : 1; Rice & Stephen, 1970 : 67.

TYPE LOCALITY. Philippines. *Type.* Brit. Mus. (Nat. Hist.).

DESCRIPTION. Introvert about equal in length to the trunk; numerous spines, and up to 230 hooks present. Trunk about 50 mm in length, covered with large and small glands that are more numerous posteriorly. The shields are darker

FIG. 28. (A–D) *Paraspidosiphon steenstrupii*. (A) Entire animal, × about 2. (B) Dissected specimen. (C) Papillae from the body. (D) Hook from the introvert; scale same as in (E). (A–D after Selenka.) (E–F) *Paraspidosiphon formosanus*. (E) Hook from the introvert. (F) Spine from the introvert; (E) and (F) to same scale. (E–F after Sato.) (G–H) *Paraspidosiphon klunzingeri*. (G) Hook from one of the posterior rows. (H) A hook from the fourteenth row. (D), (G) and (H) to same scale. (G–H after Selenka.) (I) *Paraspidosiphon grandis*. Skin papillae from the caudal shield (after Sato). KEY: See Fig. 26, p. 221.

than the trunk. Anteriorly to the caudal shield the circular muscles contract giving the posterior end a characteristic sub-conical appearance. The anus lies immediately below the anal shield. Anal shield has 12–13 furrows, visible only around the edge. Caudal shield has 30 furrows at the edge but only 12–13 visible at the centre. Longitudinal muscles split posteriorly into 32–34 bands, anteriorly into 27–28. The circular muscles are strongly developed. A single broad retractor present, the base of which covers 19 longitudinal muscle bands, in some specimens it splits into four roots. A strong spindle muscle arises just behind the anus as a fine thread and is fastened in the posterior part of the trunk. About 15–20 intestinal convolutions, oesophagus with a contractile vessel anteriorly carrying numerous villi. Two brown nephridia, reaching to the posterior end of the trunk and attached for two fifths of their length to the trunk wall. Numerous villi, appendages or caeca, 'langen zottenartigen Gebilden', are attached to the rectum, according to Selenka (1883).

REMARKS. This species is a well known inhabitant of tropical seas. In his key to the genus *Aspidosiphon* Selenka (1883 : 14) states the species possesses a rectal caecum as well.

DISTRIBUTION. West Indies (Andrew & Andrew, 1953); Red Sea (Hérubel, 1904a); Zanzibar, etc. (Fischer, 1892); Malaysia (Augener, 1903); New Guinea (Leroy, 1936); Queensland, Great Barrier Reef (Monro, 1931); Philippines (Baird, 1868).

Paraspidosiphon exostomus (Johnson, 1964)

Aspidosiphon exostomum Johnson, 1964 : 331–332, pl. 7.

TYPE LOCALITY. Andaman Islands. *Type.* Museum, Zoology Dept., Birla College, India.

DESCRIPTION. Length of trunk 30 mm, length of introvert 16 mm. Anal shield dark and oval; caudal shield dark. Introvert armed with hooks and spines. Hooks with two points are arranged in about 100 circlets. Circlets of spines with blunt tips alternate with circlets of hooks. Eleven small tentacles. Two slender, free retractor muscles which arise in the middle of the posterior half of the trunk. Nephridia fixed for a third of their length. Longitudinal muscles in 18–24 anastomosing bundles.

DISTRIBUTION. As for the type locality.

Paraspidosiphon fischeri fischeri (ten Broeke, 1925)

Aspidosiphon fischeri ten Broeke, 1925 : 92–93, figs 11–12.

TYPE LOCALITY. Caracas Bay, West Indies.

DESCRIPTION. Introvert rather more than twice the length of the trunk; covered anteriorly with numerous rows of small two-pointed hooks and posteriorly with spines. Eighteen tentacles present. Trunk very small, up to 5 mm in length, slender and covered with small inconspicuous papillae. Anal shield without furrows, composed of regularly arranged many-angled plates, smaller and darker in the centre, larger and lighter at the edge. The caudal shield is round, not clearly defined and in its centre has dark patches. Those at the periphery are larger and lighter and pass gradually into the trunk. Longitudinal muscles gathered into about 18 strongly anastomosing bundles. One retractor arising directly from the caudal shield. About 20 intestinal convolutions. A strong spindle muscle fixed posteriorly. The rectum is short. The nephridia open in front of the anus; they are short, half as long as the body and free for their posterior half.

REMARKS. Based originally on two specimens.

DISTRIBUTION. As for the type locality.

Paraspidosiphon fischeri cubanus (Murina, 1967)

Aspidosiphon fischeri cubanus Murina, 1967a : 1331; 1967b : 39–42, figs 5 (1)–(5), figs 6 (1)–(5), fig. 7.

DESCRIPTION. Introvert equal to or slightly longer than the trunk. Anal shield flat and oval. Two retractors attached to the caudal shield, uniting anteriorly.

DISTRIBUTION. Cuba.

Paraspidosiphon formosanus (Sato, 1939)

(Fig. 28E–F)

Aspidosiphon formosanus Sato, 1939 : 421–424, pl. 21, fig. 23, text-figs 55–57.

TYPE LOCALITY. Sinko, Formosa (Taiwan).

DESCRIPTION. The introvert carries about 30 circular rows of hooks. Each is yellow-brown in colour and has two bluntly pointed teeth. Behind the hooks are numerous gently curved spines. The trunk is about 18 mm in length and 3 mm in breadth and its colour in alcohol is yellowish-grey. Anal shield dark, oval and seemingly smooth to the naked eye but under the microscope it is seen to be composed of minute chitinous granules. The ventral border is hard on account of a deposit of calcareous material. Caudal shield deep brown and rounded; it is grooved both radially and concentrically and is composed of many papillae. Surface of the trunk nearly smooth to the naked eye but actually consists of numerous minute papillae, larger and darker at the extremities. Longitudinal muscles split into many frequently anastomosing bands. Two retractors arise immediately in front of the caudal shield. About 20 intestinal convolutions. Spindle muscle present. Two nephridia are about two thirds as long as the trunk, free for their posterior half and open slightly behind the anus.

REMARKS. Based originally on two specimens.

DISTRIBUTION. As for the type locality.

Paraspidosiphon gigas (Sluiter, 1884)

Aspidosiphon gigas Sluiter, 1884 : 39–57, pl. 2, figs 1–11, pl. 2a, figs 12–25; 1886 : 473; 1891 : 116; 1902 : 19.

TYPE LOCALITY.   Between Tausend Island and Java; at 26 m.

DESCRIPTION.   Introvert one fifth as long as the trunk, without hooks or spines; 26 small tentacles present.   Trunk cylindrical, 85 mm in length and about six times as long as thick.   Shields sharply marked off from the trunk.   The anal shield is darker and almost oval in shape being its broadest on the dorsal side and smallest towards the introvert; it is strongly furrowed, the furrows converging on the intro-vert.   The caudal shield is round and is drawn out to a cone-like point, with very numerous radial grooves converging on the point of the cone.   The surface of the trunk is rugose and is incised with deep furrows.   The lines are so regular that the surface is cut up into rectangular areas like it is in *Sipunculus*.   The longitudinal muscles are gathered into about 40 bands which seldom anastomose.   Oesophagus long; numerous intestinal coils present occupying about three quarters of the trunk. Rectum short and fixed by a wing muscle.   One broad retractor which reaches nearly to the anterior border of the posterior third of the trunk.   The retractor arises from two short broad roots covering 4–6 muscle bands.   Nephridia are long and thin and open behind the anus.   A prominent nephrostome is present anteriorly.

REMARKS.   Sluiter (1891 and 1902) repeated the original record.   His original paper described the anatomy and histology of the species in detail.

DISTRIBUTION.   Indonesia.

Paraspidosiphon grandis (Sato, 1939)

(Fig. 28I)

Aspidosiphon grandis Sato, 1939 : 414–419, pl. 21, fig. 21, text-figs 46–50.

TYPE LOCALITY.   Diahanratu, Formosa (Taiwan).

DESCRIPTION.   About 60 transverse rows of beak-shaped hooks on the introvert which are tall and sharply bent at the tip.   The introvert is strongly pigmented and bears numerous filamentous tentacles.   Trunk large, length about 70 mm and maximum width about 10 mm.   The skin is yellowish-brown in colour, deeper towards the anal shield.   Numerous large dark brown papillae in the anterior part of the trunk behind the anal shield.   Anal shield is solid, black and oval and its surface is marked by 15 radial grooves.   The caudal shield is dark brown in colour, conical in side-view, with many radial grooves.   Numerous papillae present on the surface of the trunk; they are large and strongly pigmented at the anterior and posterior ends, somewhat crowded behind the anal shield so as to form a zone round the trunk but small and unpigmented in the middle of the trunk.   The longitudinal muscles are split into about 28 bands in the middle of the trunk; at the anterior end they frequently anastomose.   The circular muscle-layer also splits into numer-ous shallow bands.   One retractor arises near the posterior end of the trunk; it has four roots which arise at about the same level.   The two roots next to the nerve cord divide further into two short roots. A spindle muscle beginning near the anus is fixed to the posterior end of the trunk. The rectum is attached by wing muscles. The contractile vessel is simple, without villi. The rectum carries two kinds of appendages, a small caecum and numerous short blind tubes attached to both sides of the rectum. The nephridia are long, brownish-yellow tubes and their posterior half is free; they open between bands 2 and 3, slightly in front of the anus.

REMARKS. Known only from the holotype.

DISTRIBUTION. As for the type locality.

Paraspidosiphon insularis (Lanchester, 1905)

Aspidosiphon insularis Lanchester, 1905b : 40, pl. 2, fig. 4.

TYPE LOCALITY. Pulau Bidan, Penang, Malaya. *Type.* Brit. Mus. (Nat. Hist.), no. 1924.3.1.180.

DESCRIPTION. Introvert less than half as long as the trunk; anteriorly there are a few rows of hooks and posteriorly rather large papillae each of which terminates in a dense, almost tooth-like, structure. Along the dorsal line the papillae are enclosed in a dense brown pigment. Trunk dirty white in colour, dotted with papillae which in the middle region can only be seen with a lens. Papillae larger towards the posterior end. Anal shield circular and formed of large, crowded, brown papillae. Caudal shield not described. Longitudinal muscles split into bundles which anastomose rather freely and which are strongest behind the level of the retractors where they number about 22; in front of this, however, there are only 15. Four retractors arise just behind the middle of the trunk, the ventrals from bands 2–6, the dorsals from bands 5–6 just a little in front of the ventrals. The pairs unite soon; the two retractors so formed remain separate until they almost reach the tentacles. Nephridia arise at the level of the anus and extend just posterior to the retractors. They are brown in colour and are attached only in their front portion, which is slightly swollen. There is a strong spindle muscle which is attached posteriorly.

REMARKS. Based on two damaged specimens.

DISTRIBUTION. As for the type locality.

Paraspidosiphon klunzingeri (Selenka & de Man, 1883)

(Fig. 28G–H)

Aspidosiphon klunzingeri Selenka & de Man, 1883 : 115–116, pl. 13, figs 187–189; Fischer, 1896a : 338; 1914a : 70; Sluiter, 1898 : 444; 1912 : 20; Shipley, 1898 : 471, pl. 37, fig. 9; 1899a : 153, pl. 28, fig. 1; Hérubel, 1904a : 564; Monro, 1931 : 34; Edmonds, 1956 : 308, fig. 20, pl. 3, fig. 1; Wesenberg-Lund, 1957b : 8–9, fig. 1; 1959a : 196; 1959c : 211–212; 1963 : 138.

TYPE LOCALITY. Koseir (? Red Sea).

DESCRIPTION. Introvert about as long as the trunk with regularly arranged hooks on the anterior part; hooks resemble those of *A. muelleri* but possess only a

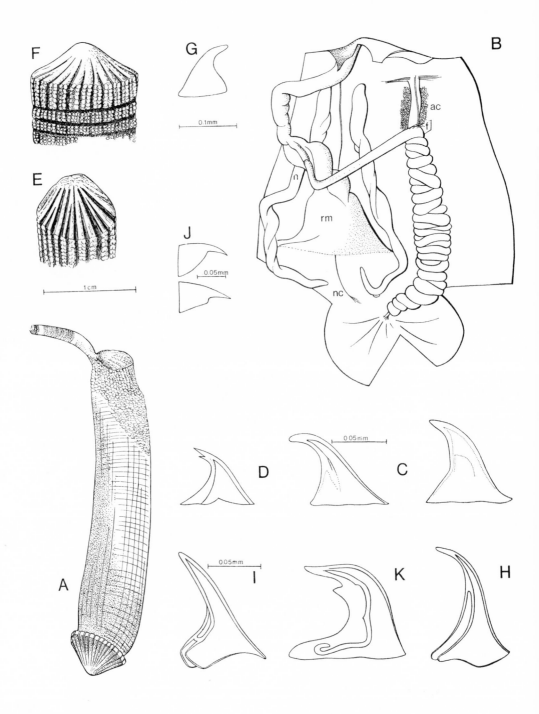

single point. The posterior portion of the introvert bears spines. Trunk up to about 32 mm, yellowish to light brown in colour, with darker shields. Anal shield oval, with 13 furrows which run from its lower edge to the trunk above the anus. Caudal shield roundish with 30–32 radial furrows. Small swellings occur on the anterior part of the trunk, but papillae are absent. Longitudinal muscles split into closely-lying bands which number 38 in the middle of the trunk. One retractor with a broad base arising from 20 bands, inserted between about the fourth and last fifth of the trunk. Intestinal coils numerous. On the rectum there is a large caecum from the sides of which numerous lappets or lobes arise ('Am Rectum sitzt ein grosser, an beiden Seiten vielfach gelappter Blindsack'). The spindle muscle arises a little in front of the anus, follows the rectum, traverses the intestinal spiral and is attached in the middle of the caudal shield. No fixing mesenteries. A contractile vessel present. The nephridia are fixed for about half their length and open between the bands 4–5 or 5–6, just posterior to the anus.

REMARKS. This species is a well known inhabitant of warm waters and especially of coral reefs.

DISTRIBUTION. Cape Verde (Sluiter, 1912; Wesenberg-Lund, 1959a); Gulf of Guinea (Wesenberg-Lund, 1959c); Red Sea (Selenka & de Man, 1883; Hérubel, 1904a; Wesenberg-Lund, 1957b, 1963); Indonesia (Fischer, 1896); Funafuti (Shipley, 1898); Great Barrier Reef (Monro, 1931, Edmonds, 1956).

Paraspidosiphon levis (Sluiter, 1886)

Aspidosiphon levis Sluiter, 1886 : 493–494, pl. 3, fig. 8; 1891 : 116; 1902 : 18.

TYPE LOCALITY. Indonesia.

DESCRIPTION. Introvert about as long as the trunk, anteriorly with many rows of double-pointed hooks, posteriorly without horny spikes but with chitinous ridges. Trunk wider posteriorly. Colour greyish-brown, lighter posteriorly. Anal shield dark black-brown, granulated and without clear furrows. Caudal shield light brown with radial furrows which do not reach the centre. Longitudinal muscles split into 21 bands, clearly seen posteriorly but less so anteriorly; few anastomoses. Papillae small, the central area is composed of a few small plates of lighter colour. Two small retractors which arise from bands 2–5 are attached near the caudal shield. Intestine has many convolutions which reach almost to the hind end of the trunk, the last coil forming a long loop that is attached posteriorly by the spindle muscle. A small caecum present on the rectum. Nephridia are

FIG. 29. (A–C) *Paraspidosiphon cumingii*. (A) Entire specimen (after Baird). (B) Dissected specimen. (C) Two hooks from the anterior region of the introvert. (B–C after Selenka.) (D) *Paraspidosiphon spinososcutatus*. Hook from introvert (after Fischer). (E–G) *Paraspidosiphon pachydermatus*. (E) Anal shield. (F) Caudal shield. (G) Hook from introvert. (A–G after Wesenberg-Lund.) (H–I) *Paraspidosiphon grandis*. Hooks from introvert (after Sato). (H) Anterior. (I) Middle. (H) and (I) to same scale. (J) *Paraspidosiphon speciosus*. Hooks from introvert (after Gerould). (K) *Paraspidosiphon ambonensis*. Hooks from introvert (after Augener). KEY: *See* Fig. 26, p. 221.

R

fairly short, opening between the second and third muscle bands and free for their whole length.

REMARKS. Described originally from one specimen. Sluiter (1891) only repeated the original record. In 1902 he recorded another specimen without any further description.

DISTRIBUTION. Bay of Bantam, Indonesia (Sluiter, 1886); Siboga station 142, Major Reef, Indonesia (Sluiter, 1902).

Paraspidosiphon makoensis (Sato, 1939)

(Fig. 30D–E)

Aspidosiphon makoensis Sato, 1939 : 419–421, pl. 21, fig. 22, text-figs 51–54.

TYPE LOCALITY. Mako, Formosa (Taiwan).

DESCRIPTION. About 100 complete circles of hooks, each with two sharp points present on the anterior region of the introvert; minute papillae are scattered between the nrigs. Trunk small 20–25 mm in length, 3·5–3·8 mm in breadth, yellowish-grey in colour. Anal shield oval consisting of many deep brown granules. Caudal shield conical in side view, rounded in surface view, with numerous radial grooves. Papillae are small and crowded near the shields. The longitudinal muscles are split into 20–25 bands which frequently anastomose. Two retractors arise close to the caudal shield and are fused for most of their length. The spindle muscle is fixed near the anus and attached to the posterior end of the trunk. There are about 13 intestinal convolutions. The nephridia, about half the length of the trunk, are fixed for their whole length and open slightly behind the anus. A simple contractile vessel without tubules is present.

REMARKS. Based on three specimens.

DISTRIBUTION. As for the type locality.

Paraspidosiphon pachydermatus (Wesenberg-Lund, 1937)

(Fig. 29E–G)

Aspidosiphon pachydermatus Wesenberg-Lund, 1937c : 9–16, text-figs 4–9.

TYPE LOCALITY. Recif Polo Kalappa, Malaya.

DESCRIPTION. Introvert with about 100 complete rows of hooks, each hook ending in a single blunt point. Trunk about 100 mm in length, dark brown in colour with a thick tough skin and a heavily developed cuticle, furrowed annularly. Anal shield shaped like a *Mytilus* shell and radially marked with alternating short and long furrows, strongest on the dorsal side; it is set at an angle to the trunk. Caudal shield terminal marked by alternating short and long furrows. The central part forms a conical protrusion. Both shields are composed of small, dark chitinous bodies. Longitudinal muscles split into 24 bands in the middle of the trunk with little anastomosing. One long broad retractor arises from the last quarter of the trunk by means of two broad flat roots which soon fuse. Each root extends over five muscle bands. The retractor is reddish-brown in colour contrasting strongly with the yellow-brown muscle layer. The oesophagus is long and slender and is closely connected with a contractile vessel carrying a large number of rounded protrusions. About 26 intestinal convolutions, the last part being fixed by a mesentery about 6 mm long and covering 16 muscle bands. Its distal part is split into numerous delicate strands. A large cluster of blind sacs, attached by a mesentery, is present close to the last part of the intestine; a stem passes through the cluster and opens into the intestine close to where the rectal mesentery arises. The spindle muscle arises about 15 mm behind the anus and is attached to the caudal shield; it is thin posteriorly but gets progressively stronger until anteriorly it is as strong as a muscle band. A number of delicate fibres split off and fix the intestinal coils. No rectal caecum. The nephridia are long, rusty-red in colour and slender; they open just posterior to the anus and extend to about the middle of the trunk. Nephrostome short and wide, the rim forming a frilly funnel.

REMARKS. Described from a single specimen. Two very fine specimens from the Philippines are in the collection of the U.S. National Museum (nos. 21430 and 24645).

DISTRIBUTION. Malay and Philippine Is.

Paraspidosiphon pygmaeus (Fischer, 1921)

Aspidosiphon pygmaeus Fischer, 1921a : 45–47, text-figs 1–7.

TYPE LOCALITY. Juan Fernandez; at 30–45 m.

DESCRIPTION. Introvert carries 6–8 tentacles and about 100–150 rows of hooks, the latter perpendicular to the skin. The hooks are clearly double-pointed with a clear inner line; between them lie the papillae, six hooks to two papillae. Posterior to the hooks are spines. Introvert 10–18 mm in length and somewhat darker than the trunk. Trunk small, and about 5–7 mm in length. With the exception of the shields, the skin is uniformly coloured yellowish-grey. Like other species of *Aspidosiphon*, it has strongly chitinized caudal and anal shields, which are marked off from the trunk by their darker colour. Both are furrowed. The anal shield is broken by seven furrows, so that there are eight plates which are not separated in the ventral half. Posterior to the plates are two rows of warts, somewhat lighter in colour than the plates. The caudal shield is rounded and carries 28–30 furrows which traverse the plates. Body and introvert smooth to the naked eye. The longitudinal muscles are split into numerous bands which anastomose so frequently that it is not possible to determine their number. They are most numerous at the anal shield and mostly run together at the caudal shield. Two retractors arise almost immediately behind the caudal shield from eight bands close to the nerve cord. The gut consists of three to four coiled spirals. These are supplemented by a strong spindle muscle attached to the middle of the caudal shield. The first coil is fastened by a mesentery. The long rectum has a caecum in its middle. The anus is fixed in a broad plate. The nephridia, which open at the same level as the anus, are wholly free, brown in colour and reach almost to the join of the retractors.

REMARKS.   Described originally from several specimens.   According to Fischer it is allied to *A. truncatus*.

DISTRIBUTION.   As for the type locality.

Paraspidosiphon schnehageni (Fischer, 1913)

Aspidosiphon schnehageni Fischer, 1913 : 99–100, text-figs 4–6; 1914b : 15; Wesenberg-Lund, 1955b : 13.

TYPE LOCALITY.   Chile.

DESCRIPTION.   Introvert, longer than the trunk, bears 70–80 rows of fine yellow single-pointed hooks and more proximally a zone of regularly arranged spines. Trunk 23 mm in length and spirally rolled like the *Scalaria* shell in which it lives. Colour light brown anteriorly, lighter posteriorly; the shields are darkest.   The papillae are covered with large, closely packed polygonal plates.   Both shields are grooved; the caudal is conical and has 16–18 grooves.   A single retractor with a long root springs from the caudal shield.   The rectum is fixed by a mesentery from the third longitudinal muscle band.   Nephridia about a third as long as the trunk, opening quite a way in front of the anus and free for their posterior half.

REMARKS.   Known only from the holotype; Wesenberg-Lund (1955b) only repeats Fischer's record.

DISTRIBUTION.   As for the type locality.

Paraspidosiphon semperi (ten Brokee, 1925)

(Fig. 30H)

Aspidosiphon semperi ten Broeke, 1925 : 92, text-figs 18–20.

TYPE LOCALITY.   Caracas Bay, West Indies.

DESCRIPTION.   Introvert about equal in length to the trunk, with eight tentacles and rows of double-pointed hooks.   Papillae present between the rows.   The posterior region of the introvert carries spines of about the same size as the hooks. Trunk up to 15 mm in length, covered with papillae, which are more or less uniform in size, except posteriorly and near the shields, where they are about double in size.   The papillae are formed of irregularly-shaped plates, uniform in size, bounded by a row of small plates round the periphery.   Longitudinal muscles gathered into 22–26 anastomosing bands.   Two pairs of retractors arise from a point about a quarter of the trunk length from the caudal shield, the ventrals springing from bands 3–6, the dorsals from bands 6–9.   They soon unite to form a single muscle. In one small specimen only one pair was present.   Four intestinal convolutions present.   A strong spindle muscle is fixed to the posterior end of the trunk and the rectum is long.   The nephridia are about as long as the trunk; their posterior third is free and they open at about the level of the anus.

REMARKS.   Based on seven specimens.

DISTRIBUTION.   As for the type locality.

Paraspidosiphon speciosus (Gerould, 1913)

(Fig. 29J)

Aspidosiphon speciosus Gerould, 1913 : 426–427, text-fig. 16, pl. 62, fig. 22; Fischer, 1922e : 13.

TYPE LOCALITY. Key West, Florida; shore. *Type.* U.S.N.M. no. 16320.

DESCRIPTION. Introvert, about as long as the trunk, with about 110 rows of fine, single-pointed hooks on its first fifth. Introvert otherwise smooth and without papillae. Trunk up to 40 mm long; its anterior and posterior ends covered with polygonal or square elevations, dark brown in colour. The middle of the trunk is smooth and yellowish-brown in colour. The shields are dark brown and furrowed. The anal shield is oval, with its long axis transverse and with 18 long and short furrows at its posterior edge, converging to the base of the introvert. The caudal shield has 22–26 radial furrows of which only about 15 reach the round elevation in the centre. The caudal shield, due to contractions of the muscles, stands out from the trunk like the roof of a pagoda. The longitudinal muscles are gathered into about 46 bands which anastomose only under the anal shield and in the region of the nephridia. One retractor arises from two roots and is fixed at about two sevenths of the trunk length in front of the caudal shield. Intestinal convolutions numerous attached by a strong muscle to the caudal shield. A large rectal caecum. Two nephridia free for three quarters of their length are present; nephrostome prominent.

REMARKS. Described originally from three specimens. Fischer (1922) records another without comment.

DISTRIBUTION. West Indies (Fischer, 1922e); Florida, Cuba, Brazil (Gerould, 1913).

Paraspidosiphon speculator (Selenka, 1885)

(Fig. 30F–G)

Aspidosiphon speculator Selenka, 1885 : 19–20, pl. 4, figs 24–27; Wesenberg-Lund, 1959c : 213.

TYPE LOCALITY. St Vincent, Cape Verde. *Type.* Brit. Mus. (Nat. Hist.) no. 1885.12.3.28.

DESCRIPTION. Introvert probably longer than the trunk, thickly studded with hooks. On the anterior half they are flattened, strongly curved, double-pointed and arranged in rows. In the posterior half they are tetrahedral with only a slightly bent point. Cutaneous glands occur between the hooks and are more numerous anteriorly. Tentacles few and short. Trunk up to 14 mm long and yellow-brown; shields dark brown. Skin glands supported by chitinous plates which from a ring round the central opening. They do not appear as papillae but as flat tubercles. Anal shield rough and granulated. Caudal shield grooved with about 30 peripheral grooves. Longitudinal muscles split into weak bands; anteriorly about 22 which anastomose in a complex manner but in the rest of the trunk they appear as 14 fine strands. Two strong retractors originate a short way in front of the caudal shield and join about half way up the trunk. Small caecum present on rectum. Two large nephridia free for half their length.

REMARKS. Described originally from three specimens. Wesenberg-Lund recorded numerous specimens, all agreeing with Selenka's description.

DISTRIBUTION. Cape Verde (Selenka, 1885); Gulf of Guinea (Wesenberg-Lund, 1959c).

Paraspidosiphon spinososcutatus (Fischer, 1922)

(Fig. 29D)

Aspidosiphon spinososcutatus Fischer, 1922e : 13–14, text-figs 2–3; Murina, 1967b : 42.

TYPE LOCALITY. St Thomas Sound, Barbados, West Indies.

DESCRIPTION. Introvert up to 30 mm long and with about 40 rows of fine transparent hooks, each with two points; papillae interspersed between hooks. Trunk up to 20 mm long; the anterior and posterior parts are brownish-yellow in colour but the middle is a lighter yellow. The shields are dark brown. The anal shield is indistinctly marked off from the trunk, with prominent spine-like papillae round the edge; it has ten furrows filled with white, chalky points. The anterior quarter of the trunk is also covered with prominent but more dome-shaped papillae. The caudal shield is conical; it has 20–25 grooves which do not reach the centre, so that it is more clearly cut off from the trunk than the anal shield. Under magnification brown, angular, papillae are clearly seen. Each pore is surrounded by a single irregular row of large plates and around these is an area covered with small polygonal plates. The longitudinal muscles are gathered into 24–25 anastomosing bands. The rectum is fixed by a wing muscle. Intestinal coils 11–12 and traversed by a strong spindle muscle which is fastened in front of the anus and posteriorly to the front of the caudal shield. The two retractors arise at the caudal shield, each from two roots from 2–4 muscle bands; they unite in the middle of the trunk. The nephridia are half the trunk length and are fastened for their whole length; they open behind the anus between bands 3 and 4.

REMARKS. Fischer's description was based on several specimens.

DISTRIBUTION. West Indies (Fischer, 1922e); Cuba (Murina, 1967b).

Paraspidosiphon steenstrupii steenstrupii (Diesing, 1859)

(Fig. 28A–D)

Aspidosiphon steenstrupii Diesing, 1859 : 767, pl. 2, figs 1–6; Selenka & de Man, 1883 : 116–118, pl. 1, figs 12–13, pl. 13, figs 190–192; Sluiter, 1886 : 489–490, pl. 3, figs 5–6; 1891 : 115; 1902 : 18; Whitelegge, 1899 : 394; Shipley, 1899a : 153–154; 1902d : 131–132, 171; Ikeda, 1904 : 40–41; 1924 : 38; Hérubel, 1904a : 564; Lanchester, 1905c : 39; Fischer, 1914a : 70–71; 1914b : 13; 1922e : 13; 1923b : 21; 1926 : 108; 1931 : 139; ten Broeke, 1925 : 93–94; Monro, 1931 : 34; Sato, 1935b : 315–316, pl. 4, fig. 16; 1939 : 424–426, pl. 21, figs 18, 19, pl. 23, fig. 44, text-figs 58–60; Leroy, 1936 : 426; 1942 : 36–38; Stephen, 1942 : 253, pl. 11, fig. 6; Stephen & Robertson, 1952 : 441; Wesenberg-Lund, 1959a : 197–198; 1963 : 138; Edmonds, 1956 : 307–308, text-fig. 19; Murina, 1967b : 42.
Aspidosiphon fuscus Sluiter, 1882a : 86–108, figs 1–12; 1886 : 474; 1891 : 116; 1902 : 19; Selenka & de Man, 1883 : 116.

TYPE LOCALITY. St Thomas.

DESCRIPTION. Introvert about as long as the trunk, armed anteriorly with rows of double-pointed hooks and posteriorly with brown spines. Cylindrical papillae are irregularly scattered between them, one set between two rows of hooks. Trunk up to 40 mm in length, darker anteriorly and posteriorly. In the middle portion, the skin is so thin that the anastomosing longitudinal muscle bands can be seen. The surface of the trunk is covered with large and small papillae, which are best seen at the ends of the trunk. The papillae are composed of closely packed polygonal plates, four or more surrounding the central opening. According to the state of contraction, the shields may be flat or hemispherical. The anal shield is usually covered with chalky points. The caudal shield has the ridges at its edge unequal in size and very irregularly arranged so that their number is indefinite. The longitudinal muscle bands are most strongly developed anteriorly; there are about 25 bands over most of the trunk but they anastomose so frequently that there may be only 16 anteriorly. A single strong retractor muscle with two roots is inserted near the anterior edge of the posterior quarter of the trunk; each root covers 3–7 or 3–8 bands. The two unite in the middle of the trunk. The oesophagus lies on the dorsal side of the retractor to which its anterior half is attached. Numerous intestinal coils, which are attached to the posterior end of the trunk by a strong spindle muscle. A contractile vessel and rectal caecum present. No fastening mesenteries. The nephridia reach to the base of the retractors; their posterior half is free. Two eye-spots present.

REMARKS. This is a well known species, collected in warm seas.

DISTRIBUTION. West Indies (ten Broeke, 1925); Brazil (Fischer, 1931); Cape Verde (Fischer, 1914a); South Africa (Stephen, 1942); Mauritius (Selenka & de Man, 1883; Wesenberg-Lund, 1959a); Red Sea (Hérubel, 1904a); Gulf of Mannar (Shipley, 1902d); Laccadive Islands (Shipley, 1902d); Indonesia (Sluiter, 1891); Siam (Fischer, 1923b); Japan (Sato, 1939); West Caroline Islands (Ikeda, 1924); Philippines (Selenka & de Man, 1883); New Guinea (Fischer, 1926); Loyalty Islands (Shipley, 1899a); New Hebrides (Leroy, 1936); Great Barrier Reef (Monro, 1931; Edmonds, 1956); Indo-China (Leroy, 1942); Cuba (Murina, 1967b).

Paraspidosiphon steenstrupii fasciatus (Augener, 1903)

Aspidosiphon steenstrupi var. *fasciatus* Augener, 1903 : 322–325, text-figs 1–4.

TYPE LOCALITY. Polo Edam, Amboina.

DESCRIPTION. The subspecies differs from the nominate form in several particulars. First, there is an extensive clear area on the hook. Secondly, the middle portion of the trunk is yellow-brown and thirdly both shields are dark brown in colour.

REMARKS. Described originally from a number of specimens. Augener gave a detailed description which we have abbreviated.

DISTRIBUTION. As for the type locality.

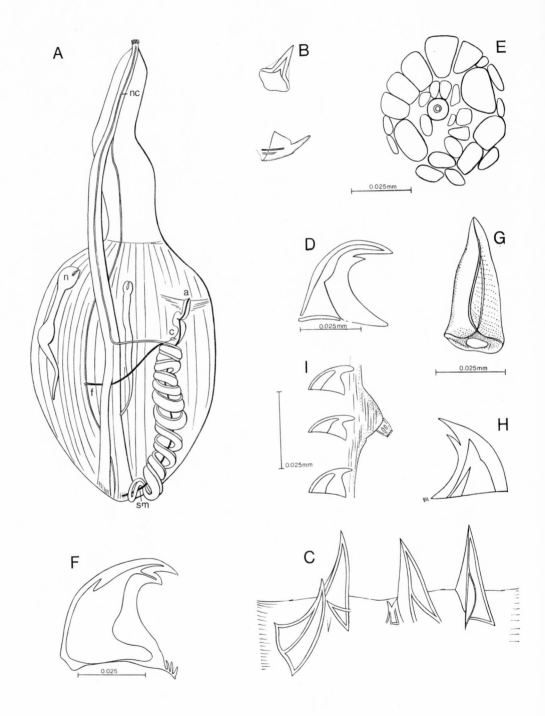

Paraspidosiphon tenuis (Sluiter, 1886)

Aspidosiphon tenuis Sluiter, 1886 : 491–492, pl. 3, fig. 7; 1891 : 116; 1902 : 19.

TYPE LOCALITY. Bay of Batavia, Malaya.

DESCRIPTION. Introvert and trunk of about equal length. Anteriorly the introvert is covered with closely packed rows of small hooks which have a very long
single point. There are no hooks or spines on the posterior part of the introvert.
Papillae very small. Trunk thicker posteriorly. The shields are dark brown and
furrowed. In the anal shield the furrows run from the base of the introvert to
the edge of the shield and there is no chalky deposit. In the caudal shield the
furrows are arranged radially and some reach the centre. The longitudinal muscles
anastomose considerably. In the middle of the trunk there are 29 bands, posteriorly
only 22. Two retractors arise close to the caudal shield from bands 2–6; they unite
at the level of the middle of the trunk. Numerous intestinal convolutions present
and a strong spindle muscle. No fastening mesentery. Rectal caecum present.
The nephridia are about half the trunk length and are free for their whole length.
A fairly well developed nephrostome anteriorly.

REMARKS. Known only from the holotype. Sluiter considered it to be closely
related to *P. steenstrupii*. Sluiter (1891, 1902) merely repeated the original record.

DISTRIBUTION. As for the type locality.

Paraspidosiphon trinidensis (Cordero & Mello-Leitao, 1952)

Aspidosiphon trinidensis Cordero & Mello-Leitao, 1952 : 277–295, pl. 1, figs 6–10.

TYPE LOCALITY. Ilha da Trinidada, Brazil; at 8 m. *Type.* Hydriol. Biol. Stn.
Oswaldo Crux, Rio de Janeiro.

DESCRIPTION. Introvert with very numerous single-pointed hooks which are
superficially set in the skin. Trunk 24 mm in length, 3·5–4 mm in breadth and with
numerous transverse furrows. Well-developed papillae scattered over the surface,
largest near the shields, smallest near the middle of the trunk. Anal shield circular,
dark brown, 4 mm in diameter with a raised irregular prominence occupying about
two thirds of the surface and set slightly nearer the base of the introvert. No
furrows, but the surface is covered with warts carrying many light brown papillae.
Caudal shield, also circular, 4 mm in diameter. The centre is well marked, 2·5 mm
in diameter and surrounded by triangular plates with a truncated apex; 18 furrows

---

FIG. 30. (A–B) *Paraspidosiphon truncatus.* (A) Dissected specimen. (B) Spines from
the introvert. (A–B after Keferstein.) (C) *Paraspidosiphon ambonensis.* Spines from
the posterior region of the introvert (after Keferstein). (D–E) *Paraspidosiphon makoensis.*
(D) Hook from the introvert. (E) Skin papillae from the anterior region of the trunk.
(D–E after Sato.) (F–G) *Paraspidosiphon speculator.* (F) Hook from the anterior part
of the introvert. (G) Hook from posterior part of introvert; (F) and (G) to same scale.
(F–G after Selenka.) (H) *Paraspidosiphon semperi.* Hook from introvert (after ten
Broeke). (I) *Paraspidosiphon angulatus.* Hooks and papillae from the introvert (after
Ikeda). KEY: *See* Fig. 26, p. 221.

present reaching to the centre of the shield. Longitudinal muscle bands fairly strong, more or less uniform in breadth and 23 in number in the middle of the trunk; some anastomoses. One relatively thin retractor attached anteriorly to the base of the introvert; posteriorly it bifurcates at the level of its distal third and is attached to the trunk wall 2 mm from the edge of the caudal shield. Each branch is identical and arises from five bands. Ten intestinal coils. A strong spindle muscle is attached posteriorly to the middle of the caudal shield. Two long, thin, tapering, cylindrical nephridia present fastened to the trunk wall for their full length and opening behind the anus.

DISTRIBUTION. As for the type locality.

Paraspidosiphon truncatus (Keferstein, 1867)

(Fig. 30A–B)

Phascolosoma truncatum Keferstein, 1867 : 50, pl. 6, figs 15–18.
Aspidosiphon truncatus: Selenka & Bülow, 1883 : 118–119, pl. 13, figs 193–195; Sluiter, 1898 : 444; 1902 : 17; Shipley, 1899a : 154; 1902d : 132; Ikeda, 1904 : 38–39, figs 66–67; Lanchester, 1905c : 34; Fischer, 1914b : 15; Benham, 1912 : 136.

TYPE LOCALITY. Panama.

DESCRIPTION. Introvert up to 13 mm in length; apparently smooth in appearance but, under magnification, is seen to carry small, elongated, irregularly scattered hooks on the anterior portion. Trunk up to 24 mm in length, brown in colour; shields darker. The furrows on the anal shield are less well defined than those on the caudal shield, they do not reach the centre and their number is indeterminate. The furrows on the caudal shield number from 20–25 and also do not reach the centre. The trunk is uniformly covered with very small rounded papillae. Longitudinal muscles are gathered into bands. They are rather stronger in the anterior part of the trunk, and anastomose so frequently that this portion of the muscle looks like a sheet with many longitudinal slits. The bands show less anastomoses under the anal shield and are fewer in number. In the posterior half of the trunk they are very strong and anastomose considerably. The retractor has two roots which arise from the caudal shield. The oesophagus follows the retractor till the roots divide when it then forms the numerous intestinal coils. A rectal caecum is present. A fastening mesentery runs from the top intestinal coil, through the angle between the roots and is attached to the trunk wall. There is also a caecum where the oesophagus and intestinal coils join. The spindle muscle arises near the anus and is attached posteriorly. The nephridia, which are free for most of their length, extend as far as the division of the retractor muscle.

REMARKS. This species is known chiefly from warmer seas.

DISTRIBUTION. Panama (Keferstein, 1867); West Indies (Fischer, 1914b); Red Sea (Hérubel, 1904a); Mauritius (Selenka & de Man, 1883); Tanganyika (Lanchester, 1905c); Natal (Sluiter, 1898); Sunday Island (Benham, 1912); Loyalty Islands (Shipley, 1899a); Japan (Ikeda, 1904).

Genus *LITHACROSIPHON* Shipley

Lithacrosiphon Shipley, 1902d : 139; Fischer, 1922b : 26–28.

DESCRIPTION. Anterior end of the trunk surmounted by a hard, calcareous, cone-shaped cap borne on a pad of skin in which the longitudinal muscles are inserted. Introvert arises on the ventral side of the cap and bears numerous rows of hooks, often double-pointed, and a few short tentacles. Longitudinal musculature grouped into bands which split and anastomose freely. Two retractor muscles and two nephridia. Spindle muscle fixed posteriorly.

TYPE SPECIES. *Lithacrosiphon maldivensis* Shipley.

REMARKS. Shipley described the genus for a single specimen from the Maldive Is. Fischer (1922b : 26) reviewed the genus and pointed out that the number of tentacles is small and that skin bodies lie between the rows of hooks. The genus lies in some respects between the genera *Paraspidosiphon* and *Cloeosiphon*; this is shown in Table 9. Nine species have been described, most of which are inhabitants of coral. Six of the species are known only from the holotypes; some are very closely related and possibly synonymous.

DISTRIBUTION. The genus is widely distributed in tropical seas.

List of Species

L. *alticonus* ten Broeke

L. *cristatus* (Sluiter)

L. *gurjanovae* Murina

L. *indicus* Fischer

L. *kukenthali* Fischer

L. *maldivensis* Shipley

L. *odhneri* Fischer

L. *poritidis* ten Broeke

L. *uniscutatus* (Ikeda)

GENUS LITHACROSIPHON—KEY TO SPECIES

1 Hooks on the introvert of two kinds, some with two-points and some with one point . 2
– Hooks on the introvert of one kind, either single or double pointed . . . 3
2 Anterior rows of hooks with one point, posteriorly placed hooks with two points
L. alticonus (p. 260)
– Anterior rows of hooks with two points, posteriorly placed hooks with one point
L. gurjanovae (p. 261)
3 Hooks uniformly single pointed 4
– Hooks uniformly double pointed 6
4 Nephridia open posterior to anus (nephridia fixed to the body wall along anterior two thirds of their length, longitudinal muscles in about 30 strongly anastomosing bands) . . . . **L. poritidis** (p. 264)
– Nephridia open at level of anus 5
5 Introvert wholly covered with more or less regularly arranged hooks (anal shield with about 52 grooves, longitudinal muscles in 18 bands) . **L. kukenthali** (p. 263)
– Only anterior region of introvert bears hooks (longitudinal muscles form a continuous sheet in the region of the introvert and posterior fourth of trunk, rectal caecum present and nephridia fixed for their whole length) . . **L. uniscutatus** (p. 265)

Lithacrosiphon alticonus ten Broeke, 1925

(Fig. 31F–G)

Lithacrosiphon alticonum ten Broeke, 1925 : 90–91, figs 13–15.

TYPE LOCALITY. Caracas Bay, West Indies.

DESCRIPTION. Introvert about half the length of the trunk; hooks prominent, anterior hooks with one point, posterior hooks with two points. Among the hooks are small, rounded papillae covered with concentrically arranged small plates which become larger towards the periphery. Skin iridescent; body wall thin, especially in the middle region. Trunk 13 mm in length and about four times as long as thick; anteriorly a high conical chalky cap is set on a base of skin. The cap is 2 mm in height and 1 mm across the base. There are 42 ridges on the lower portion of the cap. Longitudinal muscles gathered into about 20 highly anastomosed bundles, their number being hard to determine. The retractor arises posteriorly with two broad roots from longitudinal muscle bands 1–5. The oesophagus and retractors run together for half their length. Intestine with 14 convolutions. The rectum is half the length of the trunk and carries a small caecum in the middle and a larger one at the end. The two nephridia are longer than the trunk and are recurved posteriorly; their last one third is free. No caudal shield but an area of regularly radiating bands, somewhat brown in colour.

REMARKS. Known only from the holotype.

DISTRIBUTION. As for the type locality.

Lithacrosiphon cristatus (Sluiter, 1902)

Aspidosiphon cristatus Sluiter, 1902 : 26–28, pl. 3, figs 14–16.

TYPE LOCALITY. Malaya.

DESCRIPTION. Introvert, fully expanded 12 mm, transparent and smooth with only a very few papillae. In front of them there are about 20 rows of hooks which have two points and three chitinized bars running across from top to bottom. Trunk 20 mm in length and carrying at its anterior end a cylindrical shield which is 1·5 mm in height. The skin is strongly chitinized and the calcareous cap is strongly furrowed longitudinally. At its anterior end it carries a series of algal-like filaments mixed with sand and coral fragments. The anus lies on the dorsal side immediately below the cap. Posteriorly the trunk is pointed and a little darker than the middle portion. To the naked eye the skin appears smooth and transparent so that the longitudinal muscles show through but under the microscope numerous small papillae are to be seen over the entire surface. The longitudinal muscles are divided into about 20 bands, but as they anastomose greatly it is difficult to give the exact number. Two retractors which spring from the anterior end of the posterior third of the body span four longitudinal muscle bands; they join after about half their length. Oesophagus long, intestinal coils about 12 and rectum long. Spindle muscle arises behind the spirals and is fastened to the posterior end of the body. Nephridia open a little behind the anus and are about half the length of the trunk.

REMARKS. Described originally from a number of specimens. No other records known. Sluiter gave a list of the stations at which the species was taken, but did not say from which his type came.

DISTRIBUTION. Malaya. Siboga stations 53, 60, 115, 125, 142. From coral reefs.

Lithacrosiphon gurjanovae Murina, 1967

Lithacrosiphon gurjanovae Murina, 1967b : 36–39, 3 figs.

TYPE LOCALITY. Cuba.

DESCRIPTION. The species is stick-like in shape. Length of trunk 19 mm and width 3 mm. Introvert partly invaginated; length about 5 mm and width 1 mm. The anterior region of the trunk bears a hard calcareous cap from which grow several species of algae. The introvert arises ventrally to the anterior cap. The anterior region of the introvert bears hooks of two kinds, most anteriorly about 20 rings of bidentate hooks and more posteriorly irregularly scattered unidentate hooks. No posterior shield is present on the trunk. The longitudinal musculature of the body wall forms anastomosing bundles which fuse behind the roots of the retractors to form a continuous sheath. Two retractors, which are attached to the posterior third of the trunk, unite at about the level of the nephridia. Two eye-spots are present. The rectum is long and a rectal or intestinal caecum is present (in a few specimens there are two caeca). The spindle muscle is fastened posteriorly. The nephridia open at about the level of the anus. One fixing muscle is attached to the alimentary canal.

REMARKS. Described in considerable detail from 43 specimens. The species is allied to *L. alticonus* ten Broeke from the West Indies but differs most noticeably in the arrangement of the uni- or bi-dentate hooks on the introvert. The finding of specimens with two rectal caeca is of considerable interest.

Lithacrosiphon indicus Fischer, 1922

(Fig. 31C–E)

Lithacrosiphon indicus Fischer, 1922b : 28, figs 30–33.

TYPE LOCALITY. Timor, East Indies.

DESCRIPTION. Introvert 8–10 mm. The cap is short and stumpy, 1·5 mm high marked with 32–35 furrows; its base is surrounded by a ring of dark wart-like

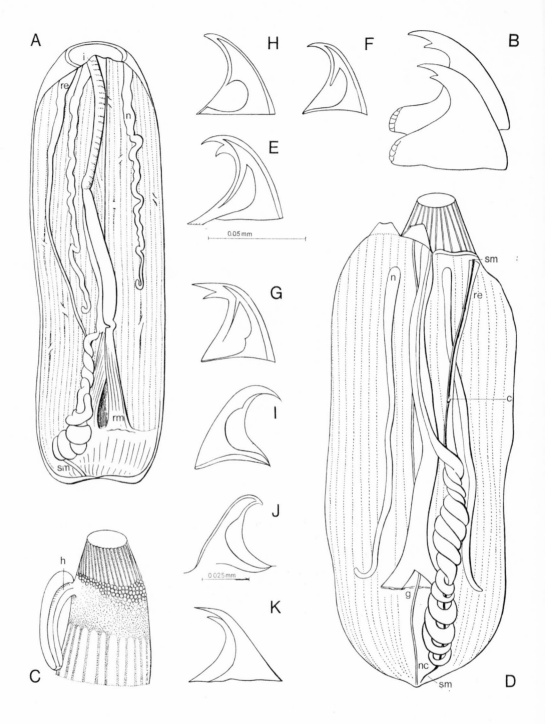

bodies. Anus situated on the dorsal side just posterior to the cap. No posterior shield. Papillae on the middle part of the body are very small and conical with fairly large angular plates; posteriorly the plates are larger and darker. Introvert arises ventrally to the cap and is transparent; it bears 6–8 broad tentacles and about 20 rows of doubly pointed hooks. Anteriorly there are 15–16 anastomosing longitudinal muscles and posteriorly 19–20. Two retractors arise from the anterior part of the last quarter of the trunk from longitudinal muscles 2–6. Oesophagus long and the contractile vessel present. Intestinal convolutions, 13–14, fixed anteriorly and posteriorly by a spindle muscle. Rectum long and a caecum is present. Two nephridia about three quarters as long as the body and fixed for their whole length. Nephridiopores just posterior to the anus.

REMARKS. The description is based on two specimens; no other records.

DISTRIBUTION. As for the type locality.

Lithacrosiphon kukenthali Fischer, 1919
(Fig. 32I)

Lithacrosiphon kukenthali Fischer, 1919b : 289–293, figs 1–5.

TYPE LOCALITY. Barbados Reef, West Indies.

DESCRIPTION. The introvert is wholly covered with more or less regularly arranged hooks of the usual form with only one point. The part of the specimen left includes most of the anterior half and is 9 mm in length and 1·5 mm in breadth. The cap is like that of *L. maldivensis*, but passes into an anal shield which, in turn, passes into the body. The anal shield is dark and grooved like the shields of *Aspidosiphon*; the grooves are chalky and number about 52. The longitudinal muscles are gathered into 18 bands. The nephridia open on a level with the anus.

REMARKS. Known only from the holotype, which was badly damaged, consisting of only the anterior half of the animal. The posterior half, including the retractors and most of the gut, was lost.

DISTRIBUTION. As for the type locality.

Lithacrosiphon maldivensis Shipley, 1902
(Figs 31A–B, 32E–F)

Lithacrosiphon maldivense Shipley, 1902d : 139–140, pl. 7, figs 1–11.

TYPE LOCALITY. Maldive Islands. *Type.* Brit. Mus. (Nat. Hist.) 1924.3.1.175.

FIG. 31. (A–B) *Lithacrosiphon maldivensis*. (A) Dissected specimen. (B) Introvert hook. (A–B after Shipley). (C–E) *Lithacrosiphon indicus*. (C) Anterior part of trunk with half-extended introvert. (D) Dissected specimen. (E) Introvert hook. (C–E) after Fischer. (F–G) *Lithacrosiphon alticonus*. (F) Introvert hook with one point. (G) Introvert hook with two points. (F–G after ten Broeke.) (H) *Lithacrosiphon poritidis*. Introvert hook (after ten Broeke). (I) *Lithacrosiphon kukenthali*. Introvert hook (after Fischer). (J) *Lithacrosiphon uniscutatus*. Introvert hook (after Ikeda). (K) *Lithacrosiphon odhneri*. Introvert hook (after Fischer). KEY: See Fig. 26, p. 221.

DESCRIPTION. Introvert with very numerous rows of doubly pointed hooks and 8–10 tentacles. Body about 30 mm in length and 4 mm in breadth and carries anteriorly a conical cap of calcareous matter showing a laminated structure. The ventral outline of the cap is in line with the body, but the dorsal outline slopes down at a very sharp angle to the ventral to near the anus. Skin thick and heavily tuberculated for the anterior sixth of the body, the remainder is smooth and transparent. The body wall is divided into 26–28 longitudinal muscle bands, which anastomose freely. One pair retractor muscles which fan out posteriorly to cover longitudinal muscles 4–12; they are inserted near the posterior end of the body. The nephridia are about half the length of the body. The alimentary canal is fixed posteriorly by a muscle strand; 10–12 intestinal coils and no rectal caecum. Brain compact with two conspicuous eye-spots on its anterior surface.

REMARKS. Known only from the holotype.

DISTRIBUTION. As for the type locality.

Lithacrosiphon odhneri Fischer, 1922

(Fig. 31K)

Lithacrosiphon odhneri Fischer, 1922b : 29–31, pl. 4, figs 34–39.

TYPE LOCALITY. Bartholomew Island, West Indies.

DESCRIPTION. Cap a tall chalk-like stump with 50 furrows surmounting an area of dark wart-like bodies; anus dorsal and lies at the base of the cap. Introvert about half the length of the trunk and bears 6–8 tentacles and numerous rows of small, doubly transparent hooks separated by papillae. Posteriorly, the skin is dark and opaque, but transparent and light in the centre; the darker part carries rectangular papillae with large dark plates. The longitudinal muscles are split into 17–18 anastomosing bands posteriorly and 13–14 anteriorly. One pair of retractors each arising from bundles 1–5, from near the hind end of the body. The oesophagus carries a small contractile vessel; intestine with about 20 convolutions fixed anteriorly and posteriorly by the spindle muscle. No rectal caecum. The anus opens between bands 5 and 6; nephridia open posterior to the anus and reach almost to the posterior end of the body; they are free.

REMARKS. Known only from the holotype.

DISTRIBUTION. As for the type locality.

Lithacrosiphon poritidis ten Broeke, 1925

(Fig. 31H)

Lithacrosiphon poritidis ten Broeke, 1925 : 91–92, figs 16–17.

TYPE LOCALITY. Caracas Bay, West Indies.

DESCRIPTION. Short introvert, bearing 12 tentacles and rows of single pointed hooks 0·04 mm high and 0·036 mm broad; papillae lie between anteriormost rows of hooks. The cap is 1 mm in height and 1 mm in breadth and covered with a brown skin with about 40 longitudinal furrows. The body is four times as long as broad. Numerous small, uniform papillae made up of closely packed plates are present at the base of the introvert and on the posterior part of the body. Longitudinal muscles gathered into about 30 very strongly anastomosing bands, so that the exact number is difficult to determine. One pair of retractors, one arising from two roots and the other from one; they fuse for about half their length. About 20 intestinal convolutions. A very strong spindle muscle is attached to the rectum and is fixed at the posterior end of the body; the rectum is long and about half the body length. Contractile vessel without villi. The nephridia are about three quarters as long as the body; their posterior third is free and they open posterior to the anus.

REMARKS. This species, known only from the holotype, is closely related to *L. kukenthali*. It differs from *L. alticonus* in the shape of its cap, in the shape of its hooks and in lacking a rectal caecum.

DISTRIBUTION. As for the type locality.

Lithacrosiphon uniscutatus (Ikeda, 1904)

(Fig. 31J)

Aspidosiphon uniscutatus Ikeda, 1904 : 43–45, fig. 10, pl. 3, figs 73–77; 1924 : 37–38.
Lithacrosiphon uniscutatus: Sato, 1939 : 429.

TYPE LOCALITY. Katura, Satsuma, Japan.

DESCRIPTION. Introvert about as long as the trunk, light yellowish in colour; anteriorly it is armed with numerous rows of reddish-yellow, single-pointed hooks; between the rows are tubular, colourless, hyaline papillae. Ten short tentacles. Mouth just below the anterior border of the anal shield. Trunk 13·5 mm in length, 3·5 mm in breadth. Skin relatively thick, yellowish-brown in colour, becoming deeper brown towards the anterior cap. The latter is deep reddish-brown in colour, shaped like a tall helmet and obliquely truncated from the dorsal basal border. The wall is made unusually thick and hard by a deposit of calcareous material; its surface is sculptured into numerous longitudinal ridges and grooves which converge towards the apex. The surface of the skin near the shield is closely set with brown papillae, structurally the same as those at the basal border of the shield. The papillae on the middle and posterior regions of the trunk are flat and formed of many polygonal plates which become smaller towards the centre. The longitudinal muscles form a continuous sheet in the region of the introvert base and the posterior fourth of the trunk; in the middle of the trunk they divide into frequently anastomosing bundles. About 12 intestinal convolutions. The spindle muscle is fixed anteriorly and posteriorly but no fixing muscles observed. A caecum occurs on the mid portion of the rectum. Anterior part of the rectum fixed by well-developed wing muscles. One pair of retractors, which are fused for most of their length; they arise from about the posterior seven eighths of the trunk where the longitudinal muscles are continuous. Two nephridia, about two thirds as long as

S

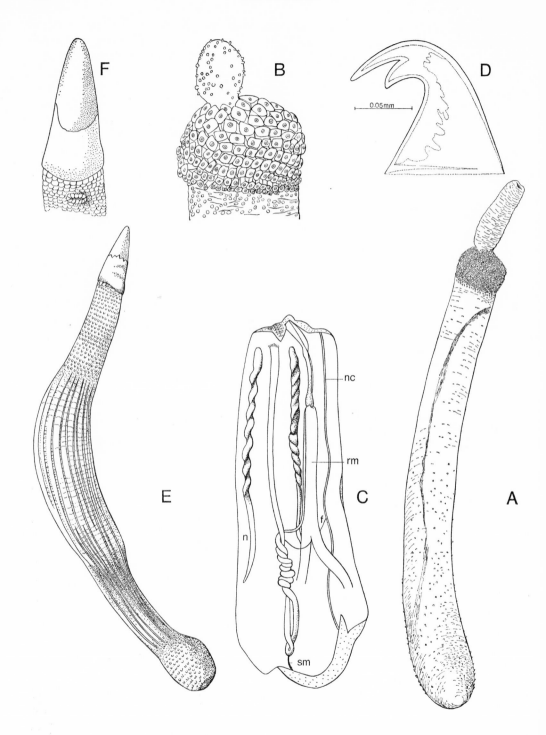

the trunk, opening at the level of the anus; they are reddish-brown in colour and are fixed for their whole length. Two eye-spots.

REMARKS. Known only from the holotype. Sato merely repeated the record. Ikeda gave a longer description which we have abbreviated.

DISTRIBUTION. Japan (Ikeda & Sato, as above).

Genus *CLOEOSIPHON* Grübe, 1868

Cloeosiphon Grübe, 1868b : 48; Selenka & de Man, 1883 : 126.

DESCRIPTION. A rounded, pineapple-like cap consisting of numerous, small, calcareous plates present at the anterior extremity of the trunk. Introvert, armed with numerous rows of doubly pointed hooks, evaginates from the centre of the cap. No shield or cap at the posterior extremity of the trunk. Longitudinal musculature continuous. A single retractor muscle with two short roots. Spindle muscle fixed posteriorly. Two nephridia.

TYPE SPECIES. *Loxosiphon aspergillus* Quatrefages, 1865.

REMARKS. Four species, other than *C. aspergillus*, have been described; *C. mollis* Selenka & de Man, 1883, *C. japonicus* Ikeda, 1904, *C. javanicus* Sluiter, 1886 and *C. carolinus* Ikeda, 1924. *C. mollis* differs from *C. aspergillus* in the size of the hooks and the shape of the cap. One of us has noticed considerable variations in the size of the hooks and the shape of the cap of about 25 specimens of *C. aspergillus* collected from one locality on the Great Barrier Reef. The differences described by Selenka we consider to be those that might be found within a species and we regard *C. mollis* and *C. aspergillus* as identical. Fischer (1922b) and Sato (1935b) considered all four species as synonymous with *C. aspergillus*.

The gender of the generic name *Cloeosiphon* has been regarded by some authors as masculine and by others as neuter. Selenka & de Man (1883 : 126) make it neuter in *C. aspergillum* and masculine in *C. mollis* (1883 : 128). Article 30(a) of the International Code of Zoological Nomenclature states that nouns that end in a Greek word 'take the gender for that word in standard Greek dictionaries unless the Commission rules otherwise'. Consequently the words ending in '-siphon' should make the gender of the Greek '*siphon*', which is masculine.

DISTRIBUTION. The species is a common inhabitant of coral reefs and has been reported from most tropical seas.

FIG. 32. (A–D) *Cloeosiphon aspergillus*. (A) Specimen showing calcareous cap and introvert partly extended. The dark structure showing through the body wall is a nephridium (original). (B) Introvert partly extended (after Ikeda). (C) Dissected specimen. (D) Hook from the introvert. (C–D after Selenka.) (E–F) *Lithacrosiphon maldivensis*. (E) Entire specimen (after Shipley). (F) Anterior region showing cone-shaped cap borne on a pad of skin. KEY: *See* Fig. 26, p. 221.

Cloeosiphon aspergillus (Quatrefages, 1865)
(Fig. 32A–D)

Loxosiphon aspergillus Quatrefages, 1865b : 605, pl. 20, fig. 20.
Echinosiphon aspergillum Sluiter, 1884 : 26–38, pl. 1, figs 1–15.
Cloeosiphon aspergillum Grübe, 1868b : 48–49; Selenka & de Man, 1883 : 126–127, pl. 2, figs
    23–24, pl. 14, figs 214–216; Fischer, 1892 : 85–86; 1895 : 18–19; 1922b : 31–33, pl. 4, figs
    40–42; 1923b : 24–25; 1926 : 109; Shipley, 1898 : 471–472; 1899c : 56; 1899a : 154; 1902d :
    132; 1903 : 174; Whitelegge, 1899 : 394; Sluiter, 1902 : 30; Augener, 1903 : 297–371;
    Lanchester, 1905b : 39; Monro, 1931 : 34; Sato, 1935b : 321–324, pl. 4, fig. 20; 1939 : 429–
    431, pl. 21, figs 24–25; Leroy, 1942 : 31–35, figs 8–9; 1936 : 426; Stephen & Robertson,
    1952 : 44; Edmonds, 1956 : 309, fig. 21; Cutler, 1965 : 58, 1 fig.
Cloeosiphon mollis Selenka & de Man, 1883 : 128, figs 217–218; Augener, 1903 : 333–334.
Cloeosiphon japonicum Ikeda, 1904 : 49–53, figs 13, 86–89.
Cloeosiphon javanicum Sluiter, 1886 : 473; 1891 : 116.
Cloeosiphon carolinum Ikeda, 1924 : 34–37, pl. 1, figs 7–11.

TYPE LOCALITY.   ? Isle de France (Quatrefages, 1865).

DESCRIPTION.   Introvert rather longer than the body and bearing many rows of doubly-pointed hooks.   Trunk up to 50 mm in length, pink in colour in living specimens and with skin translucent; anteriorly it carries a rounded, pineapple-like cap composed of small, square to rhomboidal, calcareous plates spirally set. Posteriorly the trunk is more or less pointed and lacks a shield.   A single retractor with two short roots which arise from the body wall about one fifth of the trunk length from the posterior extremity.   The oesophagus runs along the retractor to which it is bound by mesenteries.   Intestinal spiral short and with about 12 coils; anus lies just posterior to the calcareous cap.   Rectum fixed by wing muscles; no caecum.   A spindle muscle arises near the anus, traverses the spiral and is attached posteriorly to the body wall.   A fastening mesentery arises at the beginning of the spiral, runs between the roots of the retractor and is attached to the body wall near the nerve cord.   The two nephridia reach almost to the base of the retractors and are fixed by mesenteries except at the distal extremity.   Two eye-spots.

REMARKS.   A well known species of coral reefs in the Indo-Pacific region.

DISTRIBUTION.   East Africa (Fischer, 1895); Madagascar (Cutler, 1965); Zanzibar (Fischer, 1892; Lanchester, 1905c; Stephen & Robertson, 1952); Ceylon (Shipley, 1903); Maldive and Laccadive Islands (Shipley, 1902d); Indo-China (Leroy, 1942); Siam (Fischer, 1923b); Billiton (Sluiter, 1902); Penang (Lanchester, 1905b); Japan (Sato, 1939); West Caroline Islands (Sato, 1935b); Palau and Jaluit Islands (Ikeda, 1924); Loyalty Islands (Shipley, 1899a); New Hebrides (Leroy, 1936); Funafuti Atoll (Whitelegge, 1899); Christmas Island (Shipley, 1899c); Samoa (Fischer, 1895); Townsend Island (Sluiter, 1891); New Guinea (Fischer, 1926); Australia, Great Barrier Reef (Monro, 1931; Edmonds, 1956).

Genus **CENTROSIPHON** Shipley, 1903

Centrosiphon Shipley, 1903 : 173.

DESCRIPTION.   Sipunculans with anterior and posterior shields.   Introvert arises from the centre of the anterior cap or shield (and not ventral to it as in *Aspidosiphon*).

Type species. *Centrosiphon herdmani* Shipley.

Remarks. The genus contains only one species and has been reported only once. It differs from *Aspidosiphon* in that the introvert arises from the middle of the anterior shield and in possessing four retractor muscles instead of one or two. It differs from *Cloeosiphon* in possessing a posterior shield and four retractors.

Distribution. The genus is uncommon.

Centrosiphon herdmani Shipley, 1903

Centrosiphon herdmani Shipley, 1903 : 171–174, pl. 1, figs 4–10.

Type locality. Cheval Paar, Gulf of Manaar.

Description. Length of cylindrical trunk 30 mm. Width of circular anterior shield or "platform" 3 mm and that of posterior shield 2·5 mm. Introvert, about half extended, 3 mm long and arising from the middle of the anterior shield. Tentacles, 12–15, appear to surround the mouth. Chitinized projections (hooks?) on the introvert behind the mouth. Longitudinal musculature continuous. Four retractors; a thinner dorsal pair arises near the anus and a stouter ventral pair more posteriorly. Two nephridia. Eyespots present. No calcareous deposits on either shield.

Remarks. Described from two specimens.

Distribution. As for the type locality.

(6). Family **PHASCOLOSOMATIDAE** fam. nov.

Description. Sipunculans in which the tentacles are arranged in a single crescent or near circle which lies dorsal to the mouth and encloses the nuchal organ, if present. Longitudinal musculature of the body wall either in bands or continuous. No anal or caudal shield. Papillae usually with small platelets and usually most densely packed on the anterior and posterior extremities of the trunk. No integumentary or coelomic pouches in the body wall (except in one species).

Type genus. *Phascolosoma* Leuckart, 1828.

Remarks. The family contains two genera, *Phascolosoma* Leuckart, 1828 in which the longitudinal musculature is grouped into bands and *Fisherana* Stephen, 1965 in which the longitudinal musculature is continuous. *Phascolosoma* is a large genus and contains 60 species; *Fisherana* is small and contains four species.

Family Phascolosomatidae—Key to Genera

1 Species in which the longitudinal muscles are thickened into bands
   PHASCOLOSOMA (p. 270)
– Species in which the longitudinal musculature is continuous .   *FISHERANA* (p. 329)

Genus *PHASCOLOSOMA* Leuckart, 1828

Phascolosoma Leuckart, 1828 : 22, fig. 5; Keferstein, 1863 : 39, in part; 1865a : 422, in part;
    Baird, 1868 : 91; Fisher, 1950a : 551; 1952 : 422.
Phascolosomum Diesing, 1851 : 63, in part; 1859 : 758, in part.
Phymosomum Quatrefages, 1865b : 621.
Phymosoma Selenka & de Man, 1883 : 54 (emendation of *Phymosomum*).
Physcosoma Selenka, 1897 : 460; Spengel, 1898 : 50; authors.
Physconosoma Bather, 1900 : 78.

DESCRIPTION. Trunk spindle-shaped, fusiform or sub-cylindrical with longitudinal musculature divided into separate bundles which often anastomose; muscle
bands not always visible externally. Tentacles arranged in a single crescent or
near circle which lies dorsal to the mouth and which neither surrounds nor partly
surrounds the mouth. Nuchal organ, if present, enclosed within the ring of tentacles.
Surface of introvert and trunk usually covered with papillae which often bear small
chitinous platelets; papillae usually most prominent on the anterior and posterior
surfaces of the trunk. Anterior region of the introvert usually bears rings of single-
pointed hooks. Retractor muscles, usually two pairs, more rarely one pair; dorsal
and ventral retractors on each side may fuse in some species. Single contractile
vessel usually lacks villi or tubules.

TYPE SPECIES. *Phascolosoma granulatum* Leuckart, 1828.

REMARKS. The position of the tentacles dorsal to the mouth and the presence of
longitudinal muscle bands are characteristic of this genus. Sometimes a specimen
has to be dissected in order to see the arrangement of the tentacles and of the
longitudinal musculature because the latter lies internal to the circular musculature.
The anterior and posterior regions of the trunk are often made darker than the rest
of the trunk by a dense aggregation of pigmented papillae.

The synonymy of the genus, which is complicated, is explained by Fisher (1952 :
423). The genus is large and contains 60 species. We have separated them into
four subgenera according to (1) the number of retractor muscles, (2) the nature of
the contractile vessel and (3) the attachment or non-attachment of the spindle
muscle. Similar criteria have been used to divide the genus *Golfingia* into subgenera. The new subgenera are *Rueppellisoma* (p. 271), *Antillesoma* (p. 277),
Satonus (p. 282) and *Phascolosoma* (sensu stricto) (p. 289). The largest of these,
Phascolosoma (s.s.), containing 38 species, we have not been able to simplify further
nor to construct for it a satisfactory key. We have, however, arranged the species
in a list that shows some of their more important characters. A clue to the identity
of many species is given by the shape, size and structure of the introvert hooks and
of the papillae that cover the body. Therefore we have endeavoured to supply a
drawing of the hooks and/or papillae of as many species as possible.

After an examination of the type and three other specimens we agree with
Wesenberg-Lund (1959b) that *Siphonides rickettsi* Fisher is synonymous with
Phascolosoma pectinatum Keferstein. If we adopted the identical scheme used
to separate *Golfingia* into subgenera we should have placed *P. pectinatum* with
its unusual hooks and bilobed nephridia in a separate subgenus of *Phascolosoma*.

We have refrained from doing this because the only other species of the genus with bilobed nephridia is *P. kurilense* (Sato) in which the hooks are normal in shape and in which the spindle muscle is fixed posteriorly.

We also considered at one stage whether we should place *P. arcuatum* Gray (=*P. lurco* Selenka & de Man) and *P. kurilense* (Sato) with their strongly fasciculated circular muscles, into a separate subgenus. Finally we decided against further subdivision of the genus.

DISTRIBUTION. The genus is widely distributed in tropical and temperate waters. Species are commonly found under rocks and in fissures or burrows in rock and especially in limestone or coral reefs. *P. arcuatum* Gray (=*P. lurco* Selenka & de Man) is an inhabitant of mangrove swamps and is reported to live in burrows above low water level (Harms & Dragendorff, 1933).

The relationship of the four subgenera is shown in Table 10.

TABLE 10

Subgenera of the genus *Phascolosoma*

Subgenus	Retractor muscles	Contractile vessel	Spindle muscle	Type species	No. of species
1. *Rueppellisoma*	one pair	simple or with villi	attached posteriorly	*P. rueppellii*	7
2. *Antillesoma*	two pairs	with villi or tubules	attached posteriorly	*P. antillarum*	6
3. *Satonus*	two pairs	simple	absent or if present not fixed posteriorly	*P. nigritorquatum*	8
4. *Phascolosoma* (s.s.)	two pairs	simple	fixed posteriorly	*P. granulatum*	39

KEY TO SUBGENERA OF PHASCOLOSOMA

1	One pair of retractor muscles	.	.	.	.			*RUEPPELLISOMA* (p. 271)
–	Two pairs of retractor muscles	.	.	.	.	.	.	.	.	2
2	Contractile vessel with villi or tubules	.	.	.		*ANTILLESOMA* (p. 277)
–	Contractile vessel without villi or tubules	.	.	.	.	.	.	.	3
3	Spindle muscle fixed to posterior body wall	.	.	*PHASCOLOSOMA* (s.s.) (p. 289)
–	Spindle muscle absent or if present not fixed posteriorly	.		*SATONUS* (p. 282)

Subgenus *RUEPPELLISOMA* subgen. nov.

DESCRIPTION. Species with one pair of retractor muscles, contractile vessel with or without villi or tubules, spindle muscle fixed posteriorly, hooks present or absent.

TYPE SPECIES. *Phascolosoma rueppellii* Grübe.

REMARKS. This subgenus which contains seven species consists of two groups, one with and the other without introvert hooks. *P. gaudens* (Lanchester) and

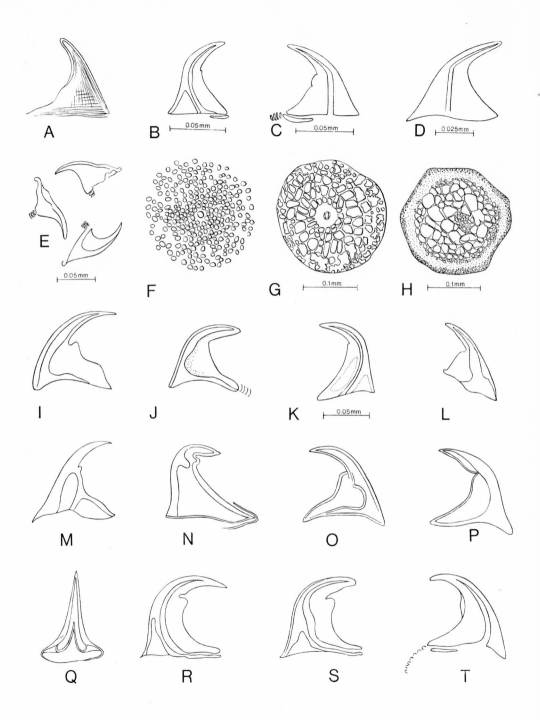

A

B   0.05mm

C   0.05mm

D   0.025mm

E   0.05mm

F

G   0.1mm

H   0.1mm

I

J

K   0.05mm

L

M

N

O

P

Q

R

S

T

P. weldoni (Shipley), according to Lanchester, are very close species. The condition of the spindle muscle is not known for *P. sewelli*.

Species without hooks	Species with hooks
P. gaudens (Lanchester)	*P. nahaense* (Ikeda)
P. onomichianum (Ikeda)	*P. rueppellii* Grübe
P. sewelli (Stephen)	
P. simile (Chen & Yeh)	
P. weldonii Shipley	

DISTRIBUTION. Tropical and temperate seas.

SUBGENUS RUEPPELLISOMA—KEY TO SPECIES

1   Hooks present on the introvert **2**
 –   Hooks absent from the introvert **3**

2   Tentacles 22 and finger-like (introvert hooks strongly curved, 20–30 anastomosing longitudinal muscles, no rectal caecum, nephridia attached for most of their length)   .   .   .   .   **P. nahaense** (p. 274)
 –   Tentacles 8 and finger-like (introvert hooks only slightly bent, 18 longitudinal muscles with little anastomosing, nephridia free for most of their length)   **P. rueppellii** (p. 275)

3   Longitudinal musculature banded over most of the surface **4**
 –   Longitudinal musculature continuous over most of the surface and banded only in the anterior quarter of the trunk where it anastomoses considerably (retractor muscles arise from the middle of the trunk and join for most of their length, nephridia free)   .   .   .   .   **P. sewelli** (p. 276)

4   Rectal caecum present (350 tentacles, 8–22 longitudinal muscles, three fastening muscles to intestine, contractile vessel with villi, nephridia free for posterior third or quarter)   .   .   .   .   **P. simile** (p. 276)
 –   Rectal caecum absent **5**

5   Nephridia open just posterior to the anal aperture (70–80 tentacles, 10–12 longitudinal muscles in middle of body, retractors arise near posterior third of trunk)   **P. weldonii** (p. 277)
 –   Nephridia arise at same level as the anal aperture **6**

6   Longitudinal muscles 16–22 (two fastening muscles, contractile vessel with villi up to 2 mm long and which may branch, nephridia entirely fixed)   **P. onomichianum** (p. 275)
 –   Longitudinal muscles 14–34 (contractile vessel with villi)   .   .   **P. gaudens** (p. 274)

FIG. 33. (A) *Phascolosoma ambonense* introvert hook (after Fischer). (B) *Phascolosoma rottnesti* introvert hook (after Edmonds). (C) *Phascolosoma kurilense* introvert hook (after Sato). (D) *Phascolosoma formosense* introvert hook (after Sato). (E) *Phascolosoma abyssorum* introvert hook (after Southern). (F) *Phascolosoma rottnesti* papilla from body (after Edmonds). (G) *Phascolosoma kurilense* papilla from body (after Sato). (H) *Phascolosoma formosense* papilla from body (after Sato). (I) *Phascolosoma demanni* introvert hook (after Sluiter). (J) *Phascolosoma diaphanes* introvert hook (after Sluiter). (K) *Phascolosoma heronis* introvert hook (after Edmonds). (L) *Phascolosoma evisceratum* introvert hook (after Lanchester). (M) *Phascolosoma extortum* introvert hook (after Sluiter). (N) *Phascolosoma glabrum* introvert hook (after Sluiter). (O) *Phascolosoma lacteum* introvert hook (after Sluiter). (P) *Phascolosoma spengeli* introvert hook (after Sluiter). (Q) *Phascolosoma spongicolum* introvert hook (after Sluiter). (R–S) *Phascolosoma thomense* introvert hooks (after Augener). (T) *Phascolosoma yezoense* introvert hook (after Ikeda).

Phascolosoma (Rueppellisoma) gaudens (Lanchester, 1905)

Physcosoma gaudens Lanchester, 1905b : 38, pl. 2, fig. 11.

TYPE LOCALITY. Palau Bidan, Penang, Malaya. *Type.* British Museum (Nat. Hist.) 1924.3.1.199–200.

DESCRIPTION. Introvert short, without hooks but densely covered with brown papillae. Trunk covered with papillae which have only two rings of small transparent plates round the central opening. These rings are surrounded by a ring of about six large brown plates and these in turn, by another more or less complete ring of smaller irregular brown plates. There is no pigment between the plates. One pair of retractors arises in the middle of the trunk. The longitudinal muscles are gathered into 14 bands anteriorly and may be as many as 34 posteriorly; in the middle of the trunk they anastomose. The contractile vessel carries villi. The nephridia open on the level of the anus.

REMARKS. Lanchester gave only a short description of the species, mainly comparing the differences between it and *P. weldonii*.

Phascolosoma (Rueppellisoma) nahaense (Ikeda, 1904)

(Fig. 38D–E)

Phymosoma nahaense Ikeda, 1904 : 29–31, text-figs 8, 59–62.

TYPE LOCALITY. Amongst dead coral, Naha, Okinawashima, Islands of Riukiu, Japan.

DESCRIPTION. Introvert with numerous rows of small hooks each with a sharp, strongly-curved apical tooth; a bar lies across the base with two rows of warts. Hooks and warts are reddish-yellow in colour. Between every second row of hooks are numerous, small, perforated papillae. There are 22 short finger-like tentacles. Trunk 45 mm in length and 8 mm in breadth, skin brownish-yellow, more deeply tinted at the introvert base and the posterior end. The surface is covered with fairly large but only slightly elevated papillae. These are thickly covered with chitinous plates which gradually become larger towards the centre of the papilla. The papillae are nearly flat and elliptical in the middle of the trunk and become larger at the posterior end and especially at the introvert base. Longitudinal muscles gathered into 20–30 separate but anastomosing bands. One pair of retractors arises from the middle of the trunk. About 10 intestinal convolutions present, with one fixing muscle which extends between the first spiral and the left side of the nerve cord. The contractile vessel runs the length of the oesophagus but is without villi. The spindle muscle is fixed anteriorly and posteriorly. The rectum is fairly long and is without a caecum. The nephridia are about half the trunk length and are attached to the trunk wall for most of their length; they open on the level of the anus.

REMARKS. Described from two specimens.

DISTRIBUTION. As for the type locality.

Phascolosoma (Rueppellisoma) onomichianum (Ikeda, 1904)

Phymosoma onomichianum Ikeda, 1904 : 26–28, text-figs 7, 56–58.
Physcosoma onomichianum: Sato, 1934 : 247; 1939 : 397–398, pl. 22, fig. 14, pl. 23, fig. 43.
Phascolosoma onomichianum: Wesenberg-Lund, 1959b : 67; 1963 : 127–128.

TYPE LOCALITY. Shore collection, Onomichie Inlet, Province of Bingo, Japan.

DESCRIPTION. Introvert slender, only 2 mm in diameter, without hooks or spines. Papillae present but there are non-papillated parts which are covered with sparsely scattered chitinous plates like those on the papillae. Eye-spots absent. Trunk 30 mm in length, 9 mm in breadth, yellowish-brown in colour and covered with deep brown coloured papillae of varying shapes. In the middle region of the trunk the papillae are only slightly elevated and consist of deep brown polygonal plates of various sizes. On the rest of the trunk and at the introvert base, the papillae are conspicuously tall cones with an obtuse apex; they consist of thick chitinous plates of irregular polygonal shape set like a pavement. The plates at the base are largest and deepest in colour. The longitudinal muscles are gathered into very frequently anastomosing bands, 16 in the region of the nephridia and 22 in the posterior part of the trunk. One pair of retractors arises at the level of the beginning of the posterior third of the trunk. There are about 15 intestinal convolutions with two fixing muscles both arising on the left of the nerve cord. One arises just behind the root of the left retractor and is joined to the posterior portion of the convolutions; the other arises at a point about 7 mm in front of the origin of the first and is joined to the first spiral. The contractile vessel has long and numerous villi, some of which may be up to 2 mm in length and show slight ramifications. The spindle muscle is attached posteriorly. Rectal caecum absent. The nephridia are about half the length of the trunk, are fixed to the trunk wall for their whole length and open at the level of the anus.

DISTRIBUTION. Japan (Sato, 1934a); Mauritius (Wesenberg-Lund, 1959b); Natal (Wesenberg-Lund, 1963).

Phascolosoma (Rueppellisoma) rueppellii Grübe, 1868

(Fig. 39B)

Phascolosoma rueppellii Grübe, 1868a : 643, pl. 8, fig. 2; Wesenberg-Lund, 1957b : 12.
Phymosoma rueppellii: Selenka & de Man, 1883 : 82–83.
Physcosoma rueppellii: Shipley, 1902d : 135.
Physcosoma rueppellii: Stephen, 1941a : 406–407.

TYPE LOCALITY. Red Sea.

DESCRIPTION. Introvert up to 8 mm in length with eight short, white, finger-like tentacles. It is white underneath, often with 11 dark cross stripes on the dorsal surface. The papillae are very small anteriorly, becoming larger, darker and club-shaped on the introvert base; 11–15 rows of very small hooks which have the point only slightly bent. Trunk up to 20 mm in length, barrel-shaped, rounded posteriorly, whitish in colour and somewhat iridescent. The skin carries papillae which appear as scattered spots; they become twice as large and more closely set in front of the anus and at the posterior end of the trunk. The longitudinal muscles are gathered into 18 bands which show few anastomoses. One pair of retractors present arising in the middle of the trunk. There are numerous intestinal convolutions. The nephridia are dark and free for most of their length.

DISTRIBUTION. Red Sea (Grübe, 1868a; Selenka & de Man, 1883; Wesenberg-Lund, 1957b); Arabian Sea (Stephen, 1941a); Maldive and Laccadive Islands (Shipley, 1902d).

Phascolosoma (Rueppellisoma) sewelli (Stephen, 1941)

Physcosoma sewelli Stephen, 1941a : 405–407.

TYPE LOCALITY. Gulf of Oman. *Type*. British Museum (Nat. Hist.) 1952.3.25.13–14.

DESCRIPTION. Introvert black or grey-brown with a few papillae; no hooks. Trunk up to 70 mm in length, grey-brown in colour. The skin is raised into strong circular ridges; in appearance it has a corky texture and is thickly covered with almost flat papillae except at the posterior end of the trunk where they become more hemispherical. Longitudinal muscles form a continuous sheet throughout most of the trunk but in the anterior quarter they are clearly gathered into bands which anastomose so much that the exact number cannot be readily counted. One pair of stout retractors arising from broad roots in the middle of the trunk; joined for much of their length. A strong spindle muscle is present but because the posterior extremity of the specimen was damaged, it is not possible to say if the muscle had been attached posteriorly. The nephridia are reddish and free for their whole length.

REMARKS. Based on two specimens.

DISTRIBUTION. Gulf of Oman. Maldive Islands. 1948–2051 m (Stephen, 1941).

Phascolosoma (Rueppellisoma) simile (Chen & Yeh, 1958)

Physcosoma similis Chen & Yeh, 1958 : 274–276, text-figs 3, 4.

TYPE LOCALITY. China.

DESCRIPTION. Introvert up to 31 mm in length and 2·6 mm in diameter with about 350 tentacles but without hooks. Two dark eye-spots present. Trunk up to 85 mm in length, yellowish-brown in colour with large, dark papillae which become darker and more closely aggregated at the introvert base and on the posterior end; they are covered with large dark and small yellowish polygonal plates. On the remainder of the trunk they are isolated, and almost invisible to the naked eye. In the holotype the longitudinal muscles are gathered into anastomosing bands, eight at the anterior end and 22 posteriorly; in the paratypes the figures are 8 and 13, and 12 and 35, respectively. One pair of retractors arises in the posterior third of the trunk. There are about 45 intestinal convolutions. The spindle muscle arises in front of the anus and is attached near the posterior end of the trunk. One fixing muscle arises from the spindle muscle in front of the rectal caecum and is attached posteriorly on the left side of the nerve cord near to the base of the retractors. Two accessory muscles separate from the anterior portion of the fixing muscle and are attached to the first intestinal coil. The contractile vessel carries very numerous villi. The rectum may be 6–8 mm in length in the male and 11–18 mm in the female; it carries a caecum. The nephridia are about half the trunk length with the posterior third or quarter free.

REMARKS. Described originally from numerous specimens.

DISTRIBUTION. China, several localities.

Phascolosoma (Rueppellisoma) weldonii (Shipley, 1892)

Physcosoma weldonii Shipley, 1892b : 77–78.

TYPE LOCALITY. Bimini Lagoon, Bahamas. *Holotype.* British Museum (Nat. Hist.) 1896.10.6.1.

DESCRIPTION. Introvert up to 10 mm long (retracted), without hooks but carrying 70–80 tentacles; a well-developed collar at its base. Introvert densely covered with brown papillae composed of horny plates; pigmented spots are scattered in between the papillae. Trunk 30–35 mm in length, plump and slightly curved. The ground colour is light yellow, modified by dark papillae of which there are two kinds on both the introvert and trunk. The first type are flat, low, brown rectangular elevations of the skin; the second are light coloured and occur as elevated protuberences on the introvert. The longitudinal muscles are gathered into 10–12 bands in the middle of the trunk and are fused into a single sheet at the anterior end. One pair of retractors arises from the anterior edge of the posterior third of the trunk. The nephridia open a little behind the anus.

REMARKS. Based originally on three specimens.

DISTRIBUTION. As for the type locality.

Subgenus ANTILLESOMA subgen. nov.

DESCRIPTION. Species with two pairs of retractor muscles, contractile vessel with villi or tubules, spindle muscle attached posteriorly, hooks present or absent.

TYPE SPECIES. *Phascolosoma antillarum* Grübe & Oersted.

REMARKS. The subgenus contains six species. We have not included *P. nigrescens* Keferstein in the subgenus although Keferstein (1865a : 424) reports that the contractile vessel bears many small, lateral pockets. Most authors state that the vessel is simple. *P. minutum* (ten Broeke) is known only from the holotype.

Species without hooks	Species with hooks
P. antillarum Grübe & Oersted	*P. horsti* (ten Broeke)
P. asser (Selenka & de Man)	*P. microdentigerum* (ten Broeke)
P. pelmum (Selenka & de Man)	*P. minutum* (ten Broeke)

DISTRIBUTION. Tropical and temperate waters.

SUBGENUS ANTILLESOMA—KEY TO SPECIES

1　Hooks present on the introvert　. 　. 　. 　. 　. 　. 　. 　. 　.3
–　Hooks absent from the introvert　. 　. 　. 　. 　. 　. 　. 　. 　2
2　Papillae on trunk bear many concentric rows of platelets　.　***P. antillarum*** (p. 278)
–　Papillae on trunk bear very few rows of platelets.　.　. ⎰　　　　***P. asser*** (p. 279)
　　　　　　　　　　　　　　　　　　　　　　　　　　　　⎱　　　***P. pelmum*** (p. 281)
3　Papillae on dorsal surface at the base of the introvert are very large and bear spines
　　(introvert with about 15–40 rows of hooks, nephridia open in front of the anus
　　and are about half as long as the trunk)　.　.　***P. microdentigerum*** (p. 280)
–　Papillae on dorsal surface at base of introvert do not bear spines .　.　.　.　4
4　Nephridia open in front of the anus, are about as long as the trunk and are free for
　　their whole length　.　.　.　.　.　.　.　.　***P. minutum*** (p. 281)
–　Nephridia open at same level as anus, are about half as long as the trunk and their
　　posterior half is free　.　.　.　.　.　.　.　***P. horsti*** (p. 280)

Phascolosoma (Antillesoma) antillarum Grübe & Oersted, 1858

(Fig. 35D–F)

Phascolosoma antillarum Grübe & Oersted, 1858 : 117–118; Diesing, 1859 : 762; Keferstein,
　　1863 : 40, pl. 3, figs 2, 11; 1865a : 435, pl. 31, fig. 11, pl. 33, fig. 37; Ikeda, 1904 : 24–25;
　　Fisher, 1952 : 434–436, pl. 39, figs 8, 9; Longhurst, 1958 : 85.
Phymosoma antillarum : Selenka & de Man, 1883 : 57, pl. 7, figs 93–96; Fischer, 1895 : 12.
Physcosoma antillarum : Gerould, 1913 : 420–421, pl. 62, figs 19–20; Fischer, 1922b : 10; Leroy,
　　1936 : 424; Sato, 1939 : 394.
Phascolosoma fuscum Keferstein, 1862 : 67.
Phascolosoma nigriceps Baird, 1868 : 90, pl. 11, fig. 1–1a; Rice & Stephen, 1970 : 63.
Phascolosoma aethiops Baird, 1868 : 90; Rice & Stephen, 1970 : 58–59

TYPE LOCALITY.　West Indies.

DESCRIPTION.　Introvert half to three quarters of the length of the trunk, up
to 18 mm long, with 50–60 long cylindrical finger-like tentacles but without hooks.
Except for a clear smooth zone on the anterior part the introvert is covered with
closely aggregated conical papillae.　Two eye-spots present.　Trunk up to 30 mm
in length, four to five times as long as it is wide.　The skin is thick, white or yellowish
in colour and covered with flat, dark brown, closely aggregated papillae.　At the
posterior end of the trunk, but especially at the introvert base, the papillae become
very large and dark, showing as dark plates with fine furrows.　The musculature
is strong and the longitudinal muscles, which are gathered into about 30 bands
in the middle of the trunk and about 20 in the anterior portion, anastomose considerably.　There are about 20 intestinal convolutions.　A strong spindle muscle
is attached near to the anus and to the posterior end of the trunk.　Two pairs of
retractors arise close together at the same level in the middle third of the trunk.
The contractile vessel carries many finger-like villi which reach to the first coil.
The nephridia are long, more than half the trunk length, and are fixed throughout
their whole length.

REMARKS.　The species was carefully redescribed by Fisher, 1952 : 434.　He
points out that there are about 200 tentacles on his specimens and that they superficially resemble those of a *Themiste*.　In addition he reports the presence of a

fixing muscle attached to the rectum and an intestinal caecum. The contractile villi are sometimes dichotomously branched. Fisher says 'on account of its more sturdy habit, short introvert and conspicuous crown of tentacles this species superficially resembles a *Dendrostomum* (=*Themiste*)'.

DISTRIBUTION. West Indies (Grübe & Oersted, 1858; Keferstein, 1863, 1865); Surinam, Barbados, Puerto Cabello (Selenka & de Man, 1883); Barbados (Fischer, 1922b); Jamaica (Baird, 1868); Punta Arenas (Grübe & Oersted, 1858); Chile (Baird, 1868); Sierra Leone (Longhurst, 1958); California (Fisher, 1952); Puerto Rico (Leroy, 1936); Hawaii (Fisher, 1952); Riukiu Is., Japan (Sato, 1939).

Phascolosoma (Antillesoma) asser (Selenka & de Man, 1883)

(Fig. 35G)

Phymosoma asser Selenka & de Man, 1883 : 59–60, pl. 1, fig. 3, pl. 7, figs 97–101; Sluiter, 1886 : 503; 1891 : 118.
Physcosoma asser: Fischer, 1895 : 12; 1914b : 5; 1922b : 10; Sluiter, 1902 : 11; Shipley, 1903 : 133, 174; Leroy, 1936 : 424.

TYPE LOCALITY. Batjan.

DESCRIPTION. Introvert very short, about one sixth of the length of the trunk; numerous finger-like tentacles present but hooks absent. It is covered with cone-shaped, closely-packed papillae. Trunk stoutly built, about three to three and a half times as long as it is wide, the diameter increases posteriorly. Posterior end rounded. The trunk is reddish-grey in the middle and posterior regions while the base of the introvert and the anal region are dark brown. The skin is crossed by fine furrows and posteriorly with longitudinal furrows. The trunk is covered with short, but prominent papillae, all of which are very similar in structure. The central pores of the papillae are surrounded by small, pale platelets which in turn are surrounded by one or two circles of red-yellow plates of chitin. The papillae occur on the anterior third of the trunk and numerous large and small plates with four or more corners lie scattered between them. More posteriorly where the skin is in the form of squares, there is one papilla to each square, the rest of the square being covered with scattered, large, red-yellow plates, often largest at the edge. Around the anus the papillae are closely packed, red-brown in colour, not divided by furrows, and form a small shield. The longitudinal muscles are gathered anteriorly into 16 bands; more numerous posteriorly. Two pairs of retractors arise at about the same level in the middle of the trunk, the weaker dorsals soon join the ventrals giving the appearance of there being only two muscles. Intestinal coils 8–10 through which passes a strong spindle muscle attached to the posterior end of the trunk. A fixing muscle extends between the first coil and the trunk wall. The contractile vessel carries many finger-like villi. The nephridia are fairly long, about half the length of the trunk and are fastened to the trunk wall for their whole length.

DISTRIBUTION. Mozambique (Fischer, 1895); Indian Ocean (Fischer, 1895); Batjan (Selenka & de Man, 1883); Java (Sluiter, 1886, 1902); Billiton (Sluiter, 1891); Loyalty Is., Laccadive Is. (Shipley, 1903); Timor (Fischer, 1922b).

Phascolosoma (Antillesoma) horsti (ten Broeke, 1925)

Physcosoma horsti ten Broeke, 1925 : 89, text-fig. 11.

TYPE LOCALITY. Caracas Bay, West Indies.

DESCRIPTION. Introvert about as long as the trunk with numerous rows of fairly small crowded hooks which have a short point bent at right angles. A dark line passes along the posterior edge of each hook and projects into the central clear space; it has a sharp point at the apical bend. Trunk 10 mm in length, 5–6 times as long as broad, skin iridescent and mottled with brown. The whole surface is covered with large papillae which are larger at the introvert base and at the posterior end of the trunk than in its middle; each papilla is covered with small chitinous plates. Longitudinal muscles gathered into 30 very strongly anastomosing bands. Two pairs of short broad retractors arise close together and soon unite, the broader ventrals arising from eight bands and the dorsals from five bands. Only eight intestinal convolutions present. The rectum is long and the contractile vessel possesses small villi. The stout spindle muscle is attached to the posterior end of the trunk. The nephridia are short and about half as long as the trunk. Their posterior half free and they open on the same level as the anus.

DISTRIBUTION. As for the type locality.

Phascolosoma (Antillesoma) microdentigerum (ten Broeke, 1925)

Physcosoma microdentigerum ten Broeke, 1925 : 88–89, text-figs 8–10; Stephen, 1960a : 517–518.

TYPE LOCALITY. In stones and coral, Caracas Bay, West Indies.

DESCRIPTION. Introvert about as long as the trunk and covered with papillae which become progressively smaller towards the tentacles. There are 15–40 rows of hooks; each hook is fairly broad, sharply bent, with a large secondary tooth on the inner side. There are 10 tentacles, dark-coloured inside. Trunk 10 mm in length, four to six times as long as thick, with a pointed posterior end and transparent musculature. The skin is covered with large papillae which are brown in colour and more closely aggregated at the introvert base and at the posterior end than in the middle of the trunk where they are small and flat. On the dorsal side of the introvert base there are several very large papillae carrying a spine on top, as in *P. dentigerum*, but the papillae are smaller and the spine about half the size of those in that species. On the ventral side the papillae are much smaller. The longitudinal muscles are gathered into 20–30 frequently anastomosing bundles. Two pairs of retractors arise at different levels but soon join; the broad ventral pair arises from 5–7 bands and the lighter dorsal pair from 2, 3 or 4 bands. There are about 10 intestinal convolutions and the oesophagus carries a contractile vessel with small villi. The convolutions are attached posteriorly by a strong spindle muscle. The rectum is long. The nephridia are short, about half as long as the trunk, and their posterior third is free; they open in front of the anus.

REMARKS. The species is closely related to *P. dentigerum*. It is said to differ in having villi attached to the contractile vessel and no warts at the base of the hooks. Further material may show that it is only a variant of the more widely distributed form. It was originally described from a number of specimens.

DISTRIBUTION. West Indies (ten Broeke, 1925); Senegal (Stephen, 1960).

Phascolosoma (Antillesoma) minutum (ten Broeke, 1925)

Physcosoma minutum ten Broeke, 1925 : 87–88, text-figs 6–7 (not *Phascolosoma minutum* Keferstein, 1863 : 40 = *Golfingia minuta* (Kef.)).

TYPE LOCALITY. Curacao, West Indies.

DESCRIPTION. Introvert about as long as the trunk, carrying about 20 tentacles and about 100 rows of hooks. Each hook has a slender tip bent at nearly a right angle, the dark line along the dorsal side of the hook projecting as a sharp point into the internal clear space about the foot of the bent point. Trunk about twice as long as thick, 5 mm in length and covered with brownish papillae which are largest at the posterior end. They are dome-shaped and the part near the central opening has many small closely-crowded chitinous plates; on the lower part of the papilla the plates are scattered irregularly. The longitudinal muscles are gathered into about 26 frequently anastomosing bands. Two pairs of retractors, which are fairly short, arise close together in the middle trunk third; the broader ventrals arise from 7 bands and the thinner dorsals from 3–4 bands. About eight intestinal convolutions are attached by a strong spindle muscle to the posterior end of the trunk. The oesophagus carries a contractile vessel with small villi. The rectum is moderately long and is fixed by a mesentery. The nephridia are almost as long as the trunk and are free for their whole length; they open in front of the anus.

REMARKS. Known only from the holotype.

DISTRIBUTION. As for the type locality.

Phascolosoma (Antillesoma) pelmum (Selenka & de Man, 1883)

Phymosoma pelma Selenka & de Man, 1883 : 60, pl. 1, fig. 4, pl. 7, fig. 102; Sluiter, 1886 : 504; 1891 : 118; Augener, 1903 : 311–312.
Physcosoma pelma : Sluiter, 1902 : 12; Shipley, 1902d : 134; Fischer, 1922b : 15; 1923b : 23–24; Sato, 1935 : 311–312, pl. 4, fig. 11.

TYPE LOCALITY. Philippines.

DESCRIPTION. Introvert very short, about a fifth as long as the trunk and carrying about 45–50 tentacles which join to form a short stalk; covered with cone-shaped papillae, but without hooks. Trunk up to 35 mm in length, slim, generally dirty-grey in colour, darker anteriorly, lighter posteriorly. Papillae are sparsely distributed over the whole surface; they resemble the papillae of *P. asser* and take the form of a clear central area surrounded by a ring of dark, elongated plates with

T

sharp corners. Between these papillae lie groups of lighter coloured papillae of varying sizes, which also have sharp corners. The papillae on the anterior portion of the trunk are darker. The longitudinal muscles are gathered into 19–21 bands which are readily evident at the anterior and posterior ends of the trunk. Two pairs of retractors arise at the same level in the middle of the trunk; the ventral pair is strong and the dorsal weak. They soon unite to give the appearance of a single pair. Intestinal coils few in number, less than 10, with a fastening mesentery from the first coil. The strong spindle muscle is attached to the posterior end of the trunk. The two nephridia are half as long as the trunk and are fastened to the trunk wall for their whole length.

REMARKS. Descriptions of the species which differ slightly in detail have been given by Selenka & de Man, 1883, Augener, 1903 and Fischer, 1923b. The species is very close to *P. asser* (Selenka & de Man).

Selenka & de Man (1883 : 56) point out that the contractile vessels of *P. antillarum*, *P. asser* and *P. pelmum* possess numerous villi or tubules. Selenka does not directly state this fact in his description of the species on page 60.

DISTRIBUTION. Mauritius (Selenka & de Man, 1883); Laccadive Islands (Shipley, 1902d); Siam (Fischer, 1923b); Amboina (Augener, 1903); Java (Selenka & de Man, 1883; Sluiter, 1891); Philippines (Selenka & de Man, 1883); West Caroline Islands (Sato, 1935).

Subgenus *SATONUS* subgen. nov.

DESCRIPTION. Species with two pairs of retractor muscles; contractile vessel simple, spindle muscle absent or if present not fixed posteriorly, hooks present or absent.

TYPE SPECIES. *Phascolosoma nigritorquatum* Sluiter.

REMARKS. After examining the holotype and paratype specimens of *Siphonides rickettsi* Fisher, 1952 we consider, like Wesenberg-Lund, 1959b, that this species is synonymous with *Phascolosoma pectinatum* Kef. Since the spindle muscle is not fixed posteriorly the species falls into this subgenus.

The subgenus contains eight species, three of which are known only from the holotypes.

DISTRIBUTION. Tropical and subtropical seas.

Species without hooks	Species with hooks
P. hebes (Sluiter)	*P. demanni* (Sluiter)
	P. duplicigranulatum (Sluiter)
	P. falcidentatum (Sluiter)
	P. maculatum (Sluiter)
	P. mauritaniense (Hérubel)
	P. nigritorquatum (Sluiter)
	P. pectinatum Keferstein

Phascolosoma (Satonus) demanni (Sluiter, 1891)

(Fig. 33I)

Physcosoma demanni Sluiter, 1891 : 121–122, pl. 2, figs 15–16.

TYPE LOCALITY. Billiton, Malaya. *Type.* Batavia Museum.

DESCRIPTION. Introvert 60 mm in length, of the same colour as the trunk and with the same type of papillae; anteriorly 13 rows of hooks. Each hook has a long, thin spine, bent at about 45°, and a well-developed secondary tooth. Trunk 35 mm in length with a moderately pointed posterior end; yellow-brown in colour. Anus is prominent. The papillae are distributed irregularly over the skin; they are fairly well dispersed over the base of the introvert and on the middle of the trunk. The longitudinal muscles are gathered into about 25 bands which anastomose very freely. They are to be seen easily at the introvert base; otherwise at the anterior and posterior ends of the trunk they are weak and less evident. Two pairs of retractors are present, uniting near the introvert; the ventrals arise near the middle of the trunk from bands 2–8, the dorsals in the anterior third from bands 4–6. About 16 intestinal convolutions are held by a fixing muscle from the first coil. The contractile vessel is without villi. The rectum is fixed by a broad wing muscle. The spindle muscle is not attached posteriorly and it does not emerge from the last coil. The two nephridia are reddish, about half the trunk length, and open a little way behind the anus; their posterior half is free.

REMARKS. Known only from the holotype.

DISTRIBUTION. As for the type locality.

Phascolosoma (Satonus) duplicigranulatum (Sluiter, 1886)

Phymosoma duplicigranulatum Sluiter, 1886 : 501–502.
Physcosoma duplicigranulatum : Shipley, 1899 : 155; Sluiter, 1902 : 13.

TYPE LOCALITY. Malaya.

DESCRIPTION. Introvert more than two and a half times the length of the trunk; with about 20 rows of anterior hooks, followed by an area scattered with single hooks. This is followed by a zone of about 80 rows of hooks and succeeding them, some more single hooks. Numerous brown papillae make the dorsal side of the introvert appear dark. Trunk tapered in front, broader posteriorly, dark yellowish-grey in colour. The papillae are of two kinds. The first are the ordinary light-coloured ones which are larger at the base of the introvert and at the posterior end than in the middle of the trunk; they are somewhat oval with the central opening surrounded by many small, almost colourless, plates. Scattered amongst these light-coloured papillae are larger, more dispersed, papillae which appear as dark brown spots; they occur mainly in the middle region of the trunk and number from 50 to 60 and their central opening is surrounded by large dark plates. The longitudinal muscles form a continuous sheet in the introvert and in the part of the trunk in front of the anus. Over the rest of the trunk the muscles are gathered into about 18 bands which show many anastomoses. Two pairs of retractors present; the ventrals arise from bands 2–6, the dorsals from bands 5–7. The intestinal tract is especially short and has only about 15 convolutions, which are not attached posteriorly by the spindle muscle. A single fastening muscle springs from the first coil. The contractile vessel is without villi. The nephridia open anteriorly close to the nerve cord where the longitudinal muscles are continuous.

DISTRIBUTION. Malayasia and Indonesia (Sluiter, 1886, 1902); New Britain (Shipley, 1899).

Phascolosoma (Satonus) falcidentatum (Sluiter, 1882)

Phymosoma falcidentatus Sluiter, 1882a : 150, pl. 1, figs 2, 7, 12; 1891 : 117.
Physcosoma falcidentatus: Sluiter, 1902 : 13.

TYPE LOCALITY. In shells of *Dentalium*. Bay of Batavia, 2 m, Onrust Island.

DESCRIPTION. Introvert half the trunk length with several rows of sickle-like hooks. Trunk 30 mm in length, about 7–8 times as long as wide, pointed posteriorly, yellow-brown in colour. The musculature is more or less transparent in the middle region. The anterior part of the trunk is sharply marked off by its darker colour and by the greater number of papillae. The papillae are sparsely distributed over the middle of the trunk but are very numerous posteriorly. The longitudinal muscles are gathered into 20–22 bands. Two pairs of retractors present; the ventrals are short and broad and the dorsals thin. Both pairs arise from four bands. There are numerous intestinal convolutions but they are not attached to the trunk wall by mesenteries, except for one which attaches the last coil to the pointed posterior end of the trunk. The spindle muscle is absent. Two nephridia, of which the right is longer, are inflated anteriorly.

REMARKS. Known only from the holotype.

DISTRIBUTION. As for the type locality.

Phascolosoma (Satonus) hebes (Sluiter, 1902)

Physcosoma hebes Sluiter, 1902 : 13–14, pl. 1, figs 5–6.

TYPE LOCALITY. Siboga stn. 117, Indonesia. (1°0′30″N, 122°56′0″E; at 80 m.)

DESCRIPTION. Introvert 24 mm in length, without hooks, Four to six cornered cuticular bodies present, arranged in circular rows on the anterior part; posteriorly they are irregularly scattered giving the same appearance as on the trunk. Trunk 22 mm in length, 8 mm in diameter, tapering at both ends. Colour in alcohol, rose-red; iridescent overall. Papillae, mostly of the same size, are spread over the surface with a few smaller ones scattered between them; they are larger and more crowded at the posterior end. The longitudinal muscles are gathered into 20 bands. Two pairs of retractors of equal length arise only 4 mm behind the anus, the ventral pair is attached to bands 2–3 and the dorsal to band 7. The intestinal tract is not coiled but arranged in loose loops; two thin fixing muscles attached where the spindle muscle joins the gut. The anus is situated 18 mm from the posterior end of the trunk and the spindle muscle which is free posteriorly arises in front of it. The nephridia are 16 mm in length; they are free for their whole length opening at band 3.

REMARKS. Known only from the holotype.

DISTRIBUTION. As for the type locality.

Phascolosoma (Satonus) maculatum (Sluiter, 1886)

Phymosoma maculatum Sluiter, 1886 : 511–512, pl. 4, fig. 4; 1891 : 118–119; Augener, 1903 : 308–310.
Physcosoma maculatum : Sluiter, 1902 : 11.

TYPE LOCALITY. Bay of Ambon, Indonesia.

DESCRIPTION. Introvert about as long as the trunk; about 22 rows of large and slightly built hooks present, the point of each hook being sickle-like, only slightly bent and bearing a small secondary tooth. Trunk eight times as long as broad, with the posterior end strongly pointed; colour dark brown mixed with flecks. The papillae are arranged irregularly; those on the pointed posterior end are very strong but not very numerous being larger and darker on the dorsal side. On the ventral side and the whole posterior area they are light yellow in colour. The longitudinal muscles are gathered into about 25 fairly broad bands, with anastomoses only at the extreme posterior end of the trunk. For a little way in front of the anus the longitudinal musculature is weakly formed and continuous. The circular muscles are also split into bands in various places. Two pairs of retractors arise at about the same level as the circular muscles; they soon fuse to form a strong muscle. The broad ventral pair arises from bands 2–8 and the dorsal more anteriorly from bands 2–7. The intestine forms about 18 convolutions; the oesophagus and rectum are short, the latter being fixed by strong wing muscles. The spindle muscle is not attached posteriorly. The nephridia open between bands 3–4; they are inflated and their posterior halves are free.

DISTRIBUTION. Bay of Ambon, Amboina, Indonesia (Sluiter, Augener, as above).

Phascolosoma (Satonus) mauritaniense (Hérubel, 1924)

Physcosoma mauritaniense Hérubel, 1924 : 110–111, text-fig. 4.

TYPE LOCALITY.   Cap Blanc, Mauritania.

DESCRIPTION.   Introvert 10 mm in length with 16 rows of hooks a little way behind the tentacular crown; they are closely crowded and without papillae between the rows.   Hooks simple, small, smooth, uniform in size and without denticulations, appearing like slightly bent spines.   Eye-spots absent.   Trunk 15 mm in length, rounded posteriorly and grey-yellow in colour.   Papillae are concentrated at the base of the introvert and at the posterior end of the trunk; they are few in number and minute on the rest of the trunk.   The longitudinal muscles are gathered into 16 bands.   Two pairs of retractors present; the ventral pair arises from four bands in the posterior third of the trunk, the dorsal from two bands half-way between the ventral pair and the anterior end.   There are 12 intestinal convolutions.   The spindle muscle is attached near the anus but is not attached posteriorly.   There is a simple contractile vessel.   Rectal caecum absent.   The two nephridia are long and free for their whole length; they open behind the anus.

REMARKS.   Described from two specimens.

DISTRIBUTION.   As for the type locality.

Phascolosoma (Satonus) nigritorquatum (Sluiter, 1882)

(Fig. 36D)

Phymosoma nigritorquatum Sluiter, 1882 : 151–152, pl. 1, figs 3, 8, 11; 1891 : 117; Selenka &
    de Man, 1883 : 68–69.

Physcosoma nigritorquatum: Sluiter, 1902 : 13; Fischer 1919a : 280; 1921b : 4–5, figs 1–2;
    1927 : 416.

TYPE LOCALITY.   Djakarta, Indonesia; (in coral).

DESCRIPTION.   Introvert about half the trunk length carrying numerous short tentacles and covered with papillae except on the basal region where the skin is smooth.   A row of dark warts and spines occurs around the mouth, which is followed by several more rows, and more posteriorly by four rows of hooks.   Trunk up to 13 mm in length and about three times as long as broad, thin and pointed anteriorly. Dark yellow to brown in colour.   There are numerous papillae, especially on the distinct fore part and pointed posterior end.   These are large, brown coloured and stand out clearly.   The papillae are covered with very small plates of chitin of uniform size surrounding the central pore.   The longitudinal muscles are gathered into 20–22 bands.   Two pairs of retractors are joined for most of their length; the posterior ends of the retractors appear as two short roots each of which again branches into two.   The intestinal tract is short, with only about nine convolutions fastened by a strong mesentery which arises near the point where the reactors branch.   The spindle muscle is lacking.   The two nephridia are not very long and are swollen at their anterior end.

DISTRIBUTION. Djakarta (Sluiter, 1882); Bay of Bantam (Sluiter, 1891); Australia, Cape Joubert (Fischer, 1921); Shark Bay (Fischer, 1919a, 1927).

Phascolosoma (Satonus) pectinatum Keferstein, 1867

(Fig. 36H–I)

Phascolosoma pectinatum Keferstein, 1867 : 47–48, pl. 6, figs 9–12; Baird, 1868 : 96; Wesenberg-Lund, 1959b : 65–66, text-figs 5–6.
Phymosoma pectinatum: Selenka & de Man, 1883 : 65–67, pl. 8, figs 113–117; Augener, 1903 : 340.
Physcosoma pectinatum: Fischer, 1895 : 12; 1922b : 15; 1922e : 11–12, 1 textfig.; Sluiter, 1900 : 13; Leroy, 1936 : 424.
Siphonides rickettsi Fisher, 1952 : 386–388, pl. 22.

TYPE LOCALITY. Panama.

DESCRIPTION. Introvert thinner than the trunk but about twice as long and with about 20 tentacles; 35–45 rows of hooks which have a long thin slightly-bent point, and, at the front end of the base, 5–9 long projections or accessory teeth. The papillae are rather smaller than those on the trunk. Two eye-spots present. Trunk moderately slim, up to 60–170 mm in length and about six times as long as wide, yellowish in colour. The skin is thrown into transverse folds in which the papillae lie. The papillae are dome-shaped and are a little larger on the trunk than on the introvert. They are rather more crowded at the introvert base and at the posterior end of the trunk. They are light in colour and built of darker concentrically arranged irregular plates; sometimes they have a truncated point. The longitudinal muscles are gathered into 25–30 frequently anastomosing bands, which are strong and separate in the anterior portion of the trunk but which posteriorly may be partly joined. Two pairs of thin retractors arise close together in the anterior third of the trunk, one pair arising near the level of the anus and the other (the ventral?) somewhat more posteriorly. There are about 46 intestinal convolutions. The spindle muscle is not attached posteriorly. The rectum is short and bears a caecum (Augener, 1903; Wesenberg-Lund, 1959b; Fischer, 1922e; Fisher, 1952). The contractile vessel is simple. Nephridia bilobed, the longer lobe being about a fifth to half as long as the trunk; they are free for most of their length. One fastening muscle runs to the last whorl of the intestine.

REMARKS. We agree with Wesenberg-Lund (1959b : 63–66) that *S. rickettsi* Fisher, 1952 is synonymous with *P. pectinatum* Kef. Our decision was made after re-examining (1) Fisher's two specimens of *S. rickettsi* (nos 21224 and 20934) in the U.S. Nat. Mus. and (2) another specimen (U.S.N.M. no. 270934) from Curacao and (3) one of Selenka's specimens of *P. pectinatum* from Surinam (cat. no. 82.5.25.1) in the Nat. Hist. Museum, London. Fisher's specimens have the same golden colour as Selenka's but are larger and more slender; they appear to be extended and distorted just as some sipunculans become if they are kept in hyposmotic fluid before they are fixed. The hooks of all the specimens have the same shape and are about the same size. We found it impossible to decide whether the tentacles of Fisher's specimens surround the mouth or lie dorsal to it. The few tentacles that

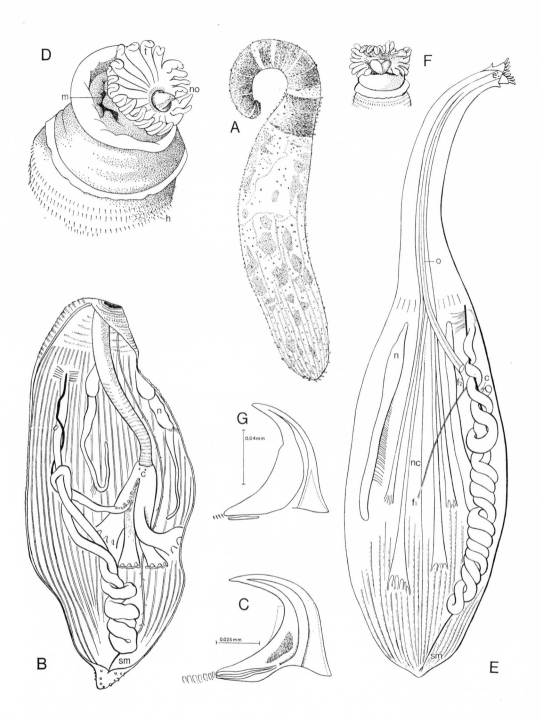

can be seen in specimen no. 20934 appear digitiform rather than as stated by Fisher filiform.

On account of the structure of its hook and its bilobed nephridia *P. pectinatum* might with justification be placed in another subgenus. We have refrained from doing this because the other species with bilobed nephridia, *P. kurilense*, has the normal hooks of a *Phascolosoma* and consequently would not fit readily into the same subgenus. It would require another subgenus of a single species to contain *P. kurilense.*

DISTRIBUTION. Panama (Keferstein, 1867), Surinam (Selenka & de Man, 1883); West Indies (Fischer, 1922e); Azores (Sluiter, 1900; Augener, 1903); Mauritius (Wesenberg-Lund, 1959b); Baja California (Fisher, 1952).

Subgenus *PHASCOLOSOMA* (sensu stricto)

DESCRIPTION. Species with two pairs of retractor muscles, simple contractile vessel, spindle muscle fastened posteriorly; hooks present or absent.

TYPE. *Phascolosoma granulatum* Leuckart, 1828.

REMARKS. This subgenus contains 39 species, many of which are closely related. It is subdivided into two groups, one with and the other without introvert hooks. We have given a key for the species without hooks but have not been able to construct a satisfactory one for those with hooks. Two of the most useful characters for the identification of species, the shape of the hook and the structure of the papillae, are difficult to describe in words. Instead of giving a conventional key to the armed species we have given a list of the species with some of their characters and references to figures of the hooks of as many species as possible. Many of the figures are illustrated at the end of the monograph. We hope that this will throw some light on the identification of the species. The size and shape of the hooks of a species, however, are not as fixed as they were formerly thought to be. The illustrations of Fisher (1952, pls 37 and 38) show some variations in the size and shape of the hooks of *P. agassizi* collected from a long stretch of coastline. Cutler (1965 : 57) showed that the length of the hooks of *P. nigrescens* lies between 40 and 80µ and Chapman (1955 : 351) illustrates the difference in the structure of some hooks of *P. granulatum.*

FIG. 34. (A–D) *Phascolosoma granulatum.* (A) Entire animal, the introvert is not fully extended (original). (B) Dissected specimen (after Wesenberg-Lund). (C) Hook from the introvert. (D) Anterior region of the introvert showing the relation between the mouth and the tentacles. (C and D after Selenka.) (E–G) *Phascolosoma agassizii.* (E) Dissected specimen. (F) Dorsal view of the head. (G) Introvert hook. (E–G after Fisher.) *a*, anus; *al*, anterior lobe of nephridium; *c*, caecum; *cv*, contractile vessel; *dr*, dorsal retractor; *e*, eye-spot; *f, f₁, f₂*, etc., fastening muscle; *g*, gonad; *h*, hooks; *m*, mouth; *n*, nephridium; *nc*, nerve cord; *no*, nuchal organ; *ns*, nephroslome; *o*, oesophagus; *rm*, retractor muscle; *sm*, spindle muscle; *t*, tentacles; *vr*, ventral retractor; *w*, wing muscle.

A re-examination of Gray's types in the British Museum by Rice & Stephen (1970) has shown that *P. arcuatum* (Gray, 1828) is a senior synonym of *P. lurco* (Selenka & de Man, 1883) and *P. perlucens* Baird, 1868, a senior synonym of *P. dentigerum* Selenka & de Man, 1883.

Five species of the subgenus are known only from the holotypes.

DISTRIBUTION.   Tropical and temperate seas; polar seas only rarely.

Species without hooks

P. corallicolum (ten Broeke)   *P. socium* (Lanchester)

P. meteori (Hérubel)

Species with hooks

P. abyssorum (Southern)   *P. japonicum* Grübe

P. agassizii Keferstein   *P. kurilense* (Sato)

P. albolineatum Baird   *P. lacteum* (Sluiter)

P. ambonense (Fischer)   *P. microdontoton* (Sluiter)

P. annulatum Hutton   *P. multiannulatum* Wes.-Lund

P. arcuatum (Gray)   *P. nigrescens* Keferstein

   (=*P. lurco* Sel. & de Man.)   *P. noduliferum* Stimpson

P. deani (Ikeda)   *P. pacificum* Keferstein

P. diaphanes (Sluiter)   *P. perlucens* Baird

P. dunwichi Edmonds   (=*P. dentigerum* Sel. & de Man)

P. esculentum Chen & Yeh   *P. puntarenae* Grübe

P. evisceratum (Lanchester)   *P. rottnesti* Edmonds

P. extortum (Sluiter)   *P. scolops* (Sel. & de Man)

P. formosense (Sato)   *P. spengeli* (Sluiter)

P. funafutiense (Fischer)   *P. spongicolum* (Sluiter)

P. glabrum (Sluiter)   *P. stephensoni* (Stephen)

P. glaucum (Sato)   *P. thomense* (Augener)

P. granulatum Leuckart   *P. varians* Keferstein

P. heronis Edmonds   *P. yezoense* (Ikeda)

KEY TO SPECIES WITHOUT HOOKS ON THE INTROVERT

1	Tentacles absent	***P. corallicolum*** (p. 298)
–	Tentacles present	2
2	Nephridia open in front of the anus	***P. meteori*** (p. 312)
–	Nephridia open behind the anus	***P. socium*** (p. 324)

TABLE II
Some characters of the armed species of the subgenus *Phascolosoma*

	pigmented bands on the introvert	length of introvert to that of the trunk	number of bands of longitudinal muscles	nephridiopore + = anterior to anus − = posterior to anus	nephridiopore on same level as anus	length of nephridia relative to that of trunk	+ = nephridia completely fixed | = nephridia almost fixed	+ = nephridia, fixed for anterior $\frac{2}{3}-\frac{3}{4}$ | = nephridia, completely free	+ = nephridia, almost free | = nephridia, free for posterior $\frac{1}{2}-\frac{2}{3}$	+ = rectal caecum present | = rectal caecum absent	hook illustrated in Fig.
P. abyssorum		1·5	18	+						—	33E
P. agassizii	+	1	20–25			0·5	—			+	34G
P. albolineatum	+	0·5	30			0·5		+		—	35A
P. ambonense*		2	17	—					+		33A
P. annulatum	+	1	20		+				+	+	35B
P. arcuatum*		1	17–18			0·33		+		—	36B
P. deani		1·5	17–18	+		0·5	+			+	—
P. diaphanes		1			+						33J
P. dunwichi	+	1	20						—	+	—
P. esculentum		2	18	+		1		+		+	—
P. eviscertum	+	1	26					+			33L
P. extortum			28	+		1	—				33M
P. formosense		3	30–40	+					+	—	33D
P. funafutiense	+	0·5	20–25	+		1	—				37C
P. glabrum		0·1	20			1	—				33N
P. glaucum			24–28	+					+	—	37E
P. granulatum	+	1	18–28						—		34C
P. heronis	+	1	20–25						—	+	33C
P. japonicum		0·5–1	20–30						—	—	37G
P. kurilense**		1	30		+				—	—	33C
P. lacteum		1·5	24		+				—		33O
P. microdontoton	+	1	25			1					38A
P. multiannulatum		1	20–24	—				+			38B
P. nigrescens	+	1	25–30			0·5		+		?	36C
P. noduliferum		1	20–26			0·5			+	—	36E
P. pacificum	+	1	30–35			1	+			?	36G
P. perlucens			22–24		+					+	37A
P. puntarenae		0·5	20–30			1				—	39A
P. rottnesti	+	1	19–24			0·5				—	33B
P. scolops	+	1	20–21			0·5		+	+		39D
P. spengeli		0·75	28	+		0·5					33P
P. spongicolum		0·33	20			0·33	—				33Q
P. stephensoni			22–23					+		—	39H
P. thomense		0·5	22–24			0·5		+		+	33R
P. varians	+	0·5	18–20	+						—	39I
P. yezoense			25	+		0·5		+		—	33T

* = Species with circular muscle in fascicles.
** = Species with bilobed nephridia.

Phascolosoma (Phascolosoma) abyssorum (Southern, 1913)

(Fig. 33E)

Physcosoma abyssorum Southern, 1913b : 12–14, pl. 1, fig. 1, pl. 2, fig. 1; Fischer, 1916 : 6, pl. 1, fig. 2 (not *Phascolosoma abyssorum* Koren & Danielssen, 1877 = *Golfingia abyssora*).

TYPE LOCALITY. South-west Ireland. 50°42′N, 11°18′W; at 1096 m.

DESCRIPTION. Introvert up to 28 mm in length carrying (1) about 28 tentacles of varying sizes, (2) papillae which increase in size towards its base and (3) 21 rows of triangular hooks with sharp points. The base of the introvert is darker, more wrinkled and with more numerous papillae than on the rest of the body. Two large eye-spots. Trunk up to 19 mm in length, tapering anteriorly, rounded posteriorly; skin very thick, wrinkled posteriorly and greyish-brown in colour. It is covered with large, conspicuous papillae which are paler and more scattered in the middle of the trunk. Posteriorly, the papillae are large, almost hemispherical, and embedded in layers of dark rust-coloured granules at the posterior end. Longitudinal muscles gathered into about 18 bands, which, except near the posterior end of the trunk, are not easily seen through the thick tissues. Two pairs of retractors which join and appear as two muscles for most of their length; they arise towards the middle region of the trunk. About 30 intestinal convolutions present. A thick spindle muscle is attached anteriorly and posteriorly. Rectal caecum absent. The nephridia are deep rust coloured, inflated at their base and open in front of the anus.

REMARKS. This species should not be confused with *Golfingia abyssora* (Koren & Danielssen, 1877), originally described as *Phascolosoma abyssorum*.

DISTRIBUTION. As for the type locality. Off Sierra Leone at 4990 m (Fischer, 1916, 1922).

Phascolosoma (Phascolosoma) agassizii Keferstein, 1867

(Fig. 34E–G)

Phascolosoma agassizii Keferstein, 1867 : 46, pl. 6, 3 figs; Fisher, 1952 : 424–430, pl. 36, figs 3–6 pl. 37, figs 4–15, pl. 38, pl. 39, fig. 1; Wesenberg-Lund, 1954a : 8–9; 1957c : 3; 1959c : 210; 1963 : 126; Stephen, 1960 : 516–517.
Phymosoma agassizii: Selenka & de Man, 1883 : 78–79.
Phymosoma lordi Baird, 1868 : 92; Rice & Stephen, 1970 : 62.
Physcosoma agassizii: Fischer, 1895 : 10; 1914a : 67–68; 1914b : 6; 1919a : 280; 1922b : 7–9; 1923b : 23; 1927 : 200; Shipley, 1899a : 155; 1902d : 133; Chamberlain, 1919 : 30; 1920 : 5D; Leroy, 1936 : 424.

TYPE LOCALITY. Mendocino, California. *Type*. Museum of Comparative Zoology, Harvard, Mass., U.S.A.

DESCRIPTION. Introvert longer than the trunk, with dark coloured half-bands on the dorsal surface, 18–24 tentacles and 15–25 rows of hooks. The first five rows are small and colourless, the last one or two may be incomplete, usually about 17 clearly visible. Two eye-spots. The trunk may measure 60–70 mm when fully extended, but it is usually half this length; posterior extremity bluntly rounded. The trunk wall varies from translucent to opaque and the skin from pinkish-grey, yellowish-grey, pale sepia to reddish-brown. The skin is rough to the touch due to the presence of numerous conical or convex papillae darker than the trunk. They are smallest midventrally, increasing in size dorsally especially at the posterior extremity and over an area just in front of the anus; in the anal region they are dark brown, conical or acorn-shaped. The papillae are composed of very numerous small platelets. The central pore is surrounded by numerous, small, irregularly-shaped plates which are themselves surrounded by an area of very small platelets interspersed with some larger ones. Longitudinal muscle bands 20–25 at the level of the base of the retractors, anastomosing rather freely. Two pairs of retractors arise at the beginning of the posterior third of the trunk, the dorsal a little way in front of the ventral pair; the dorsal arises from bands 4–7, the ventral from 6–7. A single fixing muscle with two slender roots arises from band 1 at the level of the roots of the dorsal retractors and is attached by two distal branches to the rectum and the beginning of the intestinal coils. The spindle muscle arises immediately in front of the anus and is attached to the posterior end of the trunk. The nephridia are about half the trunk length and are attached for nearly their whole length. Contractile vessel inconspicuous. An intestinal caecum is present (Fisher, 1952, pl. 39, fig. 1).

REMARKS. Fisher (1952 : 424) redescribed the species from a great number of specimens. Consequently this is one of the best known species of the genus. The principal variations that he found were in the colour, the size and shape of the larger papillae of the anal region and posterior extremity, and the hooks on the introvert—all external characters.

The Australian records of Fischer (1919, 1927) are considered by Edmonds (1956 : 284) to be doubtful.

DISTRIBUTION. Atlantic Ocean (Fischer, 1922b); Western Africa (Fischer, 1895; Fisher, 1914a; Wesenberg-Lund, 1957c, 1959c; Stephen, 1960); Indian Ocean (Fischer, 1922b); Gulf of Manaar (Shipley, 1903); Maldives and Laccadives (Shipley, 1903); Siam (Fischer, 1923); Loyalty Islands (Shipley, 1903); ? Australia (Fischer, 1919a, 1922b, 1926); California (Keferstein, 1867; Chamberlain, 1919, 1920; Fisher, 1952; Wesenberg-Lund, 1954a); Alaska (Fisher, 1952).

Phascolosoma (Phascolosoma) albolineatum Baird, 1868

(Fig. 35A)

Phascolosoma albolineatum Baird, 1868 : 91–92; Wesenberg-Lund, 1963 : 128, Rice & Stephen, 1970 : 59.
Phymosoma albolineatum: Selenka & de Man, 1883 : 71–72, pl. 9, figs 128–129; Augener, 1903 : 301–302, figs 15, 25.
Physcosoma albolineatum: Fischer, 1913 : 99; 1914b : 6; 1922b : 9; Ikeda, 1924 : 32; Leroy, 1942 : 6–9, text-figs 1–2; Sato, 1935b : 312, pl. 4, fig. 12; 1939 : 395–396, pls 20, 23, figs 10, 42; Tokioka, 1953 : 140.

TYPE LOCALITY. Philippines. *Type*. British Museum (Nat. Hist.). No. 1864.13.4.

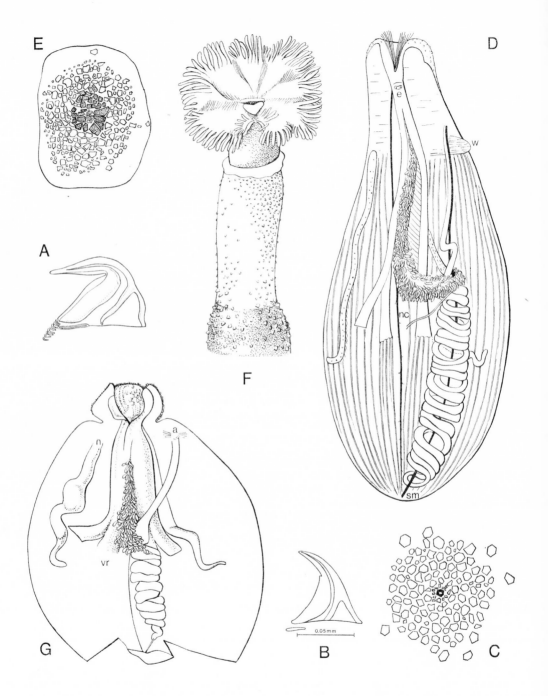

DESCRIPTION.   Introvert about half the length of the trunk but thinner, with broad, irregular, brown bands present dorsally; the tentacles are short and violet in colour.   Immediately behind them are 30 rows of hooks, their shape characteristic, each being broad and flattened with the spine bent at a right-angle.   Papillae lie

between the rows of hooks.   On the posterior half of the introvert, especially on the dorsal side, numerous dome-shaped, red-brown papillae occur, similar in size and form to those of *P. scolops*.   Trunk slim, elongated, 6–8 times as long as broad. Skin blue-grey to red-grey in colour, yellow-brown posteriorly and the longitudinal muscles are visible through it; it appears smooth to the eye but it is covered with small papillae which are smaller on the anterior half, larger and more closely packed posteriorly.   The longitudinal muscles are gathered into about 30 frequently anastomosing bands.   Two pairs of retractors arise nearly at the same level in the middle of the trunk with the dorsals a little more anteriorly.   The intestinal tract consists of about 12–15 coils, traversed by an especially strong spindle muscle which is attached posteriorly.   A fastening mesentery, with several branches, arises a little way in front of the roots of the dorsal retractors and is attached to the first intestinal coil.   The two nephridia are about half the trunk length and are free for their posterior quarter.

REMARKS.   A re-examination of the holotype shows that no rectal caecum is present and that at least two fastening muscles are present.   One gives a branch to the oesophagus and a branch to the second to last intestinal coil.   A second is connected to the last spiral and the body wall.

DISTRIBUTION.   Natal (Fischer, 1922b); Amboina (Augener, 1903); Indo-China (Leroy, 1942); Philippines (Baird, 1868); Japan (Sato, 1939); Tokara Islands (Tokioka, 1953); Palau, West Caroline Islands (Ikeda, 1924; Sato, 1935b); Java (Fischer, 1922b).

Phascolosoma (Phascolosoma) ambonense (Fischer, 1896)

(Fig. 33A)

Physcosoma ambonense Fischer, 1896a : 337–338, text-figs 1–3.

TYPE LOCALITY.   Amboina.

DESCRIPTION.   Introvert about twice as long as the trunk, not very thick and brown coloured in older animals; 20–30 tentacles followed by 47–48 rows of hooks. The hooks are very similar to those of *P. arcuatum*.   Trunk up to 14 mm in length and 7 mm in diameter posteriorly; musculature rather weak.   In young animals the colour is bluish-white, very iridescent, with the anterior and posterior ends

FIG. 35.   (A) *Phascolosoma albolineatum*.   Hook from the introvert (after Selenka).   (B–C) *Phascolosoma annulatum*.   (B) Hook from introvert.   (C) Papilla from base of trunk. (B–C after Edmonds.)   (D–F) *Phascolosoma antillarum*.   (D) Dissected specimen (after Keferstein).   (E) Papilla from mid region of body.   (F) Tentacular crown.   The heart shaped nuchal organ is shown in the centre.   (E–F after Fischer.)   (G) *Phascolosoma asser*.   Dissected specimen (after Selenka).   KEY: *See* Fig. 34, p. 289.

of the trunk rust-coloured. In older animals the whole trunk is rust-coloured. The skin is thin and transparent so that the longitudinal muscles and most of the circular muscles are clearly visible. In lighter coloured specimens the papillae are invisible to the eye but in darker forms they stand out clearly, especially at the anterior and posterior ends, as round or oval pits not showing much above the skin. The central opening is surrounded by many circular or polygonal platelets which, in turn, are surrounded by smaller platelets of uniform size. The internal surface of the body-wall is also iridescent. The longitudinal muscles are gathered into bands, 17 at the roots of the retractors, 16 at the level of the attachment of the nephridia. Circular muscles also gathered into bands. Two pairs of retractors which soon unite to form a broad muscle band; the ventral pair arises in the anterior trunk-third from bands 2–4, the dorsal about 10 mm behind them from bands 5–7. The oesophagus carries a contractile vessel without villi and is joined to the retractors at the middle fork. There are 20–22 intestinal convolutions, traversed by the spindle muscle which is attached posteriorly. The rectum is fixed by a broad wing muscle 6–7 mm behind the anus. Three fixing mesenteries present; two are attached to the rectum and a third arises from the first intestinal coil and is attached to the trunk wall near the division of the retractors. The nephridia are fairly long and reach to the roots of the ventral retractors. They are red-brown in colour, free for most of their length and open 2–3 mm behind the anus.

REMARKS. This species was described from numerous specimens. It is very close to and possibly synonymous with *P. arcuatum* Gray, 1828.

DISTRIBUTION. As for the type locality.

Phascolosoma (Phascolosoma) annulatum Hutton, 1879

(Fig. 35B–C)

Phascolosoma annulatum Hutton, 1879 : 278; Benham, 1903 : 174; Edmonds, 1960 : 160–162, text-figs 1–2, pl. 2.
Physcosoma scolops tasmaniense Fischer, 1914b : 3, pl. 1, figs 4, 6.
Physcosoma scolops: Wheeler, 1938 : 346.
Phascolosoma tasmaniense Edmonds, 1956 : 285–286, text-figs 5–6.

TYPE LOCALITY. Cape Campbell, New Zealand.

DESCRIPTION. Introvert about equal to the trunk length, 2–3 mm in width, covered with dark conical papillae; often with one to three pigmented bands on the dorsal surface, 25–30 short finger-like tentacles. Up to 28 complete rows of hooks with several incomplete ones behind them; in size and shape the hooks resemble those of *P. scolops* and *P. agassizii*. Two eye-spots in some specimens. Trunk up to 45 mm in length and 4–11 mm in width, varying in shape from cylindrical to bottle-shaped. Brown, grey or pink in colour with dark hemispherical papillae. The papillae are made up of closely-aggregated, irregularly-shaped, pentagonal platelets; detached platelets are scattered over the trunk. The longitudinal muscles are gathered into about 20 anastomosing bands. Two pairs of retractors present;

the stouter ventral pair arises in the posterior third of the trunk usually from bands 2–5 (1–5), the slenderer dorsal pair more anteriorly from bands 4–6 (3–4, 2–5, 3–6). The intestinal tract is attached to the posterior end of the trunk by the spindle muscle and by two fixing muscles. The first arises between the roots of the dorsal retractors and is attached to the first coil, the second one which is shorter, arises near to the right retractor and is attached to the last coil. The contractile vessel is weakly developed. The two nephridia open at about the level of the anus and reach to the base of the dorsal retractors; their posterior two-thirds is free.

REMARKS. This species has been dealt with at length in two papers by Edmonds following the examination of numerous specimens. A rectal caecum is present in the New Zealand specimens.

DISTRIBUTION. South Australia, Victoria, Tasmania (Edmonds, 1956); New Zealand, Chatham Islands, Stewart Islands (Edmonds, 1960).

Phascolosoma (Phascolosoma) arcuatum arcuatum (Gray, 1828)

(Fig. 36A–B)

Siphunculus arcuatum Gray, 1828 : 8; Baird, 1868 : 88; Rice & Stephen, 1970 : 50–51, pl. 1, figs. 1–5.
Phymosoma lurco Selenka & de Man, 1883 : 61–63, pl. 1, fig. 5, pl. 8, figs 103–110.
Physcosoma lurco: Fischer, 1895 : 12; 1914b : 4–5; 1922b : 15; Sluiter, 1902 : 12; Lanchester, 1905 : 37; Leroy, 1936 : 424.
Phascolosoma lurco: Edmonds, 1956 : 290–291, text-fig. 10.
Phascolosoma rhizophora Sluiter, 1891 : 119–121, pl. 1, figs 5–9, pl. 2, figs 10–12; 1902 : 13.

TYPE LOCALITY. India.

DESCRIPTION. Introvert about equal in length to the trunk; about 10 tentacles present. The papillae are similar to those on the trunk but smaller. There are numerous rows of hooks, about 60 rows in old specimens, 30–41 in young animals; the hooks are long, thin and bent. Trunk eight to nine times as long as broad. Skin thin varying in colour from light yellow-red to intense red-brown, darker at the introvert base and the posterior end of the trunk. The whole surface is covered with flat, round, moderately dispersed papillae which are much larger at the base of the introvert and at the posterior end of the trunk. Musculature strong. The longitudinal muscles are gathered into about 17–18 bands which show little anastomosis and the circular muscles are also gathered into bands. Two pairs of retractors arise near to the posterior end of the trunk; some little distance from their insertion they fuse into a broad band showing posteriorly as short roots. The intestinal tract consists of about 50 coils, the last one being attached by the spindle muscle to the posterior end of the trunk. There are no fixing muscles and the rectum is very short. There is a simple contractile vessel. The nephridia are about a third of the length of the trunk and the last quarter of each is free.

REMARKS. The circular musculature of this species forms anastomosing bundles, a fact that shows up well in Selenka's figure 103. Edmonds (1956) redescribed a number of specimens from Queensland, Australia, where it is commonly associated with mangroves. One pair of retractors arose from muscles 1–2 (2–3, 1–3) and a

U

second more anteriorly from muscle 1 and 1–2. The retractors of his specimens fused but did not separate again as described by Selenka. No rectal caecum or intestinal fastener was found. A well developed wing muscle was also present. Harms & Dragendorff (1933) report that the species is able to live in burrows above low water level. This fact is confirmed by observations in Queensland, Australia. Rice & Stephen, 1970 have redescribed the type specimen. They point out that coelomic extensions are present in the body wall.

We are adding *P. rhizophora* Sluiter, 1891 to the synonymy of the species. It possesses 17 longitudinal muscle bands, which scarcely anastomose, 50 rows of hooks similar in shape to those of *P. arcuatum*, the retractors of both species arise from the body wall in the same manner and fuse over a considerable part of their length. Sluiter's species takes its name from the fact that it was collected in mangroves (*Rhizophora*) in Java.

DISTRIBUTION. Malaya (Selenka & de Man, 1883; Lanchester, 1905); China (Fischer, 1914b; Leroy, 1936); Philippines (Selenka & de Man, 1883); Queensland, Australia (Fischer, 1895, 1914b; Edmonds, 1956); Indo-China (Leroy, 1936); India (Gray, 1828); Java (Sluiter, 1891).

Phascolosoma (Phascolosoma) arcuatum malaccense (Selenka & de Man, 1883)

Phymosoma lurco malaccensis Selenka & de Man, 1883 : 63.
Physcosoma lurco malaccensis: Sluiter, 1902 : 12.

TYPE LOCALITY. Malacca.

DESCRIPTION. The papillae on the middle of the trunk are formed of many concentric plates instead of being arranged irregularly.

REMARKS. Based originally on very numerous specimens. Sluiter only quoted the original record. Selenka & de Man's figure of the papilla from the middle of the trunk of the nominate form shows only a partial concentric arrangement of the plates.

DISTRIBUTION. As for the type locality.

Phascolosoma (Phascolosoma) corallicolum (ten Broeke, 1925)

Physcosoma corallicola ten Broeke, 1925 : 90, text-fig. 12. (Not *Sipunculus corallicolus* Pourtalés, 1851 : 41.)

TYPE LOCALITY. West Indies, Caracas Bay, in coral.

DESCRIPTION. Introvert about half the trunk length, without tentacles or hooks. Two eye-spots present. Trunk about five times as long as thick and covered with papillae which have closely-packed, small, chitinous plates around the central opening. Longitudinal muscles gathered into about 20 anastomosing bands. Two pairs of long retractors present, the dorsals however are thin and, at first sight, only one pair is readily noticed. Numerous intestinal coils are present but as they were damaged, the exact number could not be ascertained. Contractile vessel and rectum lacking. A stout spindle muscle is attached to the posterior end of the trunk. The nephridia are nearly as long as the trunk and are attached to the trunk wall for most of their length.

REMARKS. Known only from the damaged holotype. Species without tentacles are very unusual in this genus.

DISTRIBUTION. As for the type locality.

Phascolosoma (Phascolosoma) deani (Ikeda, 1905)

Phymosoma deani Ikeda, 1905a : 171–172, pl. 8, figs 5–8.

TYPE LOCALITY. Manjuyodi, South Negros, Philippines.

DESCRIPTION. Introvert one and a half times the length of the trunk, yellowish-brown, with eight lobose tentacles and about 50 complete and 150 incomplete rows of sharp pointed hooks. Between every two rows of hooks lies a ring of small, flat, papillary bodies. Each of these consists of two concentric rings of chitinous plates around the central pore. Eye-spots absent. Trunk up to 35 mm in length, 10 mm in breadth, deep brown in colour. The surface is covered with papillae which are especially large at the introvert base and at the posterior end of the trunk where they appear as deeply brownish-black spots. Each papilla is a tall cone made up of numerous polygonal plates becoming smaller and deeper in colour towards the apex which is covered with very small light brown granules. The papillae are small, sparser and lighter in colour in the middle of the trunk. The longitudinal muscles are gathered into 17–18 bands which anastomose in places. Two pairs of retractors arise near to the posterior end of the trunk; the ventrals are slender and arise from one band, the dorsals spring from bands 2 and 3 and a short way behind the roots of the ventral pair. About 20 loose intestinal convolutions present; fixing muscles absent. The contractile vessel is without villi. The spindle muscle is attached posteriorly. A small caecum is present on the rectum. The nephridia, which are deep brown in colour, extend about half the length of the trunk and are attached to the body wall along their whole length; they open slightly in front of the anus between bands 4 and 5.

REMARKS. Described originally from numerous specimens.

DISTRIBUTION. As for the type locality.

Phascolosoma (Phascolosoma) diaphanes (Sluiter, 1886)

(Fig. 33J)

Phymosoma diaphanes Sluiter, 1886 : 509–510, pl. 4, figs 2, 11; 1891 : 118.

TYPE LOCALITY. In coral, Townsend Island, Malaya.

DESCRIPTION. Introvert about as long as the trunk with an anterior set of 38 closely-set hooks followed, after an interval, by a similar, posterior set. The hooks are moderately small. The trunk is long and slender, especially in front of the anus where it is much elongated. The musculature is thin, especially at the posterior end where it is transparent and the gut is visible. The papillae are unpigmented and moderately large, somewhat stouter posteriorly than on the middle of the trunk where they are fewer and smaller. The central opening of each papilla is surrounded by a small field usually with a paired row of brown patches around the edges. On the long forepart of the trunk the papillae are numerous and each is surrounded by a strong dark rim; the result is that this part of the trunk appears to have a dark band. The musculature is weak and gathered into bands only on the posterior part of the trunk and is continuous just anterior to the anus. The retractors are set posteriorly near to the nerve cord; they are characteristic in that there appear to be only three, the right ventral apparently being absent. Only one strong branch is present at the base of the left retractor and this is inserted close to the nerve cord, a weaker branch runs to the right dorsal. Both dorsals arise very near the nerve cord. There are numerous intestinal convolutions which reach to the posterior end of the trunk where they are attached by the spindle muscle. The rectum is very short and the anus is placed far back near the level where the three retractors join. The nephridia are short, swollen anteriorly and open about the level of the anus.

REMARKS. It seems likely that the presence of three retractor muscles is due to some abnormality and that the species really possesses four. Sluiter's figure 2 shows the retractors arising at the same level.

DISTRIBUTION. As for the type locality.

Phascolosoma (Phascolosoma) dunwichi Edmonds, 1956

Phascolosoma dunwichi Edmonds, 1956 : 292–293, text-figs 12–13.

TYPE LOCALITY. Queensland, Dunwich, North Stradbroke Island. *Type*. Australian Museum, Sydney.

DESCRIPTION. Introvert about as long as the trunk, with 15–18 short stout tentacles and from 14 to 45 rows of light brown hooks. The papillae are small, conical and composed of numerous ,small, uniform, polygonal plates. A variable number of darkly pigmented bands occurs on the dorsal surface. Trunk up to 22 mm in length and 6 mm in diameter. Colour light brown except for the anterior and posterior ends which are darker. The surface is covered with papillae made up of numerous small uniform polygonal plates. They are largest and most densely aggregated at the anterior and posterior ends of the trunk; hemispherical and dark brown in colour. Thè longitudinal muscles are gathered into about 20 anastomosing bands, usually visible through the skin. Two pairs of retractors which fuse anteriorly are present; the stout ventrals arise in the posterior half of the trunk from bands 2–7 (1–6; 2–6), the slender dorsals arise more anteriorly from bands 6–7 (5–7; 6–8). The intestinal convolutions are fixed by a single mesentery which arises from band 1 near to the left dorsal retractor, the latter bifurcates and gives off one short root to the oesophagus and another to the last whorl of the intestine. The spindle muscle is attached near the anus and posteriorly to the trunk wall. The rectal caecum is well-developed. The nephridia open between bands 2–3 and 3–4 and are brown in colour; they extend to the base of the dorsal retractors and are attached to the trunk wall for half their length by a thin mesentery.

REMARKS. This species is closely related to *P. scolops*. It differs most noticeably in the possession of a rectal caecum which is not described nor reported for *P. scolops* by Selenka & de Man (1883), Sato (1930) or Wesenberg-Lund (1937).

DISTRIBUTION. Queensland, Australia.

Phascolosoma (Phascolosoma) esculentum (Chen & Yeh, 1958)

Physcosoma esculenta Chen & Yeh, 1958 : 273–274, text-figs 1–2.

TYPE LOCALITY. China.

DESCRIPTION. Introvert long and slender, nearly twice as long as the trunk, with 8–13 tentacles and, about 2 mm behind the mouth, up to 38 complete rows of hooks and 177 incomplete rows. The hooks are brownish, light in the centre and weakly curved. The papillae are light in colour and the polygonal plates scarcely visible. The papillae between the rows of hooks are flat and microscopic. Two eye-spots present. Trunk cylindrical, up to 90 mm in length and 10 mm in breadth, dusty-brown in colour. The base of the introvert and the anterior part of the trunk carry numerous deep blackish-brown papillae while on the middle of the trunk they are lightly coloured; ventrally the papillae are inconspicuous. Each consists of a light centre surrounded by numerous small chitinous plates. Longitudinal muscles are gathered into 18 bands and show slight anastomoses. Two pairs of retractors present; the thinner ventral pair are united for most of their length and arise from band 1 posteriorly to the rather stouter dorsal pair, which also arise from band 1. There are about 76 intestinal convolutions held by one fixing muscle which arises in front of the rectal caecum and is attached to the anterior coils. The prominent contractile vessel is without villi. A small round caecum is attached to the anterior part of the rectum. The nephridia are brownish and extend to the posterior end of the trunk and open in front of the anus; their anterior two thirds is attached to the trunk wall.

REMARKS. Described from numerous specimens.

DISTRIBUTION Several Chinese localities.

Phascolosoma (Phascolosoma) evisceratum (Lanchester, 1905)

(Fig. 33L)

Physcosoma evisceratum Lanchester, 1905a : 31, pl. 1, fig. 1; Stephen & Robertson, 1952 : 437.

TYPE LOCALITY. Chwaka Bay, Zanzibar. *Type*. British Museum (Nat. Hist.) 1924.3.1.163.

DESCRIPTION. Introvert about as long as the trunk, covered with large conical papillae; numerous rows of hooks, all similar in structure, which may vary in their arrangement. There may be at first 15 rows, then a hookless zone followed by another 15 rows; after another hookless zone there may be a further 30 rows of

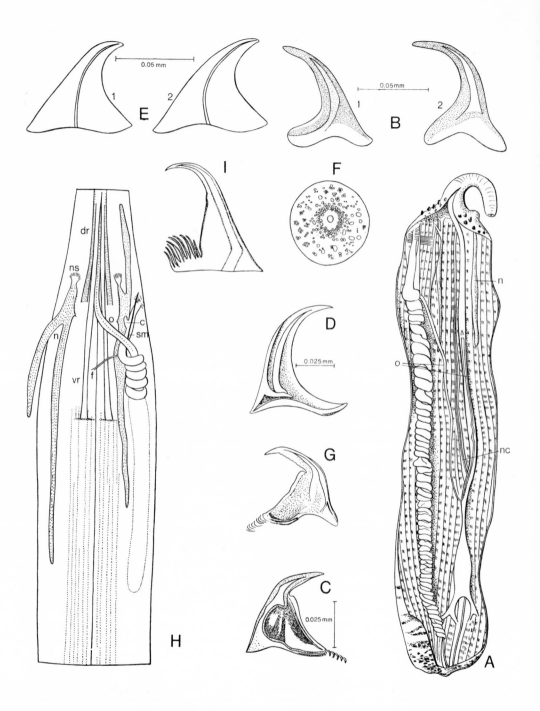

hooks (Lanchester).   Again, there may be a mass of hooks on the anterior quarter arranged in close rows followed by an area occupying about half the introvert where single rows of hooks lie scattered between the papillae (Stephen & Robertson). A dark coloured band may be present on the dorsal side.   The trunk is covered with large, conical papillae, largest on the posterior portion, smallest in the middle. They are generally colourless, but sometimes at irregular intervals a single dark brown, conspicuous papilla may occur.   The papillae are composed of very numerous platelets, closely set, and largest at the periphery.   The longitudinal muscles are gathered into about 26 bands which anastomose freely.   Two pairs of thin retractors are present, the dorsals are half the thickness of the ventrals; the ventral pair arises two thirds of the distance of the trunk from the anterior end and the dorsal pair one third of the distance.   Each ventral retractor arises from six bands, each dorsal from three.   A strong spindle muscle arises near the anus and is attached to the posterior end of the trunk.   The nephridia are long, thin, brown tubes and are attached to the trunk wall by their anterior two thirds.

REMARKS   The species was originally described from a badly damaged holotype in which the internal organs, muscle layers and part of the introvert were lacking. It was described from the structure of the hooks and papillae.   Two specimens in good condition were later secured by Robertson.

DISTRIBUTION.   Zanzibar, Chwaka Bay (Lanchester); Chukwani and Kwale Island (Stephen & Robertson).

Phascolosoma (Phascolosoma) extortum (Sluiter, 1902)

(Fig. 33M)

Physcosoma extortum Sluiter, 1902 : 15–16, pl. 1, figs 9–10.

TYPE LOCALITY.   Waingapu Reef, Indonesia.

DESCRIPTION.   Introvert black-brown in colour, darker than the trunk but with smaller papillae; about 15 complete rows of hooks present together with a few incomplete ones.   The hooks have a long, slightly bent point and a small secondary tooth.   Trunk about 34 mm in length, brown in colour with irregular dark flecks. Numerous dark brown conical papillae which are larger and more numerous at the anterior and posterior ends, are scattered over the trunk.   The opening of a papilla is at the top of the cone and the rest of its surface is covered with small, strong, chitinous plates.   The longitudinal muscles are gathered into 28 slender bands

---

FIG. 36.   (A–B) *Phascolosoma arcuatum*.   (A) Dissected specimen.   (B) Hooks from the introvert.   (A–B after Selenka.)   (C) *Phascolosoma nigrescens*.   Hook from the introvert (after Selenka).   (D) *Phascolosoma nigritorquartum*.   Hook from the introvert (after Fischer).   (E–F) *Phascolosoma noduliferum*.   (E) Two hooks from the introvert.   (F) Papilla from the posterior surface of the trunk.   (E–F after Edmonds.)   (G) *Phascolosoma pacificum*.   Hook from the introvert (after Selenka).   (H–I) *Phascolosoma pectinatum*. (H) Dissected specimen (after Fisher).   (I) Hook from the introvert (after Keferstein). KEY: *See* Fig. 34, p. 289.

which show few anastomoses.   Two pairs of retractors present; the ventral pair arises from the anterior edge of the posterior third from bands 2–9 and the slenderer dorsals arise in the middle of the trunk from bands 7–9.   The intestinal tract is in the form of a long, large, irregular loop and not in a coil; it is fastened to the posterior end of the trunk by the spindle muscle which does not traverse the hinder part of the loop.   There is a strong anterior fixing mesentery.   The nephridia are very long, reaching to the hinder part of the trunk, and only their posterior ends are free; they open in front of the anus between bands 2 and 3.

REMARKS.   Known only from the holotype.

DISTRIBUTION.   As for the type locality.

Phascolosoma (Phascolosoma) formosense (Sato, 1939)

(Fig. 33D–H)

Physcosoma formosense Sato, 1939 : 398–401, pl. 20, fig. 15, text-figs 36–41.

TYPE LOCALITY.   Suo, Formosa.

DESCRIPTION.   Introvert very long, about three times the length of the trunk, with 22 finger-like tentacles and with a small number of hooks scattered over the surface.   The papillae are smaller than on the trunk.   Trunk about 45 mm in length, 5 mm in diameter and pointed posteriorly; brown-yellow in colour but the base of the introvert and posterior end are darker.   The skin is thick and opaque and covered with numerous deep brown papillae which are largest at the base of the introvert.   The longitudinal muscles are gathered into 30–40 frequently anastomosing bands.   Two pairs of retractors are present and arise in the posterior third of the trunk; the larger ventral retractors arise from bands 3–10 and the dorsal much more anteriorly from bands 5–6.   There are about 10 intestinal convolutions.   A single fixing muscle arises at the beginning of the intestinal coil and is attached to the first band on the left side.   The rectum which is fixed by wing muscles, does not carry a caecum.   The spindle is attached to the posterior end of the trunk.   The nephridia have an inflated base, are yellowish-grey in colour and open slightly in front of the anus between bands 5 and 7; their posterior half is free.

REMARKS.   Described originally from two specimens.

DISTRIBUTION.   As for the type locality.

Phascolosoma (Phascolosoma) funafutiense (Fischer, 1914)

(Fig. 37C)

Physcosoma funafutiense Fischer, 1914b : 6–8, pl. 1, fig. 8; 1922b : 11–13.

TYPE LOCALITY.   Funafuti Atoll, Ellice Island.

DESCRIPTION.   Introvert up to 20 mm in length with 20 tentacles, four dark bands of pigment and 100–140 complete and incomplete rows of hooks.   The hooks resemble those of P. microdontoton, having a short and stumpy point, bent at a right angle.   Trunk up to 35 mm in length, cylindrical, rounded or pointed posteriorly;

generally brownish-yellow to grey-brown in colour, darker posteriorly. The longitudinal muscles are gathered into 22–23 bands in the middle of the trunk, 25 posteriorly. Two pairs of retractors join at the level of the middle of the trunk; the ventral pair arises from the front edge of the posterior trunk third from bands 2–9 and the dorsal from about the middle of the trunk from bands 4–8. About 11–13 intestinal convolutions present. A simple contractile vessel is present on the oesophagus. There is a strong spindle muscle which arises fron near the anus and is attached posteriorly. The rectum is fastened by a strong wing muscle. The nephridia are almost as long as the trunk; they open between bands 2 and 3 at the level of the anus and are fastened for most of their length.

REMARKS. Based originally on two specimens.

DISTRIBUTION. Funafuti (Fischer, 1914b); Christmas Is. in the Indian Ocean (Fischer, 1922b).

Phascolosoma (Phascolosoma) glabrum (Sluiter, 1902)

(Fig. 33N)

Physcosoma glabrum Sluiter, 1902 : 14–15, pl. 1, figs 7–8.

TYPE LOCALITY. Lucipara Island, Indonesia.

DESCRIPTION. When wholly extruded the introvert is 3 mm in length and has about 30 rows of hooks. Each hook has a short point bent at a right angle and from the thick dorsal edge a portion projects into the clear space near the tip giving it a characteristic appearance. Trunk 40 mm in length, bright yellow colour in formalin, marked on the dorsal side with dark brown to black spots and bands. The skin is more or less transparent so that muscle bands are visible. The papillae are uniform in size over most of the trunk but at the posterior end they are slightly larger. The central opening to each papilla lies in a yellow area enclosed by a small band of closely-packed plates which is surrounded by a broad glandular zone. The longitudinal muscles are gathered into about 20 bands wh'ch show some anastomoses. Two pairs of short retractors are present. The broad ventral pair is strong and arises 14 mm from the posterior end of the trunk from bands 1–5 and the dorsal pair arises 10 mm anteriorly from bands 6–7. Only 10 intestinal coils which lie in the middle third of the trunk. Two contractile vessels present, both without villi. The long spindle muscle is attached to the front of the coils and to the posterior end of the trunk. Rectal caecum absent. The nephridia are long and reach to the posterior end of the trunk and only the posterior point of each is free; they open behind the anus.

REMARKS. Known only from the holotype.

DISTRIBUTION. As for the type locality.

Phascolosoma (Phascolosoma) glaucum (Sato, 1930)

(Fig. 37D–E)

Physcosoma glaucum Sato, 1930 : 15–17, pl. 1, fig. 6, pl. 2, figs 7–8, text-fig. 4 (not *Phascolosoma glaucum* Lanchester, 1905 = *Golfingia glauca*).

TYPE LOCALITY. Urata, Mutsu Bay, Japan.

DESCRIPTION. Introvert with nine filamentous tentacles and about 50 rows of small hooks which are deep brown in colour and each with a short, not sharply bent point. A clear area which passes along the centre of the hook is sharply bent in the middle. There is a short transverse bar at the base and several minute warts arranged in a row at the anterior point. The papillae are smaller than on the trunk and perforated papillae are sparsely scattered amongst the hooks. Two eye-spots present. The trunk is 7 mm in length and 5 mm in diameter. The colour anteriorly and posteriorly is a light greenish-blue, in the middle region greenish, and in the anal region deep brown. The whole surface is covered with dark brown papillae, largest at the introvert base. The longitudinal muscles are gathered into many separate bands, some of which anastomose; there are 24 bands in the posterior region and 28 in the middle. Two pairs of retractors are present; the ventrals are the larger and arise in the middle of the trunk from bands 2–8, the dorsals far more anteriorly from bands 4–5. There are 13–14 intestinal convolutions, which are fixed by a single mesentery which arises from band 1 on the left side of the trunk and has two roots, one attached to the rectum and the other to the oesophagus in the region of the first coil. The contractile vessel is without villi. The rectum which is attached by two pairs of wing muscles carries no caecum. The spindle muscle is attached to the posterior end of the trunk. The nephridia are large, yellow-grey sacs, each with a protuberence in the middle; they open slightly in front of the anus between bands 2 and 3 and their posterior two thirds is free.

REMARKS. Described from two specimens.

DISTRIBUTION. As for the type locality.

Phascolosoma (Phascolosoma) granulatum Leuckart, 1828

(Fig. 34A–D)

Phascolosoma granulatum Leuckart, 1828 : 22, text-fig. 5; Keferstein, 1863 : 38; 1865b : 426.
?*Sipunculus tigrinus* Risso, 1826 : 292.
?*Sipunculus flavus* Risso, 1826 : 292.
?*Sipunculus genuensis* de Blainville, 1827 : 313.
Sipunculus levis Cuvier, 1830 : 243–244.
Sipunculus verrucosus Cuvier, 1830 : 243; Milne-Edwards, 1840 : 43.
Sipunculus papillosum Thompson, 1840 : 101.
Sipunculus multitorquatus de Quatrefages, 1865 : 621.
Sipunculus spinicaudus de Quatrefages, 1865 : 621.
Syrinx papillosum: Forbes, 1841 : 247.
Syrinx granulatum: McCoy, 1845 : 272.

Phascolosoma loveni Koren & Danielssen, 1877 : 128; Selenka & de Man, 1883 : 57–58; Théel,
    1905 : 50, pl. 8, figs 120–127, pl. 9, figs 128–136, pl. 15, figs 210–212.
Phascolosoma fasciatum Baird, 1868 : 89; Rice & Stephen, 1970 : 60–61.
Phascolosoma laeve Cuvier, 1830 : 243; Keferstein, 1863 : 38–39, pl. 3, fig. 4; 1865 : 200, 427,
    pl. 31, fig. 6, pl. 32, figs 20–21; 1867 : 50, pl. 6, fig. 14.
Phascolosoma jeffreysii Baird, 1868 : 88; Rice & Stephen, 1970 : 61–62.
Phascolosoma lanzarotae Harms, 1921 : 307.
Phymosoma granulatum: Collin, 1892 : 181.
Physcosoma herouardi Hérubel, 1903a : 107.
Phascolosoma granulatum: Diesing, 1851 : 63; 1859 : 759.
Physcosoma granulatum: Selenka & de Man, 1883 : 79–82, pl. 10, figs 147–151, pl. 11, figs 152–
    155; Fischer, 1895 : 9–10, fig. 6; 1914a : 69; 1914b : 2; 1922b : 11; 1931 : 139; Sluiter,
    1912 : 19; Augener, 1903 : 291; Hérubel, 1903a : 100; 1924 : 110; 1925b : 262; Southern,
    1913a : 2; Cuénot, 1922 : 16–17, fig. 9; ten Broeke, 1929 : 158–159, text-fig. 1; Sato, 1935b :
    312–313, pl. 10, fig. 13; 1939 : 2–3, text-fig. 1; Stephen, 1934 : 174; Leroy, 1936 : 424;
    Steuer, 1939 : 386, pl. 23, fig. 40; Chapman, 1955 : 351–355, text-figs 1a, 1b.
Phascolosoma granulatum: Wesenberg-Lund, 1957b : 194–197, text-figs 1–2; 1959a : 193–194;
    1959b : 61–62; 1963 : 128; Stephen, 1958 : 133; 1960b : 20, fig. 13.

TYPE LOCALITY.   Cette, France.

DESCRIPTION.   Introvert as long as the trunk, with 12–16 tentacles in young
animals and 25–26 in older ones; about 10–17 rows of hooks in young individuals
and up to 60 rows in adults.   Papillae of the same type as those in *P. varians*
occur between the rows.   The dorsal side of the introvert is often marked with
dark, transverse bands.   Trunk up to 60 mm in length, very variable in colour,
ranging from grey, brown or red to brown-yellow; young forms are often flecked with
dark spots.   Skin fairly thin and transparent in young animals.   It is covered with
dome-shaped papillae which are less numerous in the middle of the trunk than at
the anterior and posterior ends where they are more conical in shape.   The clear
space in the centre of each papilla is surrounded by several rows of dark-coloured
concentric plates.   Longitudinal muscles gathered into a variable number of bands
varying from 18–28, usually 24–25.   Two pairs of retractors spring from the middle
third of the trunk; the stronger ventral pair arises from the posterior edge, the
weaker dorsal from the anterior edge.   Intestinal tract with 6–18 coils.   A strong
spindle muscle arises near to the anus and is attached to the posterior end of the
trunk.   The contractile vessel is without villi.   A fastening mesentery arises from
between the roots of the dorsal retractors and is attached to the anterior portion
of the intestinal tract.   Each nephridium has its anterior half attached to the trunk
wall.

REMARKS.   This species appears to lack a rectal caecum.   Chapman (1955 : 351)
reported the presence of two kinds of hooks on his specimens from the Azores, one
possessing a region of different texture on the concave side of the central canal.

DISTRIBUTION.   Coast of Norway (Koren & Danielssen, 1877); Western Scotland
(Stephen, 1934); Eire (Southern, 1913a); Coast of France (Cuénot, 1922); Tangier
(Hérubel, 1924); Azores (Fischer, 1922b; Chapman, 1955); Cape Verde Island
(Sluiter, 1912; Fischer, 1914b, 1931); Mediterranean (Selenka, 1883; Fischer,
1922b); Morocco (Hérubel, 1925); Naples (Fischer, 1895); Israel (Wesenberg-Lund,
1957b; Stephen, 1958); Egypt (Steuer, 1932, 1939); Red Sea (Wesenberg-Lund,

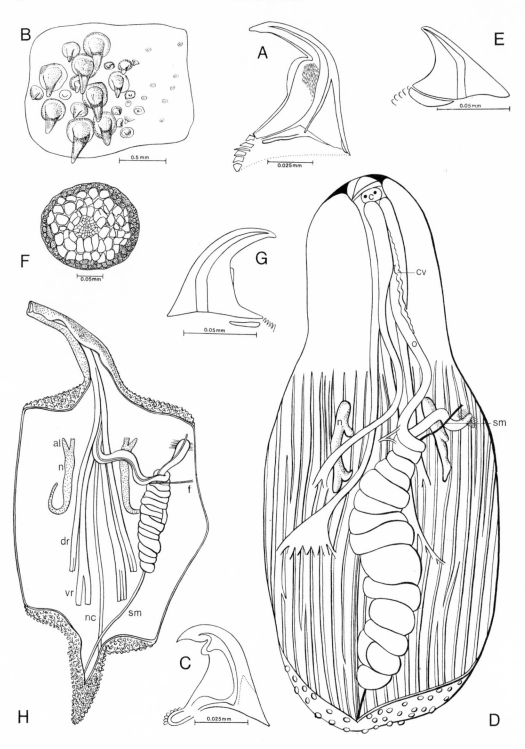

1957b); Mauritius (Wesenberg-Lund, 1959b); Cape Province (Wesenberg-Lund, 1959a, 1963); West Caroline Islands (Sato, 1935b).

Phascolosoma (Phascolosoma) heronis Edmonds, 1956

(Fig. 33K)

Phascolosoma heronis Edmonds, 1956 : 293–295, text-fig. 14.
Physcosoma scolops: Monro, 1931 : 35.

TYPE LOCALITY. Heron Island, Capricorn Group, Queensland. *Type.* Australian Museum, Sydney.

DESCRIPTION. Introvert about as long as the trunk with 14–18 white, digitiform tentacles and a varying number of darkly pigmented bands. Numerous rows of very dark brown hooks present. Papillae usually dark in colour and sharply conical. Two small eye-spots present. Trunk up to 30 mm in length and 5·5 mm in diameter, pale straw or off-white in colour, except anteriorly where it is darker being brown like the introvert. The papillae on the anterior part of the trunk are more numerous, flatter and less conical and consist of small chitinous plates of approximately uniform size. The longitudinal muscles are gathered into 20–25 anastomosing bands. Two pairs of retractors arise at different levels in the posterior third of the trunk; the ventral pair arises from bands 2–6 (1–5; 2–7) and the slenderer dorsal more anteriorly from bands 5–7 or 5–8. There is a single fixing muscle from band 1 near the left dorsal retractor; it divides into two, one strand going to the oesophagus and the other to the last intestinal coil. The spindle muscle is attached near the anus and posteriorly to the trunk wall. The rectum is fastened by strong wing muscles and carries a caecum. The nephridia open between bands 2–3 or 3–4; they extend back to the base of the dorsal retractors and are attached to the trunk wall for half their length.

REMARKS. Described from 25 specimens. *P. heronis* differs from other Australian species in the structure of the hook and the distribution of the papillae. The hook has a clear, crescentic shaped area on the concave side of the clear streak. The specimens were found embedded in coral.

DISTRIBUTION. As for the type locality.

Phascolosoma (Phascolosoma) japonicum Grübe, 1877

(Fig. 37F–G)

Phascolosoma japonicum Grübe, 1877 : 73; Wesenberg-Lund, 1963 : 116–119, text-figs 5 and 6; Fisher, 1952 : 429.

FIG. 37. (A–B) *Phascolosoma perlucens.* (A) Hook from introvert. (B) Spine from introvert. (A–B after Selenka.) (C) *Phascolosoma funafutiense.* Hook from the introvert (after Fischer). (D–E) *Phascolosoma glaucum.* (D) Dissected specimen. (E) Hook from introvert. (F–G) *Phascolosoma japonicum.* (F) Papilla from mid-region of the trunk. (G) Hook from the introvert. (H) *Phascolosoma kurilense.* Dissected specimen. (D–H after Sato.) KEY: *See* Fig. 34, p. 289.

Phymosoma japonicum: Selenka & de Man, 1883 : 76–78, pl. 2, figs 18–19, pl. 10, figs 145–146; Ikeda, 1904 : 22–23.

Physcosoma japonicum: Selenka, 1888 : 220; Fischer, 1895 : 12; 1914b : 5–6; 1916 : 15; 1922b : 13–14; 1922c : 7–8, pl. 1, fig. 3; 1923 : 3; Chamberlain, 1920 : 5d; Shipley, 1902d : 134; Ostroumov, 1909 : 319–324; Sato, 1930 : 9–11, pl. 1, fig. 5, text-fig. 2; 1937a : 149–150, pl. 2, figs 5–6; 1939 : 383–386, pl. 20, pl. 23, fig. 41, text-figs 27–29; Stephen, 1942 : 247–248; 1948 : 220 (vide *P. noduliferum*); Leroy, 1936 : 424.

TYPE LOCALITY. Japan.

DESCRIPTION. Introvert varying in length from about half to equal that of the trunk; about 28 tentacles present. It is covered with papillae which are very small on the anterior half, much smaller than those on the trunk. The number of rows of hooks varies, being up to 100 in young animals and 25–30 in mature ones. Two eye-spots present. Trunk up to 50 mm in length, about four times as long as broad. Colour greyish with numerous small red-brown papillae which appear as dark spots, larger and more closely aggregated at the introvert base and the posterior end. They are dome-shaped with small plates in the centre which become larger and more irregularly shaped towards the edge; the plates tend to be arranged in concentric rows. The longitudinal muscles are gathered into about 30 anastomosing bands in older animals and 20–25 in younger specimens. Two pairs of retractors arise in the middle third of the trunk; the ventrals from the posterior and the dorsals from the anterior limit. There are 10–12 intestinal convolutions. A simple contractile vessel is present. One fixing muscle runs from the first coil to between the roots of the dorsal retractors. A strong spindle muscle, not connected with the last coil, is attached at the posterior end of the trunk. Two red-brown nephridia reach to the roots of the dorsal retractors in most specimens and have their posterior half free.

REMARKS. Edmonds (1956 : 286) has shown that the Australian records of this species should be referred to *P. noduliferum*, to which the Tasmanian specimen (Stephen, 1948) also belongs. Fisher (1952 : 429) states that the species does not possess a rectal caecum.

DISTRIBUTION. St Paul Island (Leroy, 1936); South Africa (Fischer, 1922b; Stephen, 1942); Maldive Islands (Shipley, 1902d); Mergui Archipelago (Selenka, 1888); Japan (Ikeda, 1904; Sato, 1930, 1937, 1939); New Britain (Fischer, 1895); Vancouver (Chamberlain, 1920).

Phascolosoma (Phascolosoma) kurilense (Sato, 1937)

(Figs 37H, 33C, 33G)

Physcosoma kurilense Sato, 1937b : 117–120, text-figs 1–4.

TYPE LOCALITY. Kurile Islands, Japan.

DESCRIPTION. Introvert up to about 60 mm in length, 2·5 mm in thickness and carrying about 60 rows of hooks; the point of each hook is bent at about 45° and has a small accessory tooth and the clear central streak is narrow, sharply bent in the middle nearly bisecting the base. There is a small bar below the anterior point of the base and a number of warts. Small papillae are arranged between the hook rows. Trunk up to 65 mm in length and about 12 mm in diameter, tapering posteriorly to a blunt point. Skin dark grey covered with numerous deep-brown papillae which are larger and more crowded at the introvert base and the posterior end and small and low in the middle of the trunk; numerous brown plates surround each pore, becoming more scattered towards the periphery. The longitudinal muscles are gathered into about 30 bands with few anastomoses. Two pairs of retractors present; the ventral muscles arise about two thirds of the way down the trunk, the dorsal more anteriorly. There are about 15 intestinal convolutions with a single fixing muscle arising from the anterior part. The spindle muscle arises close to the anus and is attached to the posterior end of the trunk. The contractile vessel is without villi. The rectum is anchored by broad wing muscles but carries no caecum. The nephridia are dark grey and bilobed, the anteriorly directed lobe being much shorter than the one directed posteriorly; the anterior half of the posterior lobe is attached to the trunk wall. The nephridia open at about the same level as the anus.

REMARKS. Described originally from three specimens. The species is allied to *P. japonicum* but possesses bilobed nephridia.

DISTRIBUTION. As for the type locality.

Phascolosoma (Phascolosoma) lacteum (Sluiter, 1886)

(Fig. 33C)

Phymosoma lacteum Sluiter, 1886 : 507–508, pl. 4, fig. 1, 10, 12; 1891 : 118.
Physcosoma lacteum : Sluiter, 1902 : 13; Shipley, 1899a : 155; 1902a : 134.

TYPE LOCALITY. Malaya.

DESCRIPTION. Introvert one and a half times the trunk length; the papillae on the middle portion differ in being dark, smaller and drawn out to a point. There are about 80 rows of hooks anteriorly, followed by a fairly long section with only a few scattered hooks; then near the base of the introvert 30 similar regular rows where the hooks are thinly set. The hooks are small with a slender, strongly bent point and a broad secondary tooth. Trunk sac-like, up to 30 mm in length and 7 mm in diameter, pointed posteriorly. The skin is light dirty-yellow in colour, somewhat darker posteriorly. The papillae, which are light yellow in colour, are particularly conspicuous on the introvert base and on the posterior end of the trunk where they are more numerous. The papillae at the base of the introvert and at the posterior end are fairly large, flatly conical with the central opening surrounded by numerous small plates. The longitudinal muscles are gathered into 24 bands in the posterior section of the trunk; they are scarcely visible in the middle region, and from the anus forward they are not evident. Two pairs of retractors present; the broader ventral pair arises in the posterior third of the trunk from bands 4–7, the smaller dorsal pair from about the middle of the trunk where the bands are not clearly divided. The oesophagus is caught up in a loop with the retractors just before the spirals begin. This is followed by 10 close coils, one of which projects as a loop which is fastened to the trunk wall in front of the ventral retractor and to the fifth muscle band. The first coil is anchored by a long fixing muscle. A large rectum opens at the base of the introvert. The nephridia open close to the nerve cord on a level with the anus, their posterior halves are free.

DISTRIBUTION. Malaya (Sluiter, 1886, 1891, 1902); Loyalty Islands (Shipley, 1899, 1902).

Phascolosoma (Phascolosoma) meteori (Hérubel, 1904)

Phymosoma meteori Hérubel, 1904b : 477–478; 1904a : 563; 1907 : 123–128, text-figs 12–19.
Physcosoma meteori : Stephen, 1941 : 563.
Phascolosoma meteori : Wesenberg-Lund, 1957b : 12.

TYPE LOCALITY. Gulf of Tadjourah, Red Sea.

DESCRIPTION. Introvert shorter than the trunk, with conical papillae and 13 short digitiform tentacles. Hooks absent. Trunk up to 42 mm in length, covered with brownish papillae which have a circular or elliptical base composed of six or seven rings of concentric platelets of uniform size. The papillae are more closely crowded at the base of the introvert and on the posterior end of the trunk. In the region of the anus, the plates are thicker and resemble those of the posterior papillae. In the middle of the trunk the papillae take the form of truncated cones like those around the anus. The longitudinal muscles are gathered into 19 bands which anastomose considerably. The circular muscles are separated into about a dozen bands at the anterior extremity. Two pairs of fairly slim retractors present; the dorsals arise in the middle region of the trunk and the ventrals from the posterior third. The spindle muscle is attached posteriorly. The contractile vessel bears no villi and a caecum is lacking. The nephridia open in front of the anus and are free for their posterior third.

REMARKS. Described originally from a number of specimens.

DISTRIBUTION. Gulf of Tadjourah (Hérubel, 1904, 1907); South coast of Arabia (Stephen, 1941); Red Sea (Wesenberg-Lund, 1957b).

Phascolosoma (Phascolosoma) microdontoton (Sluiter, 1886)

(Fig. 38A)

Phymosoma microdontoton Sluiter, 1886 : 506, pl. 4, fig. 9; 1891 : 118; 1902 : 13; Shipley, 1898 : 471, pl. 37, fig. 7; 1899c : 56.
Physcosoma microdontoton : Fischer, 1914b : 6, pl. 1, fig. 9.

TYPE LOCALITY. Indonesia.

DESCRIPTION. Introvert somewhat longer than the trunk and marked with dark bands posteriorly. About 40 rows of small hooks, which measure only 0·042 mm in height and 0·05 mm across the base, and with a rough rudimentary point. Trunk up to 15 mm in length, broad and rounded posteriorly, darkish yellow in colour. The papillae are dispersed very irregularly over the surface. In the middle of the trunk they are small and few in number; at the base of the introvert and at the posterior end of the trunk, they are numerous, cone-shaped, dark brown in colour, and fairly large, reaching a height of 0·2 mm. The central opening is surrounded by small light-coloured plates which become larger and darker towards the edge. The longitudinal muscles are gathered into about 25 bands posteriorly but, owing to anastomoses, are much fewer anteriorly. Two pairs of retractors, of which the ventral are the broader, arise from the posterior end of the trunk, the ventral just posterior to the dorsal pair. The nephridia are long and reach almost to the posterior of the trunk.

DISTRIBUTION. Indonesia, Funafuti and Rotuma (Shipley, 1898); Bay of Bantam, Christmas Island, Indian Ocean (Sluiter, 1891).

Phascolosoma (Phascolosoma) multiannulatum Wesenberg-Lund, 1954

(Fig. 38B–C)

Phascolosoma multiannulata Wesenberg-Lund, 1954b : 378–383, text-figs 2–6.

TYPE LOCALITY. Hikueru, Low Archipelago.

DESCRIPTION. Introvert probably slightly shorter and narrower than the trunk and carrying 12 tentacles and about 150 rows of hooks. The point of the hook is bent at a right angle and the clear central streak is arched to form a little recess at the base; 8–12 fringes along the base. A few minute corpuscles are arranged in rings between the rows of hooks. Skin thin, light reddish in colour, with a silky lustre. A broad girdle of dark brown papillae, broadest and most deeply coloured on the dorsal side, occurs at the base of the introvert. The papillae are larger and more crowded on the dorsal side. A similar girdle occurs at the posterior end but there the papillae are smaller, more scattered and lighter in colour. In some specimens the papillae form a dark streak from the introvert to the posterior end of the trunk. The papillae are of three kinds; some are dark brown, elliptical in outline, more or less coniform, with small polygonal platelets arranged radially from the centre to the periphery which has a refractive contour. Others are low with the refractive outer ring of platelets reduced to small irregularly-arranged granules. The third kind is much smaller, circular and only slightly vaulted. The longitudinal muscles are gathered into 20–24 bands which do not anastomose. There are two pairs of retractors; the stouter ventral pair arises from double roots from four bands in the middle of the trunk and the dorsal pair from two bands slightly in front of the ventral pair. A single anchoring muscle, which has two roots, arises in the mid-ventral line at the same level as the ventral retractors. One root is attached to the presiphonal gut, the other to the rectum. The anus opens far behind the introvert, a short distance behind the nephridiopores. The rectum is fastened by a racemose wing muscle. The nephridia are long and slender, often of unequal length, and fastened for two thirds of their length.

REMARKS. Described originally from 500 specimens.

DISTRIBUTION. As for the type locality.

V

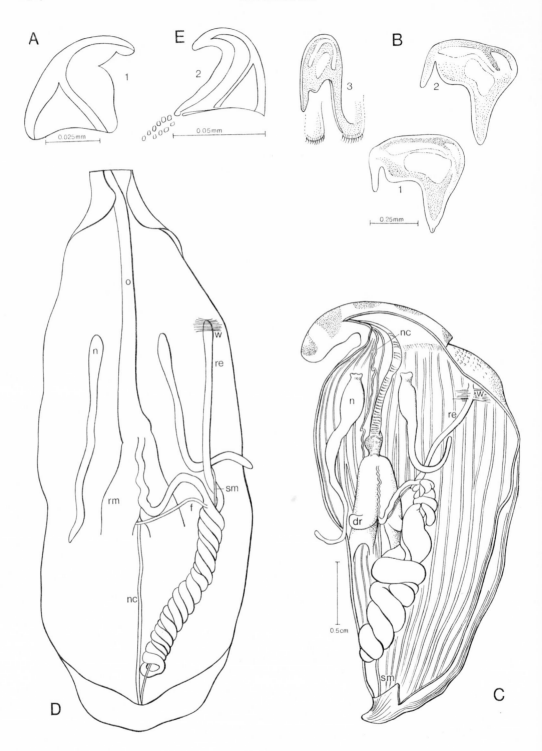

Phascolosoma (Phascolosoma) nigrescens Keferstein, 1865

(Fig. 36C)

Phascolosoma nigrescens Keferstein, 1865a : 424, pl. 31, fig. 2, pl. 32, figs 14–15; 1865b : 198–199; Baird, 1868 : 94; Stephen & Robertson, 1952 : 436–437; Stephen, 1960a : 518; Wesenberg-Lund, 1954a : 6–7; 1959a : 190; 1959c : 211; 1963 : 119–121, text-figs 5–6; Edmonds, 1956 : 289, text-fig. 9; Cutler, 1965 : 57.
Sipunculus (Phymosoma) nigrescens: Quatrefages, 1865a : 623.
Phymosoma nigrescens: Selenka & de Man, 1883 : 73–74, pl. 9, figs 130–137; Sluiter, 1891 : 119; Fischer, 1895 : 10–12; Augener, 1903 : 297; Hérubel, 1904a : 563.
Physcosoma nigrescens: Fischer, 1913 : 98; 1914a : 66–67; 1914b : 2; 1919a : 280; 1921b : 4; 1922a : 414; 1922b : 14; 1922c : 8, pl. 1, fig. 1; 1922e : 11; 1923b : 23; 1926a : 108; 1926b : 201; Shipley, 1898 : 470; 1902d : 134; Whitelegge, 1899 : 393; Collin, 1901 : 305; Lanchester, 1905b : 36; ten Broeke, 1925 : 87–88; 1933 : 4; Hammarstein, 1915a : 2; Graveley, 1927 : 87; Leroy, 1936 : 424; 1942 : 20–22, pl. 1a, fig. 6; Monro, 1931 : 34; Sato, 1935 : 311, pl. 4, fig. 10; 1939 : 387–390, pl. 20, fig. 13, text-figs 30–32; Stephen, 1941a : 404; 1941b : 256–257.
Phascolosoma planispinosum Baird, 1868 : 93; Rice & Stephen, 1970 : 65.

TYPE LOCALITY.   Fiji.

DESCRIPTION.   Introvert longer and thinner than the trunk; about 20 tentacles present.   The dorsal side is crossed by red-brown or blackish-brown bands inter-mingled with lighter ones.   The introvert is covered with dome-shaped papillae which are smaller than those on the trunk.   Anteriorly there are 30–120 rows of hooks followed by scattered hooks covering the whole posterior region.   Two eye-spots present.   The trunk is up to 30 mm in length, about 3–5 times as long as wide, greyish or brownish in colour, often marbled with brown flecks and bands.   The whole surface is covered with dome-shaped papillae which are stronger and larger on the introvert base and at the posterior end of the trunk where they are more closely set.   The papillae are darker in colour than the skin.   The longitudinal muscles are split into 25–30 bands which usually anastomose.   Two pairs of retrac-tors arise in the middle third of the trunk; the stronger ventral pair from the hind edge, the weaker dorsal pair from the front edge.   The intestinal tract is short with only 10–14 coils which are attached to the posterior end of the trunk by a strong spindle muscle.   The contractile vessel carries very numerous short villi.   The rectum is variable in length.   A single fastening muscle runs from the first intestinal coil to near to the nerve cord by the roots of the dorsal retractors.   The two nephridia are about half the trunk length and the posterior quarter of each is free.

REMARKS.   A widely distributed species showing a certain amount of variation. Sato (1939 : 389) has tabulated individual differences in the Japanese specimens. Fisher (1952 : 420) says that the hook of *P. nigrescens* is more sharply bent than that of *P. puntarenae*.   The two species, however, are very closely related.   If the two are synonymous *puntarenae* is the older name.

FIG. 38.   (A) *Phascolosoma microdontoton.*   Hook from the introvert (after Fischer). (B–C) *Phascolosoma multiannulatum.*   (B(1)–B(3)) Three hooks from the introvert.   (C) Dissected specimen.   (B–C after Wesenberg-Lund.)   (D–E) *Phascolosoma nahaense.* (D) Dissected specimen.   (E) Hook from the introvert.   (D–E after Ikeda.)   KEY: *See* Fig. 34, p. 289.

Edmonds (1956 : 289) says that his Australian specimens do not possess a caecum. Fisher (1952 : 431) reports a rectal caecum in his specimen from Hawaii. Sato (1939 : 389) shows the presence of additional fasteners and says that the species lacks a caecum.

DISTRIBUTION. West Indies (Fischer, 1922e; ten Broeke, 1925); Ascension, Tristan da Cunha (Stephen 1941b); Cape Verde (Fischer, 1922a); Western Africa (Fischer, 1895, 1914a; Stephen, 1941a, 1960a; Wesenberg-Lund, 1954a, 1959a); South Africa (Fischer, 1913); Madagascar (Hammarstein, 1915a); Zanzibar (Lanchester, 1905; Stephen & Robertson, 1952; Cutler, 1965); Mauritius (Selenka, 1883); Red Sea (Hérubel, 1904a; Stephen, 1941); Indian Seas (Leroy, 1936); Maldives (Shipley, 1903); Gulf of Manaar (Graveley, 1927); Malaya (Lanchester, 1905b); Djakarta, Amboina, Indonesia (Sluiter, 1891; Augener, 1903); Indo-China (Fischer, 1923b; Leroy, 1942); Japan (Sato, 1939); Philippines (Fischer, 1922, 1926); West Caroline Island (Sato, 1935); Funafuti (Shipley, 1898; Whitelegge, 1899); Fiji (Keferstein, 1865); New Britain (Collin, 1901); New Caledonia (Leroy, 1936); Australia (Fischer, 1919a, 1921b; Monro, 1931; Edmonds, 1956); Bas California (Leroy, 1936).

Phascolosoma (Phascolosoma) noduliferum Stimpson, 1855

(Fig. 36E–F)

Phascolosoma noduliferum Stimpson, 1855 : 390; Keferstein, 1865 : 423; Edmonds, 1956 : 286–288, text-figs 7–8.
Physcosoma japonicum Selenka & de Man, 1883 : 76 (in part); Stephen, 1948 : 220.
Phascolosoma grayi Baird 1868 : 88; Rice & Stephen, 1970 : 52
Sipunculus tuberculatus Gray, 1828 : 8 (in part); Rice & Stephen, 1970 : 52–53.

TYPE LOCALITY. Port Jackson, New South Wales, Australia.

DESCRIPTION. Introvert about as long as the trunk but lacking the dark bands found on similar species. It carries about 20–24 tentacles and a varying number of rows of dark brown hooks, the greatest number observed being 25 complete and 46 partial rows. Each hook has a broad base and is dark brown in colour except where there is a narrow, clear streak. The introvert is covered with rather large, rounded papillae, a little darker than the colour of the skin. Trunk up to 50 mm in length and 12 mm wide posteriorly. In life, light brown to buff in colour with only a slight darkening at the extremities. The skin carries rather large, rounded papillae which, like those on the introvert, are a little darker than the skin. They are largest and densest at the anterior and posterior ends of the trunk but those on the mid-region are not markedly smaller. Each papilla consists of many small scattered granules. The skin is thick and the longitudinal muscle bands are not always visible externally. The longitudinal muscles are gathered into about 20–26 bands which show numerous anastomoses. Two pairs of retractor muscles present; the stout ventral pair arises from bands 2–6 (2–7, 1–6) in the posterior half of the trunk and the slender dorsal pair more anteriorly from bands 5–7 (5–6, 6–7). They fuse in the anterior oesophageal region. The oesophagus is attached to the retractors by two thin mesenteries. The intestinal tract consists of about 10–15 convolutions, the posterior coils sometimes being light green in colour. The spindle muscle arises near the anus and is attached to the posterior end of the trunk. The rectum is fixed by two strong wing muscles. A fastening muscle arises from bands 1 and 2 near the left ventral retractor. The nephridia are about half the trunk length; they open between bands 2–3 or 3–4, and are fastened for about three quarters of their length. A dorsal contractile vessel is present. No caecum observed.

REMARKS. Some of the earlier Australian records of *P. japonicum* are referable to *P. noduliferum*. The two species are similar but are easily distinguished by the arrangement of the plates on the papillae and the shape of the hooks on the introvert.

DISTRIBUTION. New South Wales, Victoria, Tasmania (Stimpson, 1855; Keferstein, 1865a; Stephen, 1948; Edmonds, 1956).

Phascolosoma (Phascolosoma) pacificum Keferstein, 1866

(Fig. 36G)

Phascolosoma pacificum Keferstein, 1866 : 8–9; 1868 : 49–50, pl. 6, figs 1–2; Baird, 1868 : 96; Edmonds, 1956 : 291–292, text-fig. 11; Wesenberg-Lund, 1957b : 6–7; 1959b : 62–63.
Phymosoma pacificum: Selenka & de Man, 1883 : 63–65, pl. 1, fig. 6, pl. 7, figs 111–112; Fischer, 1895 : 12; 1896 : 337; Augener, 1903 : 310–311, text-fig. 20.
Physcosoma pacificum: Shipley, 1898 : 470, pl. 37, fig. 6; 1899a : 156; 1902d : 134; Sluiter, 1902 : 11; Ikeda, 1904 : 25–26; 1905 : 169; Fischer, 1914b : 6; 1922c : 8, pl. 1, fig. 5; 1926a : 108; Leroy, 1942 : 23; Monro, 1931 : 34; Sato, 1935b : 310, pl. 3, fig. 9; 1939 : 390–391; Stephen & Robertson, 1952 : 436; Stephen, 1952 : 182.
? *Phascolosoma asperum* Grübe, 1868a : 642–643, pl. 8, fig. 1.
? *Phymosoma asperum*: Selenka & de Man, 1883 : 61.

TYPE LOCALITY. Gilbert and Tarawa Is. (Kingsmill Group).

DESCRIPTION. Introvert rather longer than the trunk, similar in colour but usually marked by dark pigmented bands on its surface. It is covered with papillae which also occur between the rows of hooks. Anteriorly there are 80–100 rows of hooks, each hook with a strongly bent point. The rows of hooks are followed by scattered hooks which posteriorly become less numerous and form groups. Two eye-spots present. Trunk elongated, up to 80 mm in length, greyish, reddish or dark brown in colour, sometimes flecked or mottled with darker spots. The whole surface is covered with large cone-shaped, closely aggregated papillae which give it a hard, rough texture. These papillae are scattered irregularly and are not noticeably larger or more numerous at the introvert base or at the posterior end. The longitudinal muscles are gathered into 30–35 anastomosing bands, except in very young specimens where they may be continuous. Two pairs of strong retractors present; the ventral pair arises in the middle third of the trunk, the dorsal pair from the anterior third. The intestinal tract is short, there being only 12–14 intestinal coils. A simple contractile vessel is present. The spindle muscle is strong and attaches the last intestinal coil to the posterior end of the trunk. The rectum is short and the anus inconspicuous. The nephridia are characteristic and arise near the anus and reach to the posterior end of the trunk; they are attached for their whole length.

REMARKS. This is one of the larger species of the genus *Phascolosoma*. The anterior surface of the trunk is often mottled and the longitudinal muscles are not visible through the skin. Edmonds (1956) reports that the species lacks a rectal caecum and that the nephridia, which extend to the posterior extremity of the trunk, open just anterior to the anus.

DISTRIBUTION. Red Sea (Stephen, 1952; Wesenberg-Lund, 1957b); Madagascar (Fischer, 1914b), Zanzibar (Stephen & Robertson, 1952); Mauritius (Wesenberg-Lund, 1959b); Ambon (Sluiter, 1891); Amboina (Fischer, 1895; Augener, 1903); Indo-China (Leroy, 1942); Philippines (Ikeda, 1905); Marquesas (Fischer, 1895); Loyalty Islands (Shipley, 1899); New Britain (Fischer, 1926a); West Caroline Islands (Sato, 1935b); Japan (Ikeda, 1904; Sato, 1939); Great Barrier Reef, Australia (Monro, 1931; Edmonds, 1956).

Phascolosoma (Phascolosoma) perlucens Baird, 1868

(Fig. 37A–B)

Phascolosoma perlucens Baird, 1868 : 90–91, pl. 10, fig. 2; Rice & Stephen, 1970 : 63–64.
Phymosoma dentigerum Selenka & de Man, 1883 : 67–68, pl. 1, fig. 7, pl. 9, figs 118–123; Sluiter, 1886 : 500.
Physcosoma dentigerum: Sluiter, 1891 : 118; 1902 : 11–12; Shipley, 1898 : 474; 1903 : 134; Augener, 1903 : 304–305, text-fig. 22; Fischer, 1922b : 10–11; Monro, 1931 : 34.
Phascolosoma dentigerum: Fischer, 1952 : 432–434, pl. 30, figs 4–7; Murina, 1964b : 262; Cutler, 1965 : 58, fig. 6 (7).

TYPE LOCALITY. Jamaica.

DESCRIPTION. Introvert thinner and shorter than the trunk, carrying 12–14 tentacles and with papillae scattered over the entire surface. There are about 22 rows of hooks like those of *P. varians*, the rows alternating with rows of circular skin bodies each with a central opening. On the posterior half of the dorsal surface there are up to 40 backwardly directed, large, red-brown papillae of unequal size. Numerous red-brown bands occur on the dorsal half of the introvert. Trunk slim, skin yellow or blue-grey in colour and covered with conical papillae which differ in appearance on different parts of the trunk; they are larger on the dorsal side of the trunk and introvert than on the ventral side. Longitudinal muscles gathered into 22–24 frequently anastomosing bands which are visible through the skin. Two pairs of retractors arise in the middle of the trunk; both pairs arise from five bands. About 15 intestinal coils are traversed by a strong spindle muscle which is attached posteriorly. There is a simple contractile vessel. A fixing muscle runs from between the roots of the dorsal retractors to the first coil. The nephridia are moderately short and arise at the same level as the anus.

REMARKS. The species was redescribed by Fisher (1952 : 432) and is one of the better known ones. He reports that the dorsal retractors arise more anteriorly than the ventral pair and that there is a well-developed rectal caecum. Fisher says that it is a medium sized, slender species. Rice & Stephen (1970) consider that *P. perlucens* and *P. dentigerum* are the same species.

DISTRIBUTION. West Indies, Panama (Fischer, 1922b); Atlantic, Pacific and Indian Oceans (Fischer, 1922b); Laccadives (Shipley, 1903); Amboina (Augener, 1903); Batavia (Sluiter, 1891); Philippines (Selenka & de Man, 1883); Funafuti (Shipley, 1898); Great Barrier Reef (Monro, 1931); California, Eniwetok Atoll, Marshall Is., Hawaiian Is., Mindanao (Fisher, 1952); South China (Murina, 1964); Madagascar (Cutler, 1965); Jamaica (Baird, 1868).

Phascolosoma (Phascolosoma) psaron (Sluiter, 1886)

Phymosoma psaron Sluiter, 1886 : 505; 1891 : 118.
Physcosoma psaron: Sluiter, 1902 : 13.

TYPE LOCALITY. Billiton, Indonesia.

DESCRIPTION. The introvert carries no hooks but there are numerous papillae with fine spines, like those of *P. perlucens*; dark streaks of colour are also present. The species in general resembles *P. pelma*, but the papillae are very different. They are elliptical in form and are clearly marked off from the skin; the ventral opening is surrounded by small, clear granules, followed by numerous, large brown granules which become smaller towards the edge. (There are no numerous irregularly-shaped, cornered plates such as those which lie between the papillae in *P. pelma*.) The longitudinal muscle bands are gathered into 18 bands in the middle of the trunk. Two pairs of retractors arise at about the same level; the ventral pair springs from bands 2–5, the dorsal from bands 4–5. There are about 14 intestinal convolutions which are attached by the spindle muscle to the posterior end of the trunk. The nephridia are about three-quarters of the length of the trunk and are attached to the trunk wall along their anterior fifth; they open between bands 2 and 5.

REMARKS. Known only from the holotype. Sluiter gave only a short description and his papers of 1891 and 1902 only repeat the original record.

DISTRIBUTION. As for the type locality.

Phascolosoma (Phascolosoma) puntarenae Grübe, 1858

(Fig. 39A)

Phascolosoma puntarenae Grübe, 1858 : 13; Diesing, 1859 : 761; Keferstein, 1863 : 40; Fisher, 1952 : 430–432, pl. 36, figs 1–2, pl. 37, figs 1–3, pl. 39, fig. 3.
Sipunculus (Phymosoma) puntarenae: Quatrefages, 1865b : 624.
Phascolosoma agassizii Keferstein, partim, 1867 : 46, pl. 6, fig. 8.
Physcosoma agassizii var. *puntarenae*: Selenka & de Man, 1883 : 79.

TYPE LOCALITY. Puntarenas, Costa Rica.

DESCRIPTION. Introvert about half the trunk length, carrying 24 tentacles surrounding a heat-shaped nuchal organ. The fold surrounding the mouth and tentacles is colourless, followed by a ring-like collar, below which the hooks form a dark zone. There may be upwards of 100 complete and half rings of hooks but as the hooks are deciduous, the number is variable; in adults there are usually about 25. The hooks resemble those of *P. nigrescens* rather than *P. agassizii*. The dorsal side of the introvert is peppered with dark papillae.   Two eye-spots present.   Trunk up to about 50 mm in length, yellow-brown in colour and peppered with dark papillae, which are similar to those of *P. agassizii*.   The papillae are largest on the dorsal posterior surface and over an area immediately in front of the anus.   The difference in size between these and the papillae on the rest of the trunk is not so marked, the latter being proportionately larger and giving the trunk a shaggy appearance. The longitudinal muscles are gathered into 20–30 freely anastomosing bands, the smaller number occurring in the anterior portion of the trunk.   Two pairs of retractors present; the ventral pair has a broad base and arises from 5–7 bands in the posterior third of the trunk, the dorsal pair a little more anteriorly from bands 1 and 2.   A single fastening muscle arises by two slender roots on the mid-ventral line in front of the origin of the dorsal retractors and is attached by two branches to the rectum and oesophagus.   The spindle muscle arises in front of the anus and is attached posteriorly.   The rectal caecum is papilliform.   The nephridia are reddish-brown and reach nearly to the end of the trunk, the posterior two thirds being free.

REMARKS.   The species closely resembles both *P. agassizii* and *P. nigrescens*. Fisher (1952) has made a thorough study of the species and pointed out the differences between them.   The hook of *P. puntarenae* is less sharply bent than that of *P. nigrescens* (Fisher, 1952 : 430).

DISTRIBUTION.   Puntarenas (Grübe, 1858); Panama (Keferstein, 1867); Panama to the Gulf of California (Fisher, 1952).

Phascolosoma (Phascolosoma) rottnesti Edmonds, 1956

(Fig. 33 B & F)

Phascolosoma rottnesti Edmonds, 1956 : 282–284, text-figs 1–4.
Physcosoma agassizii: Fischer, 1919 : 277; 1926 : 200.

TYPE LOCALITY.   Rottnest Island, Freemantle, Western Australia.   *Type.* Australian Museum, Sydney.

DESCRIPTION.   Introvert about equal in length to the trunk, 1·5–2 mm in width and 15–20 finger-like tentacles.   There are varying numbers of pigmented bands present, some occur only on the dorsal surface, others encircle the introvert.   On the anterior part there are 15 to 34 rows of small light or dark brown hooks.   The papillae between the hook-rows are very small and form complete transverse rings. Towards the base they gradually become larger, more pointed or conical and darker in colour.   Two small eye-spots present.   Trunk up to 33 mm long and 5 mm wide posteriorly.   Freshly preserved specimens are straw, pale brown, or pink-brown in colour, except at the anterior and posterior ends where the skin is dark brown. The surface bears numerous papillae which vary in size and shape.   On the anterior region they are larger, circular, densely-packed and darker brown than those at the base of the introvert.   On the middle region they are smaller, rounded, more scattered and less noticeable.   On the posterior end they are large, densely-packed and dark brown.   The surface of each papilla is covered with numerous small chitinous plates of almost uniform size.   The longitudinal muscles are gathered into 19–24 anastomosing bands, usually visible externally.   Two pairs of retractor muscles present; the ventral pair arises in the posterior half from bands 2–5 (2–6, 2–7), the more slender dorsal pair more anteriorly from bands 4–6 (5–6, 5–7).   The fore part of the oesophagus is fixed by mesenteries.   The intestinal coils are held by a strong spindle muscle which is fixed posteriorly and sometimes for a short way to the rectum.   A fastening muscle arises from band 1 on the left of the nerve cord about the level of the dorsal retractor; in some specimens it is attached to the last whorl, in others, where it bifurcates, one root is attached to the last whorl and the second to the oesophagus near its junction with the intestine.   The contractile vessel is poorly developed.   A caecum is present on the intestine.   The nephridia are a half to two thirds the length of the trunk and are attached for a half to a third of their length.

REMARKS.   Described from 83 specimens.   The species closely resembles *P. agassizii*, the hooks being very similar, but the papillae are very different in kind, distribution and structure.

DISTRIBUTION.   As for the type locality.

Phascolosoma (Phascolosoma) scolops scolops (Selenka & de Man, 1883)

(Fig. 39C–F)

Phymosoma scolops Selenka & de Man, 1883 : 75–76, pl. 2, fig. 17, pl. 10, figs 138–144; Selenka, 1885 : 21–22; Sluiter, 1891 : 119; 1898 : 470; Fischer, 1892 : 86; 1895 : 10; Collin, 1901 : 304–305; Augener, 1903 : 338; Hérubel, 1904b : 563; Ikeda, 1904 : 20–22; Hammarstein, 1915a : 2–3, text-fig. 1.

Physcosoma scolops: Shipley, 1898 : 470; 1899a : 156; 1902d : 135; Sluiter, 1898 : 443–444; 1902 : 12; Whitelegge, 1899 : 393; Lanchester, 1905a : 28; 1905b : 30; 1905c : 36; Fischer, 1913 : 98; 1914a : 63–64, pl. 2, figs 6–8; 1914b : 2; 1922b : 15; 1926 : 108; Benham, 1922 : 19; Ikeda, 1924 : 31; ten Broeke, 1925 : 86; 1933 : 3; Sato, 1930 : 11–15, pl. 2, figs 9–10, text-fig. 3; 1935b : 313, pl. 4, fig. 14; 1937a : 150–151, pl. 2, fig. 7; 1939 : 381–383, pl. 2, fig. 7; Monro, 1931 : 34; Wesenberg-Lund, 1937c : 7–9; Stephen, 1941b : 257; 1942 : 248–249; Leroy, 1942 : 10–19, text-figs 3, 45; Okuda, 1946 : 223, pl. 29; Chin, 1947 : 97–100; Stephen & Robertson, 1952 : 436; Kalk, 1955 : 234.

Phascolosoma scolops: Wesenberg-Lund, 1957b : 5; 1957c : 2–3; 1959a : 191; 1959c : 209–210; 1963 : 114–115, text-figs 5–6.

TYPE LOCALITY.   Philippines.

DESCRIPTION.   Introvert about as long as the trunk, carrying 12 tentacles; greyish in colour with irregular bands and flecks of red-brown or red-yellow and covered with papillae which are slim and club-shaped on the posterior third and larger on the dorsal side than the ventral.   Towards the tentacles they become considerably smaller and sparser, so that the area behind the tentacles seems smooth. Fifteen to seventeen rows of hooks with smaller, scattered hooks behind them. Two characteristic dark lines cross the clear area of each hook.   Small round papillae lie between the rows of hooks.   Two eye-spots present.   Trunk slim, 6–9 times as long as broad, up to 40 mm in length with the muscle bands visible through the skin.   Colour blue-grey or red-grey, sometimes yellowish or brownish.   The whole

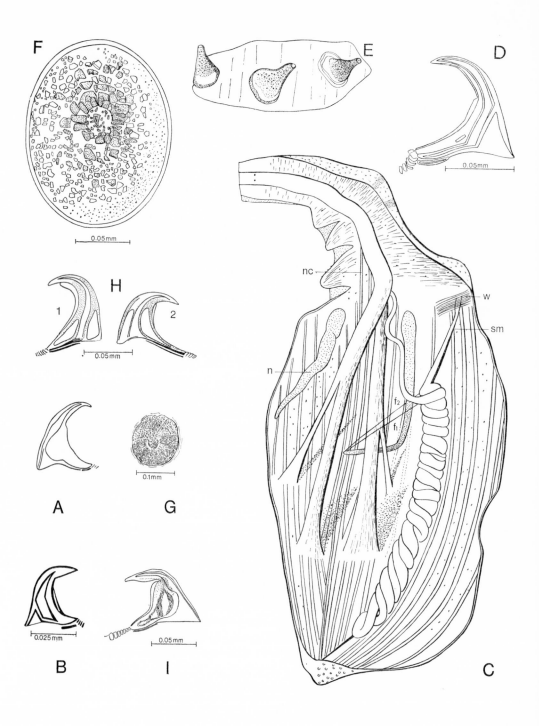

trunk is covered with dome-shaped papillae of unequal size and scattered irregularly over the surface. At the base of the introvert they are large and numerous, red-brown in colour and directed posteriorly. The longitudinal muscles are gathered into 20–21 bands which show few anastomoses. Two pairs of retractors arise in the middle of the trunk from different levels; the broader ventral pair arises from bands 5–6 from the posterior edge of the middle trunk third, the weaker dorsal from bands 1–2 from the anterior edge. The intestinal spiral comprises 12–14 coils and a fairly long rectum. The spindle muscle is specially strong and is fastened to the posterior end of the trunk. The contractile vessel is devoid of villi. One fastening mesentery arises near to the nerve cord close to the roots of the dorsal retractors; it usually has two roots, one going to the oesophagus, the other to the rectum. Two nephridia about half the trunk length, with their last third or quarter free.

REMARKS. There are two specimens from the Philippines in the British Museum (Natural History) (82.5.25.5/6) both determined and presented to the Museum by Prof. E. Selenka. No caecum is present in the dissected specimen of the two. *P. scolops* is one of the more widely reported sipunculans. The Australian records, however, are doubtful.

DISTRIBUTION. A widely distributed species which has been reported from the tropical and subtropical areas of the Atlantic, Indian and Pacific Oceans. West Indies (ten Broeke, 1925, 1933); Red Sea (Selenka, 1883; Augener, 1903; Hérubel, 1904; Fischer, 1913, 1914b; Wesenberg-Lund, 1957c); West Africa (Stephen, 1942; Wesenberg-Lund, 1959c); South Africa (Stephen, 1941b; Wesenberg-Lund, 1959a, 1963); Zanzibar (Fischer, 1892; Stephen & Robertson, 1952); Madagascar (Hammarstein, 1915a); Mozambique (Kalk, 1958); Malay Archipelago and Indonesia (Selenka, 1883; Sluiter, 1891, 1898, 1902; Lanchester, 1905a, 1905c); Philippines (Selenka, 1883); Laccadive and Maldive Islands (Shipley, 1902d); Pacific Islands (Shipley, 1898; Whitelegge, 1899); Japan (Ikeda, 1924; Sato, 1930, 1935, 1937, 1939; Okuda, 1946); China (Leroy, 1942; Chin, 1947); Great Barrier Reef (Monro, 1931); ?Tasmania (Augener, 1903; Benham, 1922).

Phascolosoma (Phascolosoma) scolops adenticulatum (Hérubel, 1904)

Physcosoma scolops var. *adenticulatum* Hérubel, 1904a : 563.

TYPE LOCALITY. Gulf of Tadjourah, Red Sea.

FIG. 39. (A) *Phascolosoma puntarenae*. Hook from introvert (after Fisher). (B) *Phascolosoma rueppelli*. Hook from introvert (after Stephen). (C–F) *Phascolosoma scolops*. (C) Dissected specimen. (D) Hook from the introvert. (E) Papilla from posterior region of trunk. (F) Papilla from the mid-region of the trunk. (C–F after Selenka.) (G–H) *Phascolosoma stephensoni*. (G) Papilla from the middle of the body. (H) Two hooks from the introvert. (G–H after Wesenberg-Lund.) (I) *Phascolosoma varians*. Hook from the introvert (after Selenka). KEY: *See* Fig. 34, p. 289.

DESCRIPTION. This subspecies differs from the nominate form in (a) lacking warts at the anterior point of the hook base, (b) the structure of the hook and (c) the shorter retractors.

REMARKS. Known only from the holotype.

DISTRIBUTION. As for the type locality.

Phascolosoma (Phascolosoma) scolops mossambiciense (Selenka & de Man, 1883)

Phymosoma scolops var. *mossambiciense* Selenka & de Man, 1883 : 443, pl. 10, fig. 14.
Physcosoma scolops var. *mossambiciense*: Sluiter, 1898 : 444; Stephen, 1942 : 249; Leroy, 1936 : 424; Edmonds, 1956 : 285; Augener, 1903 : 339.

TYPE LOCALITY. Mozambique.

DESCRIPTION. The subspecies differs from the nominate form in having a more blue-black, opaque skin and a greater number of hooks showing a different structure. The two dark lines crossing the clear area of the hook are gently curved, not acutely bent, as in the nominate form.

REMARKS. This subspecies does not occur in Australian waters. Edmonds (1956) has shown that animals referred to this species from Australia belong to *P. annulatum*, which Fischer had previously named as a variety of *P. scolops*.

DISTRIBUTION. Cape Province, eastern African coast.

KEY TO THE SUBSPECIES OF P. SCOLOPS

1	Hook narrow, no clear areas beside the central streak . .	*P.s. adenticulatum*
–	Hook broad, two clear areas beside the central streak	2
2	Hook gently curved	*P.s. mossambiciense*
–	Hook acutely bent	*P.s. scolops*

Phascolosoma (Phascolosoma) socium (Lanchester, 1905)

Physcosoma socium Lanchester, 1905b : 37–38, pl. 2, fig. 1 (not *Phascolosoma socium* Lanchester, 1908 : 1 = *Golfingia socia* (Lanchester) = *Golfingia margaritacea* (Sars)).

TYPE LOCALITY. Pulau Bidan, Penang, Malaya. *Type.* British Museum (Nat. Hist.) 1924.3.1.201–2.

DESCRIPTION. Introvert nearly half as long as the trunk; it is thickly covered with flattened dark papillae especially at the posterior end and smaller, more conical, less densely crowded and lighter coloured papillae at the posterior end. Hooks absent. Papillae are spread over the trunk. On the posterior extremity they are like those on the front of the introvert but over the trunk generally they are more widely scattered, appearing as dark spots against the transparent skin. The papillae are composed of numerous concentric plates like those of *P. psaron*. The longitudinal muscles in the middle of the trunk are gathered into 18–21 longitudinal bands and show only occasional anastomoses. Two pairs of retractors are present which soon fuse; the ventral pair arises behind the middle of the trunk from bands

2–6, the dorsal from in front of the middle of the trunk from bands 5–6.   The intestinal tract consists of only 8–10 convolutions which are attached to the posterior end of the trunk by the spindle muscle.   Two fixing muscles arise from the left of the nerve cord and are attached to the anterior convolutions.   There is a simple contractile vessel.   The rectum is long and the anus opens near the base of the introvert.   The nephridia are about half the length of the trunk, are attached for about two thirds of their own length and open just behind the anus; the anterior portion of each is much swollen.

REMARKS.   Described originally from three specimens.

DISTRIBUTION.   As for the type locality.

Phascolosoma (Phascolosoma) spengeli (Sluiter, 1886)

(Fig. 33P)

Phymosoma spengeli Sluiter, 1886 : 498–499, pl. 3, fig. 3, pl. 4, fig. 7; 1891 : 117.
Physcosoma spengeli : Shipley, 1899a : 156.

TYPE LOCALITY.   In coral, Bay of Bantam, Indonesia.

DESCRIPTION.   Introvert about three quarters of the length of the trunk.   There are 22 rows of hooks anteriorly; each hook has a long, bent point and a minute rudimentary secondary tooth.   A few slimmer hooks without a secondary tooth are scattered behind the rows together with some spines.   Trunk 5–6 times as long as broad, widest posteriorly.   The short anterior portion is covered with very numerous fairly large, brown papillae which give the trunk a brown appearance.   Dome-like papillae are widely dispersed in the middle of the trunk but are more numerous at the posterior end.   The light coloured centre of each papilla is surrounded by numerous small brown plates which become more irregularly arranged near the periphery.   The longitudinal muscles are gathered into 28 narrow bands.   Two pairs of retractor muscles present; the broader ventral pair arises in the middle of the trunk, from bands 2–9 and the slimmer dorsal pair a little more anteriorly from bands 5–9 or 4–8.   There are 18 intestinal coils with a fixing mesentery attached to band 1 at the level of the first coil.   Contractile vessel without villi.   The spindle muscle is not in contact with the posterior intestinal coils, although it is attached to the posterior end of the trunk.   The rectum is attached by a broad wing muscle. The nephridia are half as long as the trunk and open in front of the anus; anteriorly they are either dilated and brownish-yellow in colour or thin and violet.

DISTRIBUTION.   The type locality; Loyalty Islands (Shipley, 1899).

Phascolosoma (Phascolosoma) spongicolum (Sluiter, 1902)

(Fig. 33Q)

Physcosoma spongicola Sluiter, 1902 : 16–17, pl. 1, figs 11 and 12.

TYPE LOCALITY.   Indonesia (Siboga stn. 77, 3°27'S, 117°36'E), at 57 m.

DESCRIPTION. Introvert about a third of the trunk length and mostly covered with a dark pigmented network. There are about 10 rows of small, slim hooks without an accessory tooth and at the anterior base a few warts. Papillae occur between the hook rows. Trunk straight, cylindrical; 25 mm in length and 3 mm in breadth. The skin is whitish and speckled with numerous small, black spots. The papillae are dome-shaped and are larger and more crowded on the anterior end of the trunk behind the introvert and at the posterior end. The central pore is at first surrounded by a light area, then by an area of large dark chitinous plates which is followed by a zone of lighter and smaller plates. The longitudinal muscles are gathered into 20 bands. Two pairs of retractors present; the ventral pair arises from the middle of the trunk from bands 1–5 and the dorsal which are thin and strap-like, arise 3 mm anterior to the ventral from bands 5–6. The intestinal tract, which is well-developed, terminates in a long rectum and is attached posteriorly by the spindle muscle. The nephridia are about a third of the length of the trunk and are free for their whole length; they open between bands 2 and 3, about 4 mm behind the anus.

REMARKS. Known only from the holotype.

DISTRIBUTION. As for the type locality.

Phascolosoma (Phascolosoma) stephensoni (Stephen, 1942)

(Fig. 39G–H)

Physcosoma stephensoni Stephen, 1942 : 250, pl. 11, figs 3–5.
Phascolosoma stephensoni: Wesenberg-Lund, 1963 : 121–126, text-figs 7–9.

TYPE LOCALITY. Natal. *Type.* Royal Scottish Museum.

DESCRIPTION. Introvert generally dirty grey, sometimes darker, in colour with the dorsal surface red-brown. There are about 18 rows of hooks, on each hook there is a clear streak which is broad at the base and which narrows evenly forming a large, well-marked triangular area. In addition there is a crescentic, clear area which makes the species easily distinguishable; also two thickened, basal bars. The papillae have small plates arranged round the central opening like petals of a flower, with very numerous (hundreds) of small, surrounding platelets. Trunk up to 40 mm in length. Like the introvert, the colour is generally dirty grey, but sometimes darker, with the dorsal surface red-brown. In some specimens brown flecks are scattered over the dorsal surface. The surface bears prominent papillae; at the introvert base they are numerous, dark red and shaped like tall cones but smaller and less frequent on the ventral surface. On the middle of the trunk they are hemispherical and mainly light in colour with a few darker ones scattered amongst them; at the posterior end they are few, tall, conical and red in colour. The longitudinal muscles are gathered into 22–23 bands which show few anastomoses. Two pairs of retractors present, the dorsal being very much slighter than the ventral pair. The ventral pair arises in the middle of the trunk from bands 2–7 and the dorsal a little more anteriorly from band 7. The intestinal tract has about 10 coils and is fastened by the spindle muscle, which arises in front of the anus, and by a fastening mesentery which passes from the last coil to the posterior end of the trunk. Another fastening mesentery arises near the base of the dorsal retractors and is attached to the top intestinal coil. The contractile vessel is without villi. Rectal caecum absent. The nephridia are fairly long and their posterior third free.

REMARKS. Described originally from six small and much contracted specimens. It was redescribed by Wesenberg-Lund who found one or two differences from the description.

DISTRIBUTION. Natal (Stephen, 1942; Wesenberg-Lund, 1963); Portuguese East Africa (Kalk, 1954, 1958).

Phascolosoma (Phascolosoma) thomense (Augener, 1903)

(Figs. 33R–S)

Physcosoma thomense Augener, 1903 : 343–344, text-fig. 19.

TYPE LOCALITY. St Thomas, West Indies.

DESCRIPTION. Introvert 10 mm in length, with reddish-yellow bands in its dorsal half. There are 13–18 rows of hooks with some sparse groups of hooks behind them; each hook has a long point bent nearly at right angles and an accessory tooth. Trunk slender, seven times as long as broad, up to 23 mm long. The skin is soft, transparent, and yellow-white in colour. The papillae are largest at the posterior end and at the base of the introvert where they form a broad, dark girdle. Two pairs of retractors present; the ventral pair arises from a half to one third of the length of the trunk from the posterior end from bands 4–9 or 3–7 and the dorsals arise in the middle of the trunk from bands 6–8. The longitudinal muscles are gathered into 22–24 bands in the middle of the trunk. A small caecum is present on the rectum. The nephridia which are yellow in colour extend for half the length of the trunk; they are free along their posterior quarter.

REMARKS. Described originally from two specimens.

DISTRIBUTION. As for the type locality.

Phascolosoma (Phascolosoma) varians Keferstein, 1865

(Fig. 39I)

Phascolosoma varians Keferstein, 1865b : 199–200; 1865a : 424–426, pl. 32, fig. 22; 1867 : 48–49; Quatrefages, 1865b : 623; Wesenberg–Lund, 1954a : 7–8.
Phymosoma varians: Selenka & de Man, 1883 : 69–70, pl. 9, figs 124–127; Shipley, 1890 : 1–24, pls 1–4, figs 1–32; Augener, 1903 : 297–371.
Physcosoma varians: Shipley, 1898 : 468–473; 1899d : 531; Gerould, 1913 : 419–420; Fischer, 1922b : 16; ten Broeke, 1925 : 5; Sato, 1939 : 391–394, pl. 20, fig. 11, text-figs 33–35; Leroy, 1936 : 424.
Phascolosoma puntarenae: Keferstein, 1863 : 40, pl. 3, figs 1, 6, 12.

TYPE LOCALITY. West Indies.

DESCRIPTION. Introvert about half the trunk length, carrying 18–28 short, simple tentacles; divided into several regions. There is a narrow, smooth region behind the mouth then a small extensible collar which separates the smooth region from an area with about 20 rows of hooks. This is followed by a region of variable length bearing papillae and then by a region with 40–50 rows of hooks among which many papillae are scattered. The papillae are hemispherical or hemi-elliptical with 3–4 fused platelets surrounded by small platelets. Trunk up to 30 mm in length, variable in colour, but basically yellow-brown with patches of black and dark brown; iridescent. The trunk is covered with papillae which are larger and flatter than those on the introvert and without a central plate; they are marked by a much pigmented ring. The papillae are largest and most conspicuous at the anterior and posterior ends of the trunk; in the middle they are confined to the dorsal surface. The longitudinal muscles are gathered into about 22 bands at the posterior end of the introvert, 18–20 in the middle of the trunk. They anastomose to some extent and are gradually reduced posteriorly until, near the posterior end of the trunk, they form a continuous sheet. Two pairs of strong retractors present which unite in the anterior part of the introvert; the ventral pair arising from about the middle of the trunk and the dorsal a little way in front. Intestinal coils few, about 7–15, with a strong spindle muscle which is attached posteriorly. Nephridia vary much in size, they open in front of the anus and their anterior half is attached to the wall of the trunk.

REMARKS. This is a well known species. There are several specimens from Funafuti in the collection of the Museum of the Department of Zoology of the University of Cambridge, England. They were registered on June 11th, 1897 and were determined by A. E. Shipley. The dorsal surface of the introvert and the anterior part of the trunk of all the specimens are marked or mottled with bands or patches of red-brown or grey-brown pigment. The ventral retractors arise from bands 2–9 and the dorsal pair more anteriorly from bands 5–8. The nephridia open at about the same level as the anus. No caecum could be found in a dissected specimen.

Shipley (1890) and Sato (1939) give a detailed description of the species.

DISTRIBUTION. A widely distributed species, mainly West Indian. West Indies, Florida, etc. (Keferstein, 1865; Selenka & de Man, 1883; Gerould, 1913; Fischer, 1922; ten Broeke, 1925; Andrew & Andrew, 1953; Wesenberg-Lund, 1954a); Zanzibar (Augener, 1903); Formosa (Sato, 1939); Funafuti (Shipley, 1898); St Paul Is., Reunion Is., Indo-China (Leroy, 1936).

Phascolosoma (Phascolosoma) yezoense (Ikeda, 1924)

(Fig. 33T)

Physcosoma yezoense Ikeda, 1924 : 32–34, pl. 1, figs 3–6.

TYPE LOCALITY. Oshara, Hokkaido, Japan.

DESCRIPTION. The introvert carries about 12 tentacles and about 50 rows of hooks separated by rows of papillae. Each hook is deep brown in colour with two short bars and two rows of warts at the anterior base. Trunk small, about 20 mm in length and 5 mm in breadth when contracted, yellowish-brown or reddish-brown, colour is deepest at the base of the introvert and at the posterior end.   The skin is covered with low, conical papillae which are largest at the base of the introvert and at the posterior end.   The surface of each papilla is covered with a comparatively small number of plates of varying sizes.   The papillae in the middle of the trunk are smaller and have more closely set plates.   The longitudinal muscles are gathered into about 25 anastomosing bands.   Two pairs of retractors present; the broader ventral pair arises from bands 2–7 near the posterior end of the trunk and the narrower dorsals from bands 5–6, more anteriorly.   There are only a few intestinal coils and only one fixing muscle.   The spindle muscle is attached both anteriorly and posteriorly.   The contractile vessel is without villi.   Rectal caecum absent. The nephridia are about half as long as the trunk and are attached to its wall for about two thirds of their length; they open in front of the anus.

REMARKS.   Described from a number of animals found on a beach after a storm.

DISTRIBUTION.   As for the type locality.

Genus *FISHERANA* Stephen, 1965

Fisherana Stephen, 1965 : 460.

DESCRIPTION.   Small species with trunk spindle to subcylindrical in shape.   Hooks on introvert with structure and shape like those of the genus *Phascolosoma*.   Papillae dome-like to conical in shape, often capped with a small protuberence, and usually most densely packed at the anterior and posterior extremities of the trunk as in *Phascolosoma*.   Longitudinal musculature of the body wall continuous as in *Golfingia*.   One or two pairs of retractor muscles.   Tentacles in some species arranged in a crescent or near circle which lies dorsal to the mouth as in *Phascolosoma* (the arrangement of the tentacle of the type species is not known).

TYPE SPECIES.   *Phascolosoma papilliferum* Keferstein, 1865.

REMARKS.   Stephen (1965) formed this genus to contain three species with *Phascolosoma*-like hooks and papillae and continuous longitudinal musculature. He made *Phascolosoma papilliferum* Keferstein the type.   At the time Stephen was not concerned with grouping genera into families and failed to realize the generic importance of the arrangement of the tentacles.   He, however, placed *Physcosoma capitatum* Gerould with its *Phascolosoma*-like tentacles in *Fisherana*. In *Phascolosoma wasini* (Lanchester, 1905), another species which Stephen considered to be a *Fisherana*, the tentacles are also arranged in a *Phascolosoma*-like way.   How the tentacles are ordered relative to the mouth is not known for the type *F. papillifera* nor have we been able to locate the type specimen.   From a comparison with *F. capitata* and *F. wasini* it seems possible that the tentacles of *F. papillifera* are arranged in the typical *Phascolosoma*-manner.   If ever this is shown not to be so the position of *Fisherana* in the family Phascolosomatidae will be untenable.

W

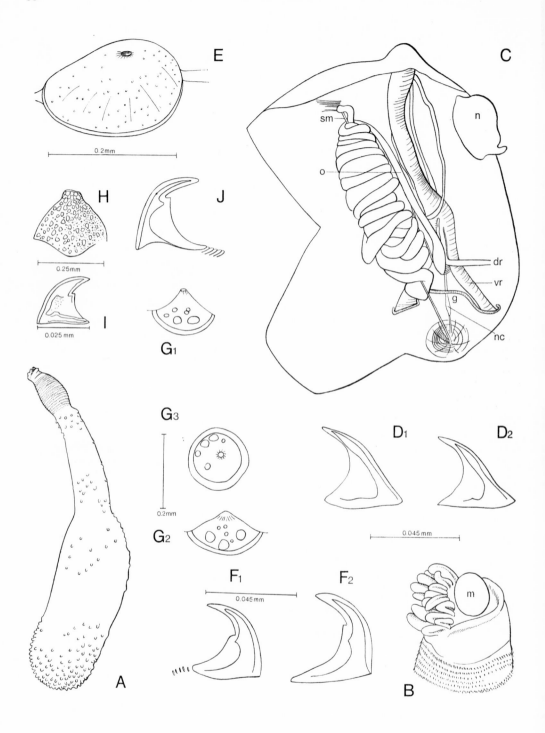

We are tentatively placing *Phascolosoma lobostomum* Fischer, 1895 in the genus. The hooks and papillae of this species are like those of *Phascolosoma* but the longitudinal musculature is continuous. The genus therefore contains four species: *F. papillifera* (Keferstein), *F. capitata* (Gerould), *F. lobostoma* (Fischer) and *F. wasini* (Lanchester).

GENUS FISHERANA—KEY TO THE SPECIES

1 One pair of retractor muscles (skin of body thin and transparent, rectum long, nephridia short and free) . . . . . . ***F. papillifera*** (p. 332)
– Two pairs of retractor muscles 2
2 Ventral retractor muscles arise from the posterior end of the trunk   ***F. capitata*** (p. 331)
– Ventral retractor muscles arise from the middle or anterior half of the trunk . . 3
3 Nephridia open just posterior to the anus and spindle muscle present
                                                   F. lobostoma (p. 334)
– Nephridia open just anterior to the anus and spindle muscle absent   ***F. wasini*** (p. 334)

Fisherana capitata (Gerould, 1913)

(Fig. 40A–E)

Physcosoma capitatum Gerould, 1913 : 421–424, pl. 61, figs 15–16, text-fig. 14; Leroy, 1936 : 434.
Fisherana capitata: Stephen, 1965 : 460 (not *Phascolosomum capitatum* Diesing, 1851 = *Phascolion strombi* Montagu).

TYPE LOCALITY. East coast of North America. *Type.* U.S.N.M. no. 4067.

DESCRIPTION. Introvert cylindrical, up to 12 mm in length and 1·5 mm in breadth and shorter than the trunk; colour similar to that of the trunk except for the anterior fourth which is light orange-yellow. The introvert is covered with light yellowish-brown papillae which are about twice as large proximally as distally and bears 35 rows of minute hooks and 14 tentacles arranged in the manner characteristic of *Phascolosoma*. Trunk up to 19 mm in length and 9 mm in diameter with conspicuous scattered papillae which are thickly studded over the posterior end. The papillae are low flat domes each capped with a central round protuberence. Longitudinal musculature continuous. Two pairs of retractors present which fuse in about the middle region of the trunk; the larger ventral pair usually arises near the posterior end of the trunk while the dorsal pair arises a little more anteriorly. The gut consists of a long oesophagus and about 20 intestinal coils. The strong spindle muscle is attached posteriorly and a single fastening mesentery runs from the middle of the oesophagus to the base of the ventral retractors. The contractile

FIG. 40. (A–E) *Fisherana capitata*. (A) Entire specimen. (B) *Phascolosoma*-like arrangement of tentacles, mouth and nuchal organ. (C) Dissected specimen. (D) Introvert hooks (from one of Gerould's specimens). (E) Papillae from anterior region of trunk. (A–C after Gerould, D–E original.) (F–G) *Fisherana wasini*. (F)–(F₂) Introvert hooks. (G₁)–(G₃) Papillae from anterior region of body. (H–I) *Fisherana lobostoma*. (H) Papilla. (I) Introvert hook. (H–I after Fischer.) (J) *Fisherana papillifera*. Introvert hook (after Keferstein). KEY: *See* Fig. 34, p. 289.

vessel is short and simple.   The nephridia are about a quarter as long as the trunk and are much inflated; they open near to the anus.

REMARKS.   We have re-examined one of Gerould's specimens from Station 2685, south of Martha's Vineyard and confirm that the tentacles are arranged as in *Phascolosoma*.   We are also supplying a figure of the introvert hooks and papillae. The hemispherical papillae are capped with a small rounded or conical shaped protuberance in the centre of which is a small aperture.   The longitudinal muscles are continuous.

F. capitata appears to be a deep water species and was dredged at depths of 1230–3240 m.

DISTRIBUTION.   East coast of North America from Cape Cod to Cape May (Gerould, 1913).   Also California (Leroy, 1936).

Fisherana papillifera (Keferstein, 1865)

(Fig. 40J)

Phascolosoma papilliferum Keferstein, 1865a : 433–434, pl. 32, figs 18–19; Sluiter, 1912 : 9; Fischer, 1914a : 76; Hérubel, 1925b : 261.
Phymosoma papilliferum: Augener, 1903 : 342–343, pl. 17, fig. 14.
Sipunculus papillifer: Quatrefages, 1865b : 620.
Phascolosoma dissors Selenka & de Man, 1883 : 31–32; Shipley, 1902d : 132–133; Fischer, 1914a : 76.
Fisherana papillifera: Stephen, 1965 : 460.

TYPE LOCALITY.   St Thomas, West Indies.

DESCRIPTION.   Introvert up to 9 mm in length, longer than the trunk; anteriorly with about 12 long, oval leaf-like tentacles.   Large, scattered elongated, finger-like papillae present over the posterior surface.   Numerous rows of closely packed hooks occur on the anterior half; hooks in the first row are, however, more widely spaced with more than a hook-breadth between each.   Trunk up to 9 mm in length, 2·5 to 3·5 times as long as wide.   Skin thin and transparent, covered with equally transparent papillae.   These are large, scattered, elongated and finger-like, especially at the posterior end of the trunk.   Musculature thin and undivided.   One pair of retractors arises in the middle of the trunk.   Intestinal coils few and fastened to the posterior end of the trunk by the spindle muscle.   A simple contractile vessel present.   Rectum long and robust.   Nephridia short and free.

REMARKS.   Described from the holotype.   Keferstein figured the hook which showed a typical *Phascolosoma* (*Physcosoma*)-like structure.   Selenka & de Man changed Keferstein's name to *dissors* in case it should be confused with *Phascolosoma papillosum* Thompson = *Golfingia vulgaris* (de Blainville).

DISTRIBUTION.   West Indies (Keferstein, 1865); Laccadives (Shipley, 1902d); Cape Verde (Sluiter, 1912).

Fisherana lobostoma (Fischer, 1895)

(Fig. 40H–I)

Phascolosoma lobostoma Fischer, 1895 : 14–15, text-figs 9–11; Hammarstein, 1915a : 3, fig. 1.

TYPE LOCALITY. Samoa.

DESCRIPTION. Introvert 1·5 mm in length, light brown posteriorly; tentacles arranged in 8–10 small bundles and two large groups. The anterior half is covered with rows of hooks which are about as broad as long, transparent and which possess a strongly bent point and a well-developed secondary tooth. Papillae occur between the rows of hooks. Trunk 20 mm in length and 4 mm in breadth; the posterior end rounded. Skin thin and transparent, light brown on the fore part, yellowish posteriorly. The papillae are hemispherical in shape and drawn to a point and are most noticeable at the anterior and posterior ends of the trunk. They are larger on the introvert base than on the rest of the trunk and the central opening is surrounded by a ring of dark plates. Two pairs of retractors; the ventral pair has a rather broader base and arises about the middle of the trunk very near to the nerve cord and the dorsal pair arises from the edge of the first third of the trunk, somewhat further away from the nerve cord. There is a single fastening muscle attached to the first spiral. The spindle muscle is attached in front of the rectum, which it anchors. The two nephridia are black-brown and open about 1 mm behind the anus; their length is about a quarter that of the trunk and they reach as far as the roots of the dorsal retractor. They are free from the trunk wall for the posterior half of their length.

REMARKS. Fischer's drawing of the hook of his species is that of a phascolosomatid. So is that of Hammarstein (1915).

DISTRIBUTION. Samoa (Fischer, 1895); Madagascar (Hammarstein, 1915).

Fisherana wasini (Lanchester, 1905)

(Fig. 40F–G)

Phascolosoma wasini Lanchester, 1905 : 32–33, pl. 1, figs 4a, 4b.
Fisherana wasini Stephen, 1965 : 460.

TYPE LOCALITY. Wasin, East Africa; at 10 m. *Type*. British Museum (Nat. Hist.) 1924.3.1.178.

DESCRIPTION. The anterior half of the introvert carries numerous rows of hooks similar to those of species of *Phascolosoma*. Flat elliptical bodies each with a conspicuous central opening are present between the rows of hooks. Papillae in the introvert more densely packed towards its base. Two eye-spots present. Trunk, up to 15 mm in length, is covered with numerous, often brown-coloured, conical papillae which are fewer and more finger-like on the middle of the trunk. Two pairs of retractors present which soon unite; the ventral pair arises close to the nerve cord just behind the middle of the trunk and the dorsal just in front of the middle region. The intestinal tract is only moderately convoluted and carries a

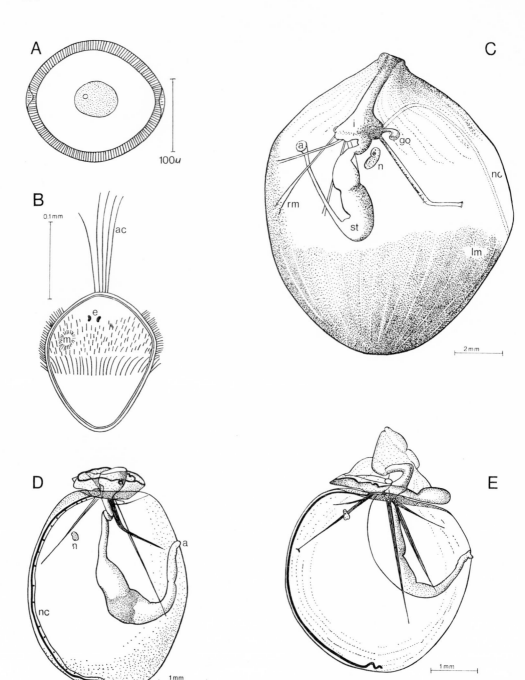

simple contractile vessel. There are three fastening mesenteries, one slender and two stout. The fine one attaches the convolutions to the posterior end of the trunk; one of the other two arises to the left of the nerve cord and is attached to the beginning of the convolutions while the other arises near to the anus and runs along the rectum to the intestine. Rectum moderately long. The anus opens a little way in front of the dorsal retractors. The nephridia are unpigmented, short and rather broad and open a little way in front of the anus.

REMARKS. Described originally from six specimens. We have re-examined two of Lanchester's specimens and are supplying a figure of the introvert hook. The tentacles lie dorsal to the mouth and the longitudinal musculature is not banded. There seems little doubt that it can be grouped with *F. capitata* to which it is closely allied. The shape of the introvert hook is very much like that of *F. papillifera* (Keferstein).

DISTRIBUTION. As for the type locality.

3. APPENDICES

(1). THE TROCHOPHORE AND PELAGOSPHAERA OF SIPUNCULANS

The work of Rice (1967) throws considerable light on the differences in the developmental processes of sipunculans of different genera. She points out that the development of the nine species of sipunculans that have been studied takes place in one of four ways. Firstly it may be direct, as in *Golfingia minuta* and *Themiste pyroides*, when pelagic stages are absent. Secondly, development may involve one larval stage, a pelagic trochophore, which metamorphoses directly to the adult form, as in *Phascolion strombi* and *Phascolopsis gouldii*. Thirdly, it may involve two larval stages, a pelagic, lecithotrophic trochophore which is transformed into a lecithotrophic pelagosphaera with a short pelagic life, the latter gradually metamorphosing into the adult. This is the pattern of development in *G. elongata*, *G. pugettensis* and *G. vulgaris*. Fourthly, development again may involve two larval stages, a pelagic lecithotrophic trochophore and a pelagic pelagosphaera with either a long planktotrophic or benthitrophic life. The adult form is then attained after the metamorphosis of the plankto- or benthi-trophic larva. This kind of development

FIG. 41. (A) Egg of *Phascolosoma albolineatum* (after Fischer). The eggs of some species are more spherical and lack indentations at the ends. (B) Trochophore larva of *Golfingia vulgaris* at about 45 hours (after Gerould). (C) Pelagosphaeric larva, introvert retracted (after Akesson). (D) Pelagosphaeric larva with anterior region partly displayed (after Damas). (E) Pelagosphaeric larva with anterior region completely displayed; lateral view (after Damas). *a*, anus; *ac*, apical tuft; *e*, eye-spot; *go*, glandular organ; *i*, introvert; *lm*, longitudinal muscle; *m*, mouth; *n*, nephridium; *nc*, nerve cord; *rm*, retractor muscle; *st*, stomach; *to*, terminal organ; *z*, zona radiata.

is found in *Phascolosoma agassizii* and *Sipunculus nudus*, the eggs of which contain little yolk.   The first three types of development take place in eggs which are rich in yolk.

The larvae of some species of sipunculans live for a month or more in a planktonic form and consequently are not uncommonly collected in hauls of plankton.   The task of identifying them, however, is a difficult one chiefly because the development of only a few species has so far been studied.   They are *Sipunculus nudus* (Hatschek, 1883), *Golfingia elongata* (Selenka, 1875 and Akesson, 1961), *Phascolopsis gouldii* and *Golfingia vulgaris* (Gerould, 1907), *Phascolion strombi* and *Golfingia minuta* (Akesson, 1958), *Golfingia pugettensis*, *Themiste pyroides* and *Phascolosoma agassizii* (Rice, 1967).

Mingazzini (1905) identified a spherical-shaped sipunculan from some samples of plankton as an adult which he called *Pelagosphaera aloysii*.   Senna (1906) subsequently showed that similar animals were not adults but larval sipunculans.   Although the generic name *Pelagosphaera* has no standing in the systemics of the phylum the term 'pelagosphaera' has been adopted to describe the plankto-pelagic larva of sipunculans.   Pelagosphaerae have been recorded and described by Heath (1910), Dawydoff (1930), Stephen (1941), Fisher (1947), Akesson (1961), Damas (1962) and Murina (1965).   Both living and preserved specimens have been studied. Jägersten (1963) reported on the morphology and behaviour of a number of pelagosphaerae.   The information in Table 12 is based on and brings up to date the details about the larvae contained in Akesson (1961 : 7).

The records show that the larvae vary considerably in size and shape, according to the stage of their development.   The smallest specimens—and even large specimens if their anterior structures are invaginated—tend to be spherical to ellipsoidal in shape.   Dawydoff, Damas, Murina and Jägersten, however, report that the anterior region of living pelagosphaerae differs considerably from that of early larvae and adult sipunculans.   A prominent head which possesses eyes, a ventrally placed mouth and a posteriorly directed flap or lip are present.   The anterior structure is covered with fine cilia and bears a well developed metatroch of very large cilia, as long as 170 μ (Akesson, 1961 : 13).   Two structures which are prominent in some pelagosphaerae are a glandular organ (or the 'lip organ' of Jägersten, 1963 : 30) and its duct, which opens on the median ventral part of the oral disc, and a terminal organ at the posterior end of the ventral nerve cord.   In some specimens longitudinal muscle bands have been distinguished and counted and retractor muscles observed.   Spengel (1907) identified Senna's specimens as probably belonging to the genus *Sipunculus* and Fisher (1947) considered his specimen distinguished by the presence of 56 longitudinal muscle bands and four retractors as *Sipunculus polymyotus*, although eight additional protractor-like muscles were attached to the introvert.   Akesson (1961) thought that his specimens were either *Sipunculus* or *Xenosiphon* and Murina (1965) considered that her specimens from Aden were probably *Sipunculus aequabilis* and those from the Pacific Ocean probably *Sipunculus norvegicus*.   Damas (1962) found that the number of muscles attached to the introvert of his specimens was 6–14 and the number of longitudinal muscle bands 36–54.   He considered them most likely to belong to the genus *Sipunculus*.

TABLE 12

Records of pelagosphaeric larvae

Author		Locality of collection	Depth	Size in mm	Number of specimens
Mingazzini	1905	Between New Zealand and New Caledonia	0–500 m	6	1
Senna	1906	Indonesian and Ceylonese waters	50–400 m	1·8–3·2	3
Heath	1910	Monterey Bay, California	surface	2·5–3·2	2
Dawydoff	1930	Off coast of Annam	surface	0·5–1·5	730
Stephen	1941	Off south-east Africa	300–1200 m	5	1
Fisher	1947	Between Bermuda and Florida	0–150 m	3–6	many
Akesson	1961	Off Natal	0–5020 m	8–10	4
Damas	1962	Parts of the Pacific, Indian and Atlantic Oceans	most above 300 m	0·7–8·8	1900
Jägersten	1963	Florida current off Key Biscayne and Bimini	surface	5–6·8	many
Murina	1965	Gulf of Aden; Northwest Pacific Ocean	0–500 m	0·7–7	12

The pelagosphaerae collected and studied alive by Jägersten (1963) were able to swim and, when placed in a dish, to crawl. They were readily separated into two groups according to the texture of the surface of their bodies, one being smooth and the other made rough by 'superficial warts'.

The information shown in Table 13 is a summary of what is known about the developmental stages of sipunculans and is based on that given by Rice (1967 : 168). Rice has suggested that the definition of a pelagosphaera, 'previously restricted to plankto-trophic, pelagic larvae, should be broadened to include any sipunculid larva resulting from the metamorphosis of a trochophore that swims by means of a prominent ciliated metatroch, and in which the prototroch either has been lost or undergone a marked regression'.

TABLE 13

The patterns of development of sipunculans (after Rice, 1967)

	Length of pelagic state			Characters of the pelagosphaeric larva			
	trochophore	pelagosphaera	total	gut	mode of life	terminal organ	anterior structures associated with the mouth
Golfingia minuta	—	—	o	—	—	—	—
Themiste pyroides	—	—	o	—	—	—	—
Phascolion strombi	8 days	—	8 days	—	—	—	—
Phascolopsis gouldii	3 days	—	3 days	—	—	—	—
Golfingia vulgaris	3 days	2 days	5 days	incomplete	benthipelagic	—	—
Golfingia elongata	2 days	4 days	6 days	incomplete	benthipelagic	present and non-retractile	—
Golfingia pugettensis	8 days	13 days	21 days	incomplete	benthipelagic	present and non-retractile	—
Phascolosoma agassizii	8–10 days	1 month +	1 month +	complete	benthipelagic	present and retractile	present
Sipunculus nudus	3 days	1 month	1 month +	complete	planktonic	present and retractile	present
unidentified pelagosphaera	?	1 month ++	?	complete	planktonic	present and retractile	present

(2). SPECIES INCERTAE SEDIS, SPECIES INQUIRENDAE, ETC.

Sipunculus clavatus de Blainville, 1827 : 312; Quatrefages, 1865b : 611. Caen (France). See under *Aspidosiphon muelleri.*

Sipunculus corallicolus Pourtalès, 1851 : 41 (not *Aspidosiphon corallicolus* Sluiter, 1902). Florida, U.S.A.

Sipunculus echinorhynchus Chiaje, 1823 : 124. Mediterranean Sea. Quatrefages, 1865b : 616 suggested that the species might be a young specimen of *S. nudus* Linn.

Sipunculus gigas Quatrefages, 1865b : 614. Brittany. Quatrefages placed the species near *S. nudus* and *S. phalloides.* Baird, 1868 : 79 thought that it was probably *S. nudus* which is common in some parts of Brittany.

Sipunculus glans Quatrefages, 1865b : 627. Indian Seas.

Sipunculus javensis Quatrefages, 1865 : 622; Baird, 1868 : 94. Java. Length 90 mm, width 10 mm. The species is eaten in Java. Is it *Siphonosoma edule* (Pallas)?

Sipunculus macrorhynchus de Blainville, 1827 : 310. Mediterranean.

Sipunculus microrhynchus de Blainville, 1827 : 310; Diesing, 1851 : 62. Mediterranean.

Sipunculus rapus Quatrefages, 1865b : 626. Locality unknown.

Sipunculus rubens Costa, 1860 : 6. Naples.

Sipunculus rufo-fimbriatus Blanchard, 1849 : 56–59. Nice.

Sipunculus saccatus Linn., 1767 : 1078. Indian Ocean. Baird (1868 : 18) placed this species, with reservations, in the synonymy of *S. phalloides* Pallas. Selenka & de Man (1883 : 111) considered that it was synonymous with *S. indicus* Peters.

Sipunculus vermiculus Quatrefages, 1865b : 619. Indian Seas.

Sipunculus violaceus Quatrefages, 1865b : 619. Indian Seas.

Phascolosoma ambiguum (Brandt, 1835 : 62); Diesing, 1851 : 67. Locality unknown.

Phascolosoma carneum Leuckart and Rüppell, 1828 : 7. Red Sea.

Phascolosoma cochlearium (Valenciennes, 1854 : 641); Baird, 1868 : 94. Indian Seas.

Phascolosoma constellatum (Quatrefages, 1865b : 622); Baird, 1868 : 94. Isle de France.

Phascolosoma exasperatum Stimpson, 1865 : 159. Puget Sound.

Phascolosoma fasciolatum (Brandt, 1835 : 61); Diesing, 1851 : 66. Caroline Is.

Phascolosoma guttatum (Quatrefages, 1865b : 621); Baird, 1868 : 93. Red Sea.

Phascolosoma johnstoni (Forbes, 1841 : 254); Baird, 1868 : 95. Berwick Bay.

Phascolosoma leachii (de Blainville, 1827 : 312); Diesing, 1851 : 67. Locality unknown.

Phascolosoma longicolle Leuck. & Rüppell, 1828 : 7; Diesing, 1851 : 64. Red Sea.

Phascolosoma loricatum (Quatrefages, 1865b : 623); Baird, 1868 : 94. Indian Ocean.

Phascolosoma nordfolcense (Brandt, 1835 : 61); Diesing, 1851 : 67. Norfolk Sound.

Phascolosoma orbiniense (Quatrefages, 1865b : 622); Baird, 1868 : 93. American Seas.

Phascolosoma placostegi Baird, 1868 : 89.   Cape of Good Hope.   This species is a
   nomen dubium according to Rice & Stephen, 1970 : 65
Phascolosoma plicatum (Quatrefages, 1865b : 622); Baird, 1868 : 93.   Indian Seas.
Phascolosoma pourtalesi (Pourtalès, 1851 : 41); Baird, 1868 : 98.   Florida.
Phascolosoma pygmaeum (Quatrefages, 1865b : 627); Baird, 1868 : 86.   Locality
   unknown.
Phascolosoma semicinctum Stimpson, 1855 : 390–391.   False Bay, South Africa.
Themiste ramosa (Quatrefages, 1865 : 629); Baird, 1868 : 98.   Brazil.   Length
   70 mm, width 10 mm.   Tentacles arise from six stems which split into 4–5 branches,
   each branch subdividing two or three times.
Themiste lutulenta (Hutton, 1879); Edmonds, 1960 : 159.   New Zealand.   A
   specimen in the British Museum (Natural History) labelled *Sipunculus lutulentus*
   appears to be a *Themiste*.
Aspidosiphon coyi Quatrefages, 1865 : 608.   Indian Seas?
Aspidosiphon eremitus Diesing, 1859 : 768.   Madeira.
Aspidosiphon laevis Quatrefages, 1865 : 608.   Indian Seas?
Aspidosiphon rhyssapsis Diesing, 1859 : 768.   West Indies.

SPECIES TRANSFERRED TO OTHER PHYLA

Chaetoderma nitidulum Löven, 1845

   Regarded by earlier writers as a gephyrean (Löven, 1845 : 169–170, pl. 2; Quatrefages, 1865b : 602, etc.).   This species is now included under the Mollusca (*Soleno-
gaster*).

Epithetosoma norvegicum Danielssen & Koren, 1881

   This species was described by Danielssen & Koren (1881 : 39–44, pl. 6, figs 9–15)
from two specimens taken off the north Norwegian coast (69°41'N, 15°50'E) at
1591 m and included by them amongst the Gephyrea.   Bock (1920) showed it to be
an heteronemertine.

Sternaspis Otto, 1821

   The genus *Sternaspis* described by Otto (1821, 10 : 619–627, pl. 50) was included
by him and others (e.g. Quatrefages, 1865b : 590–591) amongst the Gephyrea,
but is now placed in the Polychaeta (Fauvel, 1927 : 216; Hartman, 1959 : 437).

(3). Parasites and Commensals

The following list of parasites, commensals and epizoites has been compiled chiefly from the literature on the systematics of the Sipuncula. It is not necessarily a complete list.

a. Parasites of Sipunculans

Parasite	Site of Infestation	Host	Record
Protozoa			
(a) Ciliata			
unidentified ciliate	body fluid	*Sipunculus nudus*	Metalnikoff, 1900
Cryptochilidium cuenoti	oesophagus	*Golfingia vulgaris*	Cuénot, 1900
(b) Sporozoa			
unidentified gregarine	intestine	*Sipunculus nudus*	Cuénot, 1902b
unidentified sporozoon	body cavity	*Golfingia minuta*	Théel, 1905
unidentified sporozoon	body cavity	*Siphonosoma cumanense*	Augener, 1903
acephaline gregarine	gut	Sipunculus sp.	Heckmann, 1961
Schizocystis sipunculi	intestine	*Sipunculus nudus*	Dogiel, 1907
Urospora sipunculi	coelomic fluid	*Sipunculus nudus*	{ Cuénot, 1902b { Goodrich, 1950
Tetractinomyxon intermedium	blood corpuscles	*Golfingia minuta*	{ Ikeda, 1912 { Ethrington, 1953
Lecudina franciana	rectum	*Phascolion strombi*	Arvy, 1952b
Metchnikovella berliozi	intestine	*Phascolion strombi*	Arvy, 1952b
Extremocystis dendrostomi	coelomic fluid	*Themiste lageniformis* (=*Dendrostomum signifer*)	Setna, 1931
Pompholyxia sipunculi	body cavity	*Sipunculus nudus*	Fabre-Domergue, 1886
Lithocystis lankesteri	body cavity	*Sipunculus nudus*	Goodrich, 1950
Urospora hardyi	body cavity	*Sipunculus nudus*	Goodrich, 1950
Platyhelminthes			
(a) Rhabdocoela			
Callastoma monorchis	intestine	*Golfingia vulgaris*	Dörler, 1900
Callastoma minutum	intestine	*Phascolosoma granulatum*	Wahl, 1910
Callastoma eremitae	intestine	*Golfingia eremita*	Beklemischer, 1916
Callastoma pacificum	intestine	*Themiste pyroides*	Kozloff, 1953
(b) Trematoda			
metacercaria (*leptosoma*)	contractile vessel	*Golfingia vulgaris*	Cuénot, 1900
metacercaria (*capriciosa*)	brain	*Golfingia vulgaris*	Cuénot, 1900
metacercaria	brain	*Sipunculus nudus*	Akesson, 1958
metacercaria	brain	*Golfingia elongata* *Golfingia vulgaris*	} Stehle, 1954
cercaria	tentacles	*Sipunculus robustus* (=*S. angasii*)	Akesson, 1958
Cercaria rhodometropa	gonad	*Phascolion strombi*	Perez, 1924; 1925
Nematoda			
Gephyronema laeve	body cavity	*Cloeosiphon aspergillus*	Augener, 1903
Arthropoda			
Copepoda			
Siphonobius gephyreicola	body cavity	*Aspidosiphon brocki*	Augener, 1903
Myzomolgus stupendus	body surface	*Sipunculus nudus*	} Bocquet & Stock,
Catinia plana	body surface	*Sipunculus nudus*	} 1957

b. Commensals

Commensal	Sipuncula	Record
Coelenterata		
Heteropsammia sp.	⎫	⎧Bouvier, 1894; 1895
Heterocyathus sp.	⎬ *Aspidosiphon* sp.	⎨Sluiter, 1902
Stephanoceris sp.	⎭	⎩Shipley, 1903
solitary coral	*Aspidosiphon jukesii* (=*A. corallicola*)	Stephen & Robertson, 1952
Edwardsiella sp.	⎫	⎧Rickets & Calvin, 1952
Cerianthus sp.	⎬ *Golfingia hespera*	⎨Fisher, 1952
Annelida		
Mesochaetopterus sp.	*Golfingia hespera*	Fisher, 1952
	⎧ *Aspidosiphon clavatus*	⎧Southern, 1913b
Langerhansia cornuta	⎨	⎨Cuénot, 1922b
	⎩ *Phascolion strombi*	Southern, 1913b
Mollusca		
Rochefortia cuneata	*Phascolion strombi*	Hampson, 1964
Montacuta phascolionis	*Phascolion strombi*	⎧Perez, 1924; 1925 ⎩Boss, 1965
Montacuta glabra	*Sipunculus nudus*	⎧Pelseneer, 1909 ⎩Franc, 1960
Fronsella ohshimae	*Sipunculus nudus*	Habe, 1964
Mysella bidentata	⎧ *Golfingia vulgaris*	Pelseneer, 1925
Potidoma clarkiae	⎨ *Golfingia pellucida*	Orton, 1923
	⎩ *Golfingia elongata*	⎧Gardiner, 1928 ⎩Popham, 1940
Jousseaumiella concharum	*Aspidosiphon* sp.	Knudsen, 1944

c. Epizoites

Epizoite	Sipuncula	Record
Entoprocta		
Loxosomella	*Golfingia elongata*	⎫
phascolosomatum	*Golfingia margaritacea*	⎬Vogt, 1876
	Golfingia vulgaris	Cuénot, 1922
	Phascolion strombi	Bobin & Prenant, 1953a
Loxosomella marmarica	*Phascolion strombi*	Nilus, 1909
Loxosomella atkinsae	⎫	
Loxosomella arvyae	⎬ *Phascolion strombi*	Bobin & Prenant, 1953a
Loxosomella bouxini	⎫	
Loxosomella fungiformis	⎬ *Phascolion strombi*	Bobin & Prenant, 1953b
Loxosomella cuenoti	⎭	
Loxosomella sp.	*Golfingia vulgaris*	Bobin & Prenant, 1953a
Loxosoma brumpti	*Phascolion strombi*	Nilus, 1909
Loxosoma minutum	*Phascolion strombi*	⎫
	Golfingia eremita	⎬Osburn, 1912
Loxosoma sluiteri	*Phascolion convestitum*	Harmer, 1915
Loxosoma nitschei	*Phascolion strombi*	Arvy & Prenant, 1952

III Phylum (c.f. p. 2) **ECHIURA**

1. General Information

(1). *Status and name of the group*

The first echiurans to be described appear to have been *Thalassema* (=*Lumbricus*) *thalassemum* (Pallas, 1766) and *Echiurus* (=*Lumbricus*) *echiurus* (Pallas, 1766). The first bonellid described was *Bonellia viridis* Rolando, 1821. Zoologists in the middle of the nineteenth century considered that the echiurans together with sipunculans and priapulids constituted a special group of animals which they called the Gephyrea (*gephyra* a bridge) under the impression that they formed a link between the annelids and the holothurians. The taxonomic position of the Gephyrea, although at times uncertain, was usually regarded as being that of a class of the phylum Annelida. Sedgwick (1898) raised the Sipunculoidea and Priapuloidea to the rank of phyla but continued to consider the Echiuroidea as a class of the Annelida. The Echiuroidea was established as a phylum largely as a result of the studies of Newby (1940) on the embryology and development of *Urechis caupo*. He showed that annelids and echiurans differ considerably in their mode of development, that the mesodermal bands of developing echiurans show no trace of segmentation and that echiurans are no more related to annelids than they are to molluscs. He advocated that the group be considered as forming a separate phylum. The phyletic status of the group is now generally accepted (Zoological Records, Vermes Section; Hyman, 1940 : 34, 58; Fisher, 1946; Stephen, 1965; Clark, R. B., 1969).

We are also using a new term, 'echiuran' to describe an animal that belongs to the phylum. In the past some confusion has been caused by the use of the two terms 'echiuroid' and 'echiurid'. Neither is very satisfactory. It is argued that 'echiuroid' should be used for any species of a superfamily and that an 'echiurid' is a member of the family Echiuridae, just as a nereid and a eunicid belong to the families Nereidae and Eunicidae. If the name Echiura is given to the phylum (Stephen, 1965) it seems reasonable to regard the phylum as containing echiurans rather than echiuroids or echiurids. When the term 'echiurid' is used in this monograph it refers to a species of the family Echiuridae and the term 'bonellid' to a species of the family Bonelliidae. A common name for echiurans which is gaining acceptance is 'spoon-worm'.

(2). *Occurrence and distribution*

All echiurans are marine except for a few species that occur in brackish water (Annandale & Kemp, 1915). They are soft bodied, almost defenceless creatures, that always live in protected places and that are well adapted for living in burrows. They are found in sand or mud where they sometimes live in U-shaped burrows, e.g. *Echiurus echiurus*, *Ochetostoma octomyotum* and *Urechis caupo*, under rocks, in debris amongst the roots of marine angiosperms, e.g. *Anelassorhynchus adelaidensis*, in the discarded shells of echinoids that have become filled with sand, e.g. *Lissomyema mellita* and in cracks and galleries made in rocks, e.g. *Thalassema thalassemum*, limestone or coral, e.g. *Pseudobonellia biuterina*.

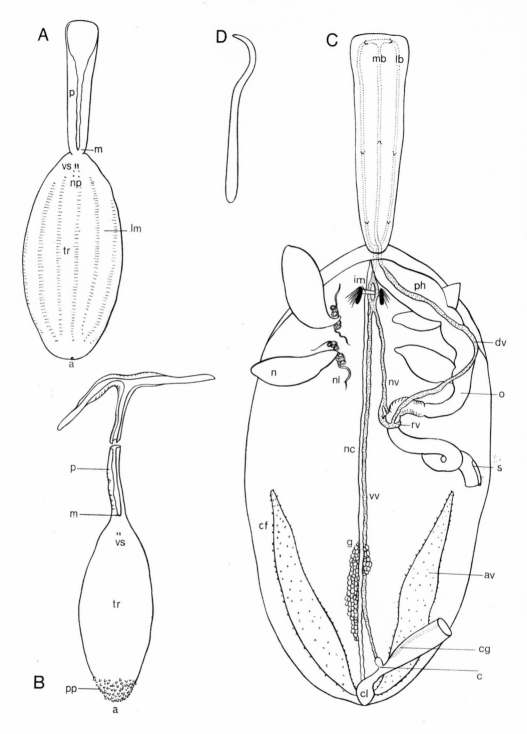

Echiurans are detritus feeders. With the aid of their highly muscular and sometimes spoon- or scoop-like proboscis they direct sand, mud, coral fragments and finely divided particles from their surroundings into their mouths and extract organic matter from the ingested material. Species belonging to the genus *Urechis*, however, trap bacteria and very fine particles of food in a slime net which is secreted from the surface of the animal.

Echiurans occur widely and their bathymetric range is extensive. They are well known in tropical, temperate and polar waters and are collected from the littoral to the abyssal regions of the ocean. Bonellids have recently been dredged from depths of 6000–10,000 m (Zenkevitch, 1957; 1958; 1964a; 1964b; 1966). Sometimes echiurans are common in a particular locality; Barnard & Hartman (1959) reported the existence of a remarkable concentration of *Listriolobus pelodes* on the sea bed at a depth of about 48 m near Santa Barbara, California.

(3). *Collection, relaxation, fixation and preservation*

The presence of an echiuran on a sand or mud flat is often shown by the openings of its burrows or sometimes by catching sight of its proboscis. The animal, however, may be difficult to collect. It is usually a waste of time and of specimens to try to remove an echiuran from its hiding place by pulling on its proboscis. The latter nearly always breaks, leaving the worm still in its burrow. Echiurans that live in sand or mud have to be removed by digging. Often the trunk may be 40–60 cm below the surface of the substrate and a considerable amount of hard work must be done to dislodge it. The position of the worm can be marked by pushing a piece of rubber tubing down the tube made by its proboscis or by two pieces if both ends of its burrow are showing. Careful digging on one side of the line connecting the ends of the burrow will ultimately expose the animal. It is best to lift up the animal by the trunk and not by the proboscis.

Sometimes echiurans are simply picked up under rocks at low tide or taken when one digs amongst the roots of some marine angiosperms. Those that live in rocks or in coral may be difficult to dislodge. Sometimes if the rock is struck sharply with a hammer it will crack along the fissure or gallery which the animal inhabits.

FIG. 42. (A) A generalized diagram of an echiurid (a species of the family Echiuridae); ventral view. In this specimen the longitudinal muscles are thickened in bands. (B) A generalized diagram of a bonellid (a species of the family Bonelliidae); ventral view. The proboscis of a bonellid is often but not always bifid. Papillae are shown only on the posterior surface of the trunk. (c) A generalized diagram to show some of the anatomy of an echiuran; dorsal view. Most of the much coiled intestine has been omitted. The nephrostome is not always basal in position nor are its lips always spirally coiled. In some species the anal vesicles may branch extensively and become bush-like. (D) Diagram showing the general shape of a ventral seta. *a*, anus; *av*, anal vesicle; *c*, caecum; *cf*, ciliated funnel; *cg*, ciliated groove; *cl*, cloaca; *cr*, crop; *dv*, dorsal vessel; *g*, gonad; *gi*, gizzard; *im*, interbasal muscle; *in*, intestine; *lb*, lateral vessel; *m*, mouth; *mb*, median vessel; *n*, nephridium; *nc*, nerve cord; *nl*, nephrostomal lips; *np*, nephridiopore; *ns*, nephrostome; *nv*, neuro-intestinal vessel; *o*, oesophagus; *p*, proboscis; *ph*, pharynx; *pp*, papillae; *rv*, ring vessel; *s*, siphon; *tr*, trunk; *vs*, ventral setae; *vv*, ventral vessel.

X

Then the animal can be lifted out with the aid of forceps.   One of the present authors has had some success in collecting a bonellid that lives in coral by immersing large pieces of the rock in a bucket containing a dilute solution (about half per cent) of formalin made up in sea water.   Under these conditions some of the bonellids will move out of their burrows.

Because the proboscis of many species is deciduous and likely to be lost echiurans must be handled carefully.   This is true particularly of specimens of the genera *Arhynchite, Thalassema, Anelassorhynchus, Ochetostoma* and *Listriolobus*.   If the proboscis is shed it is important that it be collected, fixed and stored along with the trunk because its form is an important taxonomic character.

After it has been collected the animal should be placed in plenty of cool sea water until it is to be narcotized.   It is highly desirable to relax or narcotize a specimen before it is fixed in order to prevent it from becoming distorted and contracted when it is directly plunged into fixatives.   Echiurans can be narcotized (1) by placing them in a shallow dish containing cool sea water on the top of which some crystals of menthol have been sprinkled, (2) by placing them in a 7% solution of magnesium chloride (made up in tap or distilled water), (3) by placing them in sea water to which is added very carefully a small quantity of 90% alcohol (drop by drop, if the volume of liquid is small) or (4) by immersing them in a 1% solution of propylene phenoxetol.   Often it is necessary to leave the animal in the relaxing agent for 2–12 hours, depending on its size.

When the animal no longer responds to touch it can be transferred to a 5% solution of neutral formalin in order to kill it and fix its tissues.   After it has been fixed for 24 hours it should be placed in 70% alcohol for storage.

(4). *Dissection, external and internal characters*

In order to identify an echiuran it is nearly always necessary to dissect it.   This is done by pinning out the animal under water in a dish which contains a layer of solidified paraffin wax.   The animal is placed with its ventral side down on the wax, that is the side on which the setae appear.   The dissection is performed by carefully cutting the body wall longitudinally along the mid-dorsal line of the trunk with the aid of a scalpel and forceps.   It is important to hold up the body wall before cutting it so that the incision will not damage the organs in the body cavity.   It is necessary to cut almost to the anterior and posterior extremities of the trunk.   The flaps of the body wall are then pinned back clear of the internal organs.   Sometimes the blood or reproductive cells of the animal are found to have coagulated in the body cavity during fixation, thereby obscuring some of the finer structures.   It is often possible to wash away some of the coagulated matter by directing on to it a fine stream of water from a wash bottle.

If the specimen is dissected in this way the characters that are of taxonomic importance are preserved.

The morphology and anatomy of a 'generalized' echiuran is shown in Fig. 42A–D. The external characters of a specimen viewed from the ventral side are shown in Fig. 42A; the truncated type of proboscis is shown.   The bifid type of proboscis that is found only in some bonellids is shown in Fig. 42B.   The internal anatomy of a specimen that has been dissected from the dorsal side is shown in Fig. 42C. The shape of an anterior or ventral seta is shown in Fig. 42D.

(5). *Explanation of terms as used for echiurans*

alimentary canal – A very long and much coiled tube that runs from the mouth to the anus. In an echiuran it consists typically of three chief sections: (1) a foregut, which is sub-divisible into a pharynx, oesophagus, gizzard, stomach or crop, (2) a mid-gut or intestine proper (with which are usually associated a ciliated groove and a siphon) which is sub-divisible into a pre-siphonal, a siphonal and a post siphonal region, (3) a short hind gut or cloaca into which the anal vesicles discharge. The fore- and hind-gut are ectodermal in origin and the layers of longitudinal and circular muscles are a continuation of those of the body wall. The mid-gut, however, is endodermal in origin and the position of the layers of longitudinal and circular muscle are the reverse of those that they occupy in the fore- and hind-gut.

anal rosette – A structure of unknown function that surrounds the anal aperture of the deep sea bonellid *Bruunellia* (Fig. 46F).

anal setae – One or two rings of hook-like structures that encircle the posterior extremity of the trunk and that are found only in the genera *Echiurus* and *Urechis* (Figs 52A and 59B).

anal vesicles – A pair of usually large, often tubular or sac-like excretory vessels which lie in the body cavity and discharge their products into the cloaca. Their surface usually bears a few to numerous excretory tubules, the coelomic extremity of which is modified to form a ciliated cup or funnel. Sometimes the vesicles branch simply or complexly and they may even be broom-like (Figs 42C and 51E).

androecium – A specialized part, usually the basal part, of the nephridium of some female bonellids where the male may be found (Fig. 43G).

anterior setae – see *ventral setae*.

anus – The posterior aperture of the alimentary canal which is situated at the posterior extremity of the trunk.

arborescent – Tree-like.

bifid – Forked; usually refers to the condition of the proboscis of some species of the Bonelliidae, the forked sections being called arms (Fig. 42B).

body wall – The dermal, glandular, muscular and epithelial tissues that constitute the wall of the trunk.

bonellid – A species of the family Bonelliidae.

caecum – A blind pouch of unknown function which arises from the posterior (precloacal) region of the intestine (Fig. 42C). Absent in some echiurans.

ciliated funnels – Small, ciliated funnel- or cup-shaped structures which are borne at the coelomic extremities of the excretory tubules (Fig. 52C).

ciliated groove – A ciliated channel that runs along the ventral surface of the mid-intestine as far as the precloacal caecum; it may form a ridge and sometimes is closely associated with the siphon.

circular muscle – The outermost muscular layer of the body wall of echiurans except those in the genus *Ikeda*.

cloaca – The posterior part of the intestinal tract into which pass the contents of the anal vesicles.

coelomic epithelium – The thin layer of tissue that covers the inner surfaces of the body cavity or coelom.

collateral intestine – A tube associated with the mid-gut for a considerable part of its length; its diameter is considerably less than that of the gut itself.

crop – The posterior region of the foregut; often marked by a number of longitudinal lines which correspond to the longitudinal folds of its lining. It is often surrounded by a ring blood vessel.

dendritic – Tree-like or branching.

diaphragm – A thin-walled, funnel shaped septum that incompletely separates an anterior or peripharyngeal coelom from the general body cavity of species of the genus *Echiurus* (Fig. 52E).

diverticulum – An alternative term for caecum.

dorsal blood vessel – A prominent, tubular blood vessel that lies dorsally in the anterior part of the body cavity and which is often associated with the foregut. Because in many echiurans it has been observed to pulsate it is sometimes called the 'heart'. The blood is forced anteriorly in the vessel to the median vessel of the proboscis (Fig. 42C).

excretory tubules – Small, delicate tubules which are often present in great numbers on the coelomic surface of the anal vesicles or their branches; each ends in a ciliated cup or funnel (Fig. 52C). The tubules may be short or long and may be present either separately or in tufts. In some species the tubules are minute.

fascicle – A bundle; usually refers to a thickening into bands of the oblique musculature of some genera of the Echiuridae (Fig. 55D).

fimbriated – Fringed at the margin.

fore-gut – See under *alimentary canal*.

frenulum (plural-a) – A fold of membrane.

genital groove – A depression that extends from the nephridopore(s) to the mouth on the ventral surface of some genera of the Bonelliidae; in some genera, e.g. *Acanthohamingia* setae may be present in the groove but in others e.g. *Amalosoma* they are not (Fig. 44A and B).

gizzard – A short, muscular region of the posterior section of the foregut that is usually marked by ringed or annular striations (Fig. 47D).

gonoducts – An alternative term for the nephridia.

haemoglobin – A respiratory pigment that is present in the blood of echiurans.

hind-gut – The posterior section of the alimentary canal (see under *alimentary canal*).

heart – A term sometimes used to describe the pulsating dorsal blood vessel.

interbasal muscle – A strong, narrow muscular band of tissue that connects the sheaths of the two ventral setae; very prominent in some species but absent in others (Figs 42C and 54D).

lappets – The shortened arms of the proboscis of some bonellids.

longitudinal muscle bands – The layer of longitudinal muscle of the body wall of some species of the Echiuridae is thickened into bundles which are usually visible externally (Figs 54B and 55A).

mesentery – A fold of peritoneal tissue that helps to hold an internal organ in position.

mid-gut – See *alimentary canal*.

muscular pad – A pad of muscular tissue (sometimes there are two) associated with the ventral setae of some species of the Bonelliidae, e.g. those of the genus *Acanthobonellia*.

muscular sheath of the setae – A sheath that encloses the coelomic section of each of the ventral setae.

mouth – The anterior opening of the alimentary canal.

nephridia – Thin walled, elongate or sac-like vessels, one end of which is attached to the anterior and ventral surface of the body wall and the free end of which lies in the body cavity (Fig. 44C). They act as organs for the temporary storage of eggs and sperms. There is a strong tendency throughout the phylum for the nephridia to occur in pairs; only one nephridium, however, is present in some of the Bonelliidae. In the family Ikedaidae the nephridia are numerous (about 400) and unpaired. The external opening of a nephridium is a nephridiopore and the coelomic or internal opening a nephrostome.

As a rule the number of nephridia present in a species is constant and an important taxonomic character. Occasionally, however, slight variations are found in the same species (Stewart, 1900; Fisher, 1946 : 222; Edmonds, 1963 : 244–245).

nephridiopore – The external opening of a nephridium through which eggs or sperms pass to the exterior. The nephridiopores may or may not be clearly visible on the external surface.

nephrostome – The coelomic opening of a nephridium through which sex cells pass on their way from the body cavity to the lumen of the nephridium. The position of the nephrostome is an important taxonomic character, especially of the family Bonelliidae. The nephrostome may be placed (1) basally or proximally (near the nephridiopore, Fig. 45E) or (2) terminally or distally (towards the coelomic extremity, Fig. 47D).

nephrostomal lips – The lip-like tissue that surrounds the nephrostome, the shape of which is an important taxonomic character. Nephrostomal lips may be inconspicuous, expanded or leaf-like (Fig. 53F) or extended into long threads which may or may not be spirally coiled (Fig. 55D).

nerve cord – A prominent, unsegmented thread of nervous tissue that runs longitudinally along the coelomic wall of the body on the ventral side. Anteriorly in the proboscis it is expanded into a large peripharyngeal ring (Fig. 54C).

neurointestinal blood vessel – A prominent blood vessel that branches from the ventral blood vessel at a point posterior to the setae and which connects with the dorsal blood vessel either (1) directly through a ring vessel (Fig. 42C)—the common condition in the family Echiuridae—or (2) indirectly through often spacious blood lacunae in the intestinal walls (Fig. 45E)—a common condition in the family Bonelliidae.

oesophagus – Part of the foregut; see under *alimentary canal.*

oblique muscles – The innermost muscular layer of the body wall of echiurans. In some genera of the Echiuridae it forms oblique or nearly transverse fascicles between the thickened bands of the longitudinal muscles (Fig. 55D).

papillae – Wart-like or rounded, often prominent, tubercles that are found on the surface of most echiurans. Sometimes they are almost uniform in size but usually they are largest towards the anterior and posterior extremities of the trunk. They may or may not be distributed uniformly over the surface. They are often associated with glandular cells.

pharynx – The anteriormost part of the foregut (see under *alimentary canal*).

plicate – Folded or ridged like a fan.

proboscis – A highly muscular and sensitive food gathering and respiratory organ which extends from the anterior region of the trunk near the mouth. It is present, sometimes only in a reduced form, in nearly all echiurans. It is, however, sometimes readily detached form the trunk and easily lost. In some species of Bonelliidae its anterior extremity is forked and the arms so formed may be long or short (Figs 43A and 45C). In other species of the Bonelliidae and in most species of the Echiuridae the proboscis is not bifid but either truncated (Fig. 54C) or flattened anteriorly to form a spoon-like structure (as in the genus *Arhynchite*). In the genus *Urechis* it is reduced to a scoop shaped upper lip (Fig. 59A) and it has not been described for the genera *Amalosoma* and *Nellobia*.

A ciliated groove is usually present on the ventral surface of the organ for the whole of its length. Food material mixed with mucus is directed along the groove to the mouth. The proboscis is also an important respiratory organ and contains, typically, an afferent median and two efferent lateral blood vessels. In a few species, e.g. *Anelassorhynchus branchiorhynchus* dendritic, gill-like processes extend from its lateral edges. The lateral margins of the proboscis of some species fuse at the base to form a small cup-like structure (Fig. 57D). The proboscis of some of the deep sea bonellids may be modified in different ways. Sometimes the mouth is surrounded by massive lips as in the genus *Prometor* or by a funnel-like structure as in the genus *Vitjazema*. In the genus *Choanostomellia* a deep funnel-like collar surrounds the proximal part of the proboscis and pharynx. In the genera *Bruunellia* and *Jakobia* the proboscis is oval and not crescentic in transverse section for the whole of its length and then lacks a ventral groove.

radiating muscle – A somewhat cone-like arrangement of separate muscles which radiate from the base and proximal side of the setal sheath to the body wall; their action is important in the movement of the setae.

ring vessel – A ring of vascular tissue which surrounds or almost surrounds the posterior section (crop) of the foregut. It is formed by the bifurcation of the neurointestinal vessel (Fig. 57C). It is, however, not present in some species.

reserve setae – Replacing setae, enclosed in their own sheaths which do not project from the ventral surface until they replace the functioning setae.

rugose – Wrinkled.

segmental organ – An alternative and older name for a *nephridium*.

setae – Hard, bristle or hook-like structures which are present in most genera of echiurans. See *ventral setae* and *anal setae*.

siphon – A tube associated with the mid-gut for a considerable part of its length. Its diameter is considerably less than that of the gut itself and its function not known exactly (Fig. 45E).

slime (net) glands – A group of glands present on the anterior surface of *Urechis* which secrete a funnel shaped net of mucus in which food particles are trapped.

stomach – The posterior-most subdivision of the foregut. See under *crop*.

truncate – The shape formed by cutting off the slender apex of a tapering triangle; terminating abruptly.

trunk – The cylindrical or sac-like body of an echiuran.

uterus – A term formerly used for the nephridium of a female bonellid.

ventral setae – Bristle- or hook-like structures that pierce the ventral wall of echiurans just posterior to the mouth. They are usually present as a pair. In two genera of the Bonelliidae the setae are numerous and lie in a genital groove. Setae are absent in some species of the Bonelliidae, especially those that live at great depths. A species of *Acanthobonellia* has been described as possessing only one seta which is barbed.

ventral groove – A ciliated groove or channel which traverses the ventral surface of the proboscis and along which food material and mucus is directed to the mouth. It appears to be absent in some deep sea species of the Bonelliidae.

ventral (blood) vessel – A prominent blood vessel that runs alongside the ventral nerve cord and which also supplies the gonads with blood. A neurointestinal vessel branches from it in the anterior part of the trunk.

vascular system – The vascular system consists of (typically) a ventral, a neurointestinal and dorsal vessel in the trunk and a median and two lateral vessels in the proboscis. Blood moves anteriorly in the dorsal to the median (afferent) vessel and posteriorly in the two lateral (efferent) vessels to the ventral vessel. It moves from the ventral to the dorsal vessel through the neurointestinal vessel (see under *neurointestinal vessel*). The blood is oxygenated chiefly in the proboscis. There is no blood vascular system in *Urechis*.

vas deferens – A tube through which the sperms of a male bonellid pass from the sperm receptacle to the male aperture (Fig. 60B).

(6). *General and special references*

There are two general accounts of the phylum, that (written in German) of Baltzer (1931d) in Kükenthal & Krumbach's Handbuch der Zoologie and that (in French) of Dawydoff (1959) in Grassé's Traité de Zoologie. Both are comprehensive and describe the anatomy, physiology and embryology of the phylum. That of Dawydoff is the more recent. The introduction of Fisher's paper 'Echiuroid worms of the north Pacific Ocean' (Fisher, 1946), although short, is particularly informative.

The following are references of special as opposed to general interest: Fisher & MacGinitie (1928—The natural history of an echiuroid worm, Redfield & Florkin (1931)—The function of the blood of *Urechis caupo*, Gislén (1940)—The investigations of the ecology of *Echiurus*, Newby (1940)—The embryology of the echiuroid worm

Urechis caupo, MacGinitie & MacGinitie (1968)—The natural history of marine animals, and Bridges (1963)—A laboratory looks at a peculiar worm (*Bonellia viridis*).

2. CLASSIFICATION

(1). *Systems of classification*

The most recent systems of classification of the phylum Echiura are those of Bock (1942) and Fisher (1946, 1949). The main differences between the two schemes arise from (1) the promotion of the Echiura from a class of the Annelida to a phylum, (2) the removal of the very unusual *Poeobius meseres* Heath from the phylum and (3) the upgrading of the differences between *Urechis* Ikeda and the remaining genera of the phylum from those of a family and subfamily to those of an order.

The system of classification that we have used is basically that of Fisher; we consider that the reasons underlying the changes that he made to the previously existing schemes were sound. We have, however, made one or two minor alterations. The name of the phylum becomes Echiura for reasons that are given by Stephen (1965, *footnote*) and we have placed *Sactosoma vitreum* Dan. & Kor., 1881 amongst the *species inquirendae* and *species incertae sedis* in the Appendix (p. 473). To create a class of the Echiura for a single species, inadequately described from one defective specimen, seems to us to be unwarranted and even misleading. Although we agree with Fisher's reasons for combining Bock's Thalassematidae and Echiuridae we consider that the difference between the two can be recognized with justification at the level of a subfamily. Consequently we regard the Echiuridae as consisting of two subfamilies, Echiurinae for *Echiurus* and Thalassematinae for the remaining genera of the family.

We have proposed two new genera, *Metabonellia* for two bonellids with distally placed nephrostomes and *Prashadus* for an echiurid with 20 pairs of nephridia and a distally placed nephrostome. We have followed Fisher's lead in recognizing *Listriolobus* Fischer and *Anelassorhynchus* Annandale as valid genera. Three genera, however, have not been admitted. (1) *Platylobostoma* Wesenberg-Lund, 1957 is considered to be synonymous with *Ochetostoma*; the lack of a proboscis seems insufficient grounds for its separation. (2) *Taguella* Benham, 1948, from its description and after an examination of a slide of the type specimen in the British Museum (Natural History), does not seem to us to be an echiuran (see p. 473). (3) *Austrobonellia* Fisher, 1948 for reasons that are given on p. 371 has been placed under *Archibonellia* Fischer, 1919.

The system of classification that we have followed together with those of Bock and Fisher is shown in Table 14. A note on some species that are no longer included in the Echiura and Sipuncula is given in the Appendix. According to our system of classification the phylum contains 4 families, 34 genera and 129 species.

Table 14

A comparison of three systems of classification of the phylum Echiura

Author	Phylum	Class	Order	Family	Subfamily
Bock (1942)	Annelida	Echiuroidea	Echiuroinea	⎰ Echiuridae ⎱ Thalassematidae ⎰ Bonelliidae	⎰ Ikedinae ⎱ Thalassematinae
			Sactosamatinea Poeobiinea	Sactosomatidae Poeobiidae	
Fisher (1946)	Echiuroidea	Echiurida	⎰ Echiuroinea ⎱ Xenopneusta ⎰ Heteromyota	⎰ Bonelliidae ⎱ Echiuridae Urechidae	
		Sactosomatida		Sactosomatidae	
Stephen & Edmonds	Echiura	—	⎰ Echiuroinea ⎱ Xenopneusta ⎰ Heteromyota	⎰ Bonelliidae ⎱ Echiuridae Urechidae Ikedaidae	⎰ Echiurinae ⎱ Thalassematinae

(2). *Characters of the phylum and keys to orders and families*

a. Phylum ECHIURA

Echiuroidea (class of Annelida) Sedgwick, 1898 : 527; Monro, 1927 : 616; Bock, 1942 : 7–17.
Echiurida (class of Annelida) Baltzer, 1931d; Dawydoff, 1959.
Echiuroidea (phylum) Newby, 1940 : 210; Hyman, 1940 : 34, 58; Fisher, 1946 : 219.
Echiura (phylum) Stephen, 1965 : 457 (footnote).

The phylum Echiura consists of a group of unsegmented, bilaterally symmetrical, coelomate animals, the body or trunk of which is sub-cylindrical or sac-like in shape and muscular in composition. A muscular, sensory proboscis that is usually capable of great extension is nearly always present and is attached to the anterior region of the trunk. The proboscis cannot be retracted within the body of the animal and so differs from the introvert of a sipunculan. The mouth is situated anteriorly at the base of the proboscis and the anus posteriorly at the extremity of the trunk. Within a spacious body cavity lies a long and much coiled alimentary canal. A collateral intestine or siphon is associated with the alimentary canal for a considerable part of its length. A pair of setae is usually present on the ventral surface of the body just posterior to the mouth and one or two rings of anal setae encircle the posterior region of two genera. One to numerous nephridia lie in the body cavity and are attached to the ventral surface of the body wall; they are usually present in pairs. Eggs and sperms are stored in the nephridia and are discharged to the exterior through nephridiopores. A pair of anal vesicles which usually bear ciliated funnels or tubules are attached to the cloacal region of the alimentary canal; they are excretory organs. A closed vascular system consisting of dorsal, ventral and neurointestinal blood vessels is always present except in one genus. The nerve cord is ventral and unsegmented. The gonads are diffuse and lie in a mesentery above the nerve cord or in mesenteries near the cloaca. The sexes are separate; in one family (Echiuridae) they are indistinguishable externally but in another (Bonelliidae) there is marked sexual dimorphism, the male, which is carried on or in the female, being relatively small. Fertilization is usually external and the larva is a trochophore.

The phylum comprises three orders.

Key to Orders

1   Echiurans in which the longitudinal musculature of the body wall lies between an outer layer of circular and an inner layer of oblique muscles; nephridia paired (except in the species of Bonelliidae which contain only one nephridium) and not very numerous (not more than 20 pairs)   2
–   Echiurans in which the longitudinal musculature of the body wall lies outside both the layers of circular and oblique muscles; nephridia unpaired and very numerous (400); nephrostome distal . . . . . . HETEROMYOTA (p. 354)
2   A closed vascular system present; posterior region of intestine not modified to form an anal respiratory organ . . . . . . ECHIUROINEA (p. 353)
–   No closed vascular system present but body fluid heavily charged with blood corpuscles containing haemoglobin; posterior region of intestine is thin walled and enlarged and acts as an organ of respiration, the cloaca functioning as a pump
XENOPNEUSTA (p. 354)

b. Orders of Echiura and Key to Families

Order ECHIUROINEA

Echiuroinea Bock, 1942 : 16; Fisher, 1946 : 220.

Echiurans in which the longitudinal musculature of the body wall lies between an outer layer of circular and an inner layer of oblique muscle. Closed vascular system present. Posterior region of intestine not adapted to serve as an organ of respiration. Nephridia not excessively numerous (up to 20 pairs).

Key to the Families of Echiuroinea

1   Species with marked sexual dimorphism. Female with sac-like trunk and with a proboscis which may be either simple or bifid; nephridia usually one or two; ventral setae, usually either two or absent; anal setae absent; anal vesicles usually branched. Male, usually small, degenerate and parasitic in or on the female
BONELLIIDAE (p. 354)
–   Species without sexual dimorphism; proboscis not bifid; nephridia paired; ventral setae, one pair; anal setae absent except in one genus; anal vesicles usually sac-like and not branched . . . . ECHIURIDAE (p. 406)

Order XENOPNEUSTA

Xenopneusta Fisher, 1946 : 220.

Echiurans in which the longitudinal musculature of the body wall lies between an outer layer of circular and an innermost layer of oblique muscle. Closed vascular system absent. Posterior region of intestine much enlarged and serving as an organ of respiration. Nephridia, two or three pairs.

The order contains one family, URECHIDAE (p. 465).

Order HETEROMYOTA

Heteromyota Fisher, 1946 : 220.

Echiurans in which the longitudinal musculature of the body wall lies outside both the layers of circular and oblique muscles. Nephridia unpaired and very numerous (400). Nephrostome distal.

The order contains one family, IKEDAIDAE (p. 471).

(3). Family **BONELLIIDAE**

Bonelliidae Baird, 1868 : 111; Monro, 1927 : 617; Bock, 1942 : 16 (emended); Fisher, 1946 : 249; 1949 : 489.

DESCRIPTION. Echiurans with marked sexual dimorphism.

Female. Trunk usually sac-like, about 7–140 mm long and often light to dark green in colour. Proboscis truncate or bifid and usually capable of great extension. Nephridia one or two (rarely three) with a nephrostome that is usually either basal (proximal) or terminal (distal) in position. Ventral setae usually either two or absent (numerous in two genera). Anal setae absent. Anal vesicles usually branching, dendritic or arborescent. Neurointestinal and dorsal blood vessels usually connected through blood capillaries or lacunae in the wall of the intestine.

Male. Usually small, about 1–6 mm long (except in the genera *Acanthobonellia* and *Metabonellia*), planarian-like or nematoform, without a proboscis and with alimentary, vascular, excretory and nervous systems usually reduced. Surface of body usually wholly or partly ciliated. Ventral setae present or absent. Parasitic in or on the female form; usually found in the nephridium of the female but also in the body cavity, oesophagus, pharynx or in a specialized male tube (*Pseudobonellia*). Developing males may also be found on the proboscis of a female.

TYPE GENUS. *Bonellia* Rolando.

REMARKS. The sexual dimorphism of bonellids distinguishes them from all other families of the phylum. The early larva of a bonellid may develop into a male or female, depending on its proximity to an adult female. If it finds and fastens on to the proboscis of a female the developing larva becomes a male. If it does not make contact with a female it eventually becomes a female (Baltzer, 1914; Michel, 1930; Bridges, 1963).

A comparison of the characters that distinguish between bonellids and echiurids is shown in Table 15.

TABLE 15

A comparison of the characters of the Bonelliidae and Echiuridae

	Bonelliidae	*Echiuridae*
proboscis	bifid or truncate	truncate but never bifid
nephridia	may be one, two or three; never two pairs or more	never single; always one or more pairs
musculature of body wall	never grouped into bundles	may be grouped into longitudinal bands
anal vesicles	usually branching, dendritic, arborescent or bushy	usually elongated or swollen sacs
nephrostomal lips	never spirally coiled	may be spirally coiled
vascular system	dorsal and neurointestinal vessels usually not in direct contact	dorsal and neurointestinal vessels usually in direct contact through a ring vessel near the posterior extremity of the fore-gut

Male bonellids have been described by Catta (1875), Spengel (1879a), Selenka (1878; 1885, pl. 2, fig. 7), Ikeda (1904 : 76; 1907 : 5–16), Baltzer (1914), Michel (1930) and more recently by Datta Gupta and Menon (1964) and José (1964). The anatomy of a 'generalized' male is shown in Fig. 60A.

The male is usually small and planarian-like but in *Acanthobonellia* it may be 60 mm long and nematoform. It may be green or colourless, it may or may not possess setae and its surface is sometimes ciliated. The body wall, like that of the female, consists of layers of circular, longitudinal and oblique muscles. The body cavity is usually large and contains corpuscles, developing spermatids, fat storing bodies and colourless plasma. The digestive and vascular systems are much reduced and the anterior nerve ring and ventral nerve cord may be present or absent. The male system consists of one, two or three to five sperm receptacles each with a ciliated funnel at its coelomic extremity (Fig. 60B). José (1964) found that the males of *Acanthobonellia pirotanensis* were able to live in sea water outside the female for about eight days and observed that they were able to re-enter the female.

The systematics of the Bonelliidae has been made more complex recently by the discovery of a number of species (dredged at great depths during the Russian 'Vitjaz' and the Danish 'Galathea' research expeditions) which do not belong to the older established genera. These deep-sea species differ from other species most noticeably in the shape and structure of the proboscis, in the possession of oral lips and circum-oral collars, in the shape of the nephridia and in the possession of anal structures of unknown function. When, however, soft-bodied, sac-like animals such as bonellids are brought to the surface of the ocean from depths of 5,000 to 10,000 m they are usually considerably distorted and damaged by the great changes of pressure which they suffer. Consequently very little is known about such delicate structures as the digestive, vascular and reproductive systems of females and nothing is known about the male. In spite of the difficulties of working with damaged and defective specimens Zenkevitch (1957, 1958, 1964, etc.) has added considerably to the knowledge of the Bonelliidae with his descriptions of the deep-sea forms.

The chief contributors to the systematics of the Bonelliidae during the last 60 years were Monro and Fisher. Monro (1927) recognized eight genera which he arranged in three subfamilies according to the structure of the proboscis and the number of nephridia (uteri) present. Fisher's contribution was considerable. In a series of papers Fisher (1946, 1948, 1949, 1952) described eight new genera and placed the systematics of the family on a sound footing. He based his system of classification largely on four characters: (1) the position of the nephrostome, (2) the structure of the proboscis, (3) the number of nephridia and (4) the number of ventral setae that the animal possesses. As a working hypothesis he 'assumed that the basal nephrostomes are the most primitive; that two nephridia are more ancestral than one, for the same reason that an undivided proboscis is more ancestral; and that the occurrence of two setae, with typical echiuroidean muscle apparatus precedes in evolution a condition where there are more numerous setae having a modified muscle apparatus, or none, or where the setae have disappeared altogether' (Fisher, 1949 : 490). We have accepted Fisher's criteria as a basis for the following classification of the family (the numbers in brackets give the number of setae for the genus). A list of genera arranged in alphabetical order is given in Table 16.

1. Nephrostome basal
    (1) Proboscis not bifid
        a. Two nephridia
           Maxmuelleria (2), *Alomasoma** (2 or 0), *Prometor* (2)
        b. One nephridium
           Acanthohamingia (numerous), *Protobonellia* (2), *Choanostomellia* (0), *Sluiterina* (0), ? *Nellobia*** (2).

    (2) Proboscis bifid
        a. Two nephridia
           Hamingia† (0) in part
        b. One nephridium
           Acanthobonellia (1 to numerous), *Bonellia* (2), *Hamingia*† (0) in part, *Achaetobonellia* (0), *Torbenwolffia* (0)
(Shape of proboscis not known in *Amalosoma* (0), two nephridia.)

2. Nephrostome distal
    (1) Proboscis not bifid
        a. Two nephridia
           Vitjazema (2)

(2) Proboscis bifid
    a. Two nephridia
       Pseudobonellia (2)
    b. One nephridium
       Bonelliopsis (2), *Metabonellia* (2), *Eubonellia* (0), *Ikedella* (0)

3. Position of nephrostome not known in
       Archibonellia†† (2), three nephridia; *Jakobia* (0), one nephridium and
       Bruunellia (0), nephridia not known.

  * Zenkevitch has described species of *Alomasoma* with two and no setae.
  ** The proboscis of *Nellobia* is either reduced to a small snout or absent.
  † *Hamingia arctica* possesses either two or one nephridia.
  †† We have included the related genus *Austrobonellia* Fischer in *Archibonellia* (see p. 371).

The existence of three genera in which the position of the nephrostome is not
known makes it difficult to construct a key to the family in which the first division
depends on that character. We have, however, been able to construct a key using
the same four basic characters that Fisher used by rearranging them so that the
first division depends on the number of nephridia present. The number of nephridia
is known for all genera except *Bruunellia* which can be distinguished from all
other bonellids because it possesses an anal rosette. A key to the genera is given
on p. 359. A new genus *Metabonellia* has been created for *Bonellia gigas* Nielsen
and *Bonellia haswelli* Johnston and Tiegs in which the nephrostome is distal and not
basal as in *Bonellia*. *Austrobonellia* Fischer, 1948 for reasons set out on p. 371 we
consider to be included in *Archibonellia* Fischer, 1919.

A summary of some information about the Bonelliidae is shown in Table 16.
It can be seen that the family contains 23 genera and 47 species and that 11 genera
contain only one species. The basal position of the nephrostome is more usual
than the distal, the proboscis is bifid in about half the genera and one nephridium
is more common than two. The bathymetric range of the family is wide. Species
from ten genera have been found at depths of over 4000 m and five at the depths
of over 7000 m.

Zenkevitch (1966 : 182) considered that the Echiuridae inhabit shallow and the
Bonelliidae deeper waters and that the Bonelliidae are 'a characteristic community
of the abyssal and ultra-abyssal fauna and reach to the greatest depths of the ocean'.
The information contained in Tables 16 and 17 supports his statement. Most
echiurids have been collected in shallow waters and none are known to occur at
depths of over 2000 m. Zenkevitch considered that the genera *Jakobia*, *Vitjazema*,
Alomasoma, *Bruunellia* and *Torbenwolffia* are ultra-abyssal and that *Prometor*,
Bonellia (in part) and *Sluiterina* belong to the 'mean-abyssal' zone. The genera
Choanostomellia and *Ikedella* should also be added to one or other of the two groups.
He put forward the hypothesis that the sexual dimorphism of the family and the
parasitism of the male are adaptations to life at great depths, in a way 'similar to
the conditions observed in angler fishes of the order Lophiiformes'.

TABLE 16

The genera of the family Bonelliidae (showing the position of nephrostome, condition of proboscis, etc.)

genus	author	date	nephrostome	proboscis	No. of nephridia	No. of species	bathymetric range
1. Acanthobonellia	Fisher	1948	basal	bifid	1	3	220 m
2. Acanthohamingia	Ikeda	1910	basal	not bifid	1	2	730–920 m
3. Achaetobonellia	Fisher	1953	basal	bifid	1	1	shallow water?
4. Alomasoma	Zenkevitch	1958	basal	not bifid	2	3	520–7820 m
5. Amalosoma	Fisher	1948	basal	?	2	2	220 m
6. Archibonellia	Fischer	1919	?	bifid	3	2	littoral
7. Bonellia	Rolando	1821	basal	bifid	1	6	littoral—4130 m
8. Bonelliopsis	Fisher	1946	distal	bifid	1	1	littoral
9. Bruunella	Zenkevitch	1966	?	?	?	1	1693–4930 m
10. Choanostomellia	Zenkevitch	1964	basal	not bifid	1	2	4020–7250 m
11. Eubonellia	Fisher	1946	distal	bifid	1	1	173 m
12. Hamingia	Dan. & Kor.	1881	basal	bifid	1 or 2	1	347 m
13. Ikedella	Monro	1927	distal	bifid	1	3	two species at 3500–6850 m
14. Jakobia	Zenkevitch	1958	?	not bifid	1	1	3270–8100 m
15. Maxmuelleria	Bock	1942	basal	not bifid	2	5	not deep water
16. Metabonellia	nov. gen.		distal	bifid	1	2	littoral
17. Nellobia	Fisher	1946	basal	not bifid?	1	1	134 m
18. Prometor	Fisher	1948	basal	not bifid	2	4	1670–4820 m
19. Protobonellia	Ikeda	1908	basal	not bifid	1	1	852 m
20. Pseudobonellia	Johnst. & Tiegs	1919	distal	bifid	2	1	littoral
21. Sluiterina	Monro	1927	basal	not bifid	1	1	4390 m
22. Torbenwolffia	Zenkevitch	1966	basal	bilobed	1	1	5850–8300 m.
23. Vitjazema	Zenkevitch	1958	distal	not bifid	2	2	5560–10210 m

KEY TO THE GENERA OF THE FAMILY BONELLIIDAE

1   Body wall surrounding the anus modified to form an anal rosette (number of
nephridia, position of nephrostome and form of anal vesicles not known; proboscis
in transverse section oval and not crescentic throughout its whole length and
lacking a ventral groove; only one species known which was dredged at 7250 m)
     BRUUNELLIA (p. 381)

–   No anal rosette present   2

2   Nephridium, single   3

–   Nephridia, more than one   17

3   Proboscis cleft or bifid with arms that may be long or short or reduced in one genus
to two lobes   4

–   Proboscis not cleft or bifid but truncate (reduced to a very short snout or absent
in *Nellobia*).   12

4   Setae usually numerous and set in one or two pads from which muscles radiate
(basal nephrostome; dorsal and neurointestinal vessels in direct contact; males
very large, 28–60 mm, and without setae) .   **ACANTHOBONELLIA** (in part)
     (p. 361)

–   Setae two, one or absent   5

5   Setae, two   6

–   Seta, one or absent   8

6   Nephrostome basal (dorsal and neurointestinal blood vessels indirectly connected
by lacunae or capillaries in the intestinal wall; male very small)   **BONELLIA** (p. 374)

–   Nephrostome not basal but distal (terminal)   7

7   Nephrostome on a short stalk and placed towards the distal extremity (intestinal
siphon reported to be absent; each vesicle consists of about 13 tubes; male large,
19 mm, and without setae . . . . .   **METABONELLIA** (p. 394)

–   Nephrostome trumpet-shaped and placed distally at the extremity of the nephridium
(males small, 1–2 mm, and without setae) . .   **BONELLIOPSIS** (p. 379)

8   Seta single, barbed and set in a muscular pad .   **ACANTHOBONELLIA** (in part)
     (p. 361)

–   Setae absent   9

9   Anal vesicles unbranched and short (ciliated funnels few, one nephridium, bifid
arms of proboscis reduced to two lobes; male unknown; specimens dredged at
5800–8300 m) . . . .   **TORBENWOLFFIA** (p. 404)

–   Anal vesicles branched, arborescent or dendritic.   10

10   Nephrostome on a short stalk and placed basally (alimentary canal very long with
an exceptionally long first segment and no clear distinction between the gizzard
and crop; cloaca enlarged and thin walled; males without setae)
     ACHAETOBONELLIA (p. 367)

–   Nephrostome placed distally   11

11   Nephrostome on a short stalk and placed distally (male small, 3 mm and without
setae) . . . .   **IKEDELLA** (p. 386)

–   Nephrostome not on a short stalk but is an expansion of the distal extremity of the
nephridium; lips voluminous (body wall thick; a short narrow groove extends
along the base of the proboscis near the mouth; male small, 1·2 mm, and without
setae) . . . .   **EUBONELLIA** (p. 383)

12   Setae or spinelets numerous, without radiating muscles, embedded in a genital
groove or slit that extends forwards from the nephridiopore to the mouth (nephrostome basal; male about 4 mm long and without setae)
     ACANTHOHAMINGIA (p. 364)

–   Setae two or absent   13

13   Setae two (nephrostome borne on a stalk and placed basally; male unknown)
     PROTOBONELLIA (p. 400)

– Setae absent 14

14 A wide, deep, funnel-like collar completely surrounds the basal part of the proboscis and pharynx; the collar is deeply incised on the ventral side (nephrostome basal; anal vesicles long and unbranched; male not known; dredged at 3000–5000 m)
CHOANOSTOMELLIA (p. 381)

– No wide, deep, collar surrounds the basal part of the proboscis 15

15 Nephridium unusual, consisting of two sections sharply bent to form a V, with arms that lie close together and partly fuse; nephrostome small but position uncertain (anterior extremity of proboscis flattened; proboscis in transverse section is oval and not crescentic in shape and lacks a ventral groove; well-developed lips attached to the mouth; male not known; only one species known which was dredged at 6000–8000 m) . . . . **JAKOBIA** (p. 389)

– Nephridium normal, sac-like or elongate and not bent to form a V . . . 16

16 Skin thick; proboscis a short, truncate snout or absent (anal vesicles branch profusely, hind-gut enlarged; nephrostome basal; male not known) . **NELLOBIA** (p. 395)

– Skin thin; proboscis well-developed with lateral margins fusing at the base to form a cup (nephrostome basal, male not known; species dredged at 4400 m)
SLUITERINA (p. 403)

17 Two nephridia present 18

– Three nephridia present, two being lateral and paired and one median and unpaired (in one species nephrostome of lateral nephridia is distal and of the median basal; in other species position of nephrostomes unknown; proboscis bifid; setae two)
ARCHIBONELLIA (p. 371)

18 Nephrostome basal in position 19

– Nephrostome distal in position 24

19 Setae two 20

– Setae absent 22

20 Proboscis with a specialized cup at its base (proboscis long and truncate; nephrostome with two fan-shaped lips and a common nephridiopore; neurointestinal and dorsal blood vessels directly connected; male not known; dredged at 1670–4820 m) . . . . **PROMETOR** (p. 397)

– Proboscis without a specialized cup at its base 21

21 Nephridia open to exterior by separate pores (proboscis ribbon-like and truncate, interbasal muscle well developed, anal vesicles bush-like; male not known)
MAXMUELLERIA (p. 390)

– Nephridia open (at least in *A. belyaevi*) into a common duct with a single pore (proboscis truncate; anal vesicles bush-like; male not known; dredged at 520–7820 m) . . . . **ALOMASOMA** (in part) (p. 368)

22 A narrow specialized genital groove or slit lying on the ventral side between the mouth and nephridiopore; proboscis not known; male small (1–2 mm) with setae
AMALOSOMA (p. 370)

– No narrow genital groove or slit present 23

23 Proboscis bifid (one nephridium reported in some species; male not known)
HAMINGIA (p. 385)

– Proboscis not bifid (specimens also described with two setae—see above)
ALOMASOMA (in part) (p. 368)

24 Proboscis bifid; a specialized male tube lies medianally between the two nephridio-pores (two setae with one or two pairs of reserve setae sometimes embedded in the body wall; anal vesicles open independently into the cloaca; interbasal muscle well developed; male small, 0·6 mm long, and lacking setae)
PSEUDOBONELLIA (p. 401)

– Proboscis not bifid but slightly widened anteriorly (two setae, anal vesicles sac-like: male not known; dredged at depths of 7300–9750 m) . **VITJAZEMA** (p. 405)

Genus *ACANTHOBONELLIA* Fisher, 1948

Acanthobonellia Fisher, 1948b : 857.

DESCRIPTION. *Female.* Trunk with bifid proboscis and with setae (usually numerous) embedded in one or two muscular pads anterior to the nephridiopore. Dorsal and neurointestinal blood vessels in direct communication. Single nephridium. Anal vesicles branching.

Male. Unusually large with ciliate epidermis. No setae.

TYPE SPECIES. *Bonellia miyajimai* Ikeda, 1904.

REMARKS. This genus contains three species, *A. miyajimai* (Ikeda), *A. pirotanensis* José and *A. rollandoe* Menon, Datta Gupta & Johnston. A fourth species *A. vulgaris* Menon, Datta Gupta & Johnson, we consider to be synonymous with *A. pirotanensis*.

DISTRIBUTION. Japan and the Gulf of Kutch, N.W. India.

ACANTHOBONELLIA—KEY TO SPECIES

1 Setae barbed and single . . . . **A. rollandoe** (p. 364)
– Setae not barbed and more than one **2**
2 Two to fourteen setae embedded in a single muscular cushion which is without
   radiating muscles . . . . **A. pirotanensis** (p. 363)
– Not less than twenty-nine setae embedded in two muscular cushions from which
   several muscles radiate . . . . **A. miyajimai** (p. 361)

Acanthobonellia miyajimai (Ikeda, 1904)

(Fig. 43A–D)

Bonellia miyajimai Ikeda, 1904 : 73–74; 1907 : 2–16, pl. 1, figs 1–2, pl. 2, figs 5–17; Sato,
   1939 : 363.
Acanthobonellia miyajimai : Fisher, 1948b : 857; Menon, Datta Gupta & Johnson, 1964 : 50–51;
   Datta Gupta & Menon, 1964 : 267–276, 4 text-figs.

TYPE LOCALITY. Tomari, Naha, Okinawashima, Japan.

DESCRIPTION. *Female.* Proboscis long, slender, up to about six times as long as the body and anteriorly divided into two long lobes; ventrally somewhat deeply grooved. Proboscis covered with black spots, more densely crowded on the dorsal surface and at the base. Trunk short, thick, ovoid and rounded posteriorly, 20 mm long, 10 mm wide; greyish brown in colour with innumerable black specks. Papillae relatively small and sparse, slightly larger and more crowded anteriorly and posteriorly. Ventral setae 29 in number, very small and irregularly scattered over a small area posterior to the mouth; elongate, gently bent, 0·5 to 1·5 mm in length and pale yellow in colour. Setae embedded in two pads that lie on each side of the nerve cord; several branching muscle-strands radiate from the pads to the body wall. Alimentary canal fixed by numerous delicate mesenteries. One nephridium (left)

Y

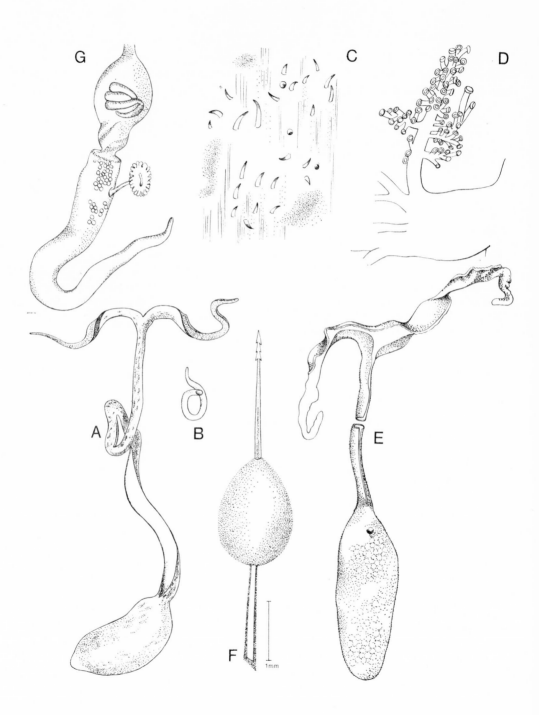

with a nephrostome placed basally. Anal vesicles relatively short; the main canal of each branches repeatedly and the final branches bear numerous ciliated funnels.

Male. Occurs in the body cavity of the female; unusually large, 28·5 mm in length, 2·0 mm in breadth. Cylindrical but pointed at both ends. Trunk uniformly covered with closely-set cilia. Ventral setae absent.

REMARKS. Described from one female and one male. Ikeda's description in 1904 is short but that in 1907 is much fuller. Sato's account in 1939 is only a summary of Ikeda's papers. Six specimens were described by Menon *et al.* (1964). These specimens possessed 16–20 setae. Menon *et al.*, also described the variations found in their material.

DISTRIBUTION. Japan (Ikeda, 1904); Gulf of Kutch (Menon *et al.*, 1964). Menon *et al.* report that this bonellid lives in coral.

Acanthobonellia pirotanensis José, 1964

(Fig. 60B)

Acanthobonellia pirotanensis José, 1964 : 53–68, 15 text-figs.
Acanthobonellia vulgaris Menon, Datta Gupta & Johnson, 1964 : 51–54, fig. 1(a–d), fig. 3(a–c);
    Datta Gupta & Menon, 1964 : 267–276, 4 text-figs.
Ikedella misakiensis: Gideon et alia, 1956 : 201–202.

TYPE LOCALITY. Pirotan Island, Gulf of Kutch.

DESCRIPTION. *Female.* Proboscis 80–200 mm long, fleshy, ribbon-like and deeply cleft anteriorly into two long arms; dark violet in colour. Trunk sausage-shaped, up to 134 mm long and ash-brown in colour. Skin wrinkled and lacking prominent papillae. Two to fourteen minute setae situated on a small circular pad of skin just anterior to the nephridiopore; the pad is on the right or left of the nerve cord according to the position of the nephridium. A single nephridium consisting of a muscular, tubular part (in which the male lives) and a membranous, sac-like distal part (in which the ova are stored); a ciliated, funnel-shaped nephrostome borne basally. The heart is a cylindrical, tubular structure which completely encircles the terminal portion of the presiphonal intestine for 10–15 mm. Anal vesicles paired and dendritic; excretory tubules elongate and with ciliated funnels terminally.

FIG. 43. (A–D) *Acanthobonellia miyajimai.* (A) Female, × about 2. (B) Male, × about 1·25. (C) Ventral setae. (D) Part of the anal vesicle showing primary, secondary and tertiary branches and ciliated funnels. (A–D after Ikeda.) (E–G) *Acanthobonellia rollandoe.* (E) Female, × about 2. (F) Barbed seta embedded in an ellipsoidal muscular pad. (G) Nephridium showing a male in the male sac, eggs and nephrostome. (E–G after Menon *et al.*) *av*, anal vesicle; *cl*, cloaca; *cr*, crop; *dv*, dorsal vessel; *ec*, egg canal; (*g*) gonad; *gi*, gizzard; *im*, interbasal muscle; *in*, intestine; *mp*, male pore; *ms*, mesentery; *mt*, male tube; *n*, nephridium; *nc*, nerve cord; *np*, nephridiopore; *nr*, nerve ring; *ns*, nephrostome; *nv*, neuro-intestinal vessel; *o*, oesophagus; *p*, proboscis; *ph*, pharynx; *pi*, posterior intestine; *rv*, ring vessel; *s*, siphon; *un*, unpaired nephridium; *vs*, ventral setae; *vv*, ventral vessel.

Male. Exceptionally long (50–60 mm) and found coiled up in the androecium of the female. Without vascular and nephridial systems and setae.

REMARKS. The type material of this species was first identified by Gideon *et al.* (1956) as *Ikedella misakiensis* but further study showed that it was a new species. José's description includes a well illustrated account of the histology of the animal. *A. vulgaris* Menon *et al.* was also described from Pirotan Is., Gulf of Kutch. Although we have not examined specimens of either *A. pirotanensis* or *A. vulgaris* it seems to us that they are synonymous. The *Ann. Mag. nat. Hist.* 7 (73)—the part for Jan. 1964 which contains the description of *A. vulgaris*—was published according to the information on the cover of the journal on Oct. 29, 1964. The *J. of Morph.* **115** (1)—the part for July 1964 which contains the description of *A. pirotanensis*—was received in the Zoological Library of the British Museum (Natural History) on Oct. 5, 1964 and must have been published before this date. Consequently the specific name contained in the latter journal has priority.

DISTRIBUTION. Pirotan Is., Gulf of Kutch (José, 1964); Andamans (Menon *et al.*, 1964).

Acanthobonellia rollandoe Menon, Datta Gupta & Johnson, 1964

(Fig. 43E–G)

Acanthobonellia rollandoe Menon, Datta Gupta & Johnson, 1964 : 54–56, 6 figs.

TYPE LOCALITY. Beacon area of Pirotan Island, Gulf of Kutch. *Type.* Museum, Birla College, Pilani.

DESCRIPTION. *Female.* Living specimens grey-black in colour. Proboscis long and bifid. Trunk 35mm long and 12·5mm wide and uniformly covered with rounded papillae. Seta, single, arrow-like, about 4 mm long and with a barbed tip. Seta appears to pierce a single muscle pad. Anal vesicles tubular and branched, the smallest branches bearing a cluster of stumpy funnels.
Male. Large.

REMARKS. Described from a single specimen. The presence of a single seta with a barbed tip, embedded in an elliptically shaped muscle pad distinguishes this species from others of the genus.

DISTRIBUTION. Gulf of Kutch, N.W. India.

Genus *ACANTHOHAMINGIA* Ikeda, 1910

Acanthohamingia Ikeda, 1910 : 146–147; Monro, 1927 : 618; Fisher, 1946 : 260; 1947 : 355.

DESCRIPTION. *Female.* Proboscis not bifid but resembling that of *Thalassema.* Skin of trunk thin, with papillae poorly developed or absent. The nephridiopore opens into a longitudinal, genital groove which extends as far as the mouth. Embedded in the skin of the groove are numerous setae which lack muscular sheaths and radial muscles. A single nephridium with a nephrostome placed basally. Anal vesicles more than two in number and branching.

Male. Body slender and surface uniformly ciliated. Ventral setae absent. Nephridium long and wide with a single funnel that opens into the body cavity.

TYPE SPECIES. *Hamingai ijimia* Ikeda.

REMARKS. Fisher (1946) emended Ikeda's description to include his new species *A. paradola.* In 1947 he erected a new genus *Amalosoma* for *A. paradola* so that the generic description of *Acanthohamingia* reverts to the original form. The genus contains the two species *A. ijimai* and *A. shiplei* both described by Ikeda. Both species were found in deep water.

DISTRIBUTION. Japanese waters.

ACANTHOHAMINGIA—KEY TO SPECIES

1 Ventral setae eight in number, with apices curved and hooked; anal vesicles with
   four main stems on each side .   .   .   .   **A. shiplei**
- Ventral setae 29 in number, with apices not sharply pointed; anal vesicles with
   three main stems on each side   .   .   .   .   .   .   **A. ijimai**

Acanthohamingia ijimai (Ikeda, 1908)

(Fig. 44A–B)

Hamingia ijimai Ikeda, 1908b : 61–68, pl. 1, figs 1–8.
Acanthohamingia ijimai : Ikeda, 1910 : 146–147; Sato, 1939 : 365.

TYPE LOCALITY. Outside Okinose, Sigami Bay, Japan; at 920 m.

DESCRIPTIONS. *Female.* Proboscis with rounded tip. Skin of trunk thin, semitransparent, devoid of papillae and bright red-yellow in colour. Ventral setae less curved and longer than those of *A. shiplei* and grouped in the middle of the genital groove. A single nephridium with a stalked nephrostome placed basally. Anal vesicles have three or four main stems on each side which branch profusely.

Male. Found in the nephridium of the female. Length 4 mm and width 0·17 mm. Surface uniformly ciliated but setae lacking. Nephridium of male long and wide and ending in a single funnel.

REMARKS. Described from a single specimen and no other records are known. The specimen was found in deep water.

DISTRIBUTION. As for the type locality.

Acanthohamingia shiplei Ikeda, 1910

Acanthohamingia shiplei Ikeda, 1910 : 135–147, pl. 10, figs 1–6, 8–9.

TYPE LOCALITY. Sagami Bay, Japan; at 740 m.

DESCRIPTION. *Female.* Proboscis about 85 mm long when fully extended, deeply and widely grooved on the ventral side and narrowing abruptly to a point. Towards the mouth the free margins come together to form a funnel-shaped passage

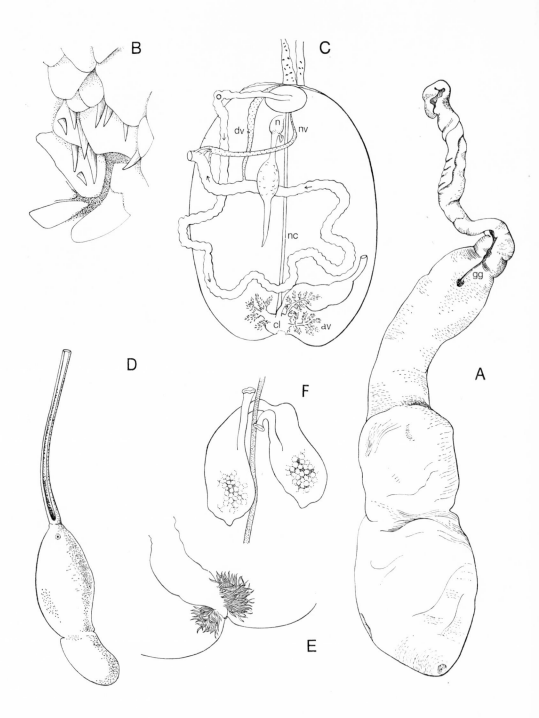

leading to the mouth. Trunk about 62 mm in length, rounded at both ends and pale yellow in colour. Skin of trunk is folded at the extremities; the rest of the trunk bears scattered papillae. Eight small ventral setae situated in the genital groove but not embedded in a muscular cushion. A single nephridium (right) with a stalked nephrostome that opens basally. Each anal vesicle consists of four profusely branched stems.

Male. Three specimens 3·8–4·2 mm long were found in the glandular part of the female nephridium. The surface is profusely ciliated and lacks setae. The internal anatomy is like that of *A. ijimai.*

REMARKS. Described in considerable detail from a single female and three males. Found at considerable depths.

DISTRIBUTION. As for the type locality.

Genus *ACHAETOBONELLIA* Fisher, 1953

Achaetobonellia Fisher, 1953 : 258.

DESCRIPTION. *Female.* Proboscis bifid. Ventral setae absent. One nephridium with a nephrostome placed sub-basally; a thick walled, bulbous expansion of the neck of the nephridium between the nephrostome and body wall serves as an *androecium.* The segment of the gut between the mouth and the point of attachment of the neurointestinal blood vessel is very long. Siphon rudimentary. The anal vesicles are numerous, aborescent structures attached to the walls of the cloaca.

Male. Trunk not ciliated and lacking ventral setae.

TYPE SPECIES. *Achaetobonellia maculata* Fisher.

REMARKS. The genus contains the single species *A. maculata* Fisher.

DISTRIBUTION. Gilbert Islands.

Achaetobonellia maculata Fisher, 1953

(Fig. 44C)

Achaetobonellia maculata Fisher, 1953 : 258–259, 1 fig.

TYPE LOCALITY. Deep central lagoon, Onota, Gilbert Islands. *Type.* U.S.N.M. no. 24618.

DESCRIPTION. *Female.* Bifid proboscis about 95 mm in length and 0·6 mm in breadth when flattened; each terminal branch is about 20 mm in length. The posterior folds of the proboscis do not fuse to form a tube. The trunk is about 45 mm

FIG. 44. (A–B) *Acanthohamingia ijimai.* (A) Ventral view of female. (B) Setae in the genital groove. (A–B after Ikeda.) (C) *Acanthobonellia maculata.* Dissected female (after Fisher). (D–F) *Alomasoma nordpacificum.* (D) Ventral view of the female. (E) Bush-like anal vesicles. (F) Nephridia, showing basally placed nephrostomes set on a long stalk. (D–F after Zenkevitch.) KEY: *See* Fig. 43, p. 363.

long, ellipsoidal in shape and covered with numerous dark spots. Ventral setae absent. The body wall is thin and generally smooth except posteriorly and anteriorly where it may be wrinkled. One nephridium (left) about 25 mm long is present; a nephrostome is situated sub-basally on a short stalk. Between the nephrostome and the body wall is a thick walled chamber which serves as an androecium. Alimentary canal very long—about 400 mm—with an especially long first segment—about 150 mm. Pharynx sub-spherical and thin-walled and oesophagus short; no clear division exists between the gizzard and stomach. Cloaca enlarged and thin walled. Anal vesicles appear as numerous arborescent structures rather than as elongated sacs.

Male. Found embedded in the androecium of the female. Ventral setae absent.

REMARKS. Known only from holotype. Fisher also discussed the relations between this genus and its nearest relative, *Nellobia*.

DISTRIBUTION. As for the type locality.

Genus *ALOMASOMA* Zenkevitch, 1958

Alomasoma Zenkevitch, 1958 : 198.

DESCRIPTION. *Female.* The genus is closely related to *Amalosoma* Fisher, but differs in having a well-developed and furrowed proboscis with an undivided tip. Two nephridia each with a basal nephrostome and a large nephridiopore are present. Anal vesicles broom-like, with a great number of separate branches. Ventral setae may or may not be present.

Male. Not known.

TYPE SPECIES. *A. chaetiferum* Zenkevitch.

REMARKS. The genus includes three species, *A. belyaevi*, *A. chaetiferum* and *A. nordpacificum*. Zenkevitch (1966 : 177–178) also reported additional specimens which he assigned to this genus.

DISTRIBUTION. The Bering Sea, the Sea of Okhotsk and the north-western Pacific. All the specimens have been found at great depths.

ALOMASOMA—KEY TO SPECIES

1 Ventral setae present	*A. chaetiferum*
– Ventral setae absent	2
2 Nephrostome set on a long stalk	*A. nordpacificum*
– Nephrostome not set on a long stalk	*A. belyaevi*

Alomasoma belyaevi Zenkevitch, 1964

Alomasoma belyaevi Zenkevitch, 1964b : 1863, figs 1(a–b); 1966 : 77.

TYPE LOCALITY. Vitjaz station 4173 (44°53·8′N, 128°32·1′W); at 2826–2843 m.

DESCRIPTION. *Female.* Proboscis up to 11 mm long, short, thin with a small lobe at its anterior extremity. Trunk 49–75 mm long, brown in colour and opaque. Setae absent. Two large nephridia open into a common duct with a single pore; nephrostomes short and basal in position. The anal trees are bushy on account of the presence of very many long tubules.

Male. Not known.

REMARKS. Described from seven specimens. The proboscis stem, however, was complete in only one.

DISTRIBUTION. North-west Pacific Ocean (Zenkevitch, 1964b); Gulf of Panama (Zenkevitch, 1966).

Alomasoma chaetiferum Zenkevitch, 1958

Alomasoma chaetiferum Zenkevitch, 1958 : 200–201, figs 8, 10 (chart).

TYPE LOCALITY. Vitjaz station 3357, Aleutian Trench, depth 7268 m.

DESCRIPTION. *Female.* Proboscis about 38 mm long and trunk about 40–44 mm long. Morphologically very similar to *A. nordpacificum*, but differs in possessing two ventral setae. Two nephridia; each with a nephrostome set on a short stalk situated at the basal end of the organ.

Male. Unknown.

REMARKS. Described from two specimens.

DISTRIBUTION. As for the type locality.

Alomasoma nordpacificum Zenkevitch, 1958

(Fig. 44D–F)

Alomasoma nordpacifica Zenkevitch, 1958 : 198–199, fig. 6, fig. 7 (chart).

TYPE LOCALITY. Sea of Okhotsk at 520–7820 m.

DESCRIPTION. *Female.* Proboscis 6–82 mm long and sometimes longer than the trunk. Ventral setae lacking. Nephridia small; nephrostome basal and set on a long stalk. Anal vesicles broom-like.

Male. Unknown.

REMARKS. Based on numerous specimens.

DISTRIBUTION. Nine 'Vitjaz' stations in the Sea of Okhotsk, Behring Sea and the north-west Pacific.

Alomasoma spp.

Zenkevitch (1966 : 177–178) recorded some specimens collected by the Galathea Expedition which he considered probably belong to this genus.

Alomasoma sp. 1 from San Tomé (Cameroons). Zenkevitch 1966 : 177, fig. 2.
Alomasoma sp. 2 from the Java Trench. Zenkevitch, 1966 : 178.
Alomasoma sp. 3 from the Java Trench. Zenkevitch, 1966 : 178.

Genus *AMALOSOMA* Fisher, 1948

Amalosoma Fisher, 1948a : 856.

DESCRIPTION. *Female.* Proboscis unknown. Two nephridia with small nephrostomes situated basally. Although a specialized genital slit is present anterior to the nephridiopores no setae or spinelets are present. Anal vesicles more or less rudimentary.

Male. Found in the genital groove of the female. Ventral setae present.

TYPE SPECIES. *Acanthohamingia paradola* Fisher, 1946.

REMARKS. Fisher (1946) described a bonellid from Japan as *Acanthohamingia paradola.* In order to do this he had to emend the original description of *Acanthohamingia*, a genus in which setae are present in the genital groove. In a revised scheme of classification Fisher (1948) erected a new genus *Amalosoma* to contain the Japanese specimens. The genus now contains two species, *A. paradolum* and *A. eddystonense.*

DISTRIBUTION. Kagoshima Gulf, Japan; Plymouth Sound, England.

AMALOSOMA—KEY TO SPECIES

Body pear-shaped and body-wall thin. Nerve cord very slender, about 0·13 mm in diameter. Anal vesicles arise as individual stems from the cloaca; branches few and short, ending in vase-shaped funnels which are widest at the base **A. paradolum**

Body cylindrical and body-wall thick. Nerve cord of normal thickness, about 0·5 mm in diameter. Anal vesicles arise as a few individual stems from the cloaca; branches numerous ending in conical-shaped funnels which are widest at the mouth

A. eddystonense

Amalosoma eddystonense Stephen, 1956

Amalosoma eddystonense Stephen, 1956 : 605–608.

TYPE LOCALITY. Rame Head grounds, Plymouth, England. *Type.* Brit. Mus. (Nat. Hist.).

DESCRIPTION. *Female.* Proboscis not present but probably lost. Trunk up to 144 mm in length. Body wall generally thick except for a few thin-walled patches and thickly covered with papillae except on the thin portions. Ventral setae absent. The pharynx is enlarged, the gut long and the arrangement of the neuro-intestinal blood system similar to that of *A. paradolum*. The nerve cord is of normal thickness. Two nephridia, each with a small nephrostome placed basally. Anal vesicles arise as a single stem from the cloaca, but are fewer, larger and more branched than in *A. paradolum*. Each branch ends in a conical funnel, widest at the mouth.

Male. Small, less than 2 mm in length and attached to the external genital groove of the female by two curved genital setae.

REMARKS. Described from several damaged specimens. Hunt (1925 : 31) in a short note on the echiurians of the Plymouth area mentioned this animal as *Hamingia papillosa* nom. nud. He did not describe it. Although he studied the species further he neither completed his work nor published any results. The name *eddystonense* was one of his suggestions.

DISTRIBUTION. As for the type locality.

Amalosoma paradolum (Fisher, 1946)

(Fig. 45A–B)

Acanthohamingia paradola Fisher, 1946 : 260–262, pls 31, 32.
Amalosoma paradola : Fisher, 1948a : 856.

TYPE LOCALITY. Albatross stn. 4912. Kagoshima Gulf, Japan; at 218 m. *Type.* U.S. Nat. Mus., no. 20601.

DESCRIPTION. *Female.* Proboscis not known. Body-wall very thin and translucent. Behind the mouth is a narrow genital groove containing the males; the openings of the nephridia lie at the posterior end of this groove. Ventral setae absent. Two thin-walled nephridia, each with a small nephrostome placed on a short stalk at the base of the nephridium. The pharynx is much inflated, thin-walled and connected by numerous frenula to the body wall. Nerve cord extremely slender and 0·13 mm in diameter. Anal vesicles in the form of numerous slender tubes with lateral branches arising independently from the wall of the cloaca. The tubes are fixed with strong but transparent frenula; the funnels are vase-shaped and widest at the foot.

Male. Lanceolate and planarian-like, 1–2 mm long. Setae present. The tube of the sperm receptacle opens medially at the anterior end.

REMARKS. The description is based on two specimens taken at the same station.

DISTRIBUTION. As for the type locality.

Genus *ARCHIBONELLIA* Fischer, 1919

Archibonellia Fischer, 1919a : 283; Fisher, 1948a : 856.
Austrobonellia Fisher, 1948a : 855.

DESCRIPTION. *Female.* Proboscis bifid. Trunk with two ventral setae. Three nephridia present, two being lateral and paired and one median and unpaired.

Male. Not known.

TYPE SPECIES. *Archibonellia michaelseni* Fischer.

REMARKS. Fischer (1919) described a single bonellid from Western Australia as *Archibonellia michaelseni* and in 1921 another single specimen from Western Australia as *Archibonellia mjoebergi.* Both are unusual in that they are described as possessing three nephridia, two being lateral and paired and one median and unpaired. The anatomy of the two species, however, is not well known and needs further investigation. It is possible that the median structure of both, and especially that of *A. mjoebergi* is a male tube like that found in *Pseudobonellia biuterina* Johnston

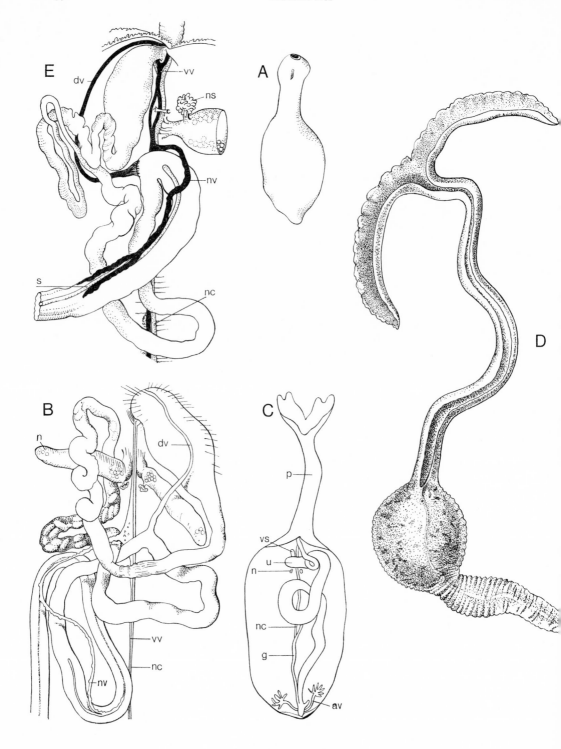

& Tiegs, also reported from Western Australia (Edmonds, 1960). Closer study of the two species is required before they can be classified satisfactorily.

Fisher (1948a) with some justification placed the two species in different genera. Because, however, the species are not fully described and in order to keep the classification of the phylum as simple as possible we are regarding the two species as falling into the same genus.

DISTRIBUTION. Western Australia.

ARCHIBONELLIA—KEY TO SPECIES

A large median nephridium lying between two smaller nephridia   .   **A. michaelseni**
A small median nephridium lying between two larger nephridia .   .   **A. mjoebergi**

Archibonellia michaelseni Fischer, 1919

(Fig. 45C)

Archibonellia michaelseni Fischer, 1919a : 283–285, 2 figs; 1926b : 207, 2 figs.

TYPE LOCALITY. West coast of Rottnest Island near Freemantle, Western Australia.

DESCRIPTION. *Female.* Proboscis not deeply cleft at the tip, but with two broad bifurcating lappets, a little over 12 mm in length. Trunk 12 mm long; in life grey in colour. Two ventral setae present with a replacement pair alongside; interbasal muscle present. Anal vesicles arise as single stems on either side of the cloaca and branch at the tip. Alimentary canal is relatively short and bears a globular, rectal caecum. Two lateral nephridia present and a larger unpaired median nephridium; position of the nephrostomes is not known.

REMARKS. Described from a single specimen. No other records or descriptions.

DISTRIBUTION. As for the type locality.

Archibonellia mjoebergi Fischer, 1921

Archibonellia mjöbergi Fischer, 1921b : 6–8, figs 3–6.
Austrabonellia mjöbergi : Fisher, 1948a : 856.

TYPE LOCALITY. Broome, Western Australia.

DESCRIPTION. *Female.* Proboscis is a short stalk, 18 mm in length and deeply cleft at the tip; arms 50 mm and 10 mm long. Body oval, 45 mm in length, a light grey in colour. Body wall transparent so that the internal organs are visible and

FIG. 45. (A–B) *Alomasoma paradolum.* (A) Ventral view of paratype, × about half. (B) Dissection of anterior part of female. (A–B after Fisher.) (C) *Archibonellia michaelseni.* Dissected specimen (after Fischer). (D–E) *Bonellia viridis.* (D) Ventral view of entire animal; the posterior half of the trunk is contracted. The ventral nerve cord lies close to the body wall and is showing through the skin (after Lacaze-Duthiers). (E) Dissection of the anterior part of a specimen from Naples (after Fisher). KEY: *See* Fig. 43, p. 363.

covered with rounded papillae that are largest and most crowded at the anterior and posterior ends. Two ventral setae which are curved at the tip. Two lateral nephridia and one small median nephridium opening into a prominent nephridiopore; nephrostomes of lateral nephridia are distal and of the median structure basal.

Male. Unknown.

REMARKS. Described from a single specimen.

DISTRIBUTION. As for the type locality.

Genus *BONELLIA* Rolando, 1821

Bonellia Rolando, 1821 : 539; Diesing, 1851 : 74; 1859 : 770; Lacaz-Duthiers, 1858 : 106; Quatrefages, 1865b : 596; Rietsch, 1886 : 509; Shipley, 1889b : 340; Monro, 1927 : 617; Fisher, 1946 : 249; 1949 : 491.

DESCRIPTION. *Female.* Proboscis bifid with arms that may be long and slender. Trunk usually green in colour and bearing irregularly scattered papillae. Ventral setae present. A single nephridium with a nephrostome placed basally. Anal vesicles sac- or tube-like which may bear ciliate funnels or tubules directly or which may branch once or twice before giving rise to funnels.

Male. Very small. Body ciliated and lacking setae in all but one species.

TYPE SPECIES. *Bonellia viridis* Rolando.

REMARKS. The status of some of the species assigned to this genus must be considered as uncertain. *B. pacifica* Zenkevitch and *B. suhmii* Selenka were described from specimens the proboscis of which was either lacking or present only as a stump. It is possible that both species should be assigned to other genera, especially as the setae of the former have tooth-like extremities and no setae at all were found in the latter. As the nephrostomes of both species are basal in position and the anal vesicles are simple structures that bear ciliated funnels we are leaving both in this genus. *B. achaeta* Zenkevitch, which lacks setae and had a distally placed nephrostome, we consider resembles *Ikedella* more closely than it does *Bonellia*. *B. pumicea* Sluiter and *B. thomensis* Fischer were described from single specimens and the only record of the latter is the type description.

B. viridis Rolando and *B. minor* Marion are closely related species and difficult to distinguish. *B. fuliginosa* Rolando for the reasons stated on page 378 we consider is synonymous with *B. viridis*.

We have assigned *B. gigas* Nielsen to a new genus *Metabonellia* because (1) the nephrostome is placed near the distal and not the basal extremity of the nephridium, (2) unlike *Bonellia* it lacks a siphon and (3) its anal vesicles are more complex than those of *Bonellia* in that about 13 branching tubes open into each anal vesicle. We have placed *B. haswelli* Johnston & Tiegs in the same genus because it closely resembles *B. gigas* in the position of its nephrostome and the structure of its anal vesicles.

According to the present scheme of classification the genus *Bonellia* therefore contains six species, *B. minor*, *B. pacifica*, *B. pumicea*, *B. suhmii*, *B. thomemsis* and *B. viridis*.

BONELLIA—PART KEY TO THE SPECIES

We have not been able to construct a satisfactory key to the six species that we have listed in this genus. *B. suhmii* was described from a damaged specimen lacking both a proboscis and setae. We have not included it in the key.

1	Setae, long hair-like with toothed extremities	*B. pacifica* (p. 376)
–	Setae not long and hair-like and lacking toothed extremities	2
2	Anal vesicles shaped like a ball	*B. thomensis* (p. 377)
–	Anal vesicles not ball-shaped	3
3	Anal vesicles branch only once	*B. minor* (p. 375)
–	Anal vesicles branch two or three times	4
4	Papillae white in colour and aggregated at the anterior and posterior end of the trunk	*B. pumicea* (p. 376)
–	Papillae dark in colour and scattered over the whole surface of the body .	*B. viridis* (p. 377)

Bonellia minor Marion, 1886

Bonellia minor Marion, vide Rietsch, 1886 : 198–313, 6 pls; Catta, 1875 : 313–319, 7 figs; Shipley, 1899b : 340; Augener, 1906 : 192–193; Ikeda, 1904 : 72–73, figs 23, 101, 102; Johnston & Tiegs, 1920 : 73; Cuénot, 1922 : 24; Baltzer, 1931 : 162; Menon, Datta Gupta & Johnson, 1964 : 56, 1 fig.
Bonellia fuliginosa: Ikeda, 1924 : 42–43, figs 18–19; Sato, 1939 : 362–363.
? *Bonellia fuliginosa:* Michel, 1930 : 1–47.

TYPE LOCALITY. Gulf of Marseilles (France).

DESCRIPTION. *Female.* Much like *B. viridis* but smaller. Total length 15–30 mm. Trunk dark green and bearing papillae. Ventral setae and interbasal muscle present. One nephridium with a basally placed nephrostome. Vascular system like that of *B. viridis* except that the neurointestinal vessel scarcely bifurcates. Anal vesicles branch only once. Eggs reddish. Larva has a ventral sucker.

Male. Surface ciliated except dorsally, where it is transversely marked or ringed. Ventral setae with recurved points.

REMARKS. This species is difficult to separate from *B. viridis* Rolando (see 'Remarks' under *B. viridis* on p. 378).

The length of the trunk of the Japanese specimens of Ikeda (1904) is up to 20 mm and that of the proboscis 40–50 mm. The males lack cilia on the dorsal surface and bear two strongly curved hooks.

The Australian record is a doubtful one.

DISTRIBUTION. Mediterranean (Marion); West Indies (Augener, 1906); Japan (Ikeda, 1904 and 1924); ? Australia (Johnston & Tiegs, 1920); Loyalty Is. (Shipley, 1899); Andaman Is. (Menon *et al.*, 1964).

Bonellia pacifica Zenkevitch, 1958

Bonellia pacifica Zenkevitch, 1958 : 201, figs 10 (chart), 11 (a–d).

TYPE LOCALITY. North part Kurile-Kamchatka Basin, at 3800–4130 m.

DESCRIPTION. *Female.* Large animals with a trunk 50–80 mm long. Only the basal part or stump of the proboscis remained on the specimens. Ventral setae long and hair-like, up to 16 mm in length with tooth-like ends; denticles situated on one plane on two opposite sides of each seta. Anal glands long and thin covered with many small funnels. Nephrostome basal.
Male. Unknown.

REMARKS. Known from 24 specimens. Collected from very deep waters. The exact position of this species cannot be decided until more information is known about its proboscis.

DISTRIBUTION. As for the type locality.

Bonellia pumicea Sluiter, 1891

Bonellia pumicea Sluiter, 1891 : 111–113, pl. 1, figs 1–4; 1902 : 50; Shipley, 1899a : 340; 1903 : 175.

TYPE LOCALITY. Krakatoa, Sunda Strait. Sumatra.

DESCRIPTION. *Female.* Proboscis 5–10 mm in length and white in colour. Body shaped like a ball, 5 mm in length and light green in colour with a reddish shimmer. Papillae, which appear as white spots, are found on the body and are denser at the anterior and posterior ends. A single nephridium with a nephrostome placed basally. Anal vesicles tube-like, branching two or three times before ending in funnels.
Male. Found in the oesophagus of the female. Posterior portion of the body drawn out into a narrow tail. Ventral setae present. Opening of the vas deferens is posterior to the setae on the ventral surface.

REMARKS. Described from a single specimen.

DISTRIBUTION. Krakatoa, Sumatra (Sluiter); Galle, Ceylon (Shipley, 1903); Loyalty Is. (Shipley, 1899).

Bonellia suhmii Selenka, 1885

Bonellia suhmii Selenka, 1885 : 9–10, pl. 1–2, figs 4–6; Shipley, 1899a : 341; Sluiter, 1912 : 25–26, pl. 1, figs 16–20; Wesenberg-Lund, 1934 : 12–15, figs 5–6.

TYPE LOCALITY. Off Nova Scotia. Challenger station 47. *Type.* Brit. Mus. (Nat. Hist.) 1885.12.3.5.

DESCRIPTION. *Female.* Proboscis unknown. Body club-shaped about 8 mm in length; posterior region damaged. Wart-like papillae thickly set on the anterior and posterior body surface; mid region of body smooth. A single nephridium with a basally placed nephrostome. Anal vesicles are two simple tubes covered with short stalked funnels. No setae present.

Male. Not found.

REMARKS. Described from a single damaged specimen, which lacked a proboscis and setae. The specimen is so damaged that one is not able to ascertain whether or not setae had been present before it was collected. The specimen, however, possesses a large nephridial pocket into which the nephridium (now detached) appears to have opened.

Wesenberg-Lund (1934) found five more specimens in a collection of the Zoological Museum at Copenhagen. The specimens were in a poor condition and she was able to add little to the original description. The trunk was 31–55 mm long and in no specimen was the proboscis complete.

DISTRIBUTION. Off Nova Scotia (Selenka, 1885); Denmark Strait, Greenland and south of Iceland (Wesenberg-Lund, 1934); North Atlantic (Sluiter, 1912). A deep water species ranging from 1540 to 2450 m.

Bonellia thomensis Fischer, 1922

Bonellia thomensis Fischer, 1922b : 15, text-figs 4–5.

TYPE LOCALITY. St Thomas, West Indies.

DESCRIPTION. *Female.* Proboscis short, stumpy and not deeply bifurcated. Body wall thin and transparent. The anterior portion and posterior half of the body are covered with prominent papillae, which are very closely packed posteriorly. The middle portion of the body bears no papillae but under the microscope shows fine transverse striations. Ventral setae present. Nephridiopore prominent on the right side above the ventral setae. One nephridium, with a stalked nephrostome placed basally and opening without a prominent funnel. The anal vesicles are ball-shaped and from them arise branches covered with funnels.

Male. Not described.

REMARKS. Described from a single specimen. No further specimens have been recorded.

DISTRIBUTION. As for the type locality.

Bonellia viridis Rolando, 1821
(Fig. 45D–E)

Bonellia viridis Rolando, 1821 : 539–556, 8 figs; Schmarda, 1852 : 117–126, 4 pls; Lacaze-Duthiers, 1858 : 49–110, 4 pls; Koren & Danielssen, 1875 : 138; Greeff, 1879 : 154, pls 6–9; Kowalevsky, 1870 : 1–8, 1 pl.; Vejdovsky, 1878 : 487–500, pl. 30; Selenka, 1885 : 9, pl. 2, figs 7–10; Levinsen, 1884 : 263; Haswell, 1886 : 331–332; Marcialis, 1892 : 246; Norman, 1894 : 150; Shipley, 1899b : 335–336, 341–342; 1902c : 127–128; Sluiter, 1900 : 17; 1902 : 50; Théel, 1906 : 23, 2 figs; Southern, 1913b : 39; Baltzer, 1914 : 162; Fischer, 1914b : 20; 1925 : 4; 1922c : 16; Bledowski, 1910a : 1–64, 3 pls, 26 figs; Augener, 1903 : 347; Cuénot, 1922 : 24; Hérubel, 1925 : 260; Wesenberg-Lund, 1939b : 29; 1939c : 11; 1957b : 11; Lindroth, 1941 : 43–44, fig. 1; Fisher, 1946 : 250, fig. 15; Mackie, 1961 : 249–251, fig. 2.

z

Bonellia fuliginosa Rolando, 1821 : 539–556, 8 figs; Greeff, 1879 : 157; Fischer, 1895 : 21;
Shipley, 1899b : 341.

TYPE LOCALITY.   Asimara Is., Sardinia.

DESCRIPTION.   *Female.*   Proboscis capable of great extension and may be as
long as 1000 mm; bifid at the tip.   Trunk more or less ovoidal in shape, green to dark
green in colour and with dark coloured papillae scattered over its whole surface.
Two ventral setae.   A single nephridium with a nephrostome placed basally.   Anal
vesicles tubular to sac-like in shape with branches that end in ciliated funnels.

Fisher's figure of a dissected specimen from Naples (Fisher, 1946, fig. 15) shows
(1) that the female possesses an interbasal muscle, (2) that the dorsal blood vessel
does not directly join the neurointestinal vessel, (3) that the neurointestinal vessel
bifurcates and that the branches run along the intestine on either side of the siphon
for some distance and (4) that the gonads lie in close relation with the posterior
part of the ventral blood vessel.

Male.   Very small.   Surface of body ciliated and without setae.

REMARKS.   Rolando's description shows that he at first confused the oral and
anal apertures of the animal.   What we now call the proboscis and the anal vesicles
he thought were a tail and a pair of salivary glands.   Lacaze-Duthiers (1858)
redescribed the species.   A considerable amount of information about its internal
anatomy can be learnt from a study of the diagrams of Théel (1906, fig. 15) and
Fisher (1946, fig. 15).   The species has been the subject of a number of anatomical,
physiological and embryological studies.

Because there seems to be no satisfactory character that will distinguish them we
are regarding *B. viridis* Rolando and *B. fuliginosa* Rolando as synonymous.   Rolando
summarized the characters of *B. viridis* as 'corps très lisse, queue longue, applatie,
divisée en deux cordons avec le bord interieur plus foncé, membraneux, ondulé
et festonné' and of *B. fuliginosa* as 'corps fusiforme parsemé de très petits tubercules,
queue ronde ainsi que les deux cordons qui sont terminés par un globule charnu'.
Lacaze-Duthiers (1858), however, says that the body of *B. viridis* is papillated.
No other description of *B. fuliginosa* from specimens collected in the Mediterranean
has been given.   Greeff (1879 : 157) thought that *B. viridis* and *B. fuliginosa* were
the same species.   The rather small bonellids from Japan which Ikeda (1924)
admitted looked like *B. minor* but which he identified as *B. fuliginosa* we have
placed in the synonymy of B. *minor*.

The type specimen of *B. minor* as described by Rietsch (1886) came from Marseilles.
B. minor is smaller than *B. viridis* and resembles it closely.   Rietsch says 'La forme
extérieure si singulière de la grande Bonellie est bien connue surtout depuis la
description et les figures de Lacaze-Duthiers.   La *Bonelia minor* lui resemble
entièrement.'   Rietsch (1886 : 510) sets out the differences between the two species
thus:

B. viridis.   Total length about 150 mm.   Anal vesicles branch twice.   Neurointestinal vessel bifurcates.   Nephridium placed usually to the right side of the nerve
cord.   Eggs yellow.   Larva without a ventral sucker.   Male entirely ciliated,
without setae and without annulations.

B. minor. Total length about 15–30 mm. Anal vesicles branch only once. Neurointestinal vessel bifurcates only slightly. Nephridium usually on the left side of the nerve cord. Eggs red. Larva with a ventral sucker. Male with recurved setae and ciliated except on the dorsal surface which is annulated.

DESCRIPTION. Mediterranean Sea (Rolando, 1821; Schmarda, 1852; Lacaze-Duthiers, 1858; Marcialis, 1892; Fischer, 1914b); Norwegian coast (Koren & Danielssen, 1875; Norman, 1894; Théel, 1906; Lindroth, 1941); Irish coast (Southern, 1913b); Azores (Sluiter, 1900; Mackie, 1961); France (Cuénot, 1922); Red Sea (Wesenberg-Lund, 1957b).

Genus *BONELLIOPSIS* Fisher, 1946

Bonelliopsis Fisher, 1946 : 252; 1948a : 856.

DESCRIPTION. *Female.* Proboscis long and bifid. Trunk with ventral setae. One nephridium (either right or left) with a conspicuous, trumpet-shaped nephrostome at the distal end; lips of nephrostome much plicated. Presiphonal gut very short. Primary branches of anal vesicles vary in number; primary and secondary branches bear ciliated bell-shaped funnels with a prominent rim.

TYPE SPECIES. *Bonelliopsis alaskana* Fisher.

REMARKS. The genus contains a single species from Alaska.

Bonelliopsis alaskana Fisher, 1946

(Fig. 46A–D)

Bonelliopsis alaskana Fisher, 1946 : 252–254, fig. 16, pls. 26, 27.

TYPE LOCALITY. Dutch Harbor, Alaska. *Type.* U.S.N.M. no. 20603.

DESCRIPTION. *Female.* Proboscis moderately long and slender, bifid at the tip and equal to or shorter than the length of the body. Body sub-cylindrical, 20–65 mm in length and blunt at both ends. Body wall thin and translucent. Ventral setae small, nearly straight and set close together. Short, broad interbasal muscle. One nephridium, either right or left, present; nephrostome distal, with much plicated lips. Anal vesicles elongate sacs, with a varying number of primary branches, which again branch; the primary and secondary branches bear ciliated bell-shaped funnels with conspicuous rims.

Male. Body not ciliated. Ventral setae absent. Sperm receptacle posterior to the middle of the body, the sperm duct opening at or near the anterior end of the body.

REMARKS. Described from several specimens collected from under rocks. No other records known.

DISTRIBUTION. Known only from the type locality.

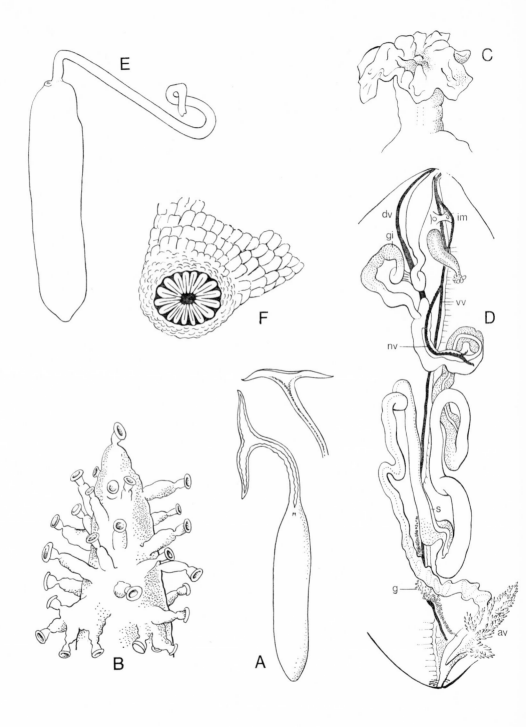

Genus *BRUUNELLIA* Zenkevitch, 1966

Bruunellia Zenkevitch, 1966 : 179.

DESCRIPTION. Proboscis in section is oval shaped and lacks a groove. Setae absent. Anal aperture surrounded by a rosette structure.

TYPE SPECIES. *Bruunellia bandae* Zenkevitch.

REMARKS. There is only one species in this genus. No information about the nephridia, the anal vesicles or the male is known.

Bruunellia bandae Zenkevitch, 1966

(Fig. 46E–F)

Bruunellia bandae Zenkevitch, 1966 : 179, fig. 4(a–e).

TYPE LOCALITY. Galathea Exped.: station 495 (Banda Trench); at 7250 m.

DESCRIPTION. *Female.* Proboscis, 13–18 mm long, oval in section throughout its whole length and lacking a groove. Mouth at base of proboscis. No setae present. Skin thick and non-transparent and entirely covered with papillae. Anal rosette, surrounds the anal aperture. No description of the nephridia, anal vesicles or vascular system was possible.

Male. Unknown.

DISTRIBUTION. Known only from the type locality. Described from **six** specimens.

Genus *CHOANOSTOMELLIA* Zenkevitch, 1964

Choanostomellia Zenkevitch, 1964b : 1864 nom. nov. pro *Choanostoma* Zenkevitch, 1964a : 178. (non *Choanostoma* Wang, 1931, nec Yamaguti, 1934).

DESCRIPTION. *Female.* Bonellids closely resembling *Prometor* Fisher but possessing a wide and deep funnel-like collar that surrounds the proximal part of the proboscis and pharynx. The collar on the ventral side is deeply incised anteriorly and posteriorly. No ventral setae. Single nephridium with a basally placed nephrostome.

Male. Not known.

TYPE SPECIES. *Choanostomellia bruuni* Zenkevitch.

FIG. 46. (A–D) *Bonelliopsis alaskana.* (A) Ventral view of female, life size. The second proboscis indicates about its maximum length in a preserved specimen. (B) Tip of one of the primary branches of an anal vesicle showing two secondary branches with their ciliated funnels. (C) Nephrstome. (D) Dissected female, × about 3. (A–D after Fisher.) (E–F) *Bruunellia bandae.* (E) General view of female. (F) Anal rosette. (E–F after Zenkevitch.) KEY: *See* Fig. 43, p. 363.

REMARKS. Zenkevitch (1964b : 1864) pointed out that the name *Choanostoma* was preoccupied. Actually it is preoccupied by Wang, 1931 (*Contributions Biol. Lab. Sc. Soc.* China, **6** : 105—Protozoa) and by Yamaguti, 1934 (*Jap. J. Zool.* **5** : 314 —Trematoda). Although Zenkevitch described his specimen as *Choanostoma filatovae*, in the title under fig. 2 he named it *Choanostomellia filatovae*. This seems to show that Zenkevitch had an alternative name in mind for the genus. We are using *Choanostomellia* in place of *Choanostoma*. The genus resembles the genus *Prometor* Fisher in having a funnel-shaped dilatation of the proboscis leading to the pharynx, but differs in that this structure occupies the ventral side only and is without incisions in *Prometor*. The genus contains only two species.

DISTRIBUTION. Known from the Arabian Sea (3676 m), from off Japan (1695 m) and from off Madagascar (4930 m).

CHOANOSTOMELLIA—KEY TO SPECIES

Collar at the base of the proboscis forming a deep pocket laterally and dorsally   *C. bruuni*
Collar at the base of the proboscis forming only a shallow groove laterally and dorsally
                                                                                    C. filatovae

Choanostomellia bruuni (Zenkevitch, 1964)

(Fig. 47A–B)

Choanostoma bruuni Zenkevitch, 1964a : 178–179, pl. 1, 4 figs, text-fig. 3; 1964b : 1864; 1966 : 178.
Choanostomellia bruuni Zenkevitch, 1964b (name *Choanostoma* changed to *Choanostomellia* in title under fig. 1).

TYPE LOCALITY. Northern Arabian Sea (18°34·8′N, 52°52·2′E), at 3676 m. (Vitjaz Expedition, Stn. 4814.)

DESCRIPTION. *Female.* Proboscis 41 mm long; tip probably missing. A narrow and deep furrow runs along the ventral surface of the proboscis. Length of trunk 103 mm and width 19 mm. No ventral setae. A single nephridium which is round and simple; nephrostome situated basally close to the nephridiopore. Anal glands long and do not branch.
Male. Not known.

REMARKS. Described from a single specimen.

DISTRIBUTION. Arabian Sea (Zenkevitch, 1964a). Off Durban at depth of 4360 m and off Madagascar at 4930 m (Zenkevitch, 1966).

Choanostomellia filatovae (Zenkevitch, 1964)

Choanostoma filatovae Zenkevitch, 1964b : 1863–1864, fig. 2(a–e). (*Choanostoma* emended to *Choanostomellia* in title under fig. 2.)

TYPE LOCALITY. Off Japan (39°45′N, 143°22′E) at 1693 m (Vitjaz Stn. 3223).

DESCRIPTION. *Female.* Proboscis 56 mm long; anterior end invaginated and bearing short papillae. The collar surrounding the basal part of the proboscis is deeply incised ventrally and dorsally. Nephridiopore borne on a papilla about 2 mm high on the ventral surface of the trunk. Skin strong and covered with papillae. Ventral setae absent. A single large nephridium with a nephrostome placed basally.

REMARKS. Described from a single specimen and a proboscis.

DISTRIBUTION. As for the type locality. A proboscis was collected at Vitjaz Stn. 3753 (20°24′N, 122°30′E) at 3120 m.

Choanostomellia sp.

Choanostomellia sp. Zenkevitch, 1966 : 178, fig. 3(a–b). From off Gabon, West Africa.

Genus *EUBONELLIA* Fisher, 1946

Eubonellia Fisher, 1946 : 255–256; 1948a : 856.

DESCRIPTION. *Female.* Proboscis well developed and bifurcate. No ventral setae. Foregut has an unusually large crop. Mesenteries in the form of strands and not sheets. Single nephridium present on the right side with a large nephrostome placed distally; rim of nephrostome is plicate. Anal vesicles tube-like with numerous branches.

Mble. Body wall thick and sperm receptacle large.

TYPE SPECIES. *Eubonellia valida* Fisher.

REMARKS. The genus contains only one species. *Eubonellia* is close to both *Bonelliopsis* Fisher, 1946 and *Ikedella* Monro, 1927. It differs from *Bonelliopsis* in that it lacks setae. Both *Eubonellia* and *Ikedella* lack setae. Fisher (1946 : 255) separated the two largely on account of the position of the nephrostome which is terminal in *Eubonellia* and lateral near the terminal extremity in *Ikedella*.

DISTRIBUTION. As for the type species.

Eubonellia valida Fisher, 1946
(Fig. 47C–D)

Eubonellia valida Fisher, 1946 : 255–257, pl. 28; Zenkevitch, 1958 : 200–201, fig. 10.

TYPE LOCALITY. Sea of Okhotsk, off east coast Sakhalin Island (at 133 m). *Type.* U.S.N.M. no. 20604.

DESCRIPTION. *Female.* Proboscis unusually broad and flat, but bifid terminally; 30 mm in length, 7–9 mm in breadth. Body cylindrical to ovoidal in shape, about 55 mm long and about 20 mm wide. Body wall tough and muscular, 1·5–2·5 mm in thickness and thrown into annular folds. From the mouth a short narrow groove extends to the constricted base of the proboscis. Ventral setae absent. A conspicuous nephridiopore lies about 8 mm behind the mouth. A single nephridium (right) bearing distally a large nephrostome with voluminous lips. Anal vesicles

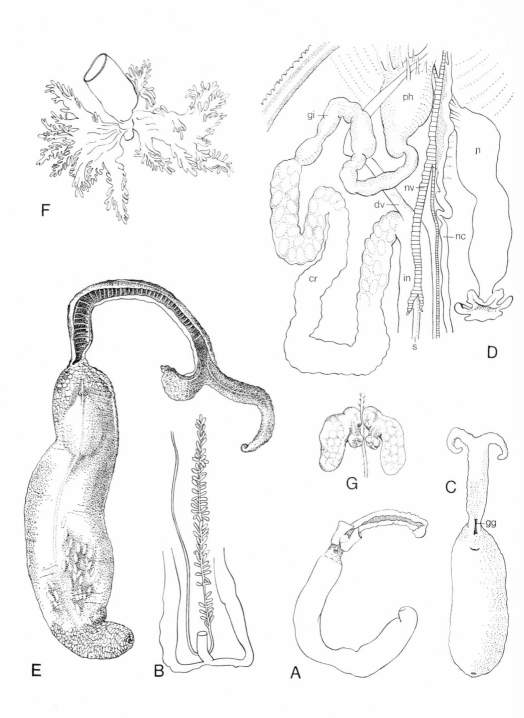

F

D

gi

ph

n

nv

dv

nc

cr

in

s

G

C

gg

E

B

A

two, long and dendritic, with a voluminous axial bladder which bears a few proximal branches. The vesicles are attached to a very large cloacal bulb, the mucosa of which is thrown into longitudinal ridges.

Male. Found in the pharynx. About 1·2 mm long; body wall thick. No ventral setae. Nephridium large and almost as long as the body.

REMARKS. Described from a single specimen.

DISTRIBUTION. Sea of Okhotsk, off the east coast of Sakhalin Island, Albatross Station 5021 (48°32′30″N, 145°08′45″E), at 135 m (Fisher, 1946); Sea of Okhotsk (Zenkevitch, 1958).

Genus *HAMINGIA* Danielssen & Koren, 1881

Hamingia Danielssen & Koren, 1881 : 20; Monro, 1927 : 618; Fisher, 1948a : 855.

DESCRIPTION. *Female*. Proboscis bifid or deeply cleft. Ventral setae absent. One or two nephridia present with a basally placed nephrostome. Anal vesicles are two thick clusters of tubules which open into a common duct.

Male. Ventral setae present.

TYPE SPECIES. *Hamingia arctica* Danielssen & Koren.

REMARKS. This genus contains only one species.

DISTRIBUTION. Arctic seas. Once recorded from the Antarctic.

Hamingia arctica Danielssen & Koren, 1881

(Fig. 47E–G)

Hamingia arctica Danielssen & Koren, 1881a : 44–62, pls 1 and 2; 1881b : 20–23; Levinsen, 1884 : 263; Lankester, 1883 : 37; Shipley, 1899b : 344; Skorikow, 1901 : 158–160; Théel, 1906 : 23; Sluiter, 1912 : 25, fig. 21; Fischer, 1922d : 244; 1928b : 479; Wesenberg-Lund, 1934 : 7, figs 1–4; 1937a : 20–22, figs 6–7; 1937b : 13; Stephen, 1941b : 249, pl. 8, fig. 1; MacGinitie, 1956 : 127–128; Brahm & Mohr, 1962 : 123.
Hamingia glacialis Horst, 1881 : 448–456.

TYPE LOCALITY. Station 290 (72°27′N, 20°51′E), Norwegian North Atlantic Expedition (1876–1878).

DESCRIPTION. *Female*. Proboscis deeply forked at the tip and one and a half times as long as the body. Body up to 120 mm in length, light to dark grassy green in colour. Ventral setae absent. One or two nephridia, each opening on a

---

FIG. 47. (A–B) *Choanostomellia bruuni*. (A) Ventral view of female. (B) Anal vesicle. (A–B after Zenkevitch.) (C–D) *Eubonellia valida*. (C) Ventral view of female. (D) Dissection of anterior region, × about 3. The crop is unusually long. (C–D after Fisher.) (E–G) *Hamingia arctica*. (E) Ventral view of female. (F) Anal vesicles. (G) Nephridia showing basal nephrostome and eggs. (E–G after Wesenberg-Lund.) KEY: *See* Fig. 43, p. 363.

well-marked papilla; nephrostome placed basally. Anal vesicles are brown tubes branching two or three times before ending in funnels.

Male. Surface ciliated. Ventral setae present.

REMARKS. The original description is brief. Wesenberg-Lund (1934, 1937a), however, has given additional information about the species.

DISTRIBUTION. Found at numerous localities in the Arctic; once recorded from the Antarctic.

Arctic: Pt. Barrow, Alaska (MacGinitie, 1956); East Greenland (Wesenberg-Lund, 1937a, 1937b); Iceland (Levinsen, 1883); Barents Sea (Horst, 1881); Murman coast (Skorikow, 1901); Norwegian coast (Danielssen & Koren, 1881; Lankester, 1883; Théel, 1906; Sluiter, 1912). Antarctic: South Shetlands (Stephen, 1941b).

Genus *IKEDELLA* Monro, 1927

Ikedella Monro, 1927 : 618; Sato, 1939 : 364; Fisher, 1948a : 856.
Pseudobonellia Onoda, 1934 : 413–422.
Parabonellia Onoda, 1935 : 141–144.

DESCRIPTION. *Female.* Proboscis long and bifid anteriorly. Ventral setae absent. One nephridium present on the left side; nephrostome on a short stalk, situated near the distal end of the nephridium. Anal vesicles comparatively short and branch at least three times; 10 to 20 funnels are present on the tertiary branches and some are present on the secondary branches.

Male. Found in the anterior part of the nephridium. Length 3·3 mm. Surface of body ciliated. No ventral setae. Vas deferens about one third of the length of the body.

TYPE SPECIES. *Bonellia misakiensis* Ikeda.

REMARKS. The genus contains two and possibly three species; *I. misakiensis* from Japan, *I. bogorovi* from the Indian Ocean and *I. achaeta* from the Sea of Okhotsk. It is very doubtful whether the last-named species should be placed in this genus.

IKEDELLA—KEY TO SPECIES

1 Nephrostome placed centrally . . . . *I. bogorovi*
– Nephrostome placed distally 2
2 Most of the branches of the anal vesicles joined to the body wall by fine mesenteries
　　　　　　　　　　　　　　　　　　　　　　　　　　I. misakiensis
– Branches of anal vesicles not joined to the body wall by fine mesenteries *I. achaeta*

Ikedella achaeta (Zenkevitch, 1958)

Bonellia achaeta Zenkevitch, 1958 : 202, figs 10–11(e–k); 1966 : 179–180.

TYPE LOCALITY. 'Vitjaz' stn. 140, southern part of Sea of Okhotsk (47°26′N, 150°16′W); collected at great depths.

DESCRIPTION. *Female*. Morphologically very similar to *Bonellia pacifica* Zenkevitch but readily separable from it in the complete absence of ventral setae. The proboscis of all specimens was missing except one where the remaining stump was 8–12 mm long. Body about 44 mm long and 16 mm wide. One large nephridium with a nephrostome placed distally. Anal glands appear to be more like those of *Bonellia*.

Male. Unknown.

REMARKS. Known from two collections of specimens. Zenkveitch (1958) placed the specimens in the genus *Bonellia* but since they lack setae and possess a distally placed nephrostome they seem nearer to the genus *Ikedella*.

DISTRIBUTION. Found at two Vitjaz stations (Zenkevitch, 1958). Station 140, Sea of Okhotsk (47°26'N, 150°16'W at 3500m). Station 167, Kurile Kamchatka Trench (41°19'N, 155°26'W at 5540 m) and at Galathea Stations.

Ikedella bogorovi Zenkevitch, 1964

Ikedella bogorovi Zenkevitch, 1964 : 179–180, fig. 2(a–c).

TYPE LOCALITY. Vitjaz stations 4535 (9°58'S, 107°56'E) Java Trench; at 6820–6850 m.

DESCRIPTION. Proboscis up to 75 mm in length. Ventral setae absent. A single large nephridium present with centrally placed nephrostome. Anal vesicles branching.

REMARKS. Described from four specimens of which only one had a more or less complete proboscis. The stumps of the proboscises of the other three specimens measured from 15–20 mm.

DISTRIBUTION. As for the type locality.

Ikedella misakiensis (Ikeda, 1904)

(Fig. 48A–B)

Bonellia misakiensis Ikeda, 1904 : 74–76, figs 24, 103–105.
Ikedella misakiensis: Monro, 1927 : 618.
Pseudobonellia misakiensis: Onoda, 1934 : 413–422, pl. 20, figs 1–6, text-figs 1–3.
Parabonellia misakiensis: Onoda, 1935 : 141–144; 1939 : 364.
Ikedella misakiensis: Gideon *et al.*, 1956 : 201–202; Menon *et al.*, 1964 : 56.

TYPE LOCALITY. Jogoshima, Misaki, Japan.

DESCRIPTION. *Female*. Proboscis 50–90 mm in length, deeply bifurcated with arms 25–30 mm long, deeply furrowed in the median line. Light greyish-brown in colour; arms dirty yellow and densely marked with bluish-black spots. Body about 40 mm long and 60 mm when fully extended; covered with minute papillae. Ventral setae absent. Only one nephridium, the left, present and it is nearly as long as the body. Anteriorly it is narrowed and muscular and posteriorly thin-walled and swollen. Nephrostome at the distal end. Anal trees comparatively short, branching at least three times. Ten to twenty-five funnels attached to each

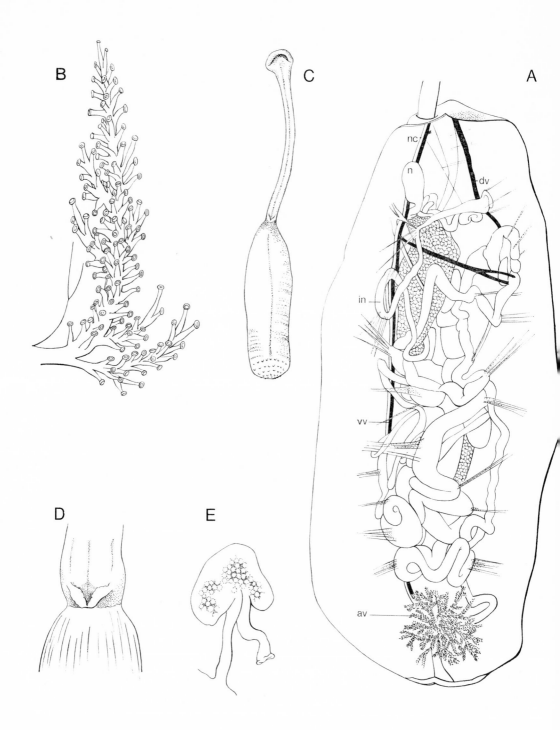

tertiary branch and others to the secondary branches. Most of the branches are joined to the body wall by fine mesenteries.

Male. Found in the anterior region of the nephridium. Length 3·3 mm, breadth 0·2 mm. Body narrows at both ends, and the surface is thickly ciliated. No ventral setae. An enlarged vas deferens, about one third of the body length, is present.

REMARKS. Ikeda in his first account, which was based on single male and female specimens, described the female as possessing numerous body spines. Later he concluded that they were not part of the animal but, possibly, parasites. Onoda (1934) described two more females and another male and placed those species in a new genus *Pseudobonellia*. Because the name *Pseudobonellia* was already preoccupied he changed his *Pseudobonellia* to *Parabonellia*. He appears to have been unaware of Monro's paper (Monro, 1927).

DISTRIBUTION. Japan (Ikeda, 1904; Onoda, 1934, 1935); Andaman Is. (Gideon *et al.*, 1956; Menon *et al.*, 1964).

Genus *JAKOBIA* Zenkevitch, 1958

Jakobia Zenkevitch, 1958 : 192–193.

DESCRIPTION. *Female.* Proboscis about as long as or longer than the trunk; the anterior end is flattened to form a 'head' which is about one and a half times as wide as the stem of the proboscises. In transverse section the stem is oval in shape. Three blood vessels, two lateral and one median, and two nerves, both lateral, run from the trunk into the proboscis. A sensory organ is situated in a small furrow which runs along the anterio-ventral border of the flattened 'head'. The mouth is surrounded on the sides and from behind by two well-developed lips. Ventral setae absent. A single nephridium consisting of two sharply bent sections lying close together and partly fused, so that it is difficult to decide whether the nephrostome is basal or distal.

Male. Not known.

TYPE SPECIES. *Jakobia birsteini* Zenkevitch.

REMARKS. The genus contains a single species, collected at great depths.

DISTRIBUTION. Kurile—Kamchatka Trench.

FIG. 48. (A–B) *Ikedella misakiensis.* (A) Dissected specimen. (B) One of the secondary branches of the anal vesicle, much magnified. (A–B after Ikeda.) (C–E) *Jakobia birsteini.* (C) Entire specimen, ventral view. (D) Posterior region of proboscis showing lips that surround the mouth. (E) Nephridium showing stalked nephrostome. (C–E after Zenkevitch.) KEY: *See* Fig. 43, p. 363.

Jakobia birsteini Zenkevitch, 1958

(Fig. 48C–E)

Jakobia birsteini Zenkevitch, 1958 : 193–194, figs 1, 2 (chart).

TYPE LOCALITY.   Kurile-Kamchatka Trench; at great depths, 6150–8100 m.

DESCRIPTION.   *Female.*   Proboscis 55–70 mm long and white in colour; consists of a flattened 'head' anteriorly and a solid stem which in transverse section is oval in shape.   A sensory structure is present on the anterio-ventral surface of the 'head'; stem supplied with three blood vessels and two nerves.   Trunk 50–70 mm long and slightly transparent.   No ventral setae.   A single nephridium bent so as to form a V with arms that lie close together.   Nephrostome small but position uncertain.

DISTRIBUTION.   Found at three stations in the Kurile-Kamchatka Trench and in the northern part of the Japanese Trench.   Found at great depths.

Genus *MAXMUELLERIA* Bock, 1942

Maxmuelleria Bock, 1942 : 22; Fisher, 1948a : 854.

DESCRIPTION.   *Female.*   Proboscis long, ribbon-like and truncate.   Two ventral setae connected by a strong interbasal muscle.   Two nephridia with nephrostomes situated basally; lips of nephrostomes not elongate or spirally coiled.   Anal vesicles sac-like and covered with a very large number of slender excretory tubules with apical funnels.

Male.   Not known.

TYPE SPECIES.   *Thalassema gigas* M. Müller.

REMARKS.   A careful study of the genus and particularly of *M. lankesteri* was made by Bock (1942).   Bock was led to place the genus in the Bonelliidae on account of the close similarity between the internal anatomy of *Maxmuelleria* and such genera as *Acanthohamingia*, *Hamingia*, *Ikedella*, *Protobonellia* and *Bonellia*, particularly the structure of (1) the nephridia or gonoducts (with their funnels and vestibular canals), (2) the anal vesicles with their numerous, long-stalked funnels and (3) the blood-vascular system.   Sexual dimorphism, however, has not yet been found in the genus.

The genus contains five species of which *M. gigas* and *M. lankesteri* are closely related and difficult to separate.   Bock (1942 : 23) thought that *Thalassema owstoni* Ikeda might also belong to the genus.

DISTRIBUTION.   Mediterranean Sea, northern Europe, southern Indian Ocean.

MAXMUELLERIA—KEY TO SPECIES

We have not been able to construct a satisfactory key to this genus from the existing descriptions of the species.   The nerve cord of *M. aulacoferum* rests in a deep furrow but that of the other species rests on a raised cushion.   The proboscis of *M. gigas* and *M. lankesteri* is said to be long and that of *M. faex* and *M. verrucosum* small.   The length of the proboscis, however, is not a satisfactory character to use for distinguishing between species because it is so variable.

M. gigas and *M. lankesteri* are very close species. The papillae of the former are said to be more densely packed on the anterior and posterior surfaces of the trunk while those of *M. lankesteri* are said to be uniformly distributed. This, also, is an unsatisfactory taxonomic character.

Maxmuelleria aulacoferum (Hérubel, 1924)

Thalassema gigas var. *aulacoferum* Hérubel, 1924 : 108, text-figs 1–2.
Maxmuelleria aulacoferum : Bock, 1942 : 23.

TYPE LOCALITY. Near Rabat, Morocco (30°37′30″N, 9°58′W).

DESCRIPTION. *Female.* This species differs from *M. gigas* because its colour is earthy grey and because the nerve cord is situated in a furrow. A further difference is in the arrangement of the muscles of the ventral setae near the nerve cord; they comprise three fine bands, well separated from each other.
Male. Unknown.

REMARKS. Described from two specimens. Boch (1942 : 24) suggested that Hérubel's specimens might be a new species.

DISTRIBUTION. Known only from the type locality.

Maxmuelleria faex (Selenka, 1885)

Thalassema faex Selenka, 1885 : 7, pl. 3, fig. 13; Shipley, 1899b : 347–348; Fischer, 1925 : 5;
    Stephen, 1941b : 247, pl. 7, fig. 2.
Maxmuelleria faex : Bock, 1942 : 23.

TYPE LOCALITY. Norwegian coast, Porcupine station 77, 1034 m. *Type.* British Museum (Nat. Hist.), no. 1885.12.3.3.

DESCRIPTION. *Female.* Proboscis short and of uniform width; anterior extremity not bifid. Body of contracted specimen 40 mm long and 15 mm wide. Skin nearly white and smooth with indistinct and scattered papillae. Ventral setae and two nephridia present. Anal vesicles of moderate size, bearing irregular branches.
Male. Unknown.

REMARKS. The branched nature of the anal vesicles is not typical for a member of this genus.

DISTRIBUTION. Norwegian coast (Selenka, 1885; Fischer, 1925); South Shetland Is. (Stephen, 1941b).

Maxmuelleria gigas (M. Müller, 1852)

Thalassema gigas M. Müller, 1852 : 14, pl. 3, figs 1–3; Greeff, 1879 : 149; Shipley, 1899b : 348;
    Vejdovsky, 1878 : 487; Cuénot, 1922 : 23.
Maxmuelleria gigas : Bock, 1942 : 26–27, pl. 1, fig. 1, pl. 3, fig. 1, pl. 4, fig. 3.

TYPE LOCALITY. Trieste (Mediterranean).

DESCRIPTION. *Female.* Proboscis long, ribbon-like and rounded at the tip; ash-grey in colour, becoming green at the base. Trunk long, up to about 450 mm, black-green in colour and conical in shape posteriorly. It bears numerous papillae,

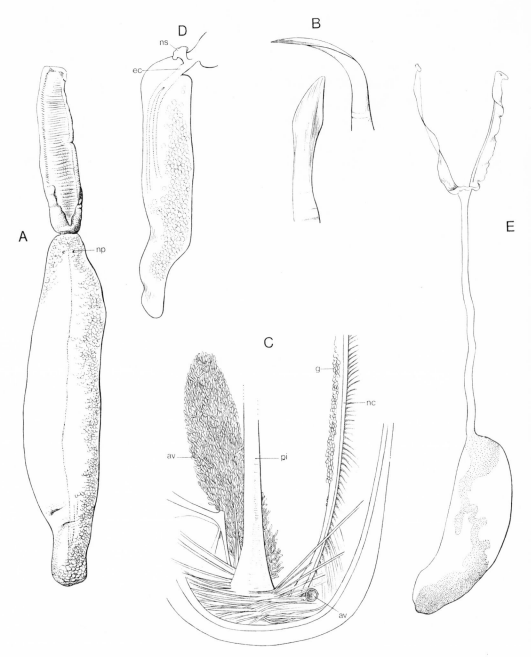

FIG. 49. (A–D) *Maxmuelleria lankesteri*. (A) Ventral view of female. (B) Two aspects of the ventral setae, × about 14. (c) Posterior part of the body. The ovary is rather small. (D) Nephridium showing nephrostome and egg canal (a proximal tube along the inside wall of the nephridum) and eggs. (A–D after Bock.) (E) *Metabonellia gigas*. Female (after Nielsen). KEY: *See* Fig. 43, p. 363.

packed most closely ventrally and dorsally. Nerve cord bound to a longitudinal cushion formed from the body wall. Two nephridia.

Male. Unknown.

REMARKS. This species was described from a single specimen and is not well known. Bock (1942) re-examined a specimen from the type locality: he claims that the eggs are smaller than those of *M. lankesteri*.

DISTRIBUTION. Mediterranean.

Maxmuelleria lankesteri (Herdman, 1898)

(Fig. 49A–D)

Thalassema lankesteri Herdman, 1898 : 381, 2 pls; Shipley, 1899b : 349; Southern, 1913b : 37–38; Stephen, 1934 : 164–165; Wesenberg-Lund, 1939c : 10–11; Lonnberg & Gustafson, 1939 : 1–4.

Maxmuelleria lankesteri: Bock, 1942 : 27–83, pl. 1, figs 2–4, pl. 2, figs 1–8, pl. 3, figs 2, 4, pl. 4, pl. 5, pl. 6, figs 2–3 and 5–10.

TYPE LOCALITY. Irish Sea.

DESCRIPTION. *Female.* Proboscis light green in colour and nearly as long as the body; anterior extremity bluntly rounded or drawn out laterally into two small ear-like horns. Trunk up to 120 mm long and 30 mm wide and apple-green in colour. Two ventral setae (and reserve setae) set in a pouch and connected by a strong interbasal muscle. Papillae more densely distributed at the ends of the trunk. Two nephridia with nephrostomes situated basally. Anal vesicles are thin walled sacs which project from the lateral sides of the rectum and which bear densely aggregated tubules. No rectal caecum.

Male. Not known.

REMARKS. Bock (1942) fully re-described and illustrated this species. His monograph is an important publication on the structure and classification of the phylum.

M. gigas and *M. lankesteri* are closely related species. Both Cuénot (1922) and Wesenberg-Lund (1939) considered that they might be one species. Herdman (1898) and Bock (1942) considered them different although the reasons for so regarding them are not clearly stated by either.

DISTRIBUTION. Irish Sea (Herdman, 1898); Firth of Clyde (Stephen, 1934); Kattegat & Skagerrack (Bock, 1942; Wesenberg-Lund, 1939c).

Maxmuelleria verrucosum (Studer, 1879)

Thalassema verrucosa Studer, 1879 : 124.

Thalassema verrucosum: Collin, 1901 : 306; Fischer, 1922c : 14–16, pl. 2, fig. 9 (a–f); 1920 : 418.

Maxmuelleria verrucosum: Bock, 1942 : 23.

TYPE LOCALITY. Kerguelen.

DESCRIPTION. *Female.* According to Studer's short description the proboscis is 5·5 mm long, spoon shaped and lacking a prominent ridge but possessing a deep channel that leads to the mouth. The trunk is reticulated and covered with

AA

numerous wart-like papillae.   There are two very small genital setae and the anal opening is set on a short papilla.

According to Fischer (1922) who examined another specimen the proboscis is 4–5 mm long and the trunk 20 mm.   The latter is ball shaped.   The whole animal is covered with large, rounded papillae; on the proboscis they are arranged regularly but on the body they are more closely packed anteriorly and posteriorly.   Ventral setae small, dark in colour but with yellow tips.   One pair of nephridia.   Anal vesicles held in place by a broad fastening membrane.

Male.   Unknown.

REMARKS.   Known from the holotype and a second specimen from Gazelle Harbour, Kerguelen (Fischer, 1922).

DISTRIBUTION.   Betsy Cove, Kerguelen (Studer, 1879); Gazelle Harbour, Kerguelen (Fischer, 1922).

METABONELLIA gen. nov.

DESCRIPTION.   *Female.*   Bonelliidae of medium to large size in which the proboscis is bifid and grooved on the ventral side.   Colour of proboscis and trunk pale to dark green.   Papillae on trunk appear to lie in transverse rows.   Two ventral setae.   One nephridium with a nephrostome at some distance from the distal end of the nephridium.   About 13–15 branching tubules opening into each of the anal vesicles.   Ovary in close relation with the posterior region of the ventral nerve cord.   An intestinal siphon may or may not be present.

Male.   Surface ciliate; ventral setae absent.

TYPE SPECIES.   *Bonellia gigas* Nielsen.

REMARKS.   The type species of the genus is closely related to the genus *Bonellia*. It differs, however, in three important respects, (1) the position of the nephrostome which in *Bonellia* is basal, (2) the absence of an intestinal siphon and (3) the structure of the anal vesicles.

The genus contains two closely related species, *M. gigas* and *M. haswelli* (Johnston and Tiegs).   The latter species is being placed in the genus because the position of its nephrostome is similar to that of *B. gigas* and its anal vesicles are of the same type.   The species, however, is described as possessing an intestinal siphon.

DISTRIBUTION.   Eastern and south-eastern Australia.

METABONELLIA—KEY TO THE SPECIES

Intestinal siphon present, ventral setae curved   .   .   .   .   .   **M. haswelli**
Intestinal siphon absent, ventral setae straight   .   .   .   .   .   **M. gigas**

Metabonellia gigas (Nielsen, 1963)
(Fig. 49E)

Bonellia gigas Nielsen, 1963 : 61–67, 3 figs, 1 pl.

TYPE LOCALITY.   Flinders, Western Port, Victoria, Australia.   *Type.*   Department of Zoology, University of Melbourne, Victoria.

DESCRIPTION. *Female.* Proboscis 300–350 mm long and bifid and the trunk 80–110 mm long and about 40 mm wide. Deep green in colour except the proboscis which is paler. Transverse rows of flattened papillae cover the trunk. Two ventral setae about 1·1 mm long and two substitute setae present. One nephridium on the left side with a nephrostome placed one third of the length of the nephridium from the distal end of the nephridium. Anal vesicles are thin-walled structures into which open about 13 tubes; the tubes branch three or four times into smaller tubes each of which branches into many ciliated funnels. Intestinal siphon absent. Ovary spread along the main ventral blood vessel.

Male. Large, about 19 mm long and deep green in colour. Found in the nephridium of the female. No setae present. There appears to be a sucker or clasper at the posterior extremity. Surface ciliated.

REMARKS. This species differs from *M. haswelli* because (1) it lacks an intestinal siphon, (2) the setae are straight and not curved and (3) the tubules of the anal vesicles are close together and divide into numerous ciliate funnels whereas in *M. haswelli* the tubules are widely separated and sparsely covered.

DISTRIBUTION. Western Port and Port Phillip, Victoria (Australia).

Metabonellia haswelli (Johnston & Tiegs, 1920)

Bonellia haswelli Johnston & Tiegs, 1920 : 72–73; Edmonds, 1960 : 95–96.
? *Bonellia viridis*: Whitelegge, 1889b : 163–323.

TYPE LOCALITY. Port Jackson, New South Wales. *Type.* Australian Museum, no. G.11220.

DESCRIPTION. *Female.* Proboscis about 100 mm, bifurcated at the tip, each branch measuring about 38 mm; a very distinct groove runs along its ventral surface. Body sac-like, coloured green in life and about 50 mm in length. The skin is marked by transverse ridges consisting of rows of papillae. Two ventral setae, 1·1 mm in length. One nephridium with a nephrostome situated about a quarter of the distance from the distal end. Two anal vesicles into which open about 15 tubes of varying length. These branch again, each ending in a circular disc fringed with a ring of cilia.

Male. Unknown.

REMARKS. Described from two immature specimens. No other records.

DISTRIBUTION. As for the type locality.

Genus *NELLOBIA* Fisher, 1946

Nellobia Fisher, 1946 : 257–258; 1948a : 855.

DESCRIPTION. *Female.* Bonelliidae without setae and possibly without a proboscis. One nephridium (left) with a basal nephrostome and a swollen basal region; no genital groove. Body wall thick. Two anal vesicles, each consisting

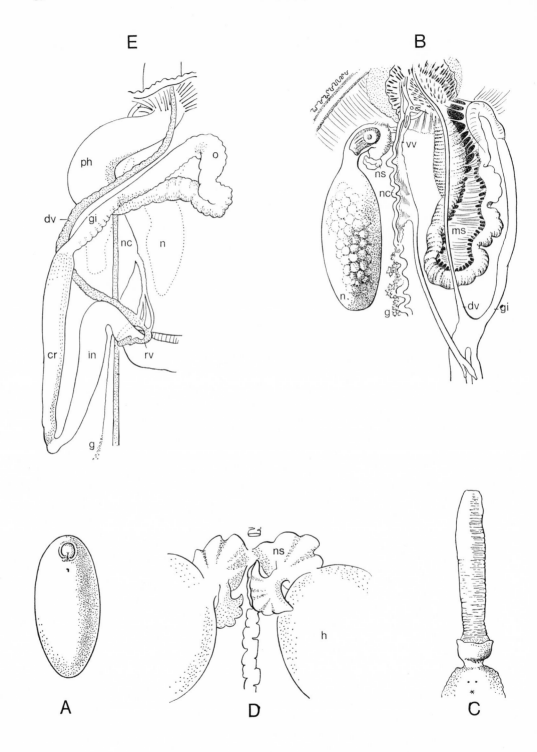

of numerous trees that arise on either side of a very muscular cloaca. Terminal region of hind-gut is very large.

TYPE SPECIES. *Nellobia eusoma* Fisher.

REMARKS. The genus contains the single species *N. eusoma*.

DISTRIBUTION. Sea of Okhotsk.

Nellobia eusoma Fisher, 1946
(Fig. 50A–B)

Nellobia eusoma Fisher, 1946 : 258–259, pl. 29, figs 1–3; pl. 30, figs 1–2.

TYPE LOCALITY. Sea of Okhotsk. Albatross stn. 5021 (48°32′30″N, 145°08′45″E); at 130 m. *Type.* U.S.N.M. no. 20605.

DESCRIPTION. *Female.* Proboscis reduced to a short truncate snout, possibly the remnants of a larger organ. Trunk, *Bonellia*-like, 44 mm in length, 15–17 mm broad in the middle. Skin thrown into irregular transverse folds. Body wall, about 2 mm thick. A conspicuous nephridiopore lies close to the median line and about 4 mm behind the mouth. Ventral setae absent. A single nephridium (left); nephrostome has simple lip and passes into the thick-walled proximal region. The pharynx is attached by numerous radiating strands. The cloaca is bulbous and attached by numerous muscle-strands to the body wall. The structure of the anal vesicles is unusual; instead of being tree-like, the main vesicles are crescent-shaped pouches, one on each side of the cloacal cavity. The opposite or free border, is produced into unequal dendritic divisions. The larger of these have a few main branches like a tree which are in turn crowded with branchlets carrying many of the glandular bulbous elements, each ending in a ciliated funnel. Vascular system like that of a bonellid.

Male. Unknown.

REMARKS. Known only from the holotype.

DISTRIBUTION. As for the type locality.

Genus *PROMETOR* Fisher, 1948

Prometor Fisher, 1948a : 857.
Tatjanella Zenkevitch, 1957 : 291; 1964a : 182.

DESCRIPTION. *Female.* Proboscis long ribbon-like not bifid but truncate, the borders fusing at the base to form a funnel or cup that leads to the mouth. Two

---

FIG. 50. (A–B) *Nellobia eusoma.* (A) Ventral view of type specimen, about natural size. (B) Dissection of anterior region. The nephridium, filled with eggs on the left, has a window cut in the wall to show the constricted duct from the egg chamber. (A–B after Fisher.) (C–E) *Prometor benthophila.* (C) Anterior end of body and proboscis with its basal cup. (D) Base of nephridia to show nephrostomes. (E) Foregut, portion of intestine and blood vessels. Nephridia shown by dotted outline. Curves of nerve cord not indicated and setae omitted. (C–E after Fisher.) KEY: *See* Fig. 43, p. 363.

well-developed ventral setae but no external bursa into which they can be retracted. One pair of nephridia with a specialized basal portion into which the large compressed, fan-shaped and bilabiate nephrostome opens; a single common nephridiopore. Anal vesicles unbranched sacs with a great number of glandular excretory tubules which have apical ciliated funnels. Dorsal and neuro-intestinal blood-vessels directly connected.

Male. Unknown.

TYPE SPECIES. *Prometor benthophila* Fisher.

REMARKS. Zenkevitch (1957 : 291) erected the genus *Tatjanella* to contain two deep water species of echiurans from the north Pacific Ocean. Later Zenkevitch (1964a) redescribed his species under the genus *Prometor* Fisher, 1948. All the species of *Prometor* have been collected from deep water.

The genus is also related to the genus *Maxmuelleria*, which, however, does not possess a cup-like structure at the base of the proboscis. There are two nephridiopores in *Maxmuelleria* and there is an external pocket into which the distal end of the two setae can be retracted (Bock, 1942, pl. 2, fig. 1).

The genus contains four species, *P. benthophila*, *P. gracilis*, *P. grandis* and *P. pocula*.

DISTRIBUTION. California coasts and the north-western Pacific Ocean.

PROMETOR—KEY TO SPECIES

1	Six setae, set on a pad	*P. gracilis* (p. 399)
–	Two or three setae, not set on a pad	2
2	Setae jointed, three in number	*P. grandis* (p. 399)
–	Setae not jointed, two in number	3
3	Tips of setae spatulate; nephridia oval sacs	*P. pocula* (p. 400)
–	Tips of setae tapering; nephridia elongate . . .	*P. benthophila* (p. 398)

Prometor benthophila Fisher, 1948

(Fig. 50C–E)

Prometor benthophila Fisher, 1948a : 957–960, figs 1–5; 1949 : 492–494, pls 33, 34.

TYPE LOCALITY. Off San Diego, California. Albatross station number 4387 (Lat. 32°32′N, long. 118°04′20″W); at 1955 m. *Type.* U.S.N.M. 21076.

DESCRIPTION. *Female.* Proboscis rather fleshy, about 55 mm in length, the base forming a cup about 7 mm long that leads to the mouth. Body somewhat slender, pear-shaped and about 110 mm in length. Anterior third of the body wall opaque, tough, finely wrinkled between very numerous flat, closely-packed granular elevations. The remainder of the body thin-walled, translucent, smooth and without glands. The common opening of the nephridia lies about 5 mm behind the base of the proboscis. Two slender ventral setae with a short interbasal muscle. Two large nephridia with a large nephrostome opening into a differentiated basal portion. The two anal vesicles are elongated sacs on each side of the cloaca; their free surface is closely covered with fusiform brown excretory tubules about 0·5 mm in length, connected to the body wall by numerous frenula. The gizzard is short and the stomach is about four times its length; the latter bends sharply where it joins the short segment of the presiphonal intestine. There is a direct connection between the neurointestinal and dorsal vessels at the beginning of the siphon. The ovary lies along the top of the ventral blood vessel.

Male. Unknown.

REMARKS. The species was described from two incomplete specimens. Fisher (1949) redescribed the material in greater detail, especially the alimentary canal (see 'Remarks' under *P. pocula*).

DISTRIBUTION. Off San Diego, California.

Prometor grandis (Zenkevitch, 1957)

Tatjanella grandis Zenkevitch, 1957 : 292–294, figs 1–4.
Prometor grandis Zenkevitch, 1964a : 181–182, fig. 3 (chart).

TYPE LOCALITY. Sea of Okhotsk, 'Vitjaz' station 23; at 2970–3400 m.

DESCRIPTION. *Female.* Proboscis very soft in texture, very long (up to 345 mm) and with a terminal lobe of 74 mm. A long funnel arises at the base of the proboscis and runs along the ventral side, enclosing about two thirds of the circumference. At the junction of the proboscis and the trunk the tissues are greatly thickened. Trunk, 82 mm in length and thin-walled. Ventral setae three in number and jointed, the terminal portion being of variable length. Two large nephridia of equal length; nephrostome large. Anal vesicles long, thin and covered with small funnels.

Male. Unknown.

REMARKS. Known from one well-preserved specimen, one distorted specimen and a fragment of a proboscis.

DISTRIBUTION. Sea of Okhotsk, at two 'Vitjaz' stations.

Prometor gracilis (Zenkevitch, 1957)

Tatjanella gracilis Zenkevitch, 1957 : 294–295, fig. 5.
Prometor gracilis Zenkevitch, 1964a : 182.

TYPE LOCALITY. Kamchatka Sound, 'Vitjaz' station 956; at 4820 m.

DESCRIPTION. *Female.* This species is closely related to *P. grandis* (Zenkevitch), but there are conspicuous differences in size and in the proportions between different parts of the body. The terminal lobe of the proboscis is elongated, its length being twice as long as its width. The proboscis is more than five times as long as the body (three times in *P. grandis*). Six setae, set on two pads and, unlike *P. grandis*, they are not jointed. Anal vesicles long and thin.

Male. Unknown.

REMARKS. Sixty-four specimens were dredged in Kamchatka Sound at 'Vitjaz' station 956. Of these only four were not distorted.

DISTRIBUTION.   Kamchatka Sound, Behring Sea and Aleutian Basin on silt or silt with pebbles (Vitjaz stations: 618, 956, 3359, 4820).

Prometor pocula Hartman & Barnard, 1960

Prometor poculum Hartman & Barnard, 1960 : 277–278, pl. 2, figs 1–4.

TYPE LOCALITY.   Long Basin stn. 6351, San Clemente Island (32°51′N, 119°01′12″W); at 1670 m.

DESCRIPTION.   *Female.*   Proboscis as long as the body, slender at the base and spreading distally into a broad triangular lobe; the cup-shaped base is pierced centrally by the oral opening.   Body shaped like a cucumber, about 95 mm long without the proboscis.   Surface of the anterior half of the body glandular and papillated, the posterior half abruptly smoother and thinner.   The anal pore on the postero-ventral side is surrounded by a ring of glandular columnar ridges. Two normal ventral setae with a third spine present on the right side; the setae have a crooked extremity which broadens distally and becomes spatulate.   A large median pore lies immediately behind the setal bases.   Two nephridia which can be seen through the body wall as oval sacs containing small spherical ova. Anal vesicles bear numerous fairly large ciliated cups.

Male.   Unknown.

REMARKS.   *P. pocula* differs from *P. benthophila* in having an oval and not a pear-shaped body.   The setae are distally spatulate and not tapering.   The paired nephridia are short and oval.   Anal pore surrounded by columnar gland cells. Known from a single specimen.

DISTRIBUTION.   As for the type locality.

Genus *PROTOBONELLIA* Ikeda, 1908

Protobonellia Ikeda, 1908a : 259–265; Monro, 1927 : 617; Fisher, 1947 : 854.

DESCRIPTION.   *Female.*   Proboscis long and tubular but not bifid distally. Two ventral setae.   One nephridium with a stalked and fimbriated nephrostome situated basally.   Anal vesicles elongate and dendritic.

Male.   Not described.

TYPE SPECIES.   *Protobonellia mitsukurii* Ikeda.

REMARKS.   The genus contains the single species *P. mitsukurii*.

DISTRIBUTION.   Japanese waters.

Protobonellia mitsukurii Ikeda

(Fig. 51A)

Protobonellia mitsukurii Ikeda, 1908a : 259–265, figs 1–4; Sato, 1939 : 363; Monro, 1927 : 617.

TYPE LOCALITY.   Sagami Bay, Japan; 554 m.

DESCRIPTION. *Female*. Proboscis very slender in comparison with the body, about 15 mm in length, colourless and covered with fine wrinkles; extremity some- what truncate. A deep groove runs along the ventral side giving it a tubular appearance; the tube closes abruptly towards the mouth forming an oval funnel. Body ovoid in form and about 9 mm in length. The papillae are closely set anteriorly and posteriorly and more minute and scattered elsewhere. The two ventral setae are carried on a papilla-like elevation about 1 mm behind the mouth and are connected internally by a very complex system of muscles. The nephridiopore is situated about 1 mm behind the mouth on the left side. The alimentary canal is attached to the body wall by numerous fine muscle-strands. One nephridium (left); nephrostome placed basally, carried on a long stalk and opening into a frilled funnel. Anal vesicles are two relatively short slender tubes about 5 mm in length that bear numerous long-stalked funnels.

Male. Unknown.

REMARKS. Known only from the holotype.

DISTRIBUTION. Known from the type locality.

Genus *PSEUDOBONELLIA* Johnston & Tiegs, 1919

Pseudobonellia Johnston & Tiegs, 1919 : 213; Monro, 1927 : 618; Fisher, 1947 : 856.

DESCRIPTION. *Female*. Proboscis bifid. Proboscis and trunk dark green in colour. Two ventral setae together with reserve setae. Two nephridia which have small nephrostomes situated laterally near the distal end. Male carried in a small blind tube which opens to the exterior between the two nephridiopores. Anal vesicles in the form of tubes that open independently into the cloaca.

Male. Small and without ventral setae; lives in a blind tube that projects into the coelom and opens on the ventral wall between the two nephridiopores.

TYPE SPECIES. *Pseudobonellia biuterina* Johnston & Tiegs.

Pseudobonellia biuterina Johnston & Tiegs, 1919

(Fig. 51B–E)

Bonellia sp. Hedley, 1906 : 462.
Pseudobonellia biuterina Johnston & Tiegs, 1919 : 213–230, pls 9–11; Monro, 1931 : 33; Fisher, 1946 : 249; Edmonds, 1960 : 96–97, pl. 2c, fig. 5.

TYPE LOCALITY. Great Barrier Reef, Australia.

DESCRIPTION. *Female*. Proboscis about 100 mm in the living state, 10–30 mm when preserved; tip bifurcated to a depth of 4–20 mm according to the state of contraction. Deeply grooved towards the mouth. Body sac-like, dark green in colour and in the preserved state 15–26 mm long and 4–8 mm wide; covered with flat-topped papillae, closely set but separated by well-marked narrow furrows.

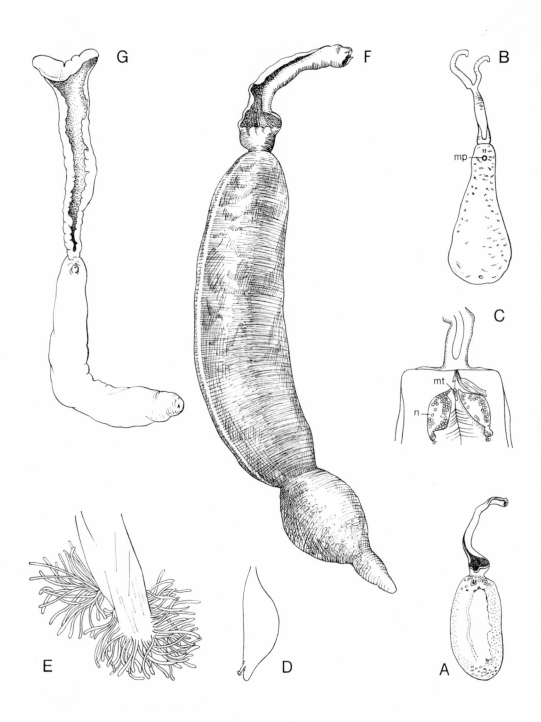

Body wall thin. Two prominent ventral setae but some specimens have one or two reserve or replacement setae as well; a well-developed interbasal muscle present. The buccal cavity leads into a muscular pharynx which becomes continuous with the long coiled intestine. Two nephridia with nephrostomes borne on a relatively thick stalk towards the posterior or distal end; the lip of the nephrostome is prominent and crenated. Anal vesicles consist of two small tuft-like masses, one on each side of the posterior end of the intestine; each is made up of a mass of delicate simple tubes opening directly into the rectum. Near its end each tubule becomes narrowed before opening into the coelom by a slightly dilated funnel fringed with long cilia.

Male. About 0·6 mm in length and 0·12–0·16 mm in breadth. Ventral setae absent. The male lies in a special blind tube projecting into the coelom and opening on the ventral wall between the two nephridiopores.

REMARKS. Described originally from several specimens.

DISTRIBUTION. Capricorn Group, Great Barrier Reef (Hedley, 1906; Johnston & Tiegs, 1919); Great Barrier Reef (Monro, 1931); Queensland and Western Australia (Edmonds, 1960).

Genus *SLUITERINA* Monro, 1927

Hamingia (part) Sluiter, 1902 : 44.
Sluiterina Monro, 1927 : 618.

DESCRIPTION. *Female.* Anterior region of proboscis is not bifid. Lateral edges of proboscis come close together to give it a tubular appearance; edges fuse near the mouth to form a cup. No ventral setae. A single nephridium with a basally placed nephrostome. Anal vesicles not described.

Male. Not known.

TYPE SPECIES. *Hamingia sibogae* Sluiter; Fisher, 1948a : 855.

REMARKS. The genus contains a single species.

DISTRIBUTION. Indonesia.

Sluiterina sibogae (Sluiter, 1902)

(Fig. 51F)

Hamingia sibogae Sluiter, 1902 : 44–46, pl. 4, fig. 12 and 1 text-fig.
Sluiterina sibogae : Monro, 1927 : 618.

TYPE LOCALITY. Indonesia. Siboga Stn. 223 (44°7′S, 126°7′30″E); at 4391 m.

FIG. 51. (A) *Protobonellia mitsukuria*. Female (after Ikeda). (B–E) *Pseudobonellia biuterina*. (B) Female. (C) Anterior region to show the male tube. (D) Nephridium showing the position of the nephrostome. (E) Anal vesicles—tuftlike. (B–E after Johnston & Tiegs.) (F) *Sluiterina sibogae*. Female; the anterior region of the proboscis of the specimen is damaged (after Sluiter). (G) *Torbenwolffia galathea*. Entire specimen, × about 1·5 (after Zenkevitch). KEY: See Fig. 43, p. 363.

DESCRIPTION. *Female.* Proboscis 70 mm in length, *Thalassema*-like; the lateral edges are close together giving it a tubular appearance and join near the mouth to form a cup. A narrow constriction cuts the cup off sharply from the body. Trunk 160 mm in length, shovel-shaped and much wrinkled transversely; anterior region bears numerous, small, scattered papillae and the posterior region is sharply pointed. No ventral setae. A single nephridium with a nephrostome situated basally. Anal vesicles not described.

Male. Not known.

REMARKS. This genus is close to *Protobonellia* and *Prometor*. It differs from both in that it possesses setae and from *Prometor* in that it possesses only one nephridium.

DISTRIBUTION. Indonesia.

Genus *TORBENWOLFFIA* Zenkevitch

Torbenwolffia Zenkevitch, 1966 : 180.

DESCRIPTION. *Female.* Proboscis large with anterior extremity bilobed; length in a living specimen several times that of the trunk. No ventral setae. One nephridium on the right side. Anal glands short and unbranched with a few funnels.

Male. Not known.

TYPE SPECIES. *Torbenwolffia galatheae.*

DISTRIBUTION. Kermadec Trench in the Pacific Ocean. Collected at great depths.

Torbenwolffia galatheae Zenkevitch, 1966

(Fig. 51G)

Torbenwolffia galatheae Zenkevitch, 1966 : 180, figs 6–8.

TYPE LOCALITY. Kermadec Trench, Pacific Ocean (Galathea Expedition).

DESCRIPTION. *Female.* Length of proboscis of fixed specimen 70–80 mm and of the trunk 90–100 mm. Proboscis terminates in a bifurcate lobe and is grooved (the shape of the proboscis may vary considerably after fixation). No ventral setae. One nephridium. Anal glands short and unbranched and only a few funnels present.

Male. Not known.

REMARKS. Described from 27 specimens.

DISTRIBUTION. Kermadec Trench (Galathea Stns. 649, 651, 654, 658 at depths of 5850–8300 m).

Genus *VITJAZEMA* Zenkevitch

Vitjazema Zenkevitch, 1958 : 194–195.

DESCRIPTION. *Female.* The structure of the unbranched proboscis is characteristic. The anterior region is expanded in a slightly widened 'head' with thickened
festoons along its anterior border; under the festoon are triangular flaps directed
inside the ventral gutter. Two ventral setae. Two nephridia. Anal vesicles
sac-like.

Male. Not known.

TYPE SPECIES. *Vitjazema ultraabyssalis* Zenkevitch.

REMARKS. The genus contains two deep-water species, *V. aleutica* and
V. ultraabyssalis.

DISTRIBUTION. The Aleutian and Kamchatka trenches in the north-west Pacific.

VITJAZEMA—KEY TO SPECIES

Ventral setae jointed; nephrostome set on a short stalk   .   .   .   .   ***V. aleutica***
Ventral setae not jointed; nephrostome set on a long stem.   .   ***V. ultraabyssalis***

Vitjazema aleutica Zenkevitch, 1958

Vitjazema aleutica Zenkevitch, 1958 : 197–198, figs 1(a–c), fig. 2 (chart).

TYPE LOCALITY. Vitjaz station 3357. Aleutian Trench (56°26'N, 170°54'W);
at 7286 m.

DESCRIPTION. *Female.* Proboscis 25 mm furrowed, slightly widened anteriorly,
without the anterior lappets and the sharply festooned border. Trunk 55 mm;
skin very transparent and green in colour. Two articulated ventral setae present.
Nephrostome carried on a short stem. Anal vesicles not preserved.

Male. Unknown.

REMARKS. In size and structure the present species is very close to *V. ultraabyssalis*. In the latter species the nephrostome is borne on a long stem and is
placed more distally. Described from two specimens.

DISTRIBUTION. As for the type locality.

Vitjazema ultraabyssalis Zenkevitch, 1958

(Fig. 53A–C)

Vitjazema ultraabyssalis Zenkevitch, 1958 : 195–197, figs 3(a–e), 4 (chart).

TYPE LOCALITY. Kurile-Kamchatka Trench, at great depths 5560–9700 m.

DESCRIPTION. *Female.* A small green-coloured bonellid with a transparent skin
and some layers of longitudinal muscle. Length of the body 14–15 mm and length
of the proboscis 9–27 mm. On the ventral side of the proboscis there is a deep
furrow; in its anterior part it is slightly widened with a festoon-like border made up
of five to six triangular lappets. Two large ventral setae with bent blades and blunt

tip. One pair of nephridia; each opening to the outside by its own nephridiopore. Nephrostome simple and situated distally or terminally on a long tube. Anal trees unbranched and covered with small funnels.

Male. Unknown.

REMARKS. Known from one specimen. Five specimens of the same genus were taken by trawl at station no. 3494, Vitjaz Expedition at depths of 9735–9750 m. Their poor state of preservation made it impossible to say whether they are con-specific with *V. ultraabyssalis.*

DISTRIBUTION. Kurile-Kamchatka Trench.

4. Family ECHIURIDAE

Echiuridae de Blainville, 1827 (restricted); Baird, 1868 : 11; Monro, 1927 : 616 (in part); Fisher, 1946 : 221; 1949 : 479.
Thalassematidae Bock, 1942 : 16.

DESCRIPTION. Echiurans without sexual dimorphism. Proboscis usually well-developed, sometimes very long but never bifid; often easily detached from the trunk. Trunk sac-like to cylindrical in shape and usually covered with papillae; sometimes green or reddish in colour. Longitudinal musculature in some genera is thickened to form longitudinal muscle bands and the oblique musculature between the longitudinal muscles may or may not form bundles. Nephridia paired and usually one to three pairs. Nephrostome basal except in one genus and the nephro-stomal lips may be inconspicuous, fan- or leaf-like, elongate and spirally coiled. A pair of ventral setae present in all genera (in one species numerous spinelets instead); interbasal muscle usual but may be absent. Anal setae and post-pharyngeal diaphragm only in *Echiurus.* Dorsal and neurointestinal blood vessels usually connected through a ring vessel in the posterior region of the foregut. Anal vesicles usually elongate or swollen sacs and not branched; their surface usually bears very small ciliated funnels.

TYPE GENUS. *Echiurus* Guérin-Ménéville.

REMARKS. The absence of sexual dimorphism distinguishes the echiurids from the bonellids. Some of the main differences between the two families are compared in Table 15. The echiurids appear to be a more homogeneous group and to show less diversity in structure than the bonellids. The 80 echiurids mentioned in this monograph are shared amongst nine genera but the 47 bonellids amongst 23 genera. One genus contains one species, a second contains two and the rest 4–29.

Monro (1927) considered the family Echiuridae to contain four genera which he grouped into three subfamilies, Echiurinae for *Echiurus,* Urechinae for *Urechis* and Thalassematinae for *Thalassema* and *Ikeda.* Bock (1942) restricted the family Echiuridae to contain *Echiurus* and *Urechis* and created a new family Thalassema-tidae to contain *Thalassema, Ochetostoma, Ikedosoma, Arhynchite* and *Ikeda.* Fisher (1946) reorganized the systematics of the phylum. He considered that the dif-ferences between *Ikeda, Urechis* and the other genera were at a higher taxonomic level than zoologists had previously believed and he created two new orders, one for *Ikeda* and the other for *Urechis*. Further, because he considered that the differences between *Echiurus* and Bock's thalassematids were at a much lower level than the differences between *Ikeda*, *Urechis* and *Echiurus*, he placed *Echiurus* and all the other *Thalassema*-like genera in one family, the Echiuridae. Fisher's reasoning and judgement seem to us to have been sound and we follow his lead in placing *Echiurus* and the 'thalassematid' genera in the family Echiuridae. We consider, however, that the Echiuridae as understood by Fisher and by us is readily divided into two subfamilies: (1) subfamily Echiurinae for Echiuridae with anal setae and a post-pharyngeal diaphragm and (2) subfamily Thalassematinae for Echiuridae without anal setae and without a post pharyngeal diaphragm. The Echiurinae contains the genus *Echiurus* and the Thalassematinae the genera *Arhynchite*, *Lissomyema*, *Listriolobus*, *Ochetostoma*. *Anelassorhynchus*, *Thalassema*, *Ikedosoma* and *Prashadus*.

The family is separated into genera largely on six characters: (1) the condition of the longitudinal muscles, (2) the condition of the oblique muscles, (3) the nature of the nephrostomal lips, (4) the number and arrangement of the nephridia, (5) the position of the nephrostome and (6) the presence of anal setae. The general plan for the subdivision of the family is shown in Table 17. It is the same as that used by Fisher (1946, 1949) but extended a little further in order to accommodate a species in which the nephrostome is placed distally.

The genera *Listriolobus* and *Anelassorhynchus* have not always been considered to be valid. Prashad and Awati (1929) and Bock (1942) found *Anelassorhynchus* unacceptable, Annandale having based his genus on the structure of the proboscis. At a later date Fisher (1946) made the presence of spirally coiled lips one of the distinguishing characters of the genus. Wharton (1913) and Bock (1942) considered *Listriolobus*, as conceived by Spengel (1912) to depend on the arrangement of the longitudinal musculature and the occurrence of small coelomic pouches in the muscle wall, to be invalid. Subsequently Fisher (1946) broadened the genus by making the shape of the nephrostomal lips one of the characters.

We have decided to accept the genera for two reasons. Firstly, on doing so we are being consistent with the view that the six characters listed in Table 17 hold the key to the classification of the family. Secondly it is of great practical advantage to be able to separate an assemblage of 36 species (*Thalassema* 14, *Anelassorhynchus* 14 and *Listriolobus* 8) into three groups. It is true that it is impossible to tell whether some of the species described by earlier workers should be classed as *Listriolobus*, *Ochetostoma* or *Anelassorhynchus* because the characters now used to separate the genera were not taken into consideration at the time (see p. 426). It is also true that because in some sexually immature specimens of *Listriolobus* the splitting of the longitudinal muscle into bands is not well developed (Wharton, 1913; Fisher, 1946), young specimens of *Listriolobus* may be confused with *Anelassorhynchus*. This is a disadvantage but similar difficulties arise in some other phyla of invertebrates.

Zenkevitch (1966 : 182) pointed out that echiurids tend to inhabit shallow waters while the bonellids extend down into very deep waters. A comparison of the information shown in Tables 16 and 17 supports his statement.

TABLE 17

Characters of the genera of the family Echiuridae

Genus	Longitudinal musculature	Oblique musculature	Nephrostomal lips	No. of nephridia	Anal setae	Position of nephrostome	No. of species	Bathymetric range
1. *Arhynchite* Sato, 1937	continuous	continuous	leaf-like	1 pair	—	basal	6	littoral—396 m
2. *Echiurus* Guérin-Ménéville, 1831	continuous	continuous	not spirally coiled	1–3 pairs	two circles	basal	4	littoral—1900 m
3. *Lissomyema* Fisher, 1946	banded	continuous	not spirally coiled	2 pairs	—	basal	2	littoral
4. *Listriolobus* Fischer 1926	banded	continuous	spirally coiled	2–3 pairs	—	basal	8	littoral 764 m
5. *Ochetostoma* Leuckart & Rüppell, 1828	banded	fasciculate	spirally coiled	1–7 pairs	—	basal	29	littoral—40 m
6. *Anelassorhynchus* Annandale, 1922	continuous	continuous	spirally coiled	1–3 pairs	—	basal	14	littoral—1936 m
7. *Thalassema* Lamarck, 1801	continuous	continuous	not spirally coiled	1–2 pairs	—	basal	14	littoral—628 m
8. *Ikedosoma* Bock, 1942	banded	weakly fasciculate	short spirals	20 pairs or 3–8 groups of 1–4 per group	—	basal	2	shallow water
9. *Prashadus* gen. nov.	?	?	not spirally coiled	20 pairs	—	distal	1	not deep water

One new genus, *Prashadus*, is described to contain a species, *Ikedosoma pirotansis* Menon & Datta Gupta with two characters unusual in the Echiuridae, 20 pairs of nephridia and a distally placed nephrostome. No information about the structure of the longitudinal and oblique musculature was given in the description of the species; it is possible that both are continuous. The position of the nephrostome, however, together with the nature of the nephrostomal lips and the number of nephridia present distinguishes *Prashadus* from all other genera in the family. It would be interesting to know how the circular and longitudinal muscle layers are arranged in the genus, because in the heteromyotan genus *Ikeda* the nephrostome is also distal.

KEY TO SUBFAMILIES

1 Two rings of setae surround the posterior or anal region of the trunk. A post-pharyngeal diaphragm incompletely separates the body cavity into two parts. Nephrostomes without spirally coiled lips . . **ECHIURINAE** (p. 409)

2 No rings of setae surround the posterior or anal region of the trunk. No post-pharyngeal diaphragm present. Nephrostomes may or may not possess spirally coiled lips . . . . **THALASSEMATINAE** (p. 413)

Subfamily **ECHIURINAE** Monro

Echiurinae Monro, 1927 : 616.

DESCRIPTION. Proboscis long and spoon-shaped. Two rings of setae surround the anus. A post-pharyngeal diaphragm incompletely separates the body cavity. Nephrostomal lips not spirally coiled.

TYPE GENUS. *Echiurus* Guérin-Méneville, 1831.

REMARKS. The subfamily contains one genus.

Genus *ECHIURUS* Guérin-Méneville

Lumbricus Pallas, 1766 : 146, pl. 11, figs 1–6 (in part).
Echiurus Guérin-Méneville, 1831 : 9, pl. 6, fig. 3; Greeff, 1879 : 136; Shipley, 1899b : 342; Skorikow, 1909 : 80; Spengel, 1912 : 173–211; Monro, 1927 : 616; Fisher, 1946 : 225.

DESCRIPTION. Two rings of anal setae at the posterior region of the trunk. Proboscis present but often easily detached. Trunk with rows of papillae which are most prominent on the posterior surface. One to three pairs of nephridia without spirally coiled lips. Ventral setae present anteriorly. Post-pharyngeal diaphragm present which almost separates the coelom into two parts. Neuro-intestinal vessel in direct connection with the dorsal blood vessel though a ring vessel as in *Thalassema*. Males and females similar.

TYPE SPECIES. *Lumbricus echiurus* Pallas.

REMARKS. The genus contains four species, one consisting of two subspecies.

DISTRIBUTION. Recorded from Arctic and Antarctic waters.

BB

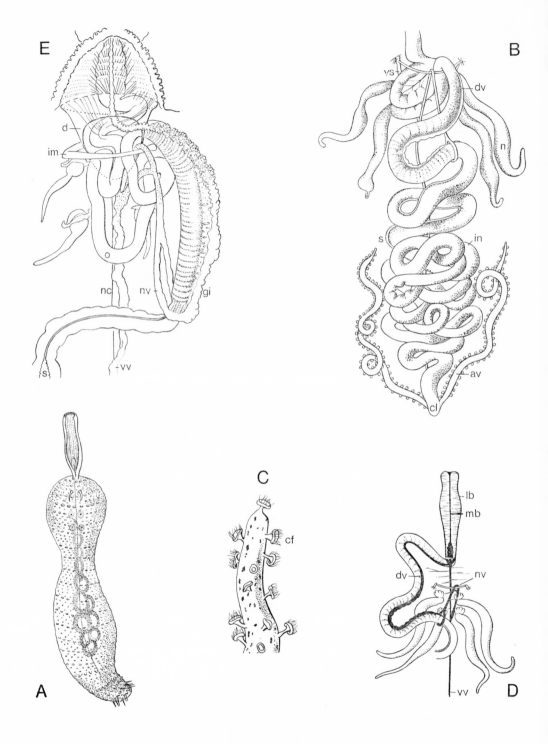

ECHIURUS—KEY TO SPECIES

1 One pair of nephridia   .   .   .   .   *E. sitchaensis* (p. 413)
– Two to three pairs of nephridia   2
2 Two pairs of nephridia   3
– Three pairs of nephridia   .   .   .   .   *E. antarcticus* (p. 411)
3 Nephrostome attached to the tube of the nephridium in the body cavity .   *E. echiurus*
                                                                              (p. 412)
– Nephrostome attached through the body wall to the tube of the nephridium
                                                                    E. abyssalis (p. 411)

Echiurus antarcticus Spengel, 1912

Echiurus antarcticus Spengel, 1912d : 200–208; Stephen, 1941b : 245–246, pl. 7, fig. 1;
    Wesenberg-Lund, 1955b : 17–18.

TYPE LOCALITY. Cumberland Bay, South Georgia. *Type.* Reichsmuseum,
Stockholm.

DESCRIPTION. Proboscis T-shaped and different from that of *Echiurus echiurus*;
the anterior region is expanded into two flaps but the anterior edge is straight.
Posterior part of the proboscis is rolled into a short tube, 2–4 mm in length and a
differentiated ridge of tissue runs along the ventral side. Trunk very similar in
appearance to that of *E. echiurus*; it has similar transverse striations and similar
longitudinal rows of large papillae. The rows of small papillae are very incomplete
and Spengel described them as being absent. The number of setae in the posterior
rows shows considerable variation, from 8–10 in the anterior row and 5–6 in the
posterior row. Three pairs of nephridia, but possibly only two in one specimen.

REMARKS. Spengel's description was given with considerable detail. The above
account is only a summary.

DISTRIBUTION. Coast of Chile (Wesenberg-Lund, 1955b); South Georgia (Spengel,
1912; Stephen, 1941b).

Echiurus abyssalis Skorikow, 1906

Echiurus pallasii Lo Bianco, 1903 : 265, pl. 7, figs 2, 4 (not Guérin-Ménéville, 1831 : 9).
Echiurus abyssalis Skorikow, 1906 : 217–221; Sluiter, 1912 : 23–24, pl. 1, figs 12–14; Spengel,
    1912d : 190–195, 1 pl., 2 figs; Southern, 1913b : 35–37; Fischer, 1920 : 422.

TYPE LOCALITY. Isle of Capri, Italy; at 1100–1500 m.

DESCRIPTION. An abyssal species with essentially the same external appearance
as *E. echiurus*. The difference between the two species as given by Skorikow, and

---

FIG. 52. (A–D) *Echiurus echiurus*. (A) Ventral view; 'the alimentary canal in living specimens is often visible through the body wall' (Greeff, 1879 : 158). (B) Dissected specimen.
(C) Enlargement of anterior part of anal vesicle. (D) Vascular system, showing the
dorsal, neuro-intestinal, ventral and ring blood vessels in the trunk and the median
and paired lateral vessels of the proboscis. (A–D after Greeff.) (E) *Echiurus echiurus
alaskanus*. Dissected specimen. The junction of the diaphragm and body wall is
indicated by dashes for the dorsal half and dots for the ventral half (after Fisher). KEY:
See Fig. 53, p. 417.

confirmed by Sluiter, is that the nephrostome is attached to the nephridium through the body wall. Sluiter (1912 : 23) says, 'L'étonnoir vibratile n'est pas situé sur l'organe segmentaire, mais s'attache immédiatement à coté de lui'. The larva of *E. abyssalis* is pelagic, that of *E. echiurus* is not.

REMARKS. Skorikow described the species from two specimens. Sluiter obtained a third from near the same locality at 1900 m.

DISTRIBUTION. Mediterranean (Lo Bianco, 1903; Skorikow, 1906; Sluiter, 1912; Fischer, 1922a); West coast of Ireland (Southern, 1913).

Echiurus echiurus echiurus (Pallas, 1767)
(Fig. 52A–D)

Lumbricus echiurus Pallas, 1766 : 146, 1 pl., figs 1–6; 1774 : 1–8, 1 pl., 5 figs.
Holothuria forcipata Fabricius, 1780 : 357.
Echiurus chrysanthophorus Pourtalès, 1851 : 39.
Thalassema vulgaris Savigny, 1809 : 102.
Bonellia fabricii Diesing, 1859 : 61.
Echiurus lutkenii Diesing, 1859 : 61.
Echiurus forcipatus: Reinhardt, 1851 : 45; Koren & Danielssen, 1877a : 151; Greeff, 1879 : 141; Shipley, 1899b : 343.
Echiurus pallasi Guérin-Méneville, 1831 : 9; Koren & Danielssen, 1877a : 151; Greeff, 1879 : 136–143, 5 pls; Spengel, 1879b : 542–547; 1880 : 460–524, pls 23–26; Rietsch, 1886 : 501–502; Fischer, 1895 : 21; Shipley, 1899b : 343; Augener, 1903 : 297–371; Théel, 1906 : 22, pl. 1, figs 7–8; Gadd, 1912 : 90–91; Ikeda, 1924 : 39, fig. 12.
Echiurus vulgaris: Forbes, 1841 : 263.
Echiurus echiurus: Wilson, 1900 : 165–170; Skorikow, 1909 : 80, pl. 1, figs 2–4; Spengel, 1912d : 173–212; Fischer, 1914b : 17; 1920 : 422; 1925 : 2–3; 1928b : 478–479; Cuénot, 1922 : 21; Ikeda, 1924 : 39, fig. 12; Wesenberg-Lund, 1925 : 83–84; 1933 : 2; 1937a : 19–20, fig. 5; 1937b : 12–13, fig. 2; 1939a : 10; 1939b : 29; ten Broeke, 1929 : 167, figs 14, 15; Stephen, 1934 : 162–164; Sato, 1939 : 350–351; Okuda, 1946 : 222, pl. 29b.

DESCRIPTION. Proboscis up to 40 mm in length; orange in colour with brown stripes. Trunk up to 150 mm, yellow-grey in colour, covered with papillae arranged in rings; 21–23 rings of large papillae alternate with 4–5 rings of small papillae. Two ventral setae and two posterior circles of setae, interrupted on the median line. Five to nine, usually 7, setae in the anterior circle, 5–8, usually 6, setae in the posterior circle. Two pairs of nephridia which lie posterior to the setae; nephrostome with a frilled border and without spiral prolongations. Anal vesicles long, thin, brown tubes which bear many funnels. Blood-vascular system with dorsal, ventral and neurointestinal vessels; dorsal and neurointestinal vessels connected through a ring vessel.

REMARKS. The species has been well described by Greeff (1879) and Spengel (1880) and its ecology by Gislen (1940).

DISTRIBUTION. Greenland (Wesenberg-Lund, 1925, 1933); Arctic, Gulf of Kola (Gadd, 1912); Iceland (Wesenberg-Lund, 1937); North Sea and Scandinavian coasts (Théel, 1906; Stephen, 1934; Wesenberg-Lund, 1933, 1937, 1939); Eastern Pacific, Alaska (Murdoch, 1885); Sea of Okhotsk (Ikeda, 1924); Japan (Sato, 1939; Okuda, 1946); U.S.A., Atlantic coast (Pourtalès, 1851).

Echiurus echiurus alaskanus Fisher, 1948

(Fig. 52E)

Echiurus echiurus alaskanus Fisher, 1946 : 225–229, pl. 20; McGinitie, 1956 : 127.
Echiurus pallasii : Wilson, 1900 : 174.

TYPE LOCALITY. Auk Bay, Juneau, Alaska. *Type*. U.S.N.M. no. 20609.

DESCRIPTION. Differs from *E. echiurus echiurus* in having (1) an adherent proboscis and (2) ventral setae that are curved and not straight. Length of sub-truncate proboscis 15–20 mm and of body 100–230 mm. Body cavity almost divided into two parts by a diaphragm; the pharynx is contained in the anterior coelom.

REMARKS. Fisher (1946) gives a very detailed account of the subspecies.

DISTRIBUTION. Alaska, Auk Bay, etc. (Fisher, 1946); Point Barrow (McGinitie, 1956).

Echiurus sitchaensis (Brandt, 1835)

Thalassema sitchaensis Brandt, 1835 : 62.
Echiurus sitchaensis : Diesing, 1859 : 777; Skorikow, 1909 : 88, pl. 1, fig. 1; Spengel, 1912d :
    184–189; Fischer, 1914b : 17–18; Fisher, 1946 : 229–230.

TYPE LOCALITY. Sitka Island, Alaska. *Type*. Formerly in the Leningrad (St Petersburg) Museum.

DESCRIPTION. Proboscis not deciduous and lacking a differentiated ridge of tissue on its ventral surface. The papillae are subequal and arranged in rather regular and numerous rings (not rings of larger papillae alternating with zones of smaller ones as in *E. echiurus*). One pair of nephridia.

REMARKS. The species is very close to *E. echiurus* and differs in having (1) two nephridia, (2) a non-deciduous proboscis and (3) the arrangement of the skin papillae. Fisher (1946) listed 120 specimens of *Echiurus* from Alaska and British Columbia. None of them he considered to be *E. sitchaensis*. Although Spengel (1912) discusses in some detail the difference between *E. echiurus* and *E. sitchaensis* there is some doubt about the validity of the species.

Subfamily THALASSEMATINAE Monro

Thalassematinae Monro, 1927 : 617; Bock, 1942 : 16.

DESCRIPTION. Proboscis long and never bifid. No rings of anal setae. No post-pharyngeal diaphragm.

TYPE GENUS. *Thalassema* Lamarck, 1801.

REMARKS. The subfamily contains eight genera.

Key to Genera

1 Nephrostome basal in position 2
– Nephrostome distal in position (proboscis and trunk very long; nephridia 20 pairs with nephrostomal lips not spirally coiled; genus contains only one species)
                      PRASHADUS (p. 462)
2 Longitudinal musculature of body wall not thickened into longitudinal bands . 3
– Longitudinal musculature of body wall thickened into longitudinal bands . . 5
3 Nephrostomal lips elongate and usually spirally coiled **ANELASSORHYNCHUS** (p. 443)
– Nephrostomal lips not elongate and spirally coiled 4
4 Nephrostomal lips expanded into a leaf-like structure with irregularly sculptured margins (one pair of nephridia, anterior extremity of proboscis expanded or fan-like, strong interbasal muscle and long presiphonal segment of the gut; ring vessel may or may not be present) . . . . . . **ARHYNCHITE** (p. 414)
– Nephrostomal lips not leaf-like but inconspicuous or semicircular (one to two pairs of nephridia, anterior extremity of proboscis not expanded or fan-like, ring vessel at the end of the foregut) . . . . . **THALASSEMA** (p. 452)
5 Nephrostomal lips not spirally coiled (inner layer of oblique muscles not differentiated into separate fascicles between the bands of longitudinal muscles)
                     LISSOMYEMA (p. 419)
– Nephrostomal lips spirally coiled 6
6 Oblique musculature between the longitudinal bands grouped into fascicles . . 7
– Oblique musculature between the longitudinal bands not grouped into fascicles (banding of longitudinal muscles may be weaker in younger specimens and visible only in the posterior region) . . . . **LISTRIOLOBUS** (p. 420)
7 Nephridia one to seven pairs (banding of longitudinal and oblique muscles well developed and a vascular ring vessel present at the beginning of the mid-gut)
                     OCHETOSTOMA (p. 426)
– Nephridia in three to fourteen groups of one to four nephridia per group, the groups being arranged in pairs (vascular ring vessel at posterior end of the pharynx)
                     IKEDOSOMA (p. 460)

Genus *ARHYNCHITE* Sato, 1937

Arhynchite Sato, 1937 : 142–143; Fisher, 1946 : 247; 1949 : 485.

DESCRIPTION. Proboscis often deciduous. If present long, slender, ribbon-like with a small expanded or fan-like extremity and a closed base forming a lower lip. One pair of nephridia; nephrostome with a single lip produced into a leaf-like organ, the margins of which are irregularly sculptured. Ventral setae connected by a strong interbasal muscle. Presiphonal segment of alimentary canal very long. Anal vesicles thin walled and unbranched as in *Thalassema*. Vascular system either with or without a ring vessel. No sexual dimorphism.

TYPE SPECIES. *Thalassema arhynchite* Ikeda.

REMARKS. The genus contains six species. No proboscis was present in the type species hence the name 'a-rhynchos'—without a snout. Some of the species in the genus are very closely related and difficult to distinguish.

DISTRIBUTION. Japan (one species), China (one species), Australia (one species), western coast of the U.S.A. (three species).

ARHYNCHITE—KEY TO SPECIES

1 Intestinal caecum present   .   .   .   .   .   .   *A. rugosus* (p. 419)
– Intestinal caecum absent **2**
2 Ring-blood-vessel present at posterior region of foregut   .   .   .   **3**
– No ring-blood-vessel present at posterior of foregut   .   .   .   **4**
3 Lip of nephrostome leaf-like with indented border   .   .   *A. pugettensis* (p. 418)
– Lip of nephrostome drawn out into a long and much expanded leaf-like appendage
                                                 A. arhynchite (p. 415)
4 Anal vesicles attached for whole length to the alimentary canal   .   *A. hiscocki* (p. 417)
– Anal vesicles not attached at all to alimentary canal **5**
5 Anal vesicles have a single opening onto the cloaca and the interbasal muscle does not
   pass through the loop of the neurointestinal canal   .   .   *A. inamoenus* (p. 418)
– Anal vesicles open separately onto the cloaca and the interbasal muscle passes
   through the loop of the neurointestinal canal   .   .   .   *A. californicus* (p. 415)

Arhynchite arhynchite (Ikeda, 1924)

(Fig. 53D)

Thalassema arhynchite Ikeda, 1924 : 41–42, pl. 1, text-figs 16–17.
Arhynchite arhynchite: Sato, 1937a : 143–145, pl. 2, fig. 3, text-fig. 2; 1939 : 351–352.

TYPE LOCALITY. Sappora, Japan. *Type.* Fisheries School, Sappora, Japan.

DESCRIPTION. Proboscis not present and no signs that the structure had been detached; 100–170 mm in length, 10–15 mm in breadth and violet-brown in colour. Papillae uniformly distributed over the surface but almost invisible to the unaided eye; rather larger and more elevated on the anterior and posterior regions of the trunk. Two nephridia lie posteriorly to the ventral setae; each has the form of a small elongated sac. The nephrostome is relatively long and leaf-like. Anal vesicles one quarter the length of the body and attached to the body wall by several muscle strands; they carry a few unstalked ciliated funnels, invisible to the naked eye.

REMARKS. Ikeda described the species from a number of specimens. Sato (1937) re-examined Ikeda's specimens and also described another found at Samé. As a result of the examination, he erected the genus *Arhynchite*. In 1939 he redescribed the species but gave no new records.

DISTRIBUTION. Sappora (Ikeda) and Samé (Sato), Japan.

Arhynchite californicus Fisher, 1949

(Fig. 53E)

Arhynchite californicus Fisher, 1949 : 486–487, pl. 30.

TYPE LOCALITY. Albatross stn. 4525, Monterey Bay, California; at 396 m. *Type.* U.S.N.M. no. 21085.

DESCRIPTION. Proboscis 65–85 mm in length, 5 mm in breadth, thin and ribbon-like; anterior extremity fan-shaped and expanded with a thickened margin. The margins join near the base to form a lip. Trunk bluntly cigar-shaped, 70–90 mm

in length, 15–20 mm in diameter. Body wall rather thick and opaque, with small glands of unequal size which form more or less distinct transverse rows or broken rings; transverse wrinkles lie between the glands. At the extremities of the body the glands are much larger, often low and papilliform. Two ventral setae, 6·5 mm in length, situated close to the anterior end of the body. Interbasal muscle well-developed, passing through a loop of the neurointestinal canal. The alimentary canal is very long with numerous coils attached to the body wall by many small frenula. Two nephridia (there is an extra right one in the type specimen); nephrostome large, flap-like, having a lobed or lacinate border and a crescentic slit near the base. Anal vesicles thin-walled, voluminous at the base and about half the length of the trunk. Vesicles anchored to the body wall by two or three broad frenula at about two thirds the length from the base and a number of smaller ones. No ring vessel present in the vascular system.

REMARKS. Described from three specimens and three proboscises.

DISTRIBUTION. As for the type locality.

Arhynchite hiscocki Edmonds, 1960

Arhynchite hiscocki Edmonds, 1960 : 90–91, pl. 1b, fig. 3; 1966 : 178.

TYPE LOCALITY. Dunwich, Queensland; from sand, 18 inches below the surface. *Type.* Australian Museum, Sydney.

DESCRIPTION. Proboscis delicate and slender, about 30 mm in length, 1–2 mm in width and fan-shaped anteriorly. Trunk pencil-like, about 100 mm in length, 4–6 mm in width; covered with small uniformly distributed papillae which are slightly larger at the anterior and posterior ends and which appear to be arranged in transverse rows. One pair of nephridia, about 15 mm long, opening behind the setae; each with a rather elaborate leaf-like nephrostomal lip. Ventral setae long and connected to strong radiating muscles arising from the body wall; well-developed interbasal muscle. Alimentary canal long and considerably coiled; oesophagus firmly fastened to the body wall by well-developed mesenteries and the presiphonal segment very long. No pre-cloacal caecum is present on the intestine. The vascular system resembles that of a bonellid and no ring vessel is present. Anal vesicles very thin, long, about one quarter of the length of the trunk; fastened

---

FIG. 53. (A–C) *Vitjazema ultra-abyssalis*. (A) Ventral view of female. (B) Anterior region of introvert. (C) Nephridia showing distally placed, stalked nephrostomes. (A–C after Zenkevitch.) (D) *Arhynchite arhynchite*. Dissection of anterior region of the trunk (after Ikeda). (E) *Arhynchite californicus*. Proboscis—ventral view (after Fisher). (F) *Arhynchite pugettensis*. Anterior region dissected (after Fisher). *av*, anal vesicle; *c*, caecum; *cf*, ciliated funnel; *cg*, ciliated groove; *cr*, crop; *d*, diaphragm; *dv*, dorsal retractor; *gi*, gizzard; *im*, interbasal muscle; *in*, intestine; *ln*, nerve loop; *lb*, lateral blood vessel; *mb*, median blood vessel; *ms*, mesentery; *n*, nephridium; *nc*, nerve cord; *nl*, nephrostomal lip; *np*, nephridiopore; *nv*, neuro-intestinal vessel; *o*, oesophagus; *om*, oblique muscle; *p*, proboscis; *ph*, pharynx; *pp*, papillae; *rv*, ring vessel; *s*, siphon; *vs*, ventral setae; *vv*, ventral vessel.

throughout their length by numerous fine mesenteries to the posterior region of the alimentary canal and only to the body wall in their last quarter. Vesicles covered with very numerous, very small ciliated funnels.

REMARKS. Described from a single specimen. Two more specimens later found in Port Phillip Bay, Victoria (Edmonds, 1966).

DISTRIBUTION. Queensland and Victoria (Australia).

Arhynchite inamoenus Fisher, 1946

Arhynchite inamoenus Fisher, 1946 : 247–249, pl. 25.

TYPE LOCALITY. 13·5 miles south of Seal Beach, Monterey Bay (U.S.A.). *Type*. U.S.N.M. no. 20615.

DESCRIPTION. Proboscis lacking. Trunk of type specimen 70 mm in length and 25 mm in breadth; the specimen, however, is much contorted. Skin roughened by low close-set papillae, largest and most irregularly set at the ends of the body. Two ventral setae, 11 mm in length, connected by an interbasal muscle which does not pass through a loop of the neurointestinal vessel. Body wall continuous and nowhere gathered into bands. Two nephrida; length in females is about four fifths that of trunk and in males about one fifth. Nephrostome set on a short stalk near the base. Anal vesicles two in number but with a single opening into a small cloaca with folded walls; ciliated funnels very small. Alimentary canal excessively long, about 600 mm, with numerous coils attached to the body wall by mesenteries. Relation of the dorsal blood vessel and the neurointestinal vessel similar to that in *Bonellia*.

REMARKS. Described from four specimens. No other records.

DISTRIBUTION. As for the type locality.

Arhynchite pugettensis Fisher, 1949
(Fig. 53F)

Arhynchite pugettensis Fisher, 1949 : 487–489, pl. 31, 32.

TYPE LOCALITY. Normandy Beach, 12 miles south of Seattle, Puget Sound, Washington. *Type*. U.S.N.M. no. 21098.

DESCRIPTION. Proboscis present, although only the basal portion remained on the specimen; reddish-brown in colour. Trunk cylindrical; skin covered with closely-packed and elevated glands of varying sizes which are larger at the extremities of the body. Two ventral setae with a strong interbasal muscle passing through a loop of the neurointestinal vessel. Two nephridia which are longer than the body; the nephrostome has a characteristically expanded lip with a lobed or slightly lacinated border. Anal vesicles unequal in size; ciliated funnels small and well-spaced. Conspicuous ring blood vessel at the end of the foregut.

REMARKS. Described from a single specimen. No other records.

DISTRIBUTION. As for the type locality.

Arhynchite rugosus Chen & Yeh, 1958

Arhynchite rugosum Chen & Yeh, 1958 : 278, text-figs 8, 9.

TYPE LOCALITY. Kiao-chow Bay, Shantung, China.

DESCRIPTION. Proboscis lacking. Trunk robust, like a sea-cucumber, tapering anteriorly to the mouth and posteriorly to the anus which is set on a low knob-like protuberence; length 90 mm and width 24 mm. Uniform fleshy-grey in colour and rugose. Body wall thick and opaque and bears closely set, ampulla-like tubercles or papillae that are largest and most conspicuous at the extremities of the body. Nephridiopores open posteriorly to the ventral setae. Digestive tract very long (about 20 times the length of the trunk); posterior part enlarged to form a cloaca. A rectal caecum about 2 mm in diameter is present on the ventral side and a pair of slender anal vesicles, about 15 mm in length. Each nephridium is 19 mm in length and has no spiral lips to the nephrostomes.

REMARKS. Described from one badly preserved specimen; no other records. The species is very close to *A. inamoenus* but distinguished from it in having a rectal caecum, a longer digestive tract and relatively short ventral setae (6 mm as against 11 mm).

DISTRIBUTION. As for the type locality.

Genus *LISSOMYEMA* Fisher, 1946

Lissomyema Fisher, 1946 : 222–223.

DESCRIPTION. Echiurans which lack posterior or anal setae. Proboscis like that of *Thalassema*. Longitudinal muscles of body wall grouped into bands. Inner layer of muscles not separated into transverse fascicles as in *Ochetostoma*. Nephro-stomal lips not spirally coiled. Blood vascular system appears to be without a ring vessel.

TYPE SPECIES. *Thalassema mellita* Conn.

REMARKS. The genus contains two species, *L. mellita* (Conn) from Carolina, U.S.A. and *L. exilii* (F. Müller) from Brazil. *L. exilii* may be synonymous with *L. mellita*. The two are difficult to distinguish.

DISTRIBUTION. North and South America.

LISSOMYEMA—KEY TO SPECIES

Anal vesicles voluminous . . . . **L. mellita**
Anal vesicles small . . . . **L. exilii**

Lissomyema exilii (F. Müller, 1883)

Thalassema exilii F. Müller [in] Lampert, 1883 : 341; Shipley, 1899b : 347.
Lissomyema exilii : De Jorge *et al.*, 1969 : 483–492.

TYPE LOCALITY. Desterro, Brazil.

DESCRIPTION. Proboscis ribbon-like, with cross furrows. Trunk 2·6 mm in length and expanded posteriorly; preserved specimens brown in colour. Papillae scattered irregularly from the middle of the trunk to the posterior end but most closely packed in the middle region of the trunk. Longitudinal muscles gathered into 8–10 bands. Two pairs of nephridia; nephrostomal lips folded and crinkly. Anal vesicles small.

REMARKS. Described originally from two specimens; no other records known. The taxonomic position of this species is uncertain. Fisher (1946 : 240) suggested that the species might fall in the genus *Lissomyema*. It is possible that the species is synonymous with *L. mellita*. If so, *exilii* is the older name.

Lissomyema mellita (Conn, 1886)

(Fig. 54A)

Thalassema mellita Conn, 1886 : 351–401, 4 pls; Shipley, 1899b : 350; Pearse *et al.*, 1942 : 184.
Lissomyema mellita: Fisher, 1946 : 222–224, text-fig. 10.

TYPE LOCALITY. Beaufort, North Carolina.

DESCRIPTION. Proboscis several times the length of the trunk according to Conn but less than the length of the trunk according to Fisher; light yellow in colour. Trunk up to 36 mm in length and dull red in colour. Skin nearly smooth with white papillae round the anus. Eight longitudinal muscle-bands, more clearly defined than in *Listriolobus* on account of the incipient fasciculation of the oblique muscle-layer. Ventral setae joined by a very strong interbasal muscle and with radiating basal muscles. Originally described as having two pairs of nephridia, but Fisher found three on one side of his specimen and two on the other. Nephrostome fan-shaped and without spirally coiled lips. Anal vesicles voluminous with numerous conspicuous ciliated funnels. Gizzard relatively short and stomach relatively long. The ventral blood vessels send a branch to the pharynx and oesophagus.

REMARKS. The description given above is based on the original one and on Fisher's description of a single specimen from the type locality. The animal is sometimes found in the empty shells of sand dollars (Pearse).

DISTRIBUTION. Beaufort, North Carolina, U.S.A. (Conn, Pearse, Fisher).

Genus *LISTRIOLOBUS* Spengel, 1912

Listriolobus Spengel, 1912b : 316 (nomen nudum); Fischer, 1926a : 110; Fisher, 1946 : 233–234; Bock, 1942 : 15.

DESCRIPTION. Proboscis like that of *Thalassema*. Longitudinal muscles of body wall grouped into bands which in young specimens are faint or visible only in the posterior region. Inner layer of muscles not separated into transverse fascicles as in *Ochetostoma*. Two to three pairs of nephridia; nephrostomal lips elongate and spirally coiled. Interbasal muscle between the setae is present.

TYPE SPECIES. *Listriolobus bahamensis* Fischer.

REMARKS. Spengel (1912b) proposed the generic name *Listriolobus* for some specimens from Billiton and the Bahamas identified as *Thalassema erythrogrammon* (Leuckart & Rüppell, 1828) by Sluiter (1883) and Wilson (1900). Fischer (1926a) subsequently provided the specific names *billitonensis* and *bahamensis* for the specimens and later Fisher (1946) designated *L. bahamensis* as the type species of *Listriolobus*. The genus contains eight species.

DISTRIBUTION. Tropical and subtropical.

GENUS LISTRIOLOBUS—KEY TO SPECIES

1	One pair of nephridia (six longitudinal muscle bands) . .	***L. hexamyotus*** (p. 424)
–	Two to three pairs of nephridia (7–16 longitudinal muscle bands)	2
2	Two pairs of nephridia (7–8 longitudinal muscle bands)	3
–	Three pairs of nephridia (12–16 longitudinal muscle bands)	5
3	Seven longitudinal muscle bands	4
–	Eight longitudinal muscle bands	***L. pelodes*** (p. 425)
4	Posterior region of trunk bulb-like	***L. bulbocaudatus*** (p. 423)
–	Posterior region of trunk without bulb	***L. brevirostris*** (p. 424)
5	Twelve to fourteen longitudinal muscle bands	6
–	Sixteen longitudinal muscle bands	***L. bahamensis*** (p. 421)
6	Twelve longitudinal muscle bands	***L. riukiuensis*** (p. 425)
–	Thirteen to fourteen longitudinal muscle bands	7
7	Thirteen longitudinal muscle bands	***L. sorbillans*** (p. 425)
–	Fourteen longitudinal muscle bands	***L. billitonensis*** (p. 423)

Listriolobus bahamensis Fischer, 1926

Thalassema erythrogrammon: Wilson, 1900 : 174 (not *Ochetostoma erythrogrammon* Leuckart & Rüppell, 1828).
Listriolobus bahamensis Fischer, 1926 : 110; Fisher, 1946 : 234.

TYPE LOCALITY. Green Turtle Quay, Great Abaco Island, Bahamas.

DESCRIPTION. Proboscis 30 mm long, lighter in colour than the body and bearing whitish papillae. Trunk spindle-shaped, 130 mm long and 24 mm wide. Papillae in dense plaques at the posterior end of the body. Longitudinal muscles gathered into 16 bands about 1·5 mm wide with interspaces 4·5–7 mm except for two bands on either side of the mid-ventral line which are close together. Three pairs of nephridia of which the most posterior pair is the largest and about 82 mm long; the anterior pair open about 3 mm in front of the ventral setae. Nephrostome with spirally coiled lips. Anal vesicles long, simple and thin walled without visible funnels.

REMARKS. Described from a single specimen.

DISTRIBUTION. As for the type locality.

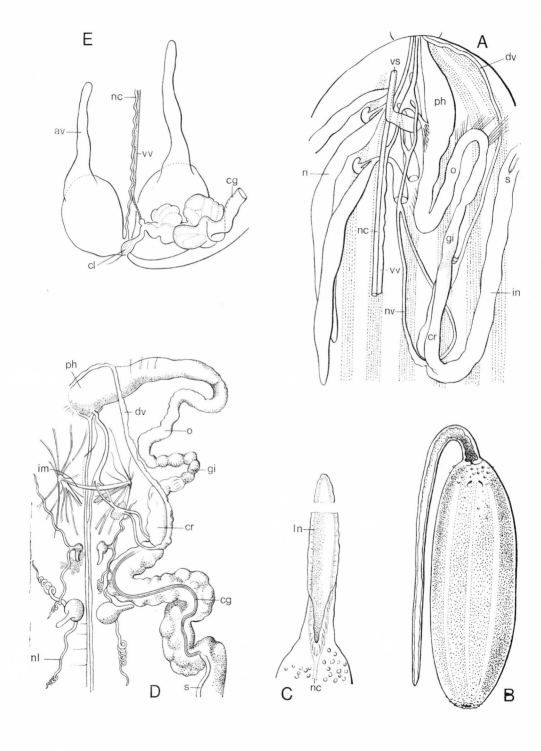

Listriolobus billitonensis Fischer, 1926

Thalassema erythrogrammon: Sluiter, 1884 : 58–60, pl. 3 (not *Ochetostoma erythrogrammon* Leuckart & Rüppell, 1828).
Listriolobus billitonensis Fischer, 1926 : 110; Fisher, 1946 : 234.

TYPE LOCALITY. Tandjong Paudau, Billiton, Indonesia.

DESCRIPTION. Proboscis up to 80 mm in length, white with yellow edges and forming a small tube at the mouth. Trunk up to 180 mm in length, dark red in colour, covered with small papillae which are largest anteriorly and posteriorly. Fourteen longitudinal muscle bands, lighter in colour than the trunk. Three pairs of nephridia, the first pair opening in front of the ventral setae. Nephrostome conspicuous with the lips drawn out into long spirally-coiled filaments. Anal vesicles short, swollen at the base. Rectal caecum present.

REMARKS. Described from numerous specimens.

DISTRIBUTION. As for the type locality.

Listriolobus bulbocaudatus Edmonds, 1963

Listriolobus bulbocaudatus Edmonds, 1963 : 243–245, pl. 1, fig. 1.

TYPE LOCALITY. Mud Island, Moreton Bay, Queensland; at 15–19 m. *Type.* Australian Museum, Sydney.

DESCRIPTION. Proboscis attached, stout and rounded about 10–16 mm long and about as wide. Trunk sausage-shaped, 48–80 mm long and 14–20 mm wide. Trunk dark red-brown in colour but the proboscis is paler. Posterior region of trunk expanded into a fleshy, pale pink bulbous structure which is slightly pointed and which bears a number of rings of very large, prominent wart-like papillae. Longitudinal muscles grouped into seven bundles which are best seen in dissected specimens. Oblique musculature between the longitudinal bands not grouped into fascicles. Two setae and a well developed interbasal muscle, and a precloacal caecum present. Two pairs of nephridia but in some there are five nephridia. Nephrostomal lips very long and much coiled. Blood system like that of *L. pelodes.* Anal vesicles long, thin and brown in colour and bearing numerous, small ciliated funnels with short stalks.

REMARKS. The description was based on four specimens. Datta Gupta, Menon & Johnson (1963 : 57–59) described *Ochetostoma septemyotum* from Quillon (India). Datta Gupta's fig. 2(a) of *O. septemyotum* and Edmond's pl. 1, fig. 1 of *L. bulbocaudatus* show that the two species look very much alike, especially as they both have seven longitudinal muscle bands. No transverse muscle fascicles were visible between the longitudinal muscles of the Australian specimens. For this reason the species was assigned to the genus *Listriolobus.*

FIG. 54. (A) *Lissomyema mellita.* Dissection of anterior region of trunk. (B–E) *Listriolobus pelodes.* (B) Entire specimen. (C) Proboscis showing the nerve loop (dotted). (D) Anterior region of the trunk. (E) Arrangement of organs at the posterior extremity of the trunk. (A–E after Fisher.) KEY: *See* Fig. 53, p. 417.

L. bulbocaudatus is also close to *L. brevirostris* Chen & Yeh, 1958 but differs most noticeably in the structure of the posterior region of the trunk which in *L. bulbo-caudatus* (1) is bulb-like and (2) is covered with large prominent papillae.

Listriolobus brevirostris Chen & Yeh, 1958

Listriolobus brevirostris Chen & Yeh, 1958 : 265–278, figs 5–7.

TYPE LOCALITY. Kiao-chow Bay, Shantung.

DESCRIPTION. Proboscis short, truncated, shovel-shaped and nearly open at the base. Trunk somewhat fusiform, narrowing at either end and up to 120 mm in length. Papillae arranged in transverse rows which are more evident on the ventral and ventro-lateral surfaces of the anterior third of the body. Trunk nearly smooth posteriorly. The papillae are small, round, ampulla-like, of variable size and either single or in groups of 2–3; generally greyish. Seven narrow thickenings of the longitudinal muscles. Two ventral setae, brownish in colour with annular orna-mentations; joined by an interbasal muscle. Two pairs of nephridia which open behind the setae. Digestive canal very long, about nine times the length of the trunk, arranged in tight coils and fixed by mesenteries. There is a round rectal caecum. A pair of anal vesicles which are long and narrow and have numerous ciliated funnels on the surface.

REMARKS. The trunk of *L. brevirostris* is nearly smooth posteriorly; that of *L. bulbocaudatus*, however, bears (1) prominent papillae and (2) is moulded into a bulb-like structure.

DISTRIBUTION. As for the type locality.

Listriolobus hexamyotus Fisher, 1949

Listriolobus hexamyotus Fisher, 1949 : 484–485, pl. 29.

TYPE LOCALITY. Albatross station 4339. Off San Diego, California; at 487–764 m. *Type.* U.S.N.M. no. 21079.

DESCRIPTION. Proboscis lacking in the specimens. Trunk up to 63 mm in length and 10 mm in breadth; grey or grey-brown in colour and covered with very small, almost microscopic, papillae. Two ventral setae, which are connected by a strong interbasal muscle. Longitudinal muscle bands six in number. Two very small nephridia; nephrostome conspicuous, with an obvious neck and with lips greatly elongated but not spirally coiled. Anal vesicles relatively very small and with no conspicuous features, 8–9 mm in length.

REMARKS. Described from four specimens. No other records known.

DISTRIBUTION. As for the type locality.

Listriolobus pelodes Fisher, 1946

(Fig. 54B–E)

Listriolobus pelodes Fisher, 1946 : 234–240, text-figs 12, 13, pl. 21, figs 1, 2, 4, 4a, pl. 22; Zenkevitch, 1958 : 220; Barnard & Hartman, 1959 : 1–16.

TYPE LOCALITY. Monterey Bay, California. *Type.* U.S.N.M. no. 20608.

DESCRIPTION. Proboscis narrow, thin, translucent and capable of extension to a length slightly greater than the trunk. Trunk 40–60 mm in length, 12–25 mm in breadth; translucent and beset with small unequal granular thickenings in close-set lines. Ventral setae with interbasal muscle. Eight longitudinal muscle-bands. Two pairs of nephridia; the ciliated funnel of the nephrostomes is set on a short stalk and the lips of the nephrostomes are long and coiled. Anal vesicles two in number, capable of great extension and with very small and scattered ciliated funnels.

REMARKS. Described from a number of specimens. According to Barnard & Hartman (1959), a remarkable concentration of *Listriolobus pelodes* is found between Santa Barbara and Ventura on the Californian coast at depths of 90–150 feet. The total weight of the species in the area is several hundred thousand tons.

DISTRIBUTION. Baja California (Fisher, 1946); California (Barnard & Hartman, 1959; Zenkevitch, 1958).

Listriolobus riukiuensis Sato, 1939

Listriolobus riukiuensis Sato, 1939 : 359–362, text-figs 10–13.

TYPE LOCALITY. Kabira, Riukiu Islands, Japan.

DESCRIPTION. Proboscis very long, 130 mm and crescentic in section. Trunk, incomplete, 75 mm in length and covered with numerous papillae which are larger in the anterior region. Ventral setae small, with no interbasal muscle and with weak radiating muscles. Longitudinal muscle-layer thickened into 12 bands. Three pairs of nephridia, the first pair opening in front of the setae. Nephrostome with spirally coiled lips. Anal vesicles lost.

REMARKS. Described from a single damaged specimen; no other records. Although Sato described *riukiuensis* as a species of *Listriolobus*, Fisher (1946 : 234) pointed out that probably it does not belong to this genus since it lacks an interbasal muscle. In addition the pattern of the blood vessels is not the same as that found in other species of *Listriolobus*.

DISTRIBUTION. As for the type locality.

Listriolobus sorbillans (Lampert, 1883)

Thalassema sorbillans Lampert, 1883 : 340–341; Shipley, 1899b : 352; Augener, 1903 : 349; Wharton, 1913 : 243–247, text-fig. 1.
Listriolobus sorbillans : Fisher, 1946 : 234.

TYPE LOCALITY. Philippines.

CC

DESCRIPTION. Length of trunk 65 mm and of proboscis 24 mm. The proboscis forms a tube at its base. Body much contracted anteriorly and posteriorly; broad in the middle and thin so that the gut can be seen. Thirteen longitudinal muscle bands which show as clearly marked stripes running from end to end. Papillae are visible at the posterior end. Three pairs of nephridia with spirally coiled lips; the first pair opens in front of the ventral setae. Ventral setae small. Anal trees long, brown tubes which under the microscope are seen to be covered with funnels. A small caecum at the end of the gut.

REMARKS. Described from a single specimen.

DISTRIBUTION. Philippines (Lampert); Syndey, Australia (Augener, 1903).

Genus *OCHETOSTOMA* Leuckart & Rüppell, 1828

Ochetostoma Leuckart & Rüppell, 1828 : 7–8; Spengel, 1912b : 316; Fisher, 1946 : 240.
Platylobostoma Wesenberg-Lund, 1957 : 8–10.

DESCRIPTION. Proboscis long, ribbon-like and without bifurcation. Longitudinal muscle layer forms a varying number of well defined bands. The intervals between the bands are crossed by numerous fascicles or small bundles of the inner oblique musculature. Nephridia, 1–7 pairs; nephrostomes with spirally coiled lips. Two ventral setae with or without an interbasal muscle. Vascular system usually with a ring vessel through which the dorsal and neurointestinal blood vessels are connected. Rectal caecum usually present.

TYPE SPECIES. *Ochetostoma erythrogrammon* Leuckart & Rüppell.

REMARKS. The most important characters of this genus are (1) that the longitudinal muscles are grouped into bundles, (2) that the oblique muscles between the longitudinal bands form fascicles and (3) that the nephrostomal lips are long and coiled. It was not, however, until the publication of Spengel's paper in 1912 and Wharton's in 1913 that the taxonomic importance of the condition of the oblique muscles was fully realized. Because some of the descriptions of the earlier species contained no information about the oblique muscles it is often almost impossible to say whether the species are *Ochetostoma* or *Listriolobus*, unless they have been re-examined recently. Sometimes if the species is well illustrated it is possible to tell whether the oblique musculature is fasciculated. For instance, it is clear from Ikeda (1904, fig. 14) that *Thalassema palense* is an *Ochetostoma*. At other times it is impossible to tell. Consequently the generic position of at least eight of the 28 species that we have assigned to this genus is doubtful. They might belong to the genus *Listriolobus*; they are: *O. arkati, O. bombayense, O. caudex, O. decameron, O. hornelli, O. kefersteini, O. kempi* and *O. kokotoniense*.

Many of the species that are listed in this genus need re-examination and redescription. This will be difficult unless specimens from or near the type locality can be found because the holotype material of a number of species has been lost. In addition some of the species were described from single specimens which means

that nothing is known about the variations that occur within the species.   The
following have been described from single specimens: *O. caudex, O. decameron,
O. formosulum, O. hupferi, O. indosinense, O. kempi, O. kokotoniense, O. manjuyodense, O. mercator, O. palense, O. senegalense, O. zanzibarense.*   In addition *O. glaucum,
O. hupferi, O. kokotoniense* and *O. stuhlmanni* were described either from damaged
specimens or specimens the proboscis of which was lacking.

The question of how much variation occurs within a species is an important one
in this genus.   The problem arises most noticeably in the classification of those
species of *Ochetostoma* which possess three pairs of nephridia and 12–18 longitudinal
muscles (see Key below, 8).   Are these 'species' synonymous, are they subspecies
or are they valid?   Wesenberg-Lund (1939d) and Sato (1939) may be correct in
their contention that they are conspecific.   We have, however, refrained from
considering them as synonymous until a closer study can be made of additional
specimens.

We have not been able to construct satisfactorily a complete key to this genus.
We have done little more than arrange the species according to the number of
nephridia that they possess.

The genus is the largest of all the Echiura, although some of the species may be
synonymous.   We have listed 29 species.   Most of them are from tropical and near
tropical waters.

GENUS OCHETOSTOMA—GUIDE TO SPECIES

1 Seven pairs of nephridia, the first pair opening in front of the ventral setae .   .   2
– Five or fewer pairs of nephridia   3
2 Twelve longitudinal muscle bands   .   .   .   .   .   *O. zanzibarense* (p. 442)
– Seven longitudinal muscle bands   .   .   .   .   .   *O. senegalense* (p. 441)
3 Five pairs of nephridia   4
– Four or fewer pairs of nephridia   5
4 First three pairs of nephridia open in front of the setae; 19 longitudinal bands
                                                        O. hornelli (p. 434)
– First two pairs of nephridia open in front of the setae; 10–11 longitudinal bands
                                                        O. bombayense (p. 429)
5 Four pairs of nephridia   6
– Three or fewer pairs of nephridia   7
6 First two pairs of nephridia open in front of the setae; 10 longitudinal bands
                                                        O. decameron (p. 432)
– All nephridia open behind the setae; 20 longitudinal bands   .   *O. kempi* (p. 437)
7 Three pairs of nephridia; only first pair opening in front of the setae   .   .   .   8
– Two pairs of nephridia   9
8 Three pairs of nephridia
      12–13 longitudinal muscle bands   .   .   .   .   .   *O. australiense* (p. 428)
      14–18 longitudinal muscle bands   .   .   .   .   *O. erythrogrammon* (p. 431)
         15 longitudinal muscle bands   .   .   .   .   .   *O. palense* (p. 440)
      15–16 longitudinal muscle bands   .   .   .   .   .   *O. stuhlmanni* (p. 442)
                                                          ⎰   *O. caudex* (p. 430)
      16–18 longitudinal muscle bands   .   .   .   .   ⎱   *O. kokotoniense* (p. 437)
      17–18 longitudinal muscle bands   .   .   .   .   .   *O. griffini* (p. 434)
         18 longitudinal muscle bands   .   .   .   .   .   *O. indosinense* (p. 435)
      21–22 longitudinal muscle bands   .   .   .   .   .   *O. multilineatum* (p. 439)

9   Two pairs of nephridia
    7 longitudinal muscle bands
        (1) with dendritic outgrowths from proboscis   .   .   ***O. septemyotum*** (p. 443)
        (2) without outgrowths from proboscis.   .   .   .   ***O. capense*** (p. 430)
    7–8 longitudinal muscle bands   .   .   .   .   ***O. formosulum*** (p. 433)
    8 longitudinal muscle bands
        (1) with gill-like structure along the basal edge of the proboscis   ***O. arkati*** (p. 428)
        (2) without gill-like structure along the basal edge of the proboscis   ***O. octomyotum***
                                        (p. 440)
    10–11 longitudinal muscle bands   .   .   .   .   ***O. hupferi*** (p. 434)
    12–13 longitudinal muscle bands, with branchial processes attached to the proboscis
                                      O. glaucum (p. 433)
    13 longitudinal muscle bands
        (1) proximal part of proboscis scalloped   .   .   .   ***O. mercator*** (p. 438)
        (2) proximal part of proboscis not scalloped   .   .   ***O. pellucidum*** (p. 441)
    14 longitudinal muscle bands .   .   .   .   .   ***O. manjuyodense*** (p. 438)
    16–17 longitudinal muscle bands; anal vesicles without branched outgrowths   ***O. edax***
                                        (p. 431)
    17–19 longitudinal muscle bands; anal vesicles with short branched outgrowths
                                        O. baronii (p. 429)
    18 longitudinal muscle bands; first pair of nephridia open anterior to the setae
                                        O. kefersteini (p. 435)
    18–21 longitudinal muscle bands; both pairs of nephridia open posterior to the setae
                                        O. myersae (p. 439)

Ochetostoma arkati (Prashad, 1935)

Thalassema arkati Prashad, 1935 : 41–42, figs 1–4.
Ochetostoma arkati : Wesenberg-Lund, 1959a : 203–204, figs 13, 14; 1963 : 141.

TYPE LOCALITY. Sandheads, Calcutta. *Type.* Museum Zoological Survey of India. Holotype W3168/1; paratypes W3176/1.

DESCRIPTION. Proboscis short and stumpy, a third to quarter of the total length of the animal; the edges of the posterior half form short, branched, gill-like processes. Trunk oval, covered with minute oval or round papillae which are very sparse or absent in the middle region. Anal opening surrounded by a number of elongate papillae. Colour creamy to yellow in preserved specimens. Longitudinal muscles gathered into eight bands. Two pairs of tubular nephridia, that are almost as long as the trunk; lips of the nephrostome drawn out into long spiral filaments. Anal vesicles yellowish, very thin and about a third of the length of the animal.

REMARKS. Described from three specimens. Wesenberg-Lund (1959a) reported 13 more specimens that agreed with Prashad's description of the species except that the number of longitudinal muscle bands was 7–8 instead of eight. Wesenberg-Lund (1959a) and Fisher (1946 : 241) consider that the species is an *Ochetostoma*.

DISTRIBUTION. Calcutta, India (Prashad, 1935); African coast, Nigeria and Cape Town (Wesenberg-Lund, 1959a).

Ochetostoma australiense Edmonds, 1960

Ochetostoma australiense Edmonds, 1960 : 93–94, pl. 2b, fig. 4.

TYPE LOCALITY. Dunwich (Stradbroke Island), Queensland. *Type.* Australian Museum, Sydney.

DESCRIPTION. This species closely resembles *Ochetostoma erythrogrammon* Leuck. & Ruep., which has 14–18 longitudinal muscle bands. The Australian specimens have 12–13, very occasionally 11–14 longitudinal bands. Proboscis up to 41 mm long and not readily deciduous. Trunk up to 102 mm long and usually reddish or violet in colour. Two ventral setae with an interbasal muscle. Three pairs of nephridia, the first pair opening in front of the setae; nephrostome lips spirally coiled. Rectal caecum present. Anal vesicles long and brown and covered with numerous tubules. Transverse muscle bands between the longitudinal bands well defined.

REMARKS. Known from about 50 specimens.

DISTRIBUTION. Known to occur along the eastern coast of Australia from near the mouth of the River Clarence, New South Wales, northwards, to Townsville, Queensland.

Ochetostoma baronii (Greeff, 1879)

Thalassema baronii Greeff, 1879 : 151, pl. 6, figs 62–67; Selenka, 1885 : 8; Shipley, 1899c : 55–56; 1899b : 336, 345–346, pl. 33, figs 1, 7; Sluiter, 1902 : 47; Augener, 1903 : 348; Verrill, 1904 : 40–41; Lanchester, 1905b : 34; Fischer, 1922e : 15; Hérubel, 1924 : 108–109; ten Broeke, 1925 : 94.
Ochetostoma baronii : Stephen, 1960a : 513; Mackie, 1961 : 247–249, fig. 1; Fischer, 1946 : 241.

TYPE LOCALITY. Arrecife, Canary Islands.

DESCRIPTION. Proboscis up to 60 mm in length, light green on the dorsal side and brownish to flesh-coloured on the ventral side. Trunk up to 80 mm in length; dark green in colour with violet longitudinal muscle bands and white papillae scattered over the surface. Longitudinal muscle bands gathered into 17–19 bundles. Two pairs of nephridia; nephrostome with spirally coiled openings. Anal vesicles are long brown tubes, pointed anteriorly and bearing short branching outgrowths.

REMARKS. Shipley (1899b, fig. 7) shows clearly that the oblique musculature between adjacent longitudinal muscle bands is grouped into transverse fascicles.

DISTRIBUTION. Atlantic Ocean: Morocco (Hérubel, 1924); Canary Is. (Greeff, 1879; Mackie, 1961); Senegal (Stephen, 1960a); Bahia (Selenka, 1885; Shipley, 1899); West Indies (Fischer, 1922e; ten Broeke, 1925); Florida (Fischer, 1922e); Bermuda (Verrill, 1904). Indian Ocean: Zanzibar (Lanchester, 1905b); Christmas Island (Shipley, 1899; Sluiter, 1902); Amboina (Augener, 1903). Pacific Ocean: Loyalty Islands; Papua (Shipley, 1899b).

Ochetostoma bombayense (Prashad & Awati, 1929)

Thalassema bombayensis Prashad & Awati, 1929 : 259–262, pl. 12.
Ochetostoma bombayense : Fisher, 1946 : 241.

TYPE LOCALITY. Intertidal beaches near Bombay. *Type.* Museum of the Zoological Survey of India. W1525/1.

DESCRIPTION. Proboscis long and tubular with the edges free to the base; broadly truncate at the anterior end and up to 24 mm long. Trunk 70–120 mm long and 25 mm wide; covered with two kinds of papillae. In the mid-region of the trunk the papillae are minute but on the anterior and posterior region of the trunk they are larger and more numerous. The longitudinal muscles are normally gathered into 10 bands but in some specimens one band is split, giving 11 bands in all. Normally there are five pairs of nephridia, but in some specimens the fifth pair is vestigial; the two anterior pairs occur in front of the setae. The nephrostomes are very much elongated and the lips drawn out into long coiled filaments. Anal vesicles almost as long as the trunk and very thin anteriorly; the funnels occur on the anterior third. No intestinal caecum present.

REMARKS. The generic position of this species is uncertain. Fisher (1946 : 241) assigned it to the genus *Ochetostoma* but there seems to be no evidence that the oblique muscles between the longitudinal bands are grouped into bundles. The species may be a *Listriolobus*. Described from numerous specimens.

DISTRIBUTION. As for the type locality.

Ochetostoma caudex (Lampert, 1883)

Thalassema caudex Lampert, 1883 : 340; Shipley, 1898 : 472, pl. 37, fig. 11; 1899b : 346; Sluiter, 1902 : 49; Prashad, 1935 : 39–40.
Ochetostoma caudex Fisher, 1946 : 241.

TYPE LOCALITY. Red Sea.

DESCRIPTION. Proboscis of preserved specimens 18–25 mm long and body 50–70 mm. Colour of preserved specimens leather-brown (Lampert) but living specimens are green with red longitudinal stripes marking the muscle bands (Shipley, 1899b : 364). Papillae lie on raised ridges which correspond to the longitudinal muscle bands; they are very numerous and are arranged in plaques posteriorly. Longitudinal muscles gathered into 16–18 bundles. Nephridia in three pairs with the anterior pair opening in front of the ventral setae; nephrostome with spirally twisted lips. Anal vesicles consist of two long, brown tubes.

REMARKS. Figure 11 (Shipley, 1898, pl. 37) suggests that the oblique muscles between the longitudinal muscle bands are formed into bundles. Both Sato (1939 : 357) and Wesenberg-Lund (1939d : 46) consider that *O. caudex* and *O. erythrogrammon* are synonymous. *O. erythrogrammon* is the older name.

DISTRIBUTION. Red Sea and Indian Ocean (Lampert, 1883); Rotuma (Shipley, 1898); Andaman and Nicobar Islands (Prashad, 1935).

Ochetostoma capense Jones & Stephen, 1955

Ochetostoma capensis Jones & Stephen, 1955 : 273–278, figs 1–3; Wesenberg-Lund, 1963 : 142.

TYPE LOCALITY. Zwartkops River, Port Elizabeth, Cape Province, South Africa.
Type. Royal Scottish Museum.

DESCRIPTION. Proboscis in preserved specimens about one eighth of the length of the body and in living specimens one twelfth to one third; the ventral edges are crenate, when the proboscis is extended, but are thrown into a series of tight ridges when contracted. Colour cream to light orange. Trunk up to 120 mm when extended, thickly covered with papillae in the anterior ventral region, but less thickly covered towards the posterior end. Trunk cylindrical or sausage shaped; the posterior region often drawn out into an apical projection. The longitudinal muscles are gathered into seven main bands which are most conspicuous at the anterior and posterior regions. Oblique muscles between the longitudinal muscles form fascicles. The longitudinal muscles are gathered into seven main bands, with a few weakly developed ones in between. Sometimes these intermediates may be as well developed as the main ones. The bands are most conspicuous at the anterior and posterior ends. Two pairs of nephridia usually half to three quarters as long as the body, but sometimes quite short; lips of nephrostomes extended into long spiral filaments. Anal vesicles two long thin brown tubes a quarter to three quarters of the length of the body and bearing minute funnels which are most numerous towards the free end. Rectal caecum present.

REMARKS. Based on a large number of specimens. The species differs from *O. septemyotum* Datta Gupta, Menon & Johnson (1963) most noticeably in the structure of the proboscis.

DISTRIBUTION. Zwartkops River and Langebaan Lagoon; Durban Bay (South Africa).

Ochetostoma edax Fisher, 1946

Ochetostoma edax Fisher, 1946 : 245–247, text-fig. 14.

TYPE LOCALITY. Pichalingue Bay, La Pas, Baja California. *Type.* U.S.N.M. no. 20606.

DESCRIPTION. Proboscis fleshy, deciduous and up to a quarter of the length of the trunk. Trunk up to 50 mm in length and translucent in the middle region. Papillae numerous and usually larger on the posterior third or fourth of the trunk. Longitudinal muscles gathered into 16–17 bands; the interspaces are very narrow. There is an interbasal muscle between the setae. Two pairs of nephridia opening posteriorly to the setae; nephrostomes with long coiled lips. Anal vesicles, often of large size, covered with ciliated funnels; unbranched. Dorsal and neuro-intestinal blood vessels connected through a ring vessel.

REMARKS. Known from several specimens. It is closely related to *O. baronii*.

DISTRIBUTION. California.

Ochetostoma erythrogrammon Leuckart & Rüppell, 1828
(Fig. 55A–B)

Ochetostoma erythrogrammon Leuckart & Rüppell, 1828 : 7–8, pl. 2, fig. 3; Fischer, 1926 : 109–116; Sato, 1935b : 298, pl. 4, fig. 21; 1939 : 341, 357–359; Wesenberg-Lund, 1939d : 46–48, figs 1 and 2; 1954b : 383–384; 1957b : 9–11, fig. 2; 1959b : 69; 1959a : 202–203; Stephen, 1952 : 181; Stephen & Robertson, 1952 : 430–432, text-fig. 2.

Thalassema erythrogrammon: M. Müller, 1852 : 16; Greeff, 1879 : 147; von Drasche, 1881 : 624; Sluiter, 1884 : 58–60, pl. 3; 1891 : 110–111; Shipley, 1899b : 337, pl. 33, fig. 4; 1902c : 128–129, pl. 6, fig. 1; Hérubel, 1904a : 564; Spengel, 1912b : 309.

TYPE LOCALITY.   Red Sea (Jubal Island).

DESCRIPTION.   Proboscis one third to three quarters of the length of the body; dorsal surface bright green, ventral side yellow with a violet line on each side. Body up to 80–160 mm in length; posterior region violet and marked with light to dark red longitudinal grooves.   Longitudinal muscles gathered into 14 bundles (14–18 according to Fischer, 1926a : 115).   Transverse fascicles of oblique muscles lie between the longitudinal muscles.   Three pairs of nephridia, the first pair opening in front of the setae; nephrostome with spirally coiled lips.   Rectal caecum present. Anal vesicles are very thin brown tubes.

REMARKS.   This species, originally described from the Red Sea, has been reported from both the Indian and Pacific Oceans.   A number of other species have been described with similar internal anatomy but with a different number of longitudinal muscle bands, usually 13–18.   The taxonomic position of some of these species, all of which are listed in the key on p. 427, is uncertain.   Wesenberg-Lund (1939d) considers that some and Sato (1939) that many of them are identical with *O. erythrogrammon*.   At the present time we are not prepared to make this assumption.

DISTRIBUTION.   Mediterranean (Hérubel, 1904); Red Sea (Stephen, 1952; Wesenberg-Lund, 1957b); Indian Ocean: Zanzibar (Stephen & Robertson, 1952); Cape Province, Mauritius (Wesenberg-Lund, 1959b); Indonesia (Sluiter, 1902); Annam (Wesenberg-Lund, 1959a); Indian Ocean (Shipley, 1899b, 1902c).   Pacific Ocean (Wesenberg-Lund, 1954b); Japan (Sato, 1935).

Ochetostoma decameron (Lanchester, 1905)

Thalassema decameron Lanchester, 1905a : 35, pl. 1, fig. 5.
Ochetostoma decameron: Fisher, 1946 : 241.

TYPE LOCALITY.   Ohwaka Bay, Zanzibar.   *Type*.   Brit. Mus. (Nat. Hist.) 1924.3.1.182.

DESCRIPTION.   Proboscis not described.   Body wall extremely thin.   Longitudinal muscles gathered into 10 bands.   Four pairs of nephridia; they are small and only slightly elongated.   Two pairs lie in front of the ventral setae.   Anal vesicles long and broad, brown at the base, tapering and largely transparent.

REMARKS.   Known only from the holotype.   This species is not well known, Lanchester's description is brief and the taxonomic position of the species is uncertain.   There is no evidence that the oblique muscles are grouped into transverse bundles and the nephrostomal lips are small and only slightly elongated.   Consequently it might justifiably be placed in the genus *Listriolobus* rather than *Ochetostoma*.   The fact that it possesses four pairs of nephridia, however, places it nearer the latter than the former genus.   The holotype is very damaged and the muscle systems are not clearly evident.

DISTRIBUTION.   As for the type locality.

ECHIURIDAE

433

Ochetostoma formosulum (Lampert, 1883)

Thalassema formosulum Lampert, 1883 : 339–340; Shipley, 1899b : 348; Sluiter, 1902 : 48;
  Wharton, 1913 : 248–249; Prashad, 1921 : 35–37.
Ochetostoma formosulum: Fisher, 1946 : 241; Wesenberg-Lund, 1963 : 140; Datta Gupta *et al.*,
  1963 : 57.

TYPE LOCALITY. Manila.

DESCRIPTION. Proboscis 8 mm long. Average length of body 30 mm; preserved
specimens white in colour. White papillae scattered uniformly over the body.
Skin very thin. Longitudinal muscles gathered into 7–8 bands. Two pairs of
nephridia, both of which open posterior to the ventral setae; nephrostomal lips
with spirally twisted openings. Rectal caecum present. Two broad, sac-like,
anal vesicles.

REMARKS. According to Prashad (1921), Thurston (1895) probably gave the name
formolosum to this echiuran without actually describing it. Wesenberg-Lund
(1963) and Datta Gupta *et al.* (1963) have classified the species as an *Ochetostoma.*
Described originally from a single specimen.

DISTRIBUTION. Manila; Shanghai (Lampert, 1883); Indonesia (Sluiter, 1902);
India (Prashad, 1921; Datta Gupta *et al.*, 1963).

Ochetostoma glaucum (Wesenberg-Lund, 1957)

Platylobostoma glaucum Wesenberg-Lund, 1957c : 8–10, figs 3–6.
Ochetostoma atlantidei Wesenberg-Lund, 1959a : 204–207, figs 15–16.

TYPE LOCALITY. West coast, Africa (5°41'S, 11°38'W); at 40 m.

DESCRIPTION. Proboscis 6 mm in length and spoon-shaped; borders not fused at
the base. Anterior edge straight and smooth; the distal part of the lateral edges
is also smooth, but the proximal part carries two rows of processes. The outer
row consists of rather long lobes with slightly scalloped edges; edges of the inner
row almost straight. Two golden sickle-shaped ventral setae. Skin smooth with
only a few rings of papillae on the posterior part of the trunk. Trunk about 22 mm
in length. Twelve to thirteen longitudinal muscle bands; the zones between them
crossed by numerous separate fascicles of oblique muscle. Intestine attached to
the body wall by numerous frenula. A pre-cloacal caecum present. Nephridia,
two pairs of small digitiform sacs of equal size, inserted just posterior to the setae.
Nephrostomal lips long and coiled. Anal vesicles are two thin-walled unbranched
tubes, one third of the length of the body.

REMARKS. *Platylobostoma glaucum* was described from two rather badly preserved
specimens without a proboscis. *O. atlantidei* was described from a single specimen
and considered to be different from *P. glaucum* because it possessed a well developed
proboscis. Because (1) the proboscis of many echiurans is easily detached, (2) the
descriptions of the two species are similar and (3) the specimens were found near
each other, we consider that *Platylobostoma* is a synonym of *Ochetostoma.*

DISTRIBUTION. As for the type locality and off the West African coast (9°28′N, 14°58′W at 50 m).

Ochetostoma griffini (Wharton, 1913)

Thalassema griffini Wharton, 1913 : 249–258, figs 2–7.
Ochetostoma griffini Fisher, 1946 : 241.

TYPE LOCALITY. Port Galera, Mindoro, Philippines.

DESCRIPTION. Proboscis 50–80 mm in length. Body 12–14 mm in length and covered with small papillae which are most prominent anteriorly and posteriorly. Three pairs of nephridia, the first opening in front of the setae. Nephrostomes, spirally coiled. Longitudinal muscles gathered into 17–18 bands. Anal vesicles one third as long as the body and covered with very small ciliated funnels.

REMARKS. Known originally from numerous specimens. There seems little doubt that this species is an *Ochetostoma* because Wharton grouped it with those echiurans with musculature like that of *T. erythrogrammon*.

DISTRIBUTION. As for the type locality.

Ochetostoma hornelli (Prashad, 1921)

Thalassema hornelli Prashad, 1921 : 36–37.
Ochetostoma hornelli : Fisher, 1946 : 241.

TYPE LOCALITY. Gulf of Manaar. *Type.* Lost.

DESCRIPTION. Proboscis short, 11 mm, covered with minute papillae; margins of proboscis free to the base. Body 82 mm long, cylindrical, covered with minute irregularly arranged papillae, which are larger at the anterior and posterior ends. Longitudinal muscles gathered into 19 bands. Five pairs of nephridia with large nephrostomes, the lips of which are long and spirally coiled; three pairs lie in front of the setae. Anal vesicles well-developed and half the length of the body; each has three rows of funnels extending over about the half length of the vesicle.

REMARKS. Described originally from two specimens; no other records. The taxonomic position of this species is uncertain. Nothing is known about the condition of the oblique musculature and the species might belong to the genus *Listriolobus*.

DISTRIBUTION. As for the type locality.

Ochetostoma hupferi (Fischer, 1895)

Thalassema hupferi Fischer, 1895 : 20–21; 1914a : 78; Shipley, 1899b : 348; Bock, 1942 : 25.
Ochetostoma hupferi Fisher, 1946 : 241.

TYPE LOCALITY. Nyango, West Africa; at 11 m.

DESCRIPTION. Proboscis 5 mm in length, edges wrinkled but smooth at the base. Trunk small, light yellow in colour and covered with small uniformly distributed papillae. Longitudinal muscles gathered into 10–11 bands. Ventral setae large, golden-yellow in colour. Two pairs of nephridia; nephrostomes with spirally coiled openings. Anal vesicles lost.

REMARKS. Described from a single damaged specimen; no other records This species seems to be an *Ochetostoma* because Fischer described the existence of fine grooves of ring muscles between the longitudinal bands of muscles. Fischer (1914a) reported the presence of two pairs of nephridia.

ISTRIBUTION. As for the type locality.

Ochetostoma indosinense Wesenberg-Lund, 1939

Ochetostoma indosinense Wesenberg-Lund, 1939d : 48–51, text-figs 3–4.

TYPE LOCALITY. Nhatrang, South Annam.

DESCRIPTION. Proboscis 9 mm long, slightly bifurcated; ventral and terminal rims crenated and the margins are rolled so that a spoon-like cavity is formed. Dorsal surface covered with ovoid or cylindrical papillae, more densely crowded at the margins; light green in life. Body 50 mm long, rather pointed at each end; body wall rather thick, tough and opaque at the ends, very much thinner and transparent in the middle. Entire surface covered with papillae like those on the proboscis; in the mid-region of the trunk they are minute and at the two ends more crowded and prominent. Colour of body pink. Two ventral setae but no inter-basal muscle. Longitudinal muscles gathered into 18 bundles with narrow inter-spaces. No rectal caecum. Three pairs of small nephridia, the anteriormost pair of which lies in front of the setae. Nephrostomal lips long but not coiled. Anal vesicles very long and ciliated funnels unstalked.

REMARKS. The proboscis of this species (Wesenberg-Lund, 1939d, fig. 3) is not that of the typical *Ochetostoma* and the nephrostomal lips are not coiled. The longitudinal muscles are grouped into bands and there are transverse bands of muscle although Wesenberg-Lund does not make it clear that the bands lie between the longitudinal muscles. She says: 'The longitudinal as well as the annular musculature of the dermal muscle layers is divided into bundles. The oblique muscle layer is very thin and continuous—following the inner side of the longitudinal muscle.' Wesenberg-Lund also likened the species to *Listriolobus sorbillans*.

Known only from the holotype.

DISTRIBUTION. As for the type locality.

Ochetostoma kefersteini (ten Broeke, 1925)

Thalassema kefersteini ten Broeke, 1925 : 94; Bock, 1942 : 25.

TYPE LOCALITY. Spanish Haven, West Indies.

DESCRIPTION. Proboscis 12 mm in length and translucent. Skin transparent so that the longitudinal muscles, gut and nerve cord are clearly seen. The two ventral setae are shining golden, 2 mm in length and bent. Small papillae are present only on the anterior and posterior ends of the body. Longitudinal muscles

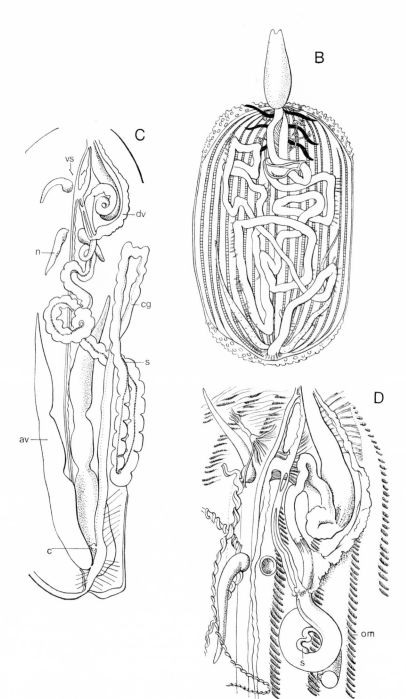
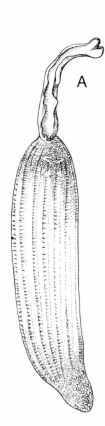

gathered into 18 bands.   The spaces between the bands are about one fifth of the width of the bands.   Two pairs of large nephridia, one pair opening anterior to the setae; nephrostomal lips spirally coiled.   The anal trees are straight and rather more than half the length of the body; they are fastened by mesenteries posteriorly.

REMARKS.   Described from several specimens.   Bock (1942 : 25) re-examined some of ten Broeke's specimens from Curaçao and found that the species possesses two pairs of nephridia with spirally coiled lips.   Ten Broeke described only one pair without coiled nephrostomal lips.

The taxonomic position of the species, however, is uncertain because nothing is known about the structure of the muscle layer between the longitudinal bands. The species may be a *Listriolobus*.

DISTRIBUTION.   West Indies.

Ochetostoma kempi (Prashad, 1919)

Thalassema kempi Prashad, 1919a : 336–337, fig. 2; 1935 : 41.
Ochetostoma kempi: Fisher, 1946 : 241.

TYPE LOCALITY.   Andaman Islands.   *Type*. Zoological Survey of India. W194/4.

DESCRIPTION.   Proboscis short and stumpy with its lateral edges rolled together; yellowish in colour and covered with minute papillae.   Body cylindrical, tapering at each end, 77 mm in length and covered with small papillae which increase in size at the posterior end where they are very large.   The longitudinal muscles are gathered into 20 bands.   Four pairs of nephridia, all of which lie behind the setae; nephrostome with spirally coiled lips.   Anal vesicles much contracted, about one third the length of the body and light yellow in colour.

REMARKS.   Nothing is known about the condition of the oblique musculature between the longitudinal muscle bands.   Consequently whether the species is an *Ochetostoma* or *Listriolobus* cannot be decided.

Known only from the holotype.

DISTRIBUTION.   As for the type locality.

Ochetostoma kokotoniense (Fischer, 1892)

Thalassema kokotoniense Fischer, 1892 : 82, fig. 1; 1895 : 20; 1914b : 18–19; Sluiter, 1902 :
    46–47; Ikeda, 1904 : 60–61, fig. 17; Shipley, 1899b : 337, pl. 33, fig. 3.
Ochetostoma kokotoniense: Fisher, 1946 : 241.

TYPE LOCALITY.   Kokotoni, Zanzibar.

DESCRIPTION.   Proboscis lacking on the type specimen.   Body 42–45 mm long, 17 mm broad and expanded posteriorly.   Colour bluish-light green; darker

FIG. 55.   (A–B) *Ochetostoma erythrogrammon*.   (A) Entire animal; about two thirds natural size (after Sluiter).   (B) Dissected specimen.   (C–D) *Ochetostoma octomyotum*.   (C) Dissected specimen.   The spiral lips of the nephridia and the longitudinal muscle bands have been omitted.   (D) Anterior region with details, showing the fasciculation of the oblique musculature between the longitudinal bands.   (C–D after Fisher.)   KEY: *See* Fig. 53, p. 417.

posteriorly.   Smaller papillae distributed over the whole surface in definite transverse rows, interrupted by rings of larger papillae.   The longitudinal muscles are
gathered into 17–18 bands.   Three pairs of nephridia, the first pair opening in front
of the setae; nephrostomal lips spirally coiled.   Anal vesicles with well marked
funnels.

REMARKS.   Described from a single specimen.   It is not clear from Fischer's
description or his fig. 1 whether the species is an *Ochetostoma* or *Listriolobus*.
Shipley's fig. 3 of a specimen from New Britain suggests that the oblique musculature
between the longitudinal bands is grouped into fascicles.   The taxonomic position
of the species, however, is uncertain.   Wesenberg-Lund (1939d : 46) and Sato
(1939 : 357) consider that the species is synonymous with *O. erythrogrammon*.
O. stuhlmanni Fischer, 1892, also from Zanzibar, is closely related but differs in
having 15–16 longitudinal muscle bands.

DISTRIBUTION.   Zanzibar (Fischer, 1892); Indonesia (Sluiter, 1902); Japan
(Ikeda, 1904); New Britain (Shipley, 1899).

Ochetostoma manjuyodense (Ikeda, 1905)

Thalassema manjuyodense Ikeda, 1905 : 172–173, pl. 8, figs 9–10.
Ochetostoma manjuyodense: Fisher, 1946 : 241; 1948b : 275.

TYPE LOCALITY.   Manjuyodi, Philippines.

DESCRIPTION.   Proboscis unknown.   Body broad, spindle-like in form, 18 mm in
length; the skin has a greyish-green tint.   The papillae are very small, almost
invisible to the naked eye, except at the posterior end of the body where they
are somewhat larger and arranged almost in circular rows.   Ventral setae relatively
large and golden-yellow in colour; interbasal muscle present which extends over the
pharynx.   Longitudinal muscles gathered into 14 broad bands.   Two pairs of
short tubular nephridia, provided with long spiral lobes; all are situated posterior
to the ventral setae.   Anal vesicles brown and longer than half the body; over their
surface are distributed numerous short-stalked funnels which are large enough to be
seen with the naked eye.   A globular rectal caecum is situated on the ventral
surface of the terminal portion of the rectum; it is attached to the nerve cord by a
delicate mesentery.

REMARKS.   Described originally from a single specimen.   Fisher (1948b : 275)
merely recorded it from Hawaii.   He must have been satisfied that it was an
Ochetostoma.   The species is closely related to *O. pellucidum* (Fischer).

DISTRIBUTION.   Manjuyodi, Philippines (Ikeda); Halape, Hawaii (Fisher).

Ochetostoma mercator Wesenberg-Lund, 1954

Ochetostoma mercator Wesenberg-Lund, 1954a : 13–16, text-figs 1–3.

TYPE LOCALITY.   Angola Bay, Cape Province.

DESCRIPTION.   Proboscis 5 mm in length, broad, fleshy and non-deciduous;
margins free to the base and proximal part scalloped.   Body 2·5 mm long with

30–35 rings of large oblong papillae. The posterior region is produced into a narrow stem, in the centre of which lies the anus. The longitudinal muscles are gathered into 13 bands. There are two pairs of nephridia; nephrostomal lips long and spirally coiled. Anal vesicles long, unbranched tubes.

REMARKS. Known only from the holotype. The species is an *Ochetostoma* because 'the interior layer of muscles is grouped into small bundles which cross the intervals between the longitudinal muscles' (Wesenberg-Lund, 1954).

DISTRIBUTION. Angola Bay, Cape Province, South Africa.

Ochetostoma multilineatum (Fischer, 1914)

Thalassema multilineatum Fischer, 1914a : 78–80, pl. 2, figs 10–11; 1914b : 20.

TYPE LOCALITY. West African coast; no precise locality.

DESCRIPTION. Proboscis lacking. Body 75 mm in length, 30–32 mm in breadth. Longitudinal muscles gathered into 21–22 longitudinal bands. Three pairs of nephridia; nephrostome with spirally coiled lips. Length of anal vesicles about one quarter that of the body. Rectal caecum present but no interbasal muscle.

REMARKS. Known only from the holotype. The 1914b reference is simply a repetition of the earlier record. No other records. Figures 10 and 11 of Fischer (1914a) clearly show that the oblique muscle between the longitudinal bands is in bundles.

DISTRIBUTION. As for the type locality.

Ochetostoma myersae Edmonds, 1963

Ochetostoma myersae Edmonds, 1963 : 245–246, pl. 1, fig. 2.

TYPE LOCALITY. Long Reef, near Sydney, N.S.W. (Australia). *Type*. Australian Museum, Sydney.

DESCRIPTION. Proboscis about one quarter as long as the trunk. Trunk sausage-shaped and green in colour; 25–35 mm long and 9–15 mm wide. Trunk covered with soft, white, wart-like papillae which are largest on the posterior third. Longitudinal muscles in 18–21 bands. Oblique muscles between the bands grouped rather weakly into fascicles. Two pairs of nephridia that lie posterior to the setae; nephrostomal lips long and thread-like and only weakly coiled. Two prominent setae and a strong interbasal muscle. Anal vesicles long and thin and do not branch. Rectal caecum present.

REMARKS. Described from four specimens. There is no possibility of these specimens being the same as the *Listriolobus sorbillans* (Lampert) reported from Sydney by Augener (1903 : 349). *L. sorbillans* has only 13 longitudinal muscle bands.

DISTRIBUTION. As for the type locality.

Ochetostoma octomyotum Fisher, 1946

(Fig. 55C–D)

Ochetostoma octomyotum Fisher, 1946 : 241–245, pl. 21, fig. 3, pls 23, 24.

TYPE LOCALITY. Cabrillo Beach, Newport Bay, Orange County, California. *Type.* U.S.N.M. no. 20607.

DESCRIPTION. Proboscis thick and fleshy in preserved specimens; length one third that of the body. Skin translucent, closely stippled everywhere with small unequal, often elliptical glands which increase markedly over the posterior region. Body in the largest specimen measures 110 mm in length. Longitudinal muscles gathered into eight bands. The ventral setae have no interbasal muscle. Two pairs of nephridia; nephrostome with specially long, spirally coiled lips. Spherical caecum present on the rectum. Anal vesicles long, with pointed apex and covered with small ciliated funnels.

REMARKS. Described originally from several specimens. No other record. The careful drawings shown in plates 23 and 24 of Fisher, 1946 show the condition of the oblique muscles between the longitudinal bands that is a characteristic of this genus.

DISTRIBUTION. As for the type locality.

Ochetostoma palense (Ikeda, 1924)

Thalassema palense Ikeda, 1924 : 39–41, figs 13–15.

TYPE LOCALITY. Misaki, Palau Islands, Japan.

DESCRIPTION. Proboscis about a quarter as long as the trunk, slender and about 2 mm in width; apex truncate. Trunk about 22 mm in length, pear-shaped and 8 mm at its widest part. Skin thin and somewhat transparent, covered with minute low papillae, larger and more crowded at the anterior and posterior ends. Bright green in life. Longitudinal muscle bands gathered into 15 bands which are apparent only on a small portion of the anterior part of the trunk. Ventral setae minute, golden-yellow in colour; no interbasal muscle. Alimentary canal short in comparison with the trunk. Three pairs of nephridia, the first pair opening in front of the ventral setae; nephrostome with curved or only slightly spirally coiled lips. Anal vesicles two large thin walled tubes, over half the length of the trunk; they carry a few unstalked funnels. No rectal caecum.

REMARKS. Known only from the holotype. Ikeda's fig. 14 shows that the muscles between the longitudinal bands are grouped into fascicles. Wesenberg-Lund (1939d : 46) considered that this species is the same as *O. erythrogrammon*. Although the resemblance between the two species is close, the Japanese specimen has a comparatively short alimentary canal and nephrostomal lips that are only slightly coiled and lacks an interbasal muscle and a rectal caecum. For these reasons we have refrained from placing the species in the synonymy of *O. erythrogrammon*.

DISTRIBUTION. As for the type locality.

Ochetostoma pellucidum (Fischer, 1895)

Thalassema pellucidum Fischer, 1895 : 19; 1914a : 78; Shipley, 1899b : 351.
Ochetostoma pellucidum: Fisher, 1946 : 241; Wesenberg-Lund, 1954a : 12.

TYPE LOCALITY.   Whydah, West Africa, at 10 m.

DESCRIPTION.   Proboscis, up to 6 mm in length, margins thick but free to the base.   Trunk up to 25 mm long, light green to bluish in colour; opaque anteriorly and posteriorly but transparent in the middle region.   The surface of the trunk is covered with papillae which are larger and more densely packed at the posterior region.   Longitudinal muscles gathered into 13 bands that are visible through the skin.   Ventral setae large.   Two pairs of nephridia with nephrostomes which have spirally coiled lips.   Anal vesicles about a quarter as long as the body, with single tubules each of which terminates in a funnel.   Rectum fastened to the body wall by numerous mesenteries.

REMARKS.   Described originally from several specimens.   No figure of this species seems to have been drawn.   Wesenberg-Lund's classification of the species as an *Ochetostoma* was made after she had examined specimens from French Guinea.

DISTRIBUTION.   Whydah, West Africa (Fischer, 1895); French Guinea (Wesenberg-Lund, 1954a).

Ochetostoma senegalense Stephen, 1960

Ochetostoma senegalense Stephen, 1960 : 513–514.

TYPE LOCALITY.   Devant Gorée, Senegal.   *Type.*   Museum d'Histoire Naturelle, Paris.

DESCRIPTION.   Proboscis 55 mm in length, thick and fleshy and covered with minute papillae; edges rolled to form a cylinder, except at the anterior tip.   Trunk 106 mm in length and more or less uniform in breadth measuring 30 mm; thick and fleshy anteriorly, thin and almost translucent towards the posterior end.   The anterior third of the trunk is thickly covered with round and oval papillae, up to about 5 mm in diameter.   The middle portion is practically smooth; the posterior portion carries papillae similar to the anterior ones except that they are larger and arranged in transverse rows.   Ventral setae not observed.   Longitudinal muscles gathered into seven strong bands, visible only on the anterior third of the animal.   Seven pairs of nephridia, full of minute ova.   Anal vesicles, long, thin, narrow tubes about one third as long as the trunk.

REMARKS.   Known only from the holotype.   It closely resembles *O. zanzibarense* Stephen, the only other species known to possess seven pairs of nephridia.

DISTRIBUTION.   As for the type locality.

DD

Ochetostoma zanzibarense Stephen & Robertson, 1952

Ochetostoma zanzibarense Stephen & Robertson, 1952 : 431–432, pl. 1, fig. 1; Wesenberg-Lund,
    1959a : 69–70; Datta Gupta & Menon, 1961 : 829–830, text-fig. 1; Datta Gupta, Menon &
    Johnson, 1963 : 61.

TYPE LOCALITY. Bat Island, Zanzibar. *Type.* Royal Scottish Museum.

DESCRIPTION. Proboscis is a short thick truncated triangle covered with papillae
and about 25 mm in length. Trunk 112 mm in length, covered with rounded papillae.
Papillae are large and crowded at the anterior end, small and scattered in the middle
region and very large at the posterior end. Longitudinal muscles gathered into
12 bands. Seven pairs of nephridia, the first pair opening in front of the ventral
setae; nephrostome with spirally coiled lips. Rectal caecum present. Anal vesicles
half as long as the body.

REMARKS. Described originally from a single specimen. Wesenberg-Lund
described another very similar to the original specimen. Datta Gupta also gave a
short description of the species.

DISTRIBUTION. Zanzibar (Stephen & Robertson, 1952); Mauritius (Wesenberg-
Lund, 1959a); Gulf of Kutch (Datta Gupta, 1961, 1963).

Ochetostoma stuhlmanni (Fischer, 1892)

Thalassema stuhlmanni Fischer, 1892 : 5–6, fig. 22; 1895 : 20, fig. 22; 1914b : 19; Shipley,
    1899b : 352; Augener, 1903 : 349.
Ochetostoma stuhlmanni: Fisher, 1946 : 241.
Thalassema leptodermon Fischer, 1892 : 6–7, fig. 3; 1895 : 20; 1914b : 19; Shipley, 1899b : 349;
    Augener, 1903 : 349.
Ochetostoma leptodermon: Fisher, 1946 : 241.

TYPE LOCALITY. Bueni Reef, Zanzibar.

DESCRIPTION. Proboscis about 0·5 mm long, broader towards the apex. Body
20 mm long and light brownish-grey in colour; body form the same as that of *O.
kokotoniense*. Darker at the posterior end. The surface of the body is covered with
papillae which are small in the anterior part and arranged more or less in transverse
rows. Papillae larger in the posterior third of the body. Longitudinal muscles
arranged in 15–16 bands. Ventral setae small, golden-yellow in colour. Three
pairs of nephridia, the first pair opening in front of the setae. A large ball-shaped
rectal caecum which is attached by a mesentery to the nerve cord. Anal vesicles
half as long as the body and with a conspicuous funnel.

REMARKS. Described from three mutilated specimens. The species is probably
an *Ochetostoma* because Fischer (1895 : 20) refers to the ring musculature of a specimen as being in bundles.

It is difficult to find any character that will distinguish *O. stuhlmanni* and *O.
leptodermon*. Both were described from Zanzibar and Fischer (1914b : 19), himself,
remarked that the two might be the same. We have refrained from placing them
in the synonymy of *O. kokotoniense*, also described from Zanzibar, because the latter

has 17–18 longitudinal muscles. Wesenberg-Lund (1963 : 46) and Sato (1939 : 357) considered that all three species were the same and identical with *O. erythrogrammon*.

DISTRIBUTION. Zanzibar (Fischer, 1892); Pangani (Fischer, 1895); Society Is. (Augener, 1903).

Ochetostoma septemyotum Datta Gupta, Menon & Johnson, 1963

Ochetostoma septemyotum Datta Gupta *et al.*, 1963 : 57–60, fig. 2A.

TYPE LOCALITY. Tangasseri, Quillon, India. *Holotype and paratype.* Zoology Museum, Birla Institute of Science and Technology, Pilani, India.

DESCRIPTION. Proboscis a fleshy structure, tapering slightly at the tip, with the lateral margins produced into a series of folds with dendritic outgrowths bent inwards towards the groove in the proboscis. A small portion of the lateral margins is without any fold, while the extreme anterior border is in the form of a series of long ridges. The proboscis is covered with minute papillae except for a narrow portion adjacent to the folded lateral margins. The surface of the trunk is also covered with minute papillae. The longitudinal muscles are gathered into seven distinct bands; there are two lateral bands, two on each side of the nerve cord and a single median band on the dorsal side. The oblique muscles are more prominent internally being fasciculated between the longitudinal bands. The posterior tip of the trunk resembles that of *O. arkati* Prashad, except that the annular thickening of the body is frilled with the edges hanging free. The two ventral setae have a replacement pair. Two pairs of small, tubular nephridia which open posterior to the setae. The lips of the nephrostomes are drawn out into coiled filaments. The anal vesicles are small and saccular.

REMARKS. Described originally from two specimens which were pale yellow in preservative, with the trunk wall almost transparent. A third specimen, taken at 55 m, was darker in colour. This species is closely related to *O. arkati* (Prashad), also described from India, but differs because the latter is described as possessing eight longitudinal muscles.

DISTRIBUTION. India. As for the type locality.

Genus *ANELASSORHYNCHUS*

Anelassorhynchus Annandale, 1922 : 148; Fisher, 1946 : 221–222; 1949 : 480–481

DESCRIPTION. Echiuridae which resemble the genus *Thalassema* in that they lack posterior setae, specialized bands of longitudinal and fascicles of oblique muscles but which differ from *Thalassema* in that the nephrostomal lips are prolonged and usually spirally coiled.

TYPE SPECIES. *Thalassema branchiorhynchus* Annandale & Kemp.

REMARKS. Annandale erected the genus to contain two estuarine species from India, *Thalassema branchiorhynchus* and *T. dendrorhynchus* the proboscides of which were unlike those of *Thalassema* in that they (1) were short and rounded and (2) possessed dendritic gill-like outgrowths. Annandale included *T. sabinum* and *T. microrhynchus* in the genus. Fisher (1946 : 222) pointed out that the gill-like modifications of the proboscis vary in complexity and considered them to be adaptations to an unusual environment. He also pointed out that a similar kind of structure was found in *Ochetostoma arkati*. The nature of the proboscis was therefore not a very satisfactory character on which to establish the genus. All the species listed by Annandale, however, were alike in that their nephrostomal lips were elongate and spirally coiled. Fisher (1946, 1949) redefined the genus so that the condition of the nephrostomal lips and not the proboscis became its distinguishing character. Many of the 14 species listed in this monograph have normal *Thalassema*-like proboscides. Fisher (1946 : 222) points out that it may sometimes be difficult to identify with certainty young specimens of *Listriolobus* in which the bands of longitudinal muscle may not be well marked.

The validity of the genus is discussed on p. 426.

The validity of the genus is discussed on p. 426.

ANELASSORHYNCHUS—KEY TO SPECIES

1 One pair of nephridia 2
– More than one pair of nephridia 3
2 Large species (trunk up to 230 mm long); nephrostomal lips prolonged but not well
      coiled (body wall translucent and no direct ring vessel) . . **A. abyssalis** (p. 445)
– Small species (trunk up to 9 mm long); nephrostomal lips prolonged and well coiled
                                                                A. indivisus (p. 448)
3 Two pairs of nephridia 4
– Three pairs of nephridia 11
4 Two ventral setae 5
– Eight very small spinelets in place of each seta . . **A. chaetiferus** (p. 447)
5 Proboscis reduced to a small collar (lateral margins of proboscis not modified
                                                            A. microrhynchus (p. 448)
– Proboscis well developed 6
6 Proboscis with dendritic or gill-like outgrowths 7
– Proboscis without dendritic outgrowths 8
7 Proboscis with conspicuous ridge between the dendritic outgrowths
                                                            A. branchiorhynchus (p. 445)
– Proboscis without ridge . . . . . **A. dendrorhynchus** (p. 447)
8 Precloacal caecum present . . . . . . **A. sabinus** (p. 450)
– Precloacal caecum absent 9
9 No ciliated funnels on the anal vesicles . . . . **A. porcellus** (p. 450)
– Ciliated funnels present on the anal vesicles 10
10 Dark green in colour (no interbasal muscle) . . . **A. adelaidensis** (p. 445)
– Blue grey in colour (sometimes with three pairs of nephridia; one pair may open in
      front of the setae) . . . . **A. semoni** (p. 451)
11 First pair of nephridia open in front of the setae 12
– All pairs of nephridia open behind the setae 13
12 Anterior extremity of anal vesicles attached to body wall by a slender muscle
                                                            A. inanensis (p. 448)
– Anterior extremity of anal vesicles not attached to body wall (neurointestinal
      vessel double for almost its whole length) . . . . **A. moebii** (p. 449)
13 Anal vesicles with ciliated funnels, set on small stalks (neurointestinal vessel double)
                                                            A. mucosus (p. 449)
– Anal vesicles without ciliated funnels . . . . . **A. vegrandis** (p. 451)

Anelassorhynchus abyssalis Fisher, 1949

Anelassorhynchus abyssalis Fisher, 1949 : 481–482, pl. 28.

TYPE LOCALITY. Albatross stn. 4547, Monterey Bay, California; at 1936 m. *Type.* U.S.N.M. no. 21082.

DESCRIPTION. Trunk up to 230 mm in length, body wall slightly translucent. Skin smooth with numerous papillae which are almost flush with the surface and more translucent than the skin. Ventral setae 10 mm in length with a relatively large, open, curved hook. Slender interbasal muscle, not surrounded by neurointestinal vessel. One pair of small nephridia; nephrostomal lips prolonged but not into a spiral. Anal vesicles lost. No well marked ring vessel in the vascular system.

REMARKS. Described from four badly preserved specimens.

DISTRIBUTION. As for the type locality.

Anelassorhynchus adelaidensis Edmonds, 1960

Anelassorhynchus adelaidensis Edmonds, 1960 : 92–93, pl. 2a; 1966a : 175.

TYPE LOCALITY. Aldinga Beach, St Vincent Gulf, South Australia. *Type.* Australian Museum, Sydney.

DESCRIPTION. Proboscis, deciduous, up to 40 mm long and tapering anteriorly; the margins, though wavy, are not frilled. The groove is light green in colour. Trunk up to 100 mm in length, rich dark green in colour. The skin is wrinkled and bears numerous, small, flat, glandular papillae. Ventral setae up to 5 mm long; no interbasal muscle. Two pairs of nephridia, all opening behind the ventral setae; they possess spirally coiled, elongate lips. Alimentary canal long and much coiled; the presiphonal section is very long. Anal vesicles long and slender and covered with numerous minute brown funnels. No precloacal caecum.

REMARKS. Described from eight specimens (five dissected). The species closely resembles *A. porcellus* Fisher and *A. semoni* Fischer. Live specimens of *A. porcellus* collected by Edmonds at the Great Barrier Reef were grey and not green in colour.

DISTRIBUTION. Southern Australia (St Vincent Gulf) and Victoria (Port Philip Bay).

Anelassorhynchus branchiorhynchus (Annandale & Kemp, 1915)

Thalassema branchiorhynchus Annandale & Kemp, 1915 : 61–63, figs 2–3; Prashad, 1919a : 324; 1919b : 399.
Anelassorhynchus branchiorhynchus : Fisher, 1946 : 222.

TYPE LOCALITY. Chandipore, Crissa, India.

DESCRIPTION. Proboscis 15 mm in length, purplish-pink in colour with bright red dendritic outgrowths; conspicuous longitudinal ridge between the two rows of dendritic outgrowths. External surface covered with very small papillae. Body 32 mm in length, 7 mm in breadth. Two pairs of nephridia; lips of the nephro-

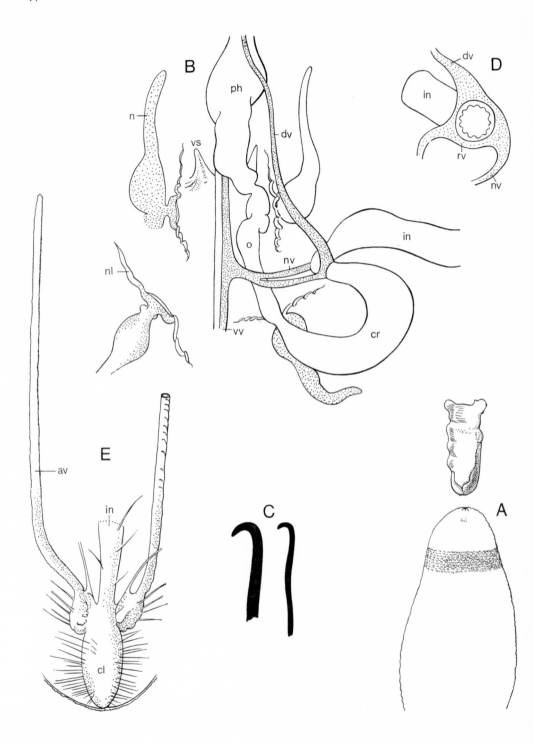

stome spirally coiled. Anal vesicles about half the length of the body and swollen at the base; each bears two rows of microscopic funnels.

REMARKS. Known only from the holotype.

DISTRIBUTION. As for the type locality.

Anelassorhynchus chaetiferus Datta Gupta, Menon & Johnson, 1963

Anelassorhynchus chaetiferus Datta Gupta, Menon & Johnson, 1963 : 61–62, fig. 2(e–i).

TYPE LOCALITY. Shingle Is., Gulf of Mannar. *Type.* Museum of Department of Zoology, Birla College, Pilani, (India).

DESCRIPTION. Proboscis is much shorter than trunk, fleshy with a shallow ventral depression that leads to mouth. Total length of proboscis and trunk 70 mm. Width of trunk 18 mm. Two conspicuous apertures plugged with muscle pads; eight minute spinelets embedded in the pads. No other setae observed. Two pairs of small nephridia with nephrostomal lips spirally coiled. Trunk covered with elliptically-shaped papillae arranged in transverse rows. Anal vesicles are elongate and sac like with few funnels.

REMARKS. The presence of muscle pads in which eight spinelets are embedded is one of the unusual features of this species. Datta Gupta says: 'The proboscis is a fleshy structure with a ventral shallow depression which leads to the mouth. Union of the proboscis and the body is strong. In this respect the animal differs from all other known echiurids and would lead one to take it for a new genus in which a typical demarcation between the proboscis and the body is wanting.'

Anelassorhynchus dendrorhynchus (Annandale & Kemp, 1915)

Thalassema dendrorhynchus Annandale & Kemp, 1915 : 58–61, fig. 1.
Anelassorhynchus dendrorhynchus: Fisher, 1946 : 222.

TYPE LOCALITY. Chilka Lake, Bengal. *Type.* Indian Museum no. Z.S.I. 6800–6803/7.

DESCRIPTION. Proboscis 8–18 mm long and shovel-shaped; the lateral edges come together to form a tube. Edges serrated; towards the proximal end they take the form of dendritic outgrowths always shorter than the proboscis. Body 46–120 mm long covered with papillae which are most numerous at the anterior and posterior ends, where they tend to become arranged in concentric rings. Ventral setae small. Two pairs of nephridia; lips of the nephrostomes with long twisted filaments. Anal vesicles about half the length of the body, swollen at the base and with two rows of microscopic funnels on each.

REMARKS. Known only from the holotype.

DISTRIBUTION. As for the type locality.

FIG. 56. (A–D) *Anelassorhynchus porcellus.* (A) Anterior two thirds of a typical specimen. (B) Anterior region of the trunk. (C) Seta, × about 10. The figure on the left shows the enlarged tip. (D) Ring vessel surrounding end of foregut. (E) Cloaca and anal vesicles. (A–D after Fisher.) KEY: *See* Fig. 53, p. 417.

Anelassorhynchus inanensis (Ikeda, 1904)

Thalassema inanense Ikeda, 1904 : 71, figs 22, 100; Sato, 1939 : 354–355; Wesenberg-Lund, 1939d : 51–55, text-figs 5, 6.
Anelassorhynchus inanense: Fisher, 1948b : 275.

TYPE LOCALITY.   Naha, Japan.

DESCRIPTION.   Proboscis 230 mm, tubular but expanded at the apex to give a bilobed appearance; yellow-grey, edged with brown on the lateral margins.   Trunk 42 mm in length, 13 mm in width; bluish-violet in colour and covered with small greenish papillae.   Ventral setae small, bright yellow in colour.   Three pairs of nephridia, the anterior pair lying in front of the setae; the lips of the nephrostome are drawn out into well-developed spiral lobes.   Anal vesicles long, reaching to the level of the second pair of nephridia and joined anteriorly to the body wall by a slender muscle; small funnels, carried on short stalks, sparsely distributed over their surface.

REMARKS.   Described originally from a single specimen.   Wesenberg-Lund (1939d) redescribed the species.   In her specimens from Annam the margins of the proboscis fold and fuse posteriorly to form a cup or funnel.   Anteriorly the proboscis is slightly bifurcated and its margins crenulated.   No interbasal muscle present.

DISTRIBUTION.   Japan (Ikeda, 1904; Sato, 1939); Hawaii (Fisher, 1948); Annam (Wesenberg-Lund, 1939d).

Anelassorhynchus indivisus (Sluiter, 1900)

Thalassema indivisum Sluiter, 1900 : 18.

TYPE LOCALITY.   Off the coast of Spain (56°43′40″N, 8°28′30″W); at 90 m.

DESCRIPTION.   Proboscis small in preserved specimens, up to 4 mm in length and broadening anteriorly; the edges join only at the base.   Rather lighter in colour than the trunk.   Trunk up to 9 mm in length and ridged by contraction; yellowish-grey in alcohol.   Papillae are scattered over the whole surface but are concentrated mainly on the ridges; they are much larger posteriorly.   One pair of nephridia; the lips of the nephrostome are drawn out into long coiled filaments.   The digestive tract is fastened to the body wall by numerous mesenteries.   Anal vesicles small, not exceeding quarter of the trunk length; they bear numerous funnels.

REMARKS.   Described from six specimens.

DISTRIBUTION.   As for the type locality.

Anelassorhynchus microrhynchus (Prashad, 1919)

Thalassema microrhynchus Prashad, 1919b : 399–400, fig. 1.
Anelassorhynchus microrhynchus: Fisher, 1946 : 222.

TYPE LOCALITY.   Chandipore, Orissa, India.

DESCRIPTION.   Proboscis 1·4 mm in length, with a small collar about one nineteenth of the body length, margins united at the base.   Trunk 25 mm in length, covered with papillae. Ventral setae with sharply curved points. Two pairs of nephridia; lips of the nephrostomes with long spiral filaments. Anal vesicles one half as long as the body with two rows of funnels on surface of the anterior half.

REMARKS. Known only from the holotype.

DISTRIBUTION. As for the type locality.

Anelassorhynchus moebii (Greeff, 1879)

Thalassema moebii Greeff, 1879 : 152, pl. 6, figs 68–69; von Drasche, 1881 : 621; Fischer, 1895 : 20; 1896a : 336; Shipley, 1899b : 350; 1902c : 129, pl. 6, figs 3(a–b); Sluiter, 1898 : 444–445; 1902 : 49; Augener, 1903 : 348; Lanchester, 1905c : 34; Wesenberg-Lund, 1959b : 71–72.
Anelassorhynchus moebii : Fisher, 1946 : 222.

TYPE LOCALITY. Mauritius.

DESCRIPTION. Proboscis 80 mm in length, light green with bright yellow edges. Trunk 70 mm long and 20 mm wide. Colour greyish-yellow, passing in places into violet, with violet stripes running diagonally round the body. Papillae irregularly scattered over the body and often arranged in clumps. Three pairs of nephridia; lips of the nephrostomes spirally coiled. Anal vesicles long brown tubes with funnels.

REMARKS. Greeff's fig. 68 shows that the lateral edges of the proboscis fuse proximally to form a short tube or funnel and that distally the proboscis is expanded slightly. The neurointestinal vessel appears to be double for most of its length.

DISTRIBUTION. Mauritius (Greeff, 1879; Wesenberg-Lund, 1959b; Sluiter, 1898); Zanzibar (Lanchester, 1905c); Maldive Islands (Shipley, 1902); Indonesia (Fischer, 1896a).

Anelassorhynchus mucosus (Ikeda, 1904)

Thalassema mucosum Ikeda, 1904 : 68–69, figs 20, 98; Sato, 1934 : 252–253; 1939 : 355–356, pl. 22, fig. 28, text-figs 6–7.
Anelassorhynchus mucosus : Fisher, 1946 : 222.

TYPE LOCALITY. Moroiso, Misaki Marine Station, Japan.

DESCRIPTION. Proboscis with a truncated apex, shorter and narrower than the trunk and tubular. Body cylindrical, 70 mm in length and 18 mm in width. Body wall thin, light green in colour but darker at both ends; covered with dark green papillae closely crowded at the extremities. Ventral setae small, recurved, bright yellow in colour. Three pairs of nephridia all lying behind the setae; lips of the nephrostome with long spirally coiled lobes. Anal vesicles long, extending to the middle of the body and bearing small ciliated funnels set on short stalks. Neuro-intestinal blood vessel is double and joins directly the dorsal blood vessel. No rectal caecum.

REMARKS. Described originally from three specimens. Sato (1939) gave a short description of some specimens found in Korea. The species is allied to *A. vegrandis* and *A. moebii*.

DISTRIBUTION. Moroiso (Ikeda, 1904); Onomichi Bay (Sato, 1934); Korea (Sato, 1939).

Anelassorhynchus porcellus Fisher, 1948

(Fig. 56A–E)

Anelassorhynchus porcellus Fisher, 1948 : 274–276, text-fig. 1; Edmonds, 1960 : 91–92, pl. 1c.

TYPE LOCALITY. Reef south of Honolulu Harbour, in tidal pools. *Type*. U.S.N.M.

DESCRIPTION. Proboscis fleshy, deciduous, the two lateral margins meeting at the base to form the lower lip. Trunk up to 70 mm in length. Body wall rather thick in large specimens, slightly translucent in smaller ones. Skin closely wrinkled transversally, so that the small, closely-packed glandular swellings have a transverse alignment; in the middle of the trunk the skin may smooth out and the glands disappear. Ventral setae small, 3 mm in length, with a well-marked hook. No interbasal muscle. Two pairs of nephridia opening behind the ventral setae; lips of the nephrostomes prolonged and usually coiled spirally. Alimentary canal very long, about 10 times the length of the trunk; no ciliated groove and no rectal caecum. Anal vesicles very long; each with a characteristically swollen base, which is attached to the body wall by numerous frenula. In some specimens they are covered with brown spots; no ciliated funnels were observed.

REMARKS. Described originally from several specimens. Edmonds found 12 more, six of which were dissected.

DISTRIBUTION. Hawaii, several localities (Fisher, 1948); Heron Island, Queensland (Edmonds, 1960).

Anelassorhynchus sabinus (Lanchester, 1905)

Thalassema sabinum Lanchester, 1905b : 40–41, pl. 2, fig. 5; Prashad, 1919 : 321–338, pl. 11, figs 2, 10, 15, text-fig. 1; Fischer, 1914 : 19.
Anelassorhynchus sabinum: Sato, 1934 : 250–251, 253, figs 4–6; 1939 : 352–354, pl. 22, fig. 29, text-figs 3–5.
Anelassorhynchus sabinus: Fisher, 1946 : 222; 1949 : 481; Datta Gupta, Menon & Johnson, 1963 : 60–61.

TYPE LOCALITY. Singora, Indonesia. *Type*. British Museum (Nat. Hist.), no. 1924.3.1.189–191.

DESCRIPTION. Proboscis short in comparison to the trunk, up to 2 mm in length. Trunk up to 8 mm in length. Ventral setae set close to the proboscis. Two pairs of nephridia; lips of the nephrostomes drawn out into spirally coiled filaments. Anal vesicles short.

REMARKS. Described rather briefly by Lanchester from five specimens. Fischer (1914 : 19) considered it to be a synonym of *A. semoni*. Prashad's figure shows a well-developed caecum and short anal vesicles. Fisher (1948b : 275) considered it to be a valid species.

DISTRIBUTION. Indonesia (Lanchester, 1905); Japan (Sato, 1934, 1939); India (Datta Gupta *et al.*, 1963).

Anelassorhynchus semoni (Fischer, 1896)

Thalassema semoni Fischer, 1896a : 338–339, text-fig. 4; 1914b : 19–20; Shipley, 1899 : 351; 1902c : 129–130, pl. 6, fig. 4; Sluiter, 1902 : 46–47; Augener, 1903 : 348; Wharton, 1913 : 247; Wesenberg-Lund, 1959c : 216.
Anelassorhynchus semoni: Fisher, 1949 : 481.

TYPE LOCALITY. Amboina.

DESCRIPTION. Proboscis lacking in type specimen. Trunk up to 5·5 mm in length, skin blue-grey in colour, thin and transparent. Covered with papillae of uniform size that are most compacted at the posterior end of the body. Ventral setae small. Two pairs of nephridia; lips of the nephrostomes drawn out into a long coiled, filament. Anal vesicles thin and brown in colour, more than half the length of the trunk; they bear ciliated funnels, and are attached to the body wall by mesenteries. No rectal caecum found.

REMARKS. Described originally from two specimens. In the larger one the right nephridium opened in front of the ventral setae, the rest behind. The smaller one had three pairs of nephridia opening behind the setae but Fischer considered this abnormal. Wharton (1913) reports two specimens with a trunk 70 mm long and a proboscis about three quarters as long as the trunk. His specimens possessed two pairs of nephridia, one pair opening in front of and one pair behind the setae.

DISTRIBUTION. Indonesia (Fischer, 1896a); Pacific (Fischer, 1914b); Maldive Islands (Shipley, 1902c); West Africa (Wesenberg-Lund, 1959c); Philippine Islands (Wharton, 1913).

Anelassorhynchus vegrandis (Lampert, 1883)

Thalassema vegrande Lampert, 1883 : 341; Shipley, 1898 : 472–473; 1899b : 352; 1901c : 130; Monro, 1931 : 33.
Anelassorhynchus vegrandis: Fisher, 1946 : 222; 1949 : 481.

TYPE LOCALITY. Philippines.

DESCRIPTION. Proboscis lacking. Trunk 35 mm in length, skin thin and papery. Papillae scattered over the whole surface; they are larger and more numerous posteriorly, where they are set in regular rows. Three pairs of nephridia which all open behind the ventral setae; lips of nephrostomes with spirally coiled filaments. Anal vesicles are long thin brown tubes without ciliated funnels.

REMARKS. Described originally from a single specimen. Shipley described a badly preserved specimen from the Maldives. Monro's specimen from the Great

Barrier Reef was also in poor condition and he made the identification with some reservation.

DISTRIBUTION. Philippines (Lampert, 1883); Maldive Islands and Rotuma (Shipley, 1902); Low Island, Great Barrier Reef (Monro, 1931).

Genus *THALASSEMA* Lamarck

Thalassema Lamarck, 1801 : 328; Diesing, 1859 : 772; Greeff, 1879 : 145; Rietsch, 1886 : 313; Shipley, 1899b : 338; Wharton, 1913 : 243; Monro, 1927 : 617; Bock, 1942 : 18; Fisher, 1946 : 230.

DESCRIPTION. Echiuridae with a well-developed proboscis but lacking anal setae; longitudinal and inner oblique layers of muscle continuous and not grouped into bands or fascicles. One or two pairs of nephridia; nephrostomal lips not elongate and not spirally coiled. No sexual dimorphism.

TYPE SPECIES. *Lumbricus thalassema* Pallas, 1766 : 8 (=*Thalassema neptuni* Gaertner of Pallas, 1774, and other authors).

REMARKS. *Lumbricas thalassema* Pallas and *Lumbricus echiurus* Pallas are the oldest known echiurans. Some uncertainty existed about the name of the type species of the genus until Fisher (1946 : 230) pointed out that *thalassema* is an older specific name for the type than *neptuni*. Lamarck (1801 : 328) ascribes the genus *Thalassema* to Cuvier. We have not, however, been able to find in any of the books at our disposal Cuvier's pre-1801 citation of *Thalassema*. The original *Thalassema* of Lamarck during the last 150 years has undergone extensive changes. It has been subdivided into a number of other genera chiefly according to the organization of the longitudinal and oblique muscle layers and the nature of the nephrostomal lips.

In this genus the dorsal and the neuro-intestinal blood vessels are in direct connection through the ring vessels at the end of the foregut. The part of the intestine that lies between the ring vessel and the beginning of the siphon is short and bears a ciliated groove. An interbasal muscle and an intestinal caecum are present in many species.

The taxonomic position of *T. marshalli* Prashad is uncertain. The proboscis of the species is short, rounded and bears branching gill-like structures, very much like those of *Anelassorhynchus branchiorhynchus* and *A. dendrorhynchus*. Fisher (1949 : 480) included the species in the genus *Anelassorhynchus*. Prashad describes the species as possessing two pairs of minute finger-like nephridia but makes no mention of the nature of the nephrostomal lips. Consequently we have decided to leave the species in the genus *Thalassema*.

The species fall into two groups, one possessing one pair of nephridia and the other two pairs. We have not been able to construct a satisfactory key to the first group. All the species seem very close and there is little critical information (except for *T. arcassonense* and *T. hartmani*) which can be used to distinguish them. Much more is known about the species in the second group. Nevertheless it is difficult to fit them into a key because *T. steinbecki* and *T. thalassemum* are indistinguishable to us.

THALASSEMA—SYNOPSIS OF SPECIES

1 Species with one pair of nephridia
   T. antarcticum; anal vesicles lacking.
   T. arcassonense; nephrostomes large, interbasal muscle lacking, caecum present.
   T. diaphanes
   T. elapsum; nephrostomal lips crumpled, caecum absent.
   T. fuscum
   T. hartmani; nephrostomes borne on stalks, lips inconspicuous, interbasal muscle and caecum present.
   T. mortenseni
   T. ovatum; nephrostomal lips are large flaps.
   T. owstoni; interbasal muscle present.

2 Species with two pairs of nephridia
   T. marshalli; has dendritic gills attached to its proboscis; remaining four species have not.
   T. sydniense; has no caecum, the remaining three species have a caecum.
   T. philostracum; nephrostomal lips fan-shaped.
   T. steinbecki; smooth lips forming an incomplete circle.
   T. thalassemum; lips form a semicircular frill.

Thalassema antarcticum Stephen, 1941

Thalassema antarcticum Stephen, 1941b : 248, figs 3, 4.

TYPE LOCALITY. Falkland Islands. *Type.* Brit. Mus. (Nat. Hist.) no. 1952.2.3.12.

DESCRIPTION. Proboscis 5·2 mm long, pale milk-white, translucent, edged with opaque porcelain white; tip not bifurcate but edges indented. Trunk up to 27 mm in length; pale yellow-white, translucent with viscera visible through body wall. One pair of nephridia; lips of nephrostomes bear no spiral filaments. Anal vesicles lacking.

REMARKS. Known only from the two specimens.

DISTRIBUTION. As for the type locality.

Thalassema arcassonense Cuénot, 1902

Thalassema arcassonensis Cuénot, 1902 : 3; 1922 : 23, fig. 13.

TYPE LOCALITY. Bay of Arcachon, France.

DESCRIPTION. Proboscis 20 mm in length, colour very pale rose-yellow; almost square at the tip. Body 110 mm in length, sausage-shaped and covered with papillae more closely packed at the anterior and posterior ends. Colour wine-red in life. Ventral setae small with no interbasal muscle. One pair of nephridia each with a large nephrostome which is not spirally coiled. Anal vesicles long

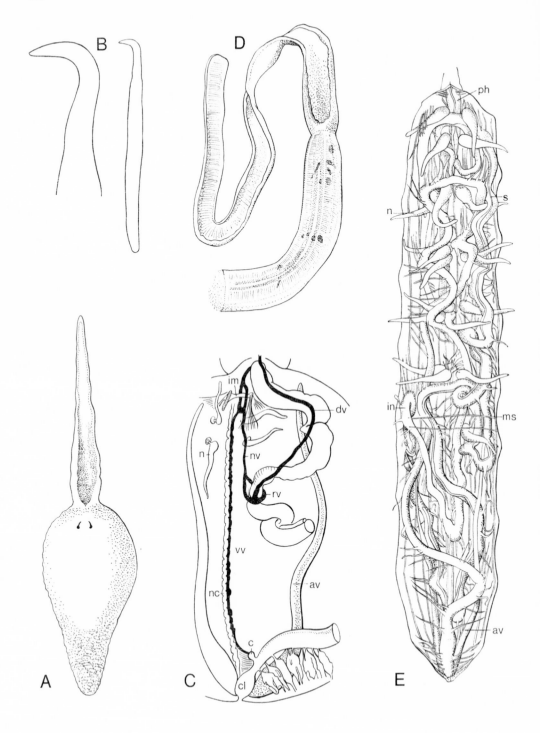

(22 mm) attached to the body by numerous mesenteries and unbranched.   A small rectal caecum present.

REMARKS.   Known only from the holotype.

DISTRIBUTION.   As for the type locality.

Thalassema diaphanes Sluiter, 1888

Thalassema diaphanes Sluiter, 1888 : 244–248, pl. 3, text-figs 1–7; 1891 : 111; 1902 : 49; Shipley, 1899b : 336–337, pl. 33, fig. 2; 1902c : 128, pl. 6, fig. 2; Prashad, 1935 : 41; Wesenberg-Lund, 1959a : 199; 1959c : 214–216.

TYPE LOCALITY.   Bay of Batavia; at 17–19 m.

DESCRIPTION.   Proboscis 30 mm long forming a tube before it joins the mouth. Body 30 mm, skin thin and transparent.   Papillae are small white specks scattered over the body; more concentrated at the anterior and posterior ends.   One pair of nephridia; the lips of the nephrostomes are not coiled.   Anal vesicles small, transparent and about 5 mm in length.   Rectal caecum lacking.

REMARKS.   According to Wesenberg-Lund (1959c : 214) the nephrostomes are large, stalked, with ovoid apertures and without curled appendages.

DISTRIBUTION.   West coast Africa; Ivory Coast (Wesenberg-Lund, 1959); South Africa, Cape Province (Wesenberg-Lund, 1959); Indian Ocean, Andaman Islands (Prashad, 1935); Maldive and Laccadive Islands (Shipley); Indonesia, Bay of Batavia (Sluiter, 1889).

Thalassema elapsum Sluiter, 1912

Thalassema elapsum Sluiter, 1912 : 24–25, fig. 15a, b; Fischer, 1914a : 80.

TYPE LOCALITY.   15°14′N, 23°03′45″W; at 628 m.

DESCRIPTION.   Proboscis lacking.   Trunk up to 35 mm in length, covered with papillae which are arranged in circles and more crowded anteriorly and posteriorly. Colour in formalin pale translucent grey.   The ventral setae are a more or less deep grey-brown in colour.   One pair of nephridia; lips of the nephrostomes merely folded or crumpled, without long filaments.   No caecum was found on the rectum, but this may be due to poor preservation.   Anal vesicles long tubes carrying funnels.

REMARKS.   Described originally from 10 specimens, in all of which the proboscis was lacking.

DISTRIBUTION.   As for the type locality.

FIG. 57.   (A–C) *Thalassema steinbecki*. (A) Ventral view of female, × about 4.   (B) Complete seta, × about 30, and an enlarged tip.   (C) Dissected specimen.   (A–C after Fisher.)   (D–E) *Ikedosoma elegans*.   (D) Anterior half of the body, about half natural size.   (E) Dissected specimen, about three eighths natural size.   (D–E after Ikeda.) KEY: *See* Fig. 53, p. 417.

Thalassema fuscum Ikeda, 1904

Thalassema fuscum Ikeda, 1904 : 69–70, figs 21, 99; Sato, 1939 : 354.

TYPE LOCALITY. Japan (actual locality not stated).

DESCRIPTION. Proboscis 20 mm in length, apex truncated. Body long, cylindrical, 75 mm in length, 1·5–1·8 mm in breadth; colour pinkish orange-yellow. Large papillae scattered over the surface, more closely set anteriorly and posteriorly. Ventral setae small with a well-developed interbasal muscle. One pair nephridia, about 20 mm in length, opening of the nephrostome without prominent lobes. Anal vesicles about as long as the body proper; ciliated funnels, sparsely distributed over the surface, are relatively small and short-stalked.

REMARKS. Known only from the holotype. Sato merely quotes the original reference. Closely allied to *T. mucosum* Ikeda. Ikeda's fig. 99 shows (1) the presence of strong radiating muscles attached to the setae, (2) that the nephrostomal lips are almost fan-like, (3) the presence of a ring vessel in the vascular system and (4) that the neurointestinal vessel does not surround the interbasal muscle and that it joins the ventral vessel more posteriorly than usual in this genus.

DISTRIBUTION. Japan (Ikeda, 1904).

Thalassema hartmani Fisher, 1947

Thalassema hartmani Fisher, 1947 : 353–354, pl. 9.

TYPE LOCALITY. Beaufort, North Carolina. *Type.* U.S.N.M. no. 20801.

DESCRIPTION. Proboscis fleshy, about 8 mm in length, forming a thick lip to the mouth. Trunk up to 40 mm, reddish in life. Papillae prominent and unequal in size; the larger ones are swollen, scale-like and bent forwards. Ventral setae 3·5 mm in length, with broadly curved flattened tips; interbasal muscle present. One pair of nephridia; the nephrostomes are borne on stalks, but the lips are inconspicuous and not drawn out into true spirals. The presiphonal segment of the alimentary canal is extremely long; small precloacal segment. Anal vesicles, relatively small, about a quarter as long as the trunk length and carrying tiny ciliated funnels. Dorsal blood vessel extends beyond the foregut on to the intestine. Very small intestinal caecum.

REMARKS. Described from two poorly preserved specimens.

DISTRIBUTION. The type locality and Chesapeake Bay, U.S.A.

Thalassema marshalli Prashad, 1935

Thalassema marshalli Prashad, 1935 : 42, figs 5–7.
Anelassorhynchus marshalli: Fisher, 1949 : 481.

TYPE LOCALITY. In the Irrawaddy, near Rangoon, Burma. *Type.* Indian Museum, Calcutta, no. W3166/1.

DESCRIPTION. Proboscis 5·8 mm in length; the ventral margins are free and are provided with greatly branching gill-like structures. Trunk 19 mm in length, rounded anteriorly but tapering posteriorly; bluish-yellow in preservative. The surface is covered with minute rounded papillae which are very minute or absent in the middle region but most prominent on the posterior third. Ventral setae prominent. Two pairs of minute finger-like nephridia; the shape of the lips of the nephrostomes was not described. Anal vesicles lost through damage to the specimen.

REMARKS. Known only from the holotype. Fisher (1949 : 480) placed this species in the genus *Anelassorhynchus*. We are unable to find any evidence to support his classification.

DISTRIBUTION. As for the type locality.

Thalassema mortenseni Fischer, 1923

Thalassema mortenseni Fischer, 1923b : 25–26, text-figs 1–3.

TYPE LOCALITY. Hong Kong.

DESCRIPTION. Proboscis lacking. Skin strong; unique in having exceedingly large overlapping papillae arranged in regular rows. Anteriorly two golden-yellow setae and a substitute one; no interbasal muscle, but numerous mesenteries run to the hooks. One pair of fairly long, free nephridia; no spiral filaments observed at the opening of the nephrostomes. Two short anal trees with single funnels.

REMARKS. Known from two specimens.

DISTRIBUTION. As for the type locality.

Thalassema ovatum Sluiter, 1902

Thalassema ovatum Sluiter, 1902 : 49–50, pl. 4, figs 14–16.

TYPE LOCALITY. Bay of Bima, Indonesia.

DESCRIPTION. Proboscis of preserved specimens up to 3 mm in length, but possibly considerably longer in life; lateral edges folded together. Trunk at most 10 mm in length, with microscopic papillae scattered regularly over it; transparent and colour of preserved material light grey. Ventral setae sickle-shaped anteriorly. One pair of nephridia, each small and ball-like; lips of the nephrostome are large flaps and lacking spirally coiled filaments. Anal vesicles not found in any of the specimens.

REMARKS. Described from numerous specimens which were probably juveniles.

DISTRIBUTION. As for the type locality.

EE

Thalassema owstoni Ikeda, 1904

Thalassema owstoni Ikeda, 1904 : 62–63, pl. 1, fig. 18; pl. 4, figs 96–97; Sato, 1934 : 249, figs 2–3;
1939 : 354.

TYPE LOCALITY.   Uraga Channel, Japan.

DESCRIPTION.   Proboscis 7·5 mm in length and deeply furrowed ventrally.
Body 17 mm long, 5 mm wide and pale reddish-brown in formalin; skin soft and
smooth except at the two extremities where the papillae are largest and most
crowded.   Two large yellow ventral setae, with a well developed interbasal muscle.
One pair of nephridia; no spiral filaments on the nephrostomal lips.   Anal vesicles
carry short funnels borne on stalks.

REMARKS.   The original description was based on the holotype.   Ikeda had doubts
as to whether this species might not be *T. diaphanes* Sluiter.

DISTRIBUTION.   Several Japanese localities (Ikeda, Sato).

Thalassema philostracum Fisher, 1947

Thalassema philostracum Fisher, 1947 : 351–353, pl. 8; Wesenberg-Lund, 1959a : 199–201,
fig. 12.

TYPE LOCALITY.   Lemon Flats, Florida.   *Type.*   U.S.N.M. no. 20802.

DESCRIPTION.   Proboscis may be as long as or slightly larger than trunk.   Margins
of the proboscis at the base do not form an upper lip to the mouth.   Body wall
rather thin, colour deep red in life.   Papillae are not prominent; they are arranged
in a transverse series in the middle region and are largest anteriorly and posteriorly.
Ventral setae up to 2·75 mm long; hooks relatively small and sharply curved.
Interbasal muscle present.   Two pairs of nephridia, nephrostomes fan-shaped.
Anal vesicles slender and half as long as the body; ciliated funnels very small.
Foregut longer than the presiphonal segment.   Precloacal caecum present.

REMARKS.   Known originally from numerous specimens.   Wesenberg-Lund
examined five more specimens but added little to the original description.

DISTRIBUTION.   Florida, North Carolina (Fisher, 1947); West Africa (Wesenberg-
Lund, 1959a).

Thalassema steinbecki Fisher, 1946

(Fig. 57A–C)

Thalassema steinbecki Fisher, 1946 : 230–231, text-fig. 11.

TYPE LOCALITY.   El Mogote, La Paz, Baja California.   *Type.*   U.S.N.M. no.
20600.

DESCRIPTION.   Proboscis about as long as the trunk, ribbon-like and expanded
distally.   Trunk small, up to 12 mm long slightly translucent in the middle portion.
Papillae are scattered over the trunk and are largest just behind the proboscis
and on the posterior third of the trunk.   The tip of the ventral setae are set at right

angles to the shaft; there is a well-developed interbasal muscle and the setae are attached to the body wall by radiating sheets of muscle. Two pairs of nephridia. The nephrostomes have simple lips, lacking any spiral filaments. Anal vesicles as long as the trunk and covered with numerous small, ciliated funnels. Rectal caecum present. Dorsal and neurointestinal blood vessels are connected through a well developed ring vessel.

REMARKS. Known from eight specimens.

DISTRIBUTION. Known from a number of localities from Baja California to Ecuador.

Thalassema sydniense Edmonds, 1960

Thalassema sydniense Edmonds, 1960 : 89–90, pl. 1a, figs 1–2.

TYPE LOCALITY. Off Watson's Bay, Port Jackson, N.S.W. *Type.* Australian Museum, Sydney.

DESCRIPTION. Proboscis about a half to one third as long as the trunk, gradually narrowing anteriorly. Colour grey-brown in preservative. Trunk 6–12 mm in length, maximum width 2–5 mm; surface covered with numerous, very small, rather flat papillae which appear to be almost in transverse rows. They are more noticeable at the anterior and posterior ends of the body. Ventral setae comparatively large, prominent and strongly recurved at the tip; prominent interbasal muscle. Another muscle runs from the base of each seta to a point on the body wall posterior to the nephridiopore of the first pair of nephridia. Two pairs of nephridia all of which open behind the ventral setae; lips of the nephrostomes are not elongated or spirally coiled and the opening is on a peduncle near the base of the nephridium. Anal vesicles about half as long as the trunk. No precloacal caecum appears to be present. Alimentary and vascular systems not able to be described.

REMARKS. The species was described from four small specimens. It resembles *Thalassema steinbecki* Fisher, which occurs along the American coast from California to Ecuador, but differs in that the nephrostomes are set on a short expanded peduncle and in that it lacks a caecum.

DISTRIBUTION. As for the type locality.

Thalassema thalassemum (Pallas, 1766)

Lumbricus thalassema Pallas, 1766 : 8–9, pl. 1, fig. 6.
Thalassema neptuni Gaertner of Pallas, 1774 : 1–15; Lamarck, 1801 : 329; Greeff, 1879 : 145; Rietsch, 1886 : 313; Lankester, 1881 : 350; Jameson, 1899b : 535, 2 pls and 1 text-fig.; Shipley, 1899b : 351, pl. 33, figs 5 and 6; Stewart, 1900 : 218; Southern, 1913 : 39; Fischer, 1914b : 20; 1922b : 14; Leigh-Sharpe, 1928 : 499–504, pls 14–15; Cuénot, 1922 : 22–23, figs 12(a–b); Wesenberg-Lund, 1959a : 199.
Thalassina mutatoria Montagu, 1815 : 24.
Thalassema thalassemum: Fisher, 1946 : 230.

TYPE LOCALITY. ?Plymouth Sound, England.

DESCRIPTION. Proboscis very contractile and when extended about three times the length of the trunk. Trunk up to 70 mm in length and may be highly coloured and there is a white median line on the ventral side. Trunk covered with papillae which are largest and most densely placed in the posterior region. Two ventral setae which are connected by an interbasal muscle. Two pairs of nephridia with nephrostomal lips that are semicircular and frilled. The anal vesicles are long brown tubes. The dorsal and the neurointestinal blood vessels are connected through a well developed ring vessel at the end of the foregut (Jameson, 1899, pl. 29, fig. 12). The neurointestinal vessel bifurcates to encircle the interbasal muscle (Lankester, 1881; Jameson, 1899b). The part of the intestine that lies between the foregut and the section which carries the siphon bears a ciliated groove (Jameson, 1899). A rectal caecum is present.

REMARKS. The species has been monographed by Rietsch (1886) and Jameson (1899). Shipley (1899) states incorrectly that the nephrostomal lips are elongate and spirally coiled. Their structure is accurately described by Lankester (1881), 'At the base of each (nephridium) is a semicircular frill, covered with cilia and leading to the internal opening of the sac. In this condition they resemble the genital pouches of *Echiurus* as figured by Greeff (1879, pl. 1, fig. 12.' Jameson (1899) describes some variations in the vascular system and Stewart (1900) some variations in the number of nephridia of *T. thalassemum*.

T. steinbecki Fisher, 1946 from the North Pacific Ocean is a very closely related species.

DISTRIBUTION. England, Ireland, France and the Mediterranean.

Thalassema viride Verrill, 1879

Thalassema viridis Verrill, 1879 : 183; Shipley, 1899 : 353.

TYPE LOCALITY. Campo Bello Island, U.S.A.

DESCRIPTION. Proboscis long, slender, spoon-shaped at the tip. Body round, thick, twice as long as broad. Bright grass-green in colour. Body covered with papillae arranged in circles. The author did not state whether the longitudinal muscles were gathered into bands or not. The anal vesicles were also not described.

REMARKS. This species cannot be included in the present keys since the description is so incomplete, leaving out most of the essential points for full identification. Since the locality is easily accessible, more specimens may be obtained and the true status ascertained.

Genus *IKEDOSOMA* Bock, 1942

Ikedosoma Bock, 1942 : 10–18; Fisher, 1946 : 224.

DESCRIPTION. Long, slender animals, the trunk and proboscis of which may each be 300–400 mm long. Longitudinal muscles gathered into bundles and the inner oblique muscles have a tendency to form fascicles between adjacent longitudinal bands. Differs from *Ochetostoma* in the number and arrangement of nephridia which may range from 20 pairs to 3–8 paired groups, each group containing 1–4 nephridia; number of nephridia may vary according to the sex of the specimen. Nephrostomes are basal and possess short, spiral lobes. Vascular ring vessel placed at the posterior end of the pharynx. Anal vesicles are long tubes which bear numerous, short, stalked funnels.

TYPE SPECIES. *Thalassema elegans* Ikeda.

REMARKS. This genus differs from the genus *Ikeda* (order Heteromyota) most noticeably in (1) the position of the longitudinal musculature, (2) the number and arrangement of the nephridia which in *Ikeda* are unpaired and (3) the position of the nephrostome which in *Ikeda* is distal.

The genus *Ikedosoma* contains two species, *I. elegans* (Ikeda) and *I. gogoshimense* (Ikeda) both from Japan. Menon & Datta Gupta (1962) described *Ikedosoma pirotansis* from the Gulf of Kutch, India. The species resembles an *Ikedosoma* in that it possesses numerous (20) pairs of nephridia. Because (1) the longitudinal musculature is not thickened into bands, (2) there is a well developed muscular pad between the setae and (3) the nephrostome is placed distally, we consider that the Indian species belongs to another genus which we have called *Prashadus*.

GENUS IKEDOSOMA—KEY TO SPECIES

Nephridia (13–27 in number), usually grouped in seven pairs   .   .   .   ***I. elegans***
Nephridia, in the female, three pairs, in the male eight groups usually arranged in pairs
   each group consisting of four nephridia   .   .   .   .   ***I. gogoshimense***

DISTRIBUTION.   Japanese waters.

Ikedosoma elegans (Ikeda, 1904)
(Fig. 57D–E)

Thalassema elegans Ikeda, 1904 : 65–66; 1907 : 47–55, pl. 1, fig. 4, pl. 4, figs 48–49; Sato, 1939 : 356.

TYPE LOCALITY.   Moroiso Inlet, near Misaki Marine Laboratory, Japan.

DESCRIPTION.   Proboscis 300–400 mm in length and 17–20 mm in width; ground colour yellow, which deepens towards the base and along its margins. Trunk 300–350 mm long and about 25 mm wide and brownish-red in colour. Longitudinal muscles thickened in places to form 10 bundles, paler in colour than the rest of the trunk. Oblique musculature between the bundles contracts into fascicles. Two ventral setae. Dermal papillae largest and most concentrated at the anterior and posterior extremities of trunk. Nephridia are elongate and club-like; nephrostomes basal and each with two short, spiral lobes.   Nephridia (13–27 in number) generally arranged in six or seven pairs.   Some of the pairs are not always perfect with respect to the number of nephridia comprising each half-pair on either side of the nerve cord.   'Thus while in some cases a pair may consist of two nephridia—one on each side of the body—and is thus perfect, in other cases a half pair may consist of a group of one to three nephridia.'   Anal vesicles are long tubes which bear numerous short stalked funnels.   Vascular ring vessel placed at the hind end of the pharynx.

REMARKS.   Ikeda in his second account (1907) gave a detailed and well illustrated description of the species.

DISTRIBUTION.   Japan.

Ikedosoma gogoshimense (Ikeda, 1904)

Thalassema gogoshimense Ikeda, 1904 : 66–67, fig. 19; Sato, 1934a : 251–253, figs 7–8; 1939 : 356.

TYPE LOCALITY.   Inlet of Gogoshima, Japan; in shallow water.

DESCRIPTION.   Proboscis up to 105 mm in length and about 20 mm in width; dorsal surface covered with small green spots and free margins coloured yellow. Trunk up to 45 mm in length and about 20 mm in width; surface closely covered with moderately large papillae, which are slightly larger and more crowded towards the extremities.   Number of nephridia varies in the two sexes; in the female there are three pairs but in the male the number ranges from three paired groups, each group consisting of one to four nephridia, to eight groups each of four nephridia.

REMARKS.   This species is closely allied to *I. elegans* and differs in minor details, such as the presence of only three groups of nephridia in the female.

DISTRIBUTION.   As for the type locality.   Inlet of Moroiso, Japan (Ikeda, 1904); Onomichi Bay, Japan (Sato, 1934).

Genus *PRASHADUS* gen. nov.

DESCRIPTION.   Long slender animals, the combined length of the proboscis and trunk being up to 740 mm.   Condition of longitudinal and oblique musculature not stated, therefore probably not grouped into bundles or fascicles as in *Ikedosoma*. Well developed muscular pad fits on to a groove between the setae.   Nephridia numerous (40) and arranged in pairs; nephrostome at distal extremity and lacking the spiral lobes found in *Ikedosoma*. Anal vesicles slender and tubular and bear numerous long stalked funnels.

TYPE SPECIES. *Ikedosoma pirotansis* Menon & Datta Gupta.

REMARKS. The genus is unique in the family Echiuridae on account of the distal position of its nephrostome. It resembles *Ikedosoma* in its general shape and in the number and arrangement of the nephridia. It differs most noticeably in (1) the presence of a setal pad and (2) the position and structure of the nephrostomes which in *Ikedosoma* are basal and bear two short coiled lobes. In *Ikedosoma* the longitudinal musculature is thickened into bands and the oblique muscles between the bands form fascicles. Menon & Datta Gupta make no mention of the condition of the musculature of their species and their figure shows no thickening of longitudinal muscles and no fasciculation of the oblique muscles. All that they say is that the cuticle is thin. It would seem, then, that the musculature is continuous. Although it resembles the heteromyotid genus *Ikeda* in possessing a distally placed nephrostome, *Prashadus* differs from *Ikeda* where the nephridia are very numerous (400) and arranged neither segmentally nor in pairs.

DISTRIBUTION. Gulf of Kutch, India.

Prashadus pirotansis (Menon & Datta Gupta, 1962)

(Fig. 58A–B)

Ikedosoma pirotansis Menon & Datta Gupta, 1962 : 305–309, figs 1–3.

TYPE LOCALITY. Pirotan Island. Gulf of Kutch, littoral. *Type.* Museum, Zoology Department, Birla College, Pilani, India.

DESCRIPTION. Animal large, length 740 mm or more, including the proboscis and width 160 mm. Proboscis white with dark spots on the dorsal surface. Trunk pale to bright red in life. Papillae most pronounced dorsally at the anterior and posterior ends of the body. Ventral setae paired and sickle-like; internally the setae are lodged in a muscular sheath provided with strands of muscles. There is a well-defined muscular pad between the setae. There are twenty pairs of nephridia which open independently to the exterior; a typical nephridium has a sac-like basal portion and a narrow neck. The distally placed nephrostome is ciliated, has a petaloid lip and hangs freely in the coelom. Anal vesicles long with numerous unbranched tubules. The ventral nerve cord bifurcates anteriorly to run as a paired nerve cord in the proboscis.

REMARKS. The species was described originally from three specimens, all females. The condition of the muscle layers of the body wall needs examination.

DISTRIBUTION. Several localities in the Gulf of Kutch, India.

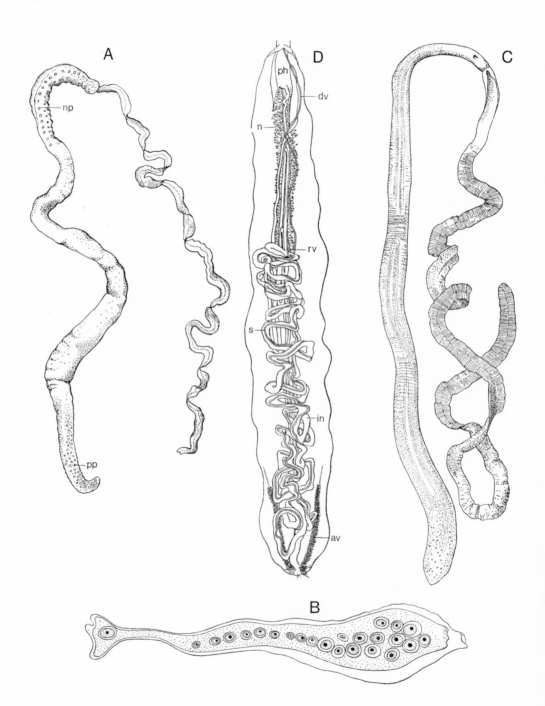

(5). Family **URECHIDAE** Fisher & MacGinitie, 1928

Fisher & MacGinitie, 1928a : 199.

DESCRIPTION. Echiurans with the characters of the order Xenopneusta. Proboscis very much reduced. Distal part of the mid-gut greatly enlarged and acts as a respiratory chamber, water entering and leaving it through the cloaca and anus. Foregut very long and contains a gizzard. No sexual dimorphism.

TYPE GENUS. *Urechis* Seitz.

REMARKS. Amor (1965 : 165) has pointed out with justification that since it has now been shown that *Echiurus chilensis* M. Müller, 1852 = *Pinuca edulis* Gay, 1854 the generic name should be *Pinuca* and the family name Pinucidae. Because an application has been made to the International Committee of Zoological Nomenclature for the suppression of the name *Pinuca* we have refrained from using the term in this monograph.

Genus *URECHIS* Seitz, 1907

Echiurus authors, in part.
Pinuca Hupé in Gay, 1854 : 475; Riveros-Zuniga, 1942 : 1–15; 1951 : 475; Amor, 1965 : 165.
Urechis Seitz, 1907 : 352; Fisher & MacGinitie, 1928 : 200; Fisher, 1946 : 263–264.
Spiroctetor Skorikov, 1909 : 94.

DESCRIPTION. Echiurans of the family Urechidae. Longitudinal musculature of the body wall lies between an outermost layer of circular and innermost layer of oblique muscles; innermost layer appears fasciculate. Two anterior, ventral setae connected by a strong interbasal muscle and one circle of curved, anal setae. Slime glands present on the anterior part of the trunk near the posterior nephridiopores. Internally, paired dorso-ventral muscles are present anterior to the setae. Blood vascular system lacking. Two to three pairs of nephridia with nephrostomal lips that are long and spirally coiled. Alimentary canal long and attached to the body wall by mesenteries; anus eccentrically placed in relation to the posterior ring of setae. Anal vesicles are large sacs which open into the posterior part of the cloaca and bear very small and scattered funnels. Sexes separate.

TYPE SPECIES. *Echiurus chilensis* M. Müller.

REMARKS. *Pinuca edulis* Hupé in Gay (1854) was rather briefly and inadequately described from a specimen collected at Chiloe Is., Chile. The type locality of *Echiuris chilensis* M. Müller, 1852 is Magellan Strait. Seitz (1907) transferred *E. chilensis* to a new genus which he called *Urechis*. Riveros-Zuniga (1951) and Amor (1965) claim that *U. chilensis* = *Pinuca edulis* and consequently the names

---

FIG. 58. (A–B) *Prashadus pirotansis*. (A) Entire specimen, about half size. (B) Nephridium with distally placed nephrostome and containing eggs. (A–B after Menon & Datta Gupta.) (C–D) *Ikeda taenioides*. (C) Entire specimen; about half-size. (D) Dissected female specimen, about one third natural size. (C–D after Ikeda.) KEY: *See* Fig. 53, p. 417.

Pinuca and Pinucidae have priority over *Urechis* and Urechidae. A proposal for the suppression of the name *Punica* has been made to the International Committee of Zoological Nomenclature on two grounds: firstly on the inadequacy of the description of *P. edulis* Hupé in Gay (1854) and secondly that the name *Urechis* is thoroughly established in the literature of the physiology, embryology and ecology of the phylum. Because we think that the application might be successful we have not used the names *Pinuca* and Punicidae in this monograph.

Urechis is an unusual group of echiurans. Fisher (1946 : 265) says 'The curious respiratory mechanism of *Urechis*, in connection with the loss of its blood vessels and the complexity of its blood physiology, relegates the genus to a very isolated position. Not less important is the behaviour pattern whereby the requirements of respiration and food are beautifully met and coordinated. At every point specialization of habit is matched by structural and physiological adjustment of the most delicate and efficient description. Along with this specialization and complexity is an amazing viability best expressed by the term "tough".

All signs point to *Urechis* as being the last of a very ancient stock, one that may have flowered into many species during Paleozoic times. It belongs to the honourable company of *Lingula* and those other aristocrats sometimes referred to as, "living fossils".'.

DISTRIBUTION. Japanese, Californian, New Zealand and South American seas.

GENUS URECHIS—KEY TO SPECIES

1	Two pairs of nephridia	2
–	Three pairs of nephridia	3
2	Trunk papillated . . . . *U. unicinctus* (p. 469)	
–	Trunk smooth . . . . *U. novae-zealandiae* (p. 467)	
3	Ventral setae sharp and strongly tapered . . . . . *U. caupo* (p. 466)	
–	Ventral setae blunt and scarcely tapered . . . . . *U. chilensis* (p. 467)	

Urechis caupo Fisher & MacGinitie, 1928

(Fig. 59A–F & Fig. 60C–F)

Urechis caupo Fisher & MacGinitie, 1928a : 200, pl. 9, figs 1–6; 1928b : 204, figs 1–3, pl. 10; Baumberger & Michaelis, 1931 : 417; Redfield & Florkin, 1931 : 185; Hall, 1931 : 400; Sato, 1931 : 178; Newby, 1932 : 387; 1940 : 1–219; 1941 : 303; MacGinitie, 1935a : 341; 1935c : 483; Fisher, 1946 : 265–280, figs 17–19, pls 33–35, pl. 36, figs 2, 4, pl. 37; Wesenberg-Lund, 1954a : 11–12.

TYPE LOCALITY. Elkhorn Slough, Monterey Bay, California. *Type.* U.S.N.M. no. 19616.

DESCRIPTION. Proboscis reduced to a short collar. Body large, usually 150–180 mm long but sometimes 500 mm; surface traversed by fine irregular channels, giving it a rugose appearance which is most pronounced in the region anterior to the zone of slime glands. Ventral setae tapered, sharp, curved and situated 3·5 mm behind the groove leading to the mouth; a strong interbasal muscle present.

Anal setae, terminally sharp, 10–11 in number and strongly marked by cross-banding. Three pairs of nephridia, the anterior pair set close to the setae; the nephrostome is placed on the anterior side at the base and its ciliated lips are long, grooved and spirally coiled. Anal vesicles cauliflower-like when contracted and bear minute ciliated funnels. No sexual dimorphism.

REMARKS. This species is a well known echiuran and many papers have been written about its structure, natural history, physiology, embryology and ecology. Papers of importance are those on its structure and natural history (Fisher & MacGinitie, 1928a, 1928b), its embryology (Newby, 1940) and its respiration (Redfield & Florkin, 1931). The description and illustrations of Fisher (1946) are particularly good. The mature egg, sperm and two larval stages are illustrated in Fig. 60C–F.

Fisher (1946 : 264) discusses the possibility of *U. caupo* and *U. chilensis* being the same species.

DISTRIBUTION. California, numerous localities.

Urechis chilensis (M. Müller, 1852)

Echiurus chilensis M. Müller, 1852 : 21; Baird, 1868 : 111; Greeff, 1879 : 144; Fischer, 1896a : 6; 1896b : 97; Collin, 1891 : 463; Shipley, 1899b : 342–343; Riveros-Zuniga, 1951 : 156.
Pinuca edulis Gay, 1854 : 475.
Echiurus farcimen Baird, 1873 : 97; Rice & Stephen, 1970 : 69–70.
Urechis chilensis: Seitz, 1907 : 323–356, 3 pls, 44 figs; Fischer, 1914b : 16; 1920 : 418; Stephen, 1941 : 246–247; Wesenberg-Lund, 1955 : 14–16.
  246–247; Wesenberg-Lund, 1955 : 14–16.
Spiroctetor chilensis: Skorikov, 1909 : 97–98.
Pinuca chilensis: Riveros-Zuniga, 1942 : 1–15 1–3; Amor, 1965 : 165–168.

TYPE LOCALITY. Straits of Magellan.

DESCRIPTION. Proboscis short and pointed. Trunk up to 225 mm in length; surface of the middle region traversed by fine furrows giving a rugose appearance more pronounced at the posterior extremity and in an area behind the introvert, where the skin appears scaly and where the slime glands are concentrated. Anal ring of 7–11 setae. Three pairs of nephridia; nephrostomes with long spirally coiled lips. Anal vesicles long, simple sacs, about half the length of the trunk.

REMARKS. Seitz's description is given in considerable detail. The use of the name *Pinuca* is discussed on p. 465.

DISTRIBUTION. Known from numerous areas from Chile and Patagonia.

Urechis novaezealandiae (Dendy, 1897)

Echiurus novaezealandiae Dendy, 1898 : 323–324.
Urechis novaezealandiae: Poche, 1920 : 102; Knox, 1957 : 141–148, figs 1–8.

TYPE LOCALITY. Brighton Beach, Christchurch, New Zealand. *Type.* Canterbury Museum, New Zealand.

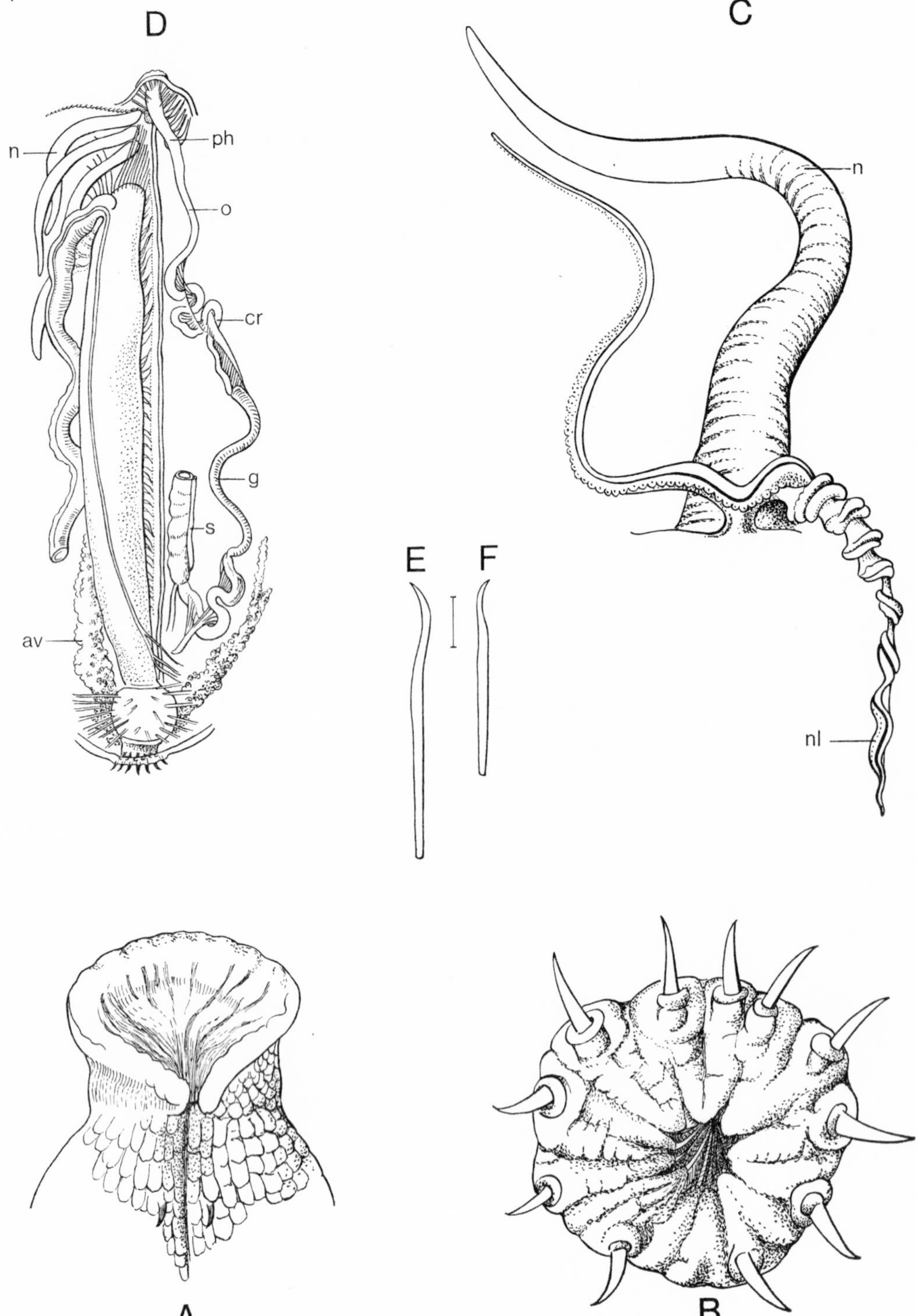
D
n
ph
o
cr
g
s
av
C
n
nl
E
F
A
B

DESCRIPTION. Proboscis short and scoop-like. Trunk cylindrical, sausage-shaped, up to 230 mm in length, when fully extended; surface traversed by fine irregular channels giving it a rugose appearance, most pronounced at the anterior and posterior ends. The anterior portion from about 10 mm behind the ventral setae deeply cut by channels into irregular areas; this region passes abruptly into the region of the slime-glands, defined by rather close irregular channels. Ventral setae up to 13 mm in length, iridescent, bluish-yellow and brownish at the tip. Posterior ring has 10–11 setae, which are cylindrical, tapering and curved at the tip. Normally two pairs of nephridia, but Knox reported a third nephridium in an adult and a juvenile specimen which he examined; one nephridium had two nephrostomes, each with spirally coiled lips. Anal vesicles long and large.

REMARKS. The original description was rather short. Knox's description is fuller and well illustrated.

DISTRIBUTION. As for the type locality (Dendy, 1898); numerous New Zealand localities (Knox, 1958).

Urechis unicinctus (von Drasche, 1881)

Echiurus unicinctus von Drasche, 1881 : 621–623, pl. 20, fig. 1; Selenka, 1885 : 6–7, pl. 1, fig. 2, pl. 3, figs 11, 12; Fischer, 1895 : 21; Shipley, 1899b : 344; Embleton, 1900 : 77–97, fig. 1, pls 7–10; Ikeda, 1904 : 59–60; 1924 : 38; Ostroumoff, 1909 : 319.
Urechis unicinctus: Seitz, 1907 : 326; Spengel, 1912c : 356; 1912d : 173–212; Fischer, 1612 : 17; 1921 : 423; Sato, 1931 : 171–178, figs 1–3; 1934 : 247–249; 1937 : 141–142, pl. 2, fig. i; 1939 : 349–350, pl. 22, figs 26–27; Chen & Yeh, 1958 : 276.
Spiroctetor unicinctus: Skorikow, 1909 : 77–96.

TYPE LOCALITY. East coast of south Japan.

DESCRIPTION. Proboscis short and reduced to a bluntly-pointed conical pre-oral lobe. Trunk up to 250 mm in length, densely covered with papillae which are extremely variable in size and form and which are roughly arranged in transverse rows. Ventral setae strongly re-curved at the tip; their bases are attached to the body wall by numerous strong radiating muscle-bands. There are 10–13 nearly straight and sharply pointed setae in the posterior circle. Two pairs of nephridia; nephrostomes with long spirally coiled lips. Anal vesicles about one third as long as the trunk and fastened over the basal quarter of their length to the body wall by several fine muscles; they carry numerous ciliated funnels.

REMARKS. The species has been studied in detail by Embleton (1900) and Sato (1931). Both have given detailed and well illustrated accounts.

DISTRIBUTION. A common species in Japanese waters and recorded from numerous localities. China: Daren, Shantung (Chen & Yeh, 1958).

FIG. 59. (A–F) *Urechis caupo.* (A) Ventral surface of proboscis and anterior end of body. (B) Posterior end of body showing the eccentrically placed anus and a circle of setae. (c) Anterior view of a nephridium of the second pair. (D) Dissection of a contracted specimen showing some of the internal structures. (E) Anterior or ventral setae; the scale line is 2 mm. (F) Anal setae; (E) and (F) to same scale. (A–F after Fisher.) KEY: See Fig. 53, p. 417.

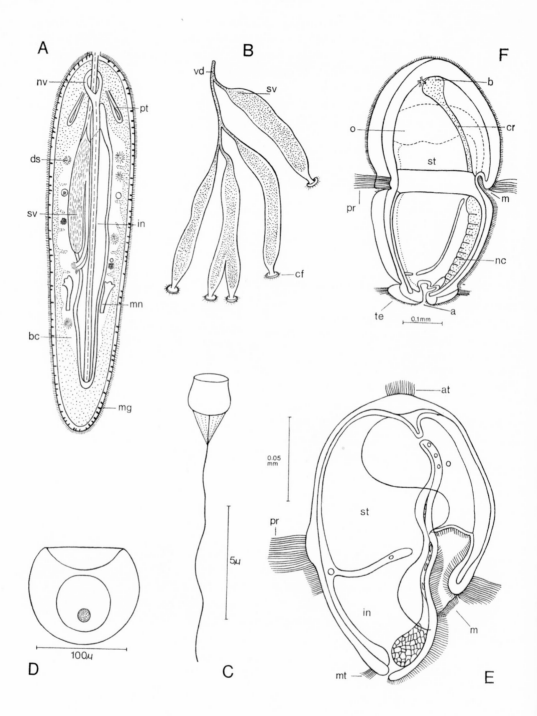

(6). Family **IKEDAIDAE**

Ikedaidae Dawydoff, 1959 : 899.

DESCRIPTION. As for the order Heteromyota (p. 354). The family contains a single genus *Ikeda*.

Genus *IKEDA* Wharton, 1913

Ikeda Wharton, 1913 : 260–261; Fisher, 1946 : 220.

DESCRIPTION. Longitudinal muscle layer of body wall lies exterior to both circular and oblique musculature; longitudinal musculature also thickened to form bands. Proboscis very long. Nephridia unpaired and numerous (200–400), nephrostome distal. A 'heart' placed at posterior end of mid-gut.

TYPE SPECIES. *Thalassema taenioides* Ikeda.

REMARKS. The genus contains one species *Ikeda taenioides* described by Ikeda, 1904 and 1907.

DISTRIBUTION. Japanese waters.

Ikeda taenioides (Ikeda) 1904

(Fig. 58C–D)

Thalassema taenioides Ikeda, 1904 : 63–64; 1907 : 16–47, pl. 1, fig. 3, pl. 2, figs 18–22, pl. 3 figs 23–36, pl. 4, figs 37–47.
Ikeda taenioides: Wharton, 1913 : 260–261; Sato, 1931 : 179–180, fig. 4; 1934a : 252–253, fig. 9; 1937a : 142, pl. 2, fig. 2; 1939 : 356–357.

TYPE LOCALITY. Onomichi Bay, Japan.

DESCRIPTION. Proboscis exceedingly long reaching, when extended, a length of up to a metre; decorated with narrow transverse brown stripes. Trunk very long, up to 400 mm with a breadth of 20–30 mm; deep reddish-brown in colour.

FIG. 60. (A) Generalized view of a sexually mature male (after Baltzer). (B) Male structures of *Acanthobonellia pirotanensis* (after Josè). (C) Mature sperm of *Urechis caupo* (after Newby). The middle piece appears to be a hyaline cone. (D) Mature egg of *Urechis caupo* (after Newby). The egg when taken from a nephridium is indented. The egg of *Lissomyema mellita* is also indented (Conn, 1886 : 359) but that of *Echiurus* appears to be spherical (Baltzer, 1917, fig. 30). (E) Larva of *Urechis caupo* during trochophore stage (after Newby). The larva is a trochophore from about 40 hours to 30 days. During this time 'no great growth or visible differentiation takes place' (Newby, 1940 : 79). (F) Larva of *Urechis caupo* after about 50 days and nearing the end of the post-trochophore period (after Newby). *a*, anus; *at*, apical tuft; *b*, brain; *bc*, body cavity; *cf*, ciliate funnel; *cr*, circumoesophageal ring; *ds*, developing sperms; *in*, intestine; *m*, mouth; *mg*, mucous glands; *mn*, metanephridium; *mt*, metatroch; *nc*, nerve cord; *nv*, nerve ring; *o*, oesophagus; *pr*, prototroch; *pt*, protonephridium; *st*, stomach; *sv*, seminal vesicle; *te*, telotroch.

The papillae, which are irregular in shape, are largest and most densely crowded at either end. Five pale yellow narrow lines which mark the longitudinal muscle bands. Base of the ventral setae bulbous; setae connected by an interbasal muscle. Pharynx carries two large wing muscles. Nephridia very numerous, never less than 200 with no indication of a segmental arrangement nor of a strictly paired disposition; nephrostome at the distal extremity. Anal vesicles 60–70 mm long and appear hairy on account of the presence of very long funnels. No rectal caecum. Dorsal blood vessel long and the heart situated posteriorly at the end of the mid-gut. A large part of the dorsal vessel in front of the crop is fixed to the body wall by a mesentery-like suspensory ligament.

REMARKS. Described originally from six specimens and redescribed very fully by Ikeda (1907). *I. taenioides*, in which the nephridia are crowded together without apparent order, fully justifies Ikeda's description, ' a remarkable species of echiuroid'.

DISTRIBUTION. Several Japanese localities (Ikeda, Sato).

3. APPENDICES

1. PARASITES AND COMMENSALS OF ECHIURANS

The following list of parasites and commensals has been compiled chiefly from the literature about the systematics of the phylum Echiura. It is not necessarily complete.

a. Parasites

Parasite	Site of infestation	Host	Record
Protozoa			
Zygosoma globosum	body cavity	*Urechis caupo*	Noble, 1938
Conorhynchus gibbosus	gut	*Echiurus echiuris*	Greeff, 1879
undetermined species	mid-gut	*Ikeda taenioides*	Ikeda, 1907
Platyhelminthes			
Nemertoscolex parasiticus	body cavity	*Echiurus echiuris*	Greeff, 1879
Distomum echiuri	nephridia	*Echiuris echiuris*	Spengel, 1880
cestode larva	siphon	*Urechis caupo*	Fisher, 1946
Nematoda			
unidentified nematodes	mid-gut	*Pseudobonellia biuterina*	Edmonds, 1960a
Annelida			
Oligognathus bonelliae	{ gut { body cavity	*Bonellia viridis*	Spengel, 1882 Fauvel, 1923 Pettibone, 1957

b. Commensals

Commensal	Echiuran	Record
Annelida		
Hesperonoe adventor	*Urechis caupo*	Fisher, 1946
Arthropoda (Crustacea)		
Scleroplax granulator	*Urechis caupo*	Fisher, 1946
Pinnixia franciscana	*Urechis caupo*	Fisher, 1946
Betaeus longidactylus	*Urechis caupo*	Fisher, 1946
Crangon californicus	*Urechis caupo*	Fisher, 1946
Mollusca		
Cryptomya californica	*Urechis caupo*	Fisher, 1946
Achasmea thalassemicola	*Anelassorhynchus mucosus*	Habe, 1962

2. SPECIES INCERTAE SEDIS, ETC.

Echiurus caraibicus Diesing, 1859 : 777; Quatrefages, 1965b : 594; West Indies.
Thalassema brevipalpis Quatrefages, 1865b : 595; locality not known.
Thalassema peltzelnii Diesing, 1859 : 774; West Indies.
Thalassema peronii Quatrefages, 1865b : 595; Indian Ocean?
Taguella aucklandica Benham, 1948 : 761–764, 6 figs.

Benham (1948) classified with reservations a worm from Auckland Is. as an 'animal allied to the echiurid gephyrea'. He called it *Taguella aucklandica*. One of us has re-examined the specimen in the British Museum but can throw no further light on its identity. It is very difficult to see how it can be an echiuran because it lacks setae, a long convoluted gut, a terminal anus and anal vesicles. It may be that it is the posterior part of some other animal, possibly a sipunculan. It is a *species inquirenda*.

Sactosoma vitreum Danielssen & Koren, 1881.

Sactosoma vitreum Danielssen & Koren, 1881 : 34–39, pl. 6, figs 1–6. The species was described from a single incomplete specimen taken off the northern Norwegian coast (63°22′N, 5°29′E) at 2222 m. It was put in the class Saccosomatidae by Théel (1906 : 14). Fisher (1946 : 220) pointed out that the name was pre-occupied and suggested the name Sactosomatidae. Both he and Bock (1942) included it in their classification of the Echiura, Bock creating an order and Fisher a class to contain it. We question whether it is wise to give the species such an elevated status. According to Danielssen & Koren (1881) and Théel (1906) the specimen is small and was dredged at a depth of 2190 m near the Faroe Is. The layers of muscle that make up the body wall are not arranged in the echiuran manner, the innermost circular layer being either missing or reduced. No proboscis is present, no tentacles, no setae, no retractor muscles and no anal vesicles. The mouth and anus are at opposite ends of the animal and the alimentary canal is convoluted but appears to lack a siphon. One nephridium, containing eggs, opened near the mouth. We consider that it is a *species inquirenda*.

FF

Poeobius meseres Heath, 1930.

    Poeobius meseres Heath, 1930 : 223–249, 1 pl., 2 text-figs. This species has had a chequered history having been placed at various times in several phyla. Heath (1930) considered it to be a connecting link between the Annelida and Echiura. Remane (Pickford, 1947a) considered it to be an echiuran but Fisher (1946) removed it from that phylum. After a detailed study Pickford (1947) came to the conclusion that it was an aberrant annelid, a view later accepted by Fisher (1952) and McGowan (1960 : 125). Berkeley & Berkeley (1960) have suggested that it might be an archiannelid. It is a common pelagic species off the Californian coast.

IV. ACKNOWLEDGEMENTS

    I should like to acknowledge the help that has been given by the following: Mr R. W. Sims (British Museum (Natural History), London) for encouragement, advice and editorial supervision; Dr Mary Rice (U.S. National Museum, Washington), Professor E. Cutler (University College of Utica, U.S.A.) and Dr V. V. Murina (Institute of Biology, Sevastopol, U.S.S.R.) for specimens and records; Mr E. G. Easton for assistance with specimens; Mrs M. Newman who typed the manuscript and especially to Mrs M. Shaffer who drew the illustrations.

                                                          S. J. E.

V. BIBLIOGRAPHY

ADOLPH, E. F. 1936. Differential permeability to water and osmotic exchanges in the marine worm *Phascolosoma*. *J. cell. comp. Physiol.* **9** : 117–135, 7 figs.

AGGARAWALA, A. C. 1924. Polychaeta and Gephyrea from Karachi. *Proc. Lahore phil. Soc.* **3** : 69–75.

AKESSON, B. 1958. A study of the nervous system of the Sipunculoideae, with some remarks on the development of the two species *Phascolion strombi* (Montagu) and *Golfingia minuta* (Keferstein). *Undersökningar över Öresund.* **38** : 1–149, 105 figs.

—— 1961a. The development of *Golfingia elongata* Keferstein (Sipunculidae), with some remarks on the development of the neurosecretory cells in sipunculids. *Ark. Zool.* **13** : 511–531, figs 1–11.

—— 1961b. Some observations on Pelagosphaera larvae (Sipunculoidea). *Galathea Report* **5** : 7–16, 6 pls, figs 1–11.

ALBERT, PRINCE DE MONACO. 1899. Sur la distribution bathymétrique de certaines espèces d'animaux marins. *Cinquantenaire de la Société de Biologie*, Paris : 55–56.

ALDER, J. 1860. Description of a zoophyte and two species of Echinodermata new to Britain. *Ann. Mag. nat. Hist.* Ser. 3, **5** : 73–75, pl. 5.

ALLEN, J. A. & TOD, R. A. 1900. The fauna of the Salcombe Estuary. *J. mar. biol. Ass. U.K.* n. ser. **6** : 151–217.

—— 1902. The fauna of the Exe Estuary. *J. Mar. biol. Ass. U.K.* n. ser. **6** : 295–335.

AMOR, A. 1964. El genero *Dendrostomum* (Sipunculida) en la Argentina. *Physis.* **24** (68) : 457–470, 5 figs.

—— 1965. Una nueva localidad para *Pinuca chilensis* (Max Müller) en el Atlantico sur (Echiurida). Aclaracion sobre su sinonimia: Pinucidae nom. nov. para Urechidae Fisher and Macginitie. *Physis* **25** (69) : 165–168.

ᴀMOR, A.   1970.   A proposito del hallazgo de *Themiste hennahi* Gray en la Bahia Concepcion, Chile (Sipuncula).   *Physis*, 29 (79) : 495–504, 1 fig. ,3 pls.

ᴀNDREAE, J.   1881.   Zur Anatomie des *Sipunculus nudus* L.   *Zool. Anz.* **4** : 477–481.

—— 1882.   Beiträge zur Anatomie und Histologie des *Sipunculus nudus* L.   *Z. wiss. Zool.* **36** : 201–255, pls 12–13.

ᴀNDREWS, E. A.   1889.   Reproductive organs of *Phascolosoma gouldii*.   *Zool. Anz.* **12** : 140–142.

—— 1890a.   Notes on the body-cavity liquid of *Sipunculus gouldii* Pourtalès.   *John Hopkins Univ. Circ.* **9** : 65.

—— 1890b.   Notes on the anatomy of *Sipunculus gouldii* Pourtalès.   *Studies Biol. Lab. John Hopkins Univ.* **4** : 389–430, pls 44–47.

ᴀNDREW, M. & ANDREW, N. V.   1953.   Some annelid and sipunculid worms of the Bimini region.   *Am. Mus. Novit.* (1617) : 1–16, 4 figs.

ᴀNNANDALE, N.   1922.   The marine element in the fauna of the Ganges.   Feestnummer 70 Geboortedag von Dr. Max. Weber.   *Bijdr. Dierk.* **22** : 143–154.

ᴀNNANDALE, N. & KEMP, S.   1915.   Fauna of the Chilka Lake.   The Echiuroidea of the lake and the Gangetic Delta.   *Mem. Indian Mus.* **5** : 55–63.

ᴀPPELLÖF, A.   1892.   Om Bergensfjordenes faunistike praeg.   *Bergens Mus. Arsberetn,* **1892** (2) : 4–14.

ᴀRVY, L.   1952a.   Quelques particularités histochemiques d'une loxosome fixé sur *Phascolion strombi* (Mont).   *Bull. Soc. zool. Fr.* **77** : 229.

—— 1952b.   Sur deux parasites de *Phascolion strombi* (Mont).   *Bull. Lab. marit. Dinard.* **36** : 7–13.

ᴀRVY, L. & GABE, M.   1952.   Particularités histochimiques du tube digestif de *Phascolion strombi* (Montagu).   *Bull. Lab. marit. Dinard.* **36** : 24–31.

ᴀRVY, L. & PRENANT, M.   1952.   *Loxosoma nitschei* Vigelius sur les phascolions de Dinard.   *Bull. Lab. marit. Dinard.* **36** : 2–5.

ᴀUGENER, H.   1903.   Beiträge zur Kenntnis der Gephyreen nach Untersuchung der im Göttinger zoologischen Museum befindlichen Sipunculiden und Echiuriden.   *Arch. Naturgesch.* **69** : 297–371, pls 16–20.   Also as Inaugural Dissertation : 1–78, pls 16–20.   Nicolaische Verlags-Buchhandlung (Berlin).

—— 1906.   Westindische Polychaeten.   Blake Rept. 42.   *Bull. Mus. comp. Zool. Harv.* **43** : 191–196, pl. 8.

ᴀWATI, P. H.   1936.   Proboscis of *Thalassema bombayensis* (Prashad & Awati).   *J. Univ. Bombay* **4** : 96–104, 8 figs.

—— 1938.   A short note on the ciliated apparatus in *Echiurus* larva.   *J. Univ. Bombay* **6** : 92–103, 10 figs.

ᴀWATI, P. R. & DESHPANDE, D. S.   1933a.   The reproductive system and the segmental organs in *Thalassema bombayensis* (Prashad & Awati).   *J. Univ. Bombay* **1** : 96–107. 9 figs.

—— 1933b.   A note on the development of *Thalassema bombayensis*.   *Proc. Indian Sci. Congr.* **18** : 223.

—— 1935a.   Burrows of *Thalassema bombayensis*.   *Proc. Indian Sci. Congr.* **22** : 320.

—— 1935b.   Food-getting in *Thalassema bombayensis*.   *Proc. Indian Sci. Congr.* **22** : 320.

—— 1935c.   Respiratory movements in *Thalassema bombayensis*.   *Proc. Indian Sci. Congr.* **22** : 320–321.

—— 1936.   The alimentary canal of *Thalassema bombayensis* (Prashad & Awati).   *J. Univ. Bombay* **4** : 68–85, 15 figs.

ᴀWATI, P. R. & PRADHAN, L. B.   1935.   The anatomy of *Dendrostoma signifer* Sel. & de Man. I.   *J. Univ. Bombay* **3** : 102–113, 2 pls, 7 text-figs.

—— 1936.   The anatomy of *Dendrostoma signifer* Sel. & de Man. II.   *J. Univ. Bombay* **4** : 114–131, 11 figs.

ʙAIRD, W. B.   1868.   Monograph of the species of worms belonging to the sub-class Gephyrea.   *Proc. zool. Soc. Lond.* **1868** : 76–114, pls 9–11.

BAIRD, W. B. 1873. Descriptions of some new species of Annelida and Gephyrea in the collections of the British Museum. *J. Linn. Soc.* (Zool.) **11** : 94–97.

BALTZER, F. 1912. Über die Entwicklungsgeschichte von *Bonellia*. *Verh. dtsch. zool. Ges.* **22** : 252–261, 10 figs.

—— 1914a. Entwicklungsgeschichte und Metamorphose des *Echiurus*. *Verh. schweiz naturf. Ges.* **2** : 208–212.

—— 1914b. Die Bestimmung des Geschlechts nebst einer Analyse des Geschlechtsdimorphismus bei *Bonellia*. *Mitt. zool. Stn. Neapel.* **22** : 1–44.

—— 1914c. Die Bestimmung und der Dimorphismus des Geschlechts bei *Bonellia*. *Sber. phys-med. Ges. Wurzburg.* **43** : 14–19.

—— 1917a. Monographie des Echiuriden des Golfes von Neapel. I. *Echiurus abyssalis* Skor. *Fauna u Flora Golf Neapel.* Berlin Monogr. **34** : 1–234, 12 pls.

—— 1917b. Über die Eibildung der *Bonellia*. *Verh. phys-med. Ges. Wurzb.* **45** : 103–110, 1 pl.

—— 1923. Zur Entwicklungsgeschichte und Auffassung des Männchens der *Bonellia*. *Verh. dtsch. zool. Ges.* **28** : 65–68.

—— 1924. Über die Giftwirkung der weiblichen *Bonellia*-gewebe auf die *Bonellia*-männchen und andere Organismen und ihre Beziehung zur Bestimmung des Geschlechts der Bonellien-larve. *Mitt. naturf. Ges. Bern.* **1924** : 98–117.

—— 1925a. Über die Giftwirkung der weiblichen *Bonellia* und ihre Beziehung zur Geschlechtsbestimmung der Larve. *Revue suisse Zool.* **32** : 87–93.

—— 1925b. Untersuchungen über die Entwicklung und Geschlechtsbestimmung der *Bonellia*. *Pubbl. Staz. zool. Napoli.* **6** : 223–286.

—— 1926. Über die Vermännlichung indifferenter *Bonellia*-larven durch *Bonellia* Extrakte. *Revue suisse Zool.* **33** : 359–374, 6 text-figs.

—— 1928a. Neue Versuche über die Bestimmung des Geschlechts bei *Bonellia viridis*. *Revue suisse Zool.* **35** : 225–231.

—— 1928b. Über metagame Geschlechtsbestimmung und ihre Beziehung zu einigen Problemem der Entwicklungsmechanik und Verebung (auf Grund von Versuchen an *Bonellia*). *Verh. dtsch. zool. Ges.* **32** : 273–325, 2 figs.

—— 1931a. Entwicklungsmechanische Untersuchungen an *Bonellia viridis*. Die Abhängigkeit der Entwicklungsgeschwindigkeit und des Entwicklungsgrades der männlichen Larve von der Dauer der Rüssel-parasitismus. *Revue suisse Zool.* **38** : 361–371.

—— 1931b. Priapulida. **2** (9) : 1–14, figs 1–14. *Handbuch der Zoologie* (Berlin); ed. Kükenthal, W. & Krumbach, T.

—— 1931c. Sipunculida **2** (9) : 15–61, figs 15–47. *Handbuch der Zoologie* (Berlin); ed Kükenthal, W. & Krumbach, T.

—— 1931d. Echiurida. **2** (9) : 62–168, figs 49–132. *Handbuch der Zoologie* (Berlin); ed. Kükenthal, W. & Krumbach, T.

—— 1932. Über die ohne Rüssel-parasitismus entstehenden Spatmännchen (genetische Männchen) der *Bonellia viridis*. *Revue suisse Zool.* **39** : 281–305.

—— 1933. Demonstration von männlichen *Bonellia* larven. *Revue suisse Zool.* **40** : 243–246, 1 fig.

—— 1934a. Über die Zuchtmöglichkeit der *Bonellia viridis*, vom Ei bis zum erwachsenen Zustand. *Revue suisse Zool.* **41** : 407–409, 2 figs.

—— 1934b. Zucht und Versuchsmethoden (Geschlechtsbestimmung) der *Bonellia viridis*. *Hand. Biol. Arb. Meth.* **9** : 437–444.

—— 1934c. Experiments on sex-development in *Bonellia viridis*. *Collecting Net.* (Woods Hole) **10** (3) : 1–8.

—— 1937a. Entwicklungmechanische Untersuchungen an *Bonellia viridis* iii. Über die Entwicklung und Bestimmung des Geschlechts und die Anwendbarkeit der Goldschmidt-schen Zeitgesetzes der Intersexualität bei *Bonellia viridis*. *Pubbl. Staz. zool. Napoli.* **16** : 89–159, 2 figs.

BALTZER, F. 1937b. Entwicklungsphysiologishe Analyse der Intersexualität. *Revue suisse Zool.* **44** : 331–352, 1 fig.
—— 1937c. Analyse des Goldschmidtschen Zeitgesetzes der Intersexualität auf Grund eines Vergleiches der Entwicklung der *Bonellia* und *Lymantria*-Intersexe. Zeitlich Gestaffelte Wirkung der Geschlechtsfaktoren (Zeitgesetz) und Faktoren Gleichzeitigkeit (Gen-Gleichgewicht). *Wilhelm Roux Arch. Entw-Mech. Organ.* **136** : 1–43.
BARNARD, J. L. & HARTMAN, O. 1959. The sea bottom off Santa Barbara, California. Biomass and community structure. *Pacif. Nat.* **1** : 1–16, 7 figs.
BASSINGDALE, R. 1945. Studies on the biology of the Bristol Channel. 16. The fauna of Skomer Island. *Proc. Bristol Nat. Soc.* **27** : 109–120, 1 map.
BASSINGDALE, R. & CLARK, R. B. 1960. The Gann Flat, Dale. Studies on the ecology of a muddy beach. *Fld. Stud.* **1** : 1–22, 12 figs.
BATHER, F. A. 1900. Zoological Record. Echinodermata : 78.
BAUMBERGER, J. P. & MICHAELIS, L. 1931. The blood pigments of *Urechis caupo*. *Biol. Bull. mar. biol. Lab., Woods Hole* **61** : 417–421.
BEKLEMISEV, V. N. 1915. Sur les turbellaries parasites de la côte Mourmanne. *Trav. Soc. Nat. Petrograd.* ser. 4, **43** : 103–156; 168–172 (in Russian). Résumé francais: 156–167.
BELLOC, G. 1959. Catalogue des types de géphyriens du Musée océanographique de Monaco. *Bull. Inst. océanogr. Monaco* (**1149**) : 1–4.
BENHAM, W. B. 1903. The sipunculids of New Zealand. *Trans. Proc. N.Z. Inst.* **36** : 172–184, pl. 7.
—— 1904. Further notes on the sipunculids of New Zealand. *Trans. Proc. N.Z. Inst.* **37** : 301–308, pls 15–16.
—— 1909. Annelida and Sipunculoidea. *Rec. Canterbury (N.Z.) Mus.* **1** : 71–82.
—— 1912. Report on sundry invertebrates from the Kermadec Islands. *Trans. Proc. N.Z. Inst.* **44** : 135–138.
—— 1922. Gephyrea inermia. Australian Antarctic Expedition 1911–1914, under the leadership of Sir Douglas Mawson. *Sci. Rep. Aust. antarct. Exped.* Ser. C, Zoology and Botany, **6** : 1–22, pl. 11, figs 1–15.
—— 1948. *Taguella aucklandica* gen. et sp. nov. an animal allied to the echiurid Gephyrea. *Proc. zool. Soc. Lond.* **118** : 761–764, figs 1–6.
BERKELEY, G. & BERKELEY, C. 1960. Some further records of pelagic polychaetes from the northeastern Pacific north of latitude 60°N and east of longitude 175°W, together with records of Siphonophora, Mollusca and Tunicata from the same region. *Canad. J. Zool.* **38** : 787–799.
BIANCHI, S. G. (Janus Plancus). 1760. *See* Plancus, J.
BIANCO, S. Lo. 1903. Le pesche abissali eseguite da F. A. Krupp. *Mitteil. Zool. St. Neapol.* **16** : 265–266.
BLAINVILLE, H. M. D. de. 1827. Dictionnaire des sciences naturelles. Vers. **49** : 305–313.
BLANCHARD, E. 1849. Recherches sur l'organisation des Vers. *Annls. Sci. nat.* ser. 3, **12** : 5–68.
BLEDOVSKI, R. 1910a. Beiträge zur Kenntnis der *Bonellia viridis* (Rol.) und der Phylogenie einiger Coelhelminthen. Vloclavek. **1910**. (Inaug. Diss. Univ. Bern), 1–69, 3 pls.
—— 1910b. Ze Studyow nad *Bonellia* (Quelques observations sur le Bonellie). *C.R. Soc. Sci. Varsovie* **3** : 399–409.
BOBIN, G. & PRENANT, M. 1953a. Sur les loxosomes du *Phascolion strombi* (Montagu) et sur la spécificitié de l'inquilisme des loxosomes. *Archs. Zool. exp. gén.* Notes et Revue. **90** : 18–41, 7 text-figs.
—— 1953b. Les populations de loxosomes du *Phascolion strombi* (Montagu). *Archs. Zool. exp. gén.* Notes et Revue. **90** : 93–104, 3 text-figs.
—— 1953c. Deux loxosomes nouveaux de Roscoff. *Archs. Zool. exp. gén.* Notes et Revue. **91** : 25–35.
—— 1953d. Sur trois loxosomes Mediterraneens. *Bull. Inst. Océanogr.* Monaco (**1030**) : 1–9, 3 text-figs.

Bobin, G. & Prenant, M. 1953e. La classification des loxosomes selon Mortensen et la *Loxosome singulaire* de Keferstein et de Claparède. *Bull. Soc. zool. Fr.* **78** : 84–96, 5 text-figs.

Bock, S. 1920. *Epithetosoma* not a gephyrean but an indeterminate heteronemertine. *Bergens Mus. Arb.* **1920-1921**, (9) : 1–5.

—— 1942. On the structure and affinities of '*Thalassema*' *lankesteri* Herdman and the classification of the Group *Echiuroidea*. *Goteborgs. Vetensk.- o. Vitterh Samh. Handl.* ser. B, **2** (6) : 1–94, 6 pls, 11 text-figs.

Bocquet, C. & Stock, J. H. 1957. Copépodes parasites d'Invertébrés des côtes de France. 4a, b, c. Le double parasitisme de *Sipunculus nudus* par *Myzomolgus stupendus* nov. gen. nov. sp. et *Catania plana* nov. gen. nov. sp. Copépodes cyclopoidea très remarquables. *Proc. K. ned. Akad. Wet.* **60**c (3) : 410–431, 6 text-figs.

Bohadsch, J. B. 1761. De quisbusdam animalibus marinis liber. Dresden. **4** : 93–97.

Bosc, L. A. G. 1802. Histoire naturelle des Vers. **1** : 113–323, Paris.

Boss, K. J. 1965. Symbiotic Erycinacean bivalves. *Malacologia.* **3** (2) : 183–195.

Bouvier, E. L. 1894. Un nouveau cas de commensalisme: association de vers du genre *Aspidosiphon* avec des polypes madréporaires et un mollusque bivalve. *C. r. hebd. Séanc. Acad. Sci., Paris* **119** : 96–98.

—— 1895. Le commensalisme chez certaines polypes madreporaires. *Annls. Sci. nat. Zool* **20** : 1–32.

Brahm, Carolyn & Mohr, John L. 1962. Report on an echiurid worm *Hamingia arctica* Dan. & Kor. from the Beaufort Sea. *Bull. Sth. Calif. Acad. Sci.* **61** (2) : 123.

Brandt, A. 1835. Prodromus descriptionis animalium ab H. Mertensio in orbis terrarum circumnavigatione observatorum **1** : 62, also [in] Lamarck, Animaux sans vertébrés **2**, 3 : 472.

—— 1870. Anatomisch-histologische Untersuchungen über den *Sipunculus nudus* L. *Mem. Acad. Sci. St. Petersburg (Sci. math. phys. nat.)* ser. 7, **16** (8) : 1–42, 2 pls.

Bridges, William. 1963. A laboratory looks at a peculiar worm (*Bonellia viridis*). *Anim. Kingd.* **66** (6) : 184–186, 1 pl.

Broch, H. 1927. Untersuchungen über die marine Bodenfauna bei Lindesness im Juni 1926. *Meddr. Zool. mus. Oslo* **10** : 1–32, 2 figs.

Broeke, A. ten. 1925. Westindische Sipunculiden und Echiuriden. *Bijdr. Dierk.* **24** : 81–96, figs 1–25.

—— 1929. *Sipunculoidea* und *Echiuroidea*. *Tierwelt Dtl.* **15** : 156–168, 15 figs.

—— 1933. Sipunculiden. Résultats scientifiques du voyage aux Indes Orientales Néerlandaises de LL AA RR le Prince et la Princesse Leopold de Belgique. *Mem. Mus. r. Hist. nat. Belg.* ser. 2, **13** : 1–4.

Broekhuysen, G. J. & Taylor, H. 1959. The ecology of South African estuaries. Pt. 8. Kosi Bay Estuary system. *Ann. S. Afr. Mus.* **44** : 279–296.

Brumpt, E. 1897. Quelques faits relatifs à l'histoire du *Phascolion strombi* (Montagu). *Archs. Zool. exp. gén.* ser. 3, **5** : 483–496, 4 figs.

Bruun, A. F. 1953. See Wolff, T. 1960.

Bülow, C. 1883. Über anscheinend freiwillige und künstliche Teilung mit nachfolgender Regeneration bei Coelenteraten, Echinodermen und Wurmer. *Biol. Zbl.* **3** : 14–20.

Bureau, L. 1898. Coup d'oeil sur la faune du departement de la Loire-Inférieure. 2. *C. r. Ass. fr. Advanc. Sci.* **3** : 15.

Buytendyk, F. J. 1909a. Zur Physiologie der Urnen von *Sipunculus nudus*. *Biol. Zbl.* **29** : 365–369.

—— 1909b. Beiträge zur Muskelphysiologie von *Sipunculus nudus*. *Biol. Zbl.* **29** : 753–759.

Cantacuzène, J. 1922a. Sur le rôle agglutinant des urnes chez *Sipunculus nudus*. *C. r. Séanc. Soc. Biol.* **87** : 259–262.

—— 1922b. Réactions d'immunité chez *Sipunculus nudus* vacciné contre une bactérie. *C. r. Séanc. Soc. Biol.* **87** : 264–267.

—— 1922c. Sur le sort ultérieur des urnes chez *Sipunculus nudus* au cours de l'infection et de l'immunisation. *C. r. Séanc. Soc. Biol.* **87** : 283–285.

CANTACUZÉNE, J. 1928. Recherches sur les réactions d'immunité chez les invertébrés. I. Réactions d'immunité chez *Sipunculus nudus.* *Archs. roum. Path. exp. Microbiol.* **1** : 1–70.

CANTACUZÈNE, J. & VLÈS, F. 1922. Sur les facteurs électriques dans les réactions du sang chez *Sipunculus nudus.* *C. r. Séanc. Soc. Biol.* **87** : 1155–1157.

CARLISLE, DAVID B. 1959a. On the neurosecretory system of the brain and associated structures in *Sipunculus nudus* with a note on the cuticle. *Gumna J. Med. Sci.* **8** : 183- 194, 9 figs.

CARUS, J. V. 1863. [In] Peters, W. C. H., Carus, J. V. & Gerstaecker, C. E. A. *Handbuch der Zoologie* **2** : 450.

—— 1884. *Prodromus faunae mediterraneae sive descriptio animalium maris mediterraneae incolarum.* Pars. I.

CATTA, J. D. (& MARION). 1875. Du male planariforme de la Bonellie. *Revue Sci. nat. de E. Dubreil* **4** : 313–319, pl. 7. [Translation of Russian article Kowalevsky (1870) with additions by Marion.]

CHAMBERLAIN, R. V. 1919. Notes on the Sipunculida of Laguna Beach. *Pomona Coll. J. Ent.* **12** : 30–31.

—— 1920. The Gephyrea collected by the Canadian National Arctic Expedition 1913–1918 (with a bibliography of sipunculids, echiurids and priapulids until 1919). *Rep. Can. arct. Exped.* **9** (D) : 1–21, figs 1–4.

CHAET, A. 1955. Further studies on the toxic factor in *Phascolosoma.* *Biol. Bull. mar. biol. Lab., Woods Hole,* **109** : 356.

CHAMISSO, A. DE & EYSENHARDT, C. G. 1821. De animalibus quisbusdam e classe vermium linneana etc. *Nova. Acta Acad. Caesar Leop. Carol* **10** : 343–374.

CHAPHEAU, M. 1928. Recherches sur la respiration des hématies du Siponcle. *Bull. Stn. Biol. d'Arcachon* **25** : 157–187.

CHAPMAN, G. 1955. Aspects of the fauna and flora of the Azores. iii. Gephyrea. *Ann. Mag. nat. Hist.* ser. 12, **8** : 351–352, 1 fig.

CHASE, H. Y. 1937. The effects of ultra-violet light upon early development in eggs of *Urechis caupo.* *Biol. Bull. mar. biol. Lab. Woods Hole* **72** : 377–383, 3 tables.

CHEN, Y. & YEH, C. C. 1958. Notes on some Gephyrea of China with descriptions of four new species. (Chinese with English summary.) *Acta. zool. sin.* **10** : 265–278, figs 1–9.

CHIAJI, S. DELLE. 1823. *Memorie sulla storia e notomia degli animali senza Verteb.* **1** : 1–184.

—— 1828. Su la notomia e la classificazione del *Sifunculo nudo* di Linneo. *Attl. Ist. Incoragg. Sci. nat.* **4** : 1–24, pl. 1.

CHIN, T. G. 1947. Studies of Fukien Sipunculoidea. *Biol. Bull. Fukien Christ. Univ.* **3** : 97– 104, 2 pls. (Chinese with English Summary.)

CHIN, T. G. & WU, C. S. 1950. Diatoms in the intestine of Amoy Sipunculids (Annelida Gephyrea). The food of Sipunculida. *Lingnan Sci. J.* **23** : 43–52.

CHITWOOD, B. G. 1958. The designation of official names for higher taxa of invertebrates. *Bull. zool. Nomencl.* **15** : 860–895.

CHUANG, S. H. 1963. Digestive enzymes of the echiuroid *Ochetostoma erythrogrammon.* *Biol. Bull. mar. biol. Lab., Woods Hole* **125** : 464–469.

CLAPARÈDE, E. 1861. Beitrag zur Kenntnis der Gephyrea. *Arch. Anat. Physiol.* **1861** : 538– 542, pl. 12, figs 1–11.

—— 1867. Sur la loxosome Kefersteini. *Ann. Sci. nat.* **5** (8) : 28–30.

CLARK, R. B. 1969. Systematics and phylogeny: Annelida, Echiura and Sipuncula. In Florkin & Scheer's *Chemical Zoology* **4** (1) : 1–68.

COLE, J. B. 1952. *The morphology of Golfingia pugettensis, a sipunculid worm.* M.Sc. Thesis: University of Washington. 78 pp.

COLLIN, A. 1891. Über *Echiurus chilensis* M. Müller. *Zool. Anz.* **14** : 463–464.

—— 1892. Gephyreen gesammelt von Herrn Oberstabsarzt Dr. Sander auf der Reise S.M.S. 'Prinz Adalbert'. *Arch. Naturgesch* **58** : 177–182, pl. 11.

—— 1901. Die Gephyreen der deutschen Expedition S.M.S. 'Gazelle'. *Arch. Naturgesch* **67** (Festschrift) : 299–306.

Conn, H. W. 1886. Life history of *Thalassema mellita* Conn. *Stud. biol. Lab. Johns Hopkins Univ.* (1884–1887), **3** : 351–401, 4 pls.

Cordero, E. H. & Mello-Leitao, A. 1952. Duas novas espécies do género *Aspidosiphon* da Ihla Trinadade. *Mems. Inst. Oswaldo Cruz* **50** : 277–295, 1 pl., col., 10 figs. Portuguese section : 277–287. English translation : 288–295.

Cosmovici, L. C. 1879a. Quelques remarques sur le genre *Phascolosoma*. *C. r. hebd. Séanc. Akad. Sci. Paris* **88** : 1092–1094.

—— 1879b. On the body cavity of some sedentary annelids and their segmental organs; with some remarks on the genus *Phascolosoma*. *Ann. Mag. nat. Hist.* ser. 5, **4** : 94–95.

Costa, A. 1853. *Sipunculus nudus*—var. *tessellatus*. *Fauna del Regno di Napoli*. Echinodermi apodi. **9** (11) : 17–20, pl. 2.

—— 1869. Di un nouyo genere di Chaetognathi und di un genere di Sipunculidei. *Annuar. Mus. zool. Univ. Napoli* (1865) **5** : 54–57, pl. 3.

Coupin, R. 1903. Les Géphyriens. *Nature, Paris* **31** : 91–92, 10 figs.

Cuénot, L. 1887. Études sur le sang, son rôle et sa formation dans la série animale. 2me partie. Invertébrés. *Archs. Zool. exp. gén.* **5** : 63–67.

—— 1889. Formation des produits génitaux par les glandes lymphatiques (invertébrés). *C. r. Ass. fr. Avanc. Sci.* **2** : 581–586.

—— 1891. Études sur le sang des glandes lymphatiques dans la série animale. *Archs. Zool. exp. gén.* ser. 2, **9** : 593.

—— 1897. Les globules sanguins et les organes lymphoides des Invertébrés. *Archs. Anat. microsc.* **8** : 153–192.

—— 1900. Le *Phascolosoma* commun (*Phascolosoma vulgare* de Blainv.) [in] Boutan, L. (ed.), *Zool. descriptive des invertébrés*, Paris **1** : 386–422.

—— 1901. La valeur respiratoire du liquide cavitaire chez quelques invertébrés. *Trav. Lab. Soc. Scient. Arcachon.* **5** : 107–125.

—— 1902a. Contributions à la faune du Bassin d'Arcachon. Echiuriens et Sipunculidens. *P. v. Soc. linn. Bordeaux* **61** : 1–28. Also: *Bull. Soc. Sci. Arcachon* **1902** : 1–28, 2 pl.

—— 1902b. Organes agglutinants et organes cilio-phagocytaires. *Archs. Zool. exp. gén.* ser. 3, **9** : 79.

—— 1913. Excrétion et phagocytose chez les Sipunculiens. *C. r. Séanc. Soc. Biol.* **74**: 159–161.

—— 1922. Sipunculiens, Echiuriens, Priapuliens. *Faune de France*, Paris **4** : 1–30, 14 textfigs.

—— 1927. Contributions à la faune du bassin d'Arcachon. ix. Revue générale de la faune et bibliographie. *Bull. Stn. biol. Arachon* **24** : 229–308.

Cutler, E. B. 1965. Sipunculids of Madagascar. *Océanographie* **3** (4) : 51–63, 6 figs.

Cuvier, G. 1830. *Règne animal*, ser. 2, **3** : 244.

Dahl, E. 1958. The integument of *Echiurus echiurus*. *K. fysiog. Sällsk Lund Forh.* **28** : 33–44, 7 figs.

Dakin, W. J. 1952. Gephyrea [in] *Australian seashores*. 157–158, pl. 33. Angus & Robertson, Sydney.

Damas, H. 1962. La collection de *Pelagosphaera* du 'Dana'. *Dana Rep.* **59** : 1–22, 10 figs, map. (In French, English summary.)

Dambroviceanu, A. 1926. Détermination de certains constitutants du plasma de *Sipunculus nudus* au cours de l'immunisation. *C. r. Séanc. Soc. Biol.* **95** : 115–118.

—— 1928. Sur la nature des formations crystalloides contenues dans les vésicules énigmatiques des Siponculides. *C. r. Séanc. Soc. Biol.* **98** : 249–250.

Danielssen, D. C. 1859. Beretning om en Zoologisk Reise, fonetagen i sommeren 1857. *Nytt. Mag. Zool.* **11** : 1–55.

—— 1869. Sipunculus norvegicus. *Ford. skand. Naturf. Kristiana Möte* **10** : 541–542.

Danielssen, D. C. & Koren, J. 1880. New northern gephyrea. *Ann. Mag. nat. Hist.* ser. 5, **6** : 462–465.

—— 1881a. Fraden norske Nordhavse expedition (1876–1878). 3. Zoologie. Gephyreer. *Nytt. Mag. Naturvid* **26** : 44–66.

DANIELSSEN, D. C. & KOREN, J. 1881b. Gephyrea. *The Norwegian North Atlantic Expedition of* 1876–1878. 1–58, 6 pls.

DATTA GUPTA, A. K. & MENON, P. K. B. 1961. Miscellaneous note. Occurrence of the echiuroid *Ochetostoma zanzibarense* Stephen in the Gulf of Kutch. *J. Bombay nat. Hist. Soc.* ser. 3, **48** : 829–830, 1 fig.

—— 1964. Morphology and histology of the males of *Acanthobonellia*. *Proc. R. Soc. Edinb.* sect. B, **68** : 267–276, 4 text-figs.

—— 1965. Additions to Indian echiurid fauna. *Ann. Mag. nat. Hist.* ser. 13, **8** : 193–201, 2 figs.

DATTA GUPTA, A. K., MENON, P. K. B. & JOHNSON, P. 1963. Echiurids from Indian waters with the description of two new species. *Ann. Mag. nat. Hist.* ser. 13, **6** : 57–63, 2 text-figs.

DAWYDOFF, C. N. 1930a. Une trochophore géante d'un echiurien des côtes d'Annam, quelques phases de son évolution. *Bull. Soc. zool. Fr.* **55** : 86–88.

—— 1930b. Quelques observations de *Pelagosphaera*, larve de Sipunculide des côtes d'Annam. *Bull. Soc. zool. Fr.* **55** : 88–90.

—— 1952. Contributions à l'étude des invertébrés de la faune marine benthique de l'Indochine. *Bull. Biol. Fr. Belg.* suppl. **37** : 158.

—— 1959. Classe des Echiuriens [in] Grassé: *Traite de Zoologie* **5** : 855–907, 1081–1082 (suppl.), text-figs 674–717.

DAY, J. H. 1959. The biology of Langebaan Lagoon: a study of the effect of shelter from wave action. *Trans. roy. Soc. S. Afr.* **35** : 475–547.

DAY, J. H., MILLAR, N. A. H. & HARRISON, A. D. 1952. The ecology of South African Estuaries. Pt. 3. Knysna: a clear open estuary. *Trans. roy. Soc. S. Afr.* **33** : 367–413, 1 pl., 4 figs.

DAY, J. H. & MORGANS, J. F. C. 1956. The ecology of South African Estuaries. Pt. 7. The biology of Durban Bay. *Ann. Natal Mus.* **13** : 259–312, 1 pl., 1 map.

DEHERE, C. & FONTAINE, M. 1932. Recherches spectrochemique sur la bonelline pigment tegumentaire de la *Bonellia viridis*. *Annls. Inst. océanogr. Monaco* **12** : 345–381.

DE JORGE, F. B., DITADI, A. S. F. & PETERSEN, J. A. 1969. Influence of prolonged fasting on the biochemistry of *Lissomyema exilii* (Echiura). *Comp. Biochem. Physiol.* **31** : 483–492.

DEKHUYZEN, M. C. 1921. Sur la semi-perméabilité biologique des parois extérieures des Sipunculides. *C. r. hebd. Séanc. Acad. Sci. Paris* **172** : 238–241.

DELAGE, T. & HEROUARD, E. 1897. Vermidiens. *Traité de Zoologie concrète* **5** : 12.

DELAMARE-DEBOUTTEVILLE, C. 1950. Description d'une trompe tératologique de Bonellie (*Bonellia viridis*). *Vie et Milieu* **1** : 361–362.

DELAUNAY, M. H. 1926. Sur l'excrétion azotée des vers. La surcharge en urée des hématies du siponcle, *Sipunculus nudus*. *C. r. Seanc. Soc. biol.* **95** : 1357–1358.

—— 1927. Recherches biochemiques sur l'excrétion azotée des invertébrés. *Bull. Stn. biol. Arcachon* **21** : 41–84.

—— 1931. L'excrétion azotée des invertébrés. *Biol. Rev.* **6** : 265–301.

DELLE CHIAJI, S. *See* Chiaji.

DENDY, A. 1898. Notes on a remarkable collection of marine animals found on New Brighton Beach near Christchurch, New Zealand. *Trans. R. Soc. N.Z.* **30** : 320–386.

DIESING, C. M. 1851. *Systema helminthum.* **2** : 1–588. Vindobonae.

—— 1859. Revision der Rhyngodeen. *Sber. Akad. Wiss. Wien* **37** : 719–782, 3 pls.

DOGIEL, V. A. 1907. Beiträge zur Kenntnis der Gregarinen. II. *Schistocytiss sipunculi*. *Arch. Protistenk* **8** : 203–215, pl. 9.

—— 1916. Sur la fonction des 'vésicules énigmatiques' du sang de *Sipunculus nudus*. *Russk. zool. Zh.* **1** : 6–8 (French translation).

DONS, C. 1938. Norges strandfauna. 20. Gephyreer. *K. norsk. Ned. selsk. Forh.* **11** (51) : 199–200.

DÖRLER, A. 1900. Neue und wenig bekannte rhabdocöle Turbellarien. *Z. wiss. Zool.* **68** : 1–42, 1 pl. 3 text-figs.

DRASCHE, R. VON. 1880. Zur Kenntnis des Baues der Segmentalorgane bei Echiuren. *Zool. Anz.* **3** : 517–519.

—— 1881. Über eine neue *Echiurus* Art aus Japan nebst Bermerkungen über *Thalassema erythrogrammon* Leuckart von der Insel Bourbon. *Verh. zool.—bot. Ges. Wien* **30** : 621–628, pl. 20, fig. 1.

DUBOIS, R. 1907. Action de la lumière sur le pigment vert flourescent de *Bonellia viridis* et émission du pigment pars certains vers marins exposés à la lumière solaire. *C. r. Séanc. Soc. Biol.* **62** : 654–655.

DUJARDIN, F. 1816. [In] Lamarck: *Histoire naturelle des animaux sans vertébrés* **3** : 76–79.

—— 1840. [In] Lamarck, *Histoire naturelle des animaux sans vertébrés* (Ed. 2) **3** : 466–475.

EDMONDS, S. J. 1955. Australian Sipunculoidea. 1. The genera *Sipunculus, Xenosiphon* and *Siphonosoma. Aust. J. mar. Freshwat. Res.* **6** : 82–97, 1 pl., 9 text-figs.

—— 1956. Australian Sipunculoidea. 2. The genera *Phascolosoma, Dendrostomum, Golfingia, Aspidosiphon* and *Cloeosiphon. Aust. J. mar. Freshwat. Res.* **7** : 281–315, 3 pls, 21 text-figs.

—— 1957a. The catabolism of nitrogen compounds in *Dendrostomum cymodoceae* Edm. (Sipunculoidea). *Aust. J. mar. Freshwat. Res.* **8** : 131–135, 1 pl.

—— 1957b. The respiratory metabolism of *Dendrostomum cymodoceae* Edm. (Sipunculoidea). *Aust. J. mar. Freshwat. Res.* **8** : 53–63, 1 fig.

—— 1960a. Some Australian echiuroids (Echiuroidea). *Trans. R. Soc. S. Aust.* **83** : 89–96, 2 pls, 5 text-figs.

—— 1960b. Sipunculids from New Zealand and the Chatham Islands. *N.Z. Dep. Sci. Industr. Res. Bull.* (**139**) : 159–167, 3 pls, 8 text-figs.

—— 1961. On *Sipunculus aeneus* Baird. *Ann. Mag. nat. Hist.* ser. 13, **4** : 217–220.

—— 1962. Some notes on the abundance, environment and nutrition of *Sipunculus nudus* L. (Sipunculoidea) at Morgat, Brittany. *Cah. Biol. mar.* **3** : 183–190.

—— 1963. Two new echiuroids (Echiuroidea) from Australia. *Trans. R. Soc. S. Aust.* **87** : 243–247, 1 pl.

—— 1965. Sipunculoidea of the Ross Sea. *N.Z. Dep. Sci. Industr. Res. Bull.* **167** : 27–33, 3 pls, 1 text-fig.

—— 1966a. Sipunculoidea and Echiuroidea. Port Phillip Survey 1957–1963. *Mem. Nat. Mus. Vict.* **1966** : 175–178.

—— 1966b. *Siphonosoma hawaiense*, a new sipunculid from Hawaii. *Pacific Sci.* **20** (3) : 386–388, 4 figs.

EDWARDS, MILNE. 1840. Zoophytes. [In] Cuvier, *Le Règne Animal* 41–45, pl. 21, figs 2–3 22, 23.

EHLERS, E. 1871. On the Vermes collected by Mr. von Heuglin in the Sea of Spitzbergen. *Ann. Mag. nat. Hist.* ser. 4, **8** : 53–61. Also *S.B. Soc. Erlang.* **1871** : 77–79.

ELLIS, D. V. 1953. Some observations on the shore fauna of Baffin Island. *Arctic*, ser. 8, **4** : 224–336.

EMBLETON, A. L. 1900. On the structure and affinities of *Echiurus unicinctus. Trans. Linn. Soc. Lond. Zool.* ser. 2, **8** : 77–97, pls 7–10, 1 text-fig.

ENRIQUES, P. 1902. Note fisiologiche sul *Sipunculus nudus. Monit. Zool. ital.* **13,** suppl. : 51–52.

—— 1903. I corpi pigmentati del *Sipunculus nudus. Arch. zool. ital.* **1** : 253–287, pl. 12.

—— 1906. Sur les vaisseaux du *Sipunculus nudus. Arch. Zool. exp. gén.* ser. 4, **4** : 23–26.

ETHRINGTON, D. 1953. On a sporozoon in the coelomic corpuscles of *Phascolosoma minutum* Keferstein (Sipunculoidea). *Parasitology* **43** : 160–169.

FABRE-DOMERGUE, 1886. Sur l'infusoire parasite de la cavité générale du *Sipunculus nudus. Pompholyxia* n.g. *sipunculi* n. sp. *C. r. Ass. fr. Avanc. Sci.* **1886** : 593–596, pl. 13.

FABRICIUS, O. 1780. *Fauna Groenlandica.* 452 pp.

FARRAN, D. 1851. *Thalassema neptuni. Ann. Mag. nat. Hist.* ser. 2, **7** : 156.

FARRAN, G. P. 1915. Results of a biological survey of Blacksod Bay, Co. Mayo. *Scient. Invest. Fish. Brch. Ire.* **3** : 1–72, 1 pl.

FAUVEL, P. 1923. Polychètes errantes. *Faune de France* **5** (1) : 1–488.
—— 1927. Polychètes sédentaires. *Faune de France* **5** (2) : 1–494.
FERRONIERE, G. 1901. Études biologiques sur les zones supralittorales de la Loire-Inférieure. *Bul.. Soc. Sci. nat. Ouest. Fr.* **2** (1) : 1–451, 6 pls.
FISCHER, J. 1914. Die Sipunculiden der Nord-und Ostsee, unter Beruchsichtigung von Formen des nordatlantischen Gebietes. *Wiss. Meeresunters.* (Kiel) **16** : 85–125, 1 pl., 9 figs.
FISCHER, W. 1892. Übersicht der von Herrn Dr. F. Stuhlmann auf Sanzibar und an der gegenüberliegenden Festlands-küste gesammelten Gephyreen. *Jb. hamb. wiss. Anst.* **9** (2) : 79–89, 1 pl., figs 1–7.
—— 1893. Weitere Beiträge zur Anatomie und Histologie des *Sipunculus indicus* Peters. *Jb. hamb. wiss. Anst.* **10** : 1–12.
—— 1894. Über kiemenartige Organe einiger *Sipunculus*- Arten. *Zool. Anz.* **17** : 333–335.
—— 1895. Die Gephyreen des naturhistorischen Museums zu Hamburg. *Abh. Geb. naturw. Hamburg* **13** : 1–24, 1 pl.
—— 1896a. Gephyreen. [In] Semon, 'Zoologische Forschungsreisen in Australien und Malayischen Archipel'. *Denkschr. med.-naturw. Ges. Jena* **8** : 337–339, 4 text-figs.
—— 1896b. Gephyreen. *Ergeb. Hamburg Magelhaen. Sammelreise* **1** (4) : 1–7.
—— 1913. Über einige Sipunculiden des naturhistorischen Museums zu Hamburg. *Jb. hamb. wiss. Anst.* **30** : 93–101, figs 1–7.
—— 1914a. Beiträge zur Kenntnis des Meeresfauna West Afrikas. *Beitr. Kennt. Meeresfauna Westft.* **1** : 57–84, pl. 2.
—— 1914b. Weitere Mitteilungen über die Gephyreen des naturhistorischen (zoologischen) Museums zu Hamburg. *Jb. hamb. wiss. Anst.* **31** : 1–28, 1 pl.
—— 1916. Die Gephyreensausbeute der deutschen Tief-see Expedition (1898–1899). Vorlaufige mitteilung. *Zool. Anz.* **48** : 14–20.
—— 1919a. Gephyreen der Sud-westküste Australiens. *Zool. Anz.* **50** : 277–285, text-figs 1–6.
—— 1919b. Über die Gattung *Lithacrosiphon*, eine neue Sipunculiden-Gattung. *Zool. Anz.* **50** : 289–293, 5 text-figs.
—— 1920. Gephyreen der antarktischen und sub-antarktischen Meere. *Dts. Sud. Pol. Exped.* 16, Zoologie (**8**) : 409–430, figs 1–4.
—— 1921a. *Aspidosiphon pygmaeus* n. sp. Eine neue Gephyrea aus Jan Fernandez. *The natural history of Juan Fernandez and Easter Island.* Ed. C. Skottsberg, **3** : 45–47, 1 fig.
—— 1921b. Results of Dr. E. Mjöberg's Swedish scientific expeditions to Australia. 1910–1913. 27. Gephyreen. *K. svenska. Vetensk-Akad. Handl.* **61** (8) : 1–8, 6 text-figs.
—— 1922b. Gephyreen des Reichsmuseums zu Stockholm. *Ark. Zool.* **14** (19) : 1–39, pl. 1–3, figs 1–42.
—— 1922c. Gephyreen der Deutschen Tiefsee Expedition, auf dem Dampher 'Valdivia' 1898–1899. *Wiss. Ergebn. dt. Tiefsee Exped. Valdivia* **22**, 1 : 1–26, 2 pls.
—— 1922d. Gephyreen der arktischen Meere. *Wiss. Meeresunters. Helgol.* **13** : 229–246, 9 text-figs.
—— 1922e. Westindische Gephyreen. *Zool. Anz.* **55** : 10–18, 5 figs.
—— 1923a. Zwei Sipunculiden des Kapgebietes nebst einer Zustammenstellung der bekannten Arten dieses Gebietes, und ihrer faunistischen Beziehung zur Ost-und Westkuste. *Goteborgs K. Vetensk. o. Vitterh. Sammh. Handl.* ser. 4, **25** (4) : 1–8, 4 text-figs.
—— 1923b. Gephyreen des Golfes von Siam. *Vidensk. Meddr. dansk. naturh. Foren. Kbh.* **76** : 21–27, figs 1–3.
—— 1924. Beitrag zur Kenntnis der Sipunculiden. Über die verwandtschaftlichen Beziehungen der Arten *Phascolosoma margaritaceum* Sars, *Phasc. hanseni* Kor. u. Dan. und *Phasc. trybomi* Théel. *Zool. Anz.* **58** : 69–74.
—— 1925. Echiuriden Sipunculiden und Priapuliden. *Tierwelt N-u. Ostsee* **6d** : 1–55, 20 figs.
—— 1926. Sipunculiden und Echiuriden der Hamburger Südsee-Expedition 1908–1909. *Mitt. zool. Staatinst. und Zool. Mus. Hamb.* **42** : 104–117, pl. 3, figs 5, 7–13.

484   SIPUNCULA & ECHIURA

484   SIPUNCULA & ECHIURA

484   SIPUNCULA & ECHIURA

484   SIPUNCULA & ECHIURA

484   SIPUNCULA & ECHIURA

484 SIPUNCULA & ECHIURA

FISCHER, W. 1927. Sipunculoidea und Echiuroidea. [In] Michaelsen & Hartmeyer, *Die Fauna Sudwest-Australiens.* **5** : 199–216, pl. 2, figs 1–7.

—— 1928a. Über zwei neue *Siphonosoma*-Arten der Würtembergischen naturalien Sammlung zu Stuttgart. *Zool. Anz.* **76** : 138–143, 2 figs.

—— 1928b. Die Sipunculiden, Priapuliden und Echiuriden der Arktis. [In] Römer & Schuadum, *Fauna Arctica,* Jena **5** : 451–490, pl. 6, 3 figs.

—— 1931. Sipunculidae. *Mitt. zool. St. Inst. Hamb.* **44** : 139–140.

FISHER, N. 1932. Gephyrean new to northern Ireland. *Ir. Nat. J.* **4** : 80–81.

FISHER, W. K. 1928. New Sipunculoidea from California. *Ann. Mag. nat. Hist.* ser. 10, **1** : 194–199, pls 6–8.

—— 1946. Echiuroid worms of the North Pacific Ocean. *Proc. U.S. natn. Mus.* **96** : 215–292, pls 20–37.

—— 1947. New genera and species of echiuroid and sipunculoid worms. *Proc. U.S. natn. Mus.* **97** : 351–372, pls 8–15.

—— 1948. A review of the Bonelliidae. *Ann. Mag. nat. Hist.* ser. 11, **14** : 857–860, figs 1–5.

—— 1948b. A new echiuroid worm from the Hawaiian Islands and a key to the genera of the Echiuridae. *Pacif. Sci.* **2** : 274–277, fig. 1.

—— 1949. Additions to the echiuroid fauna of the North Pacific Ocean. *Proc. U.S. natn. Mus.* **99** : 479–497, pls 28–34.

—— 1950a. The sipunculid genus *Phascolosoma. Ann. Mag. nat. Hist.* ser. 12, **3** : 547–552.

—— 1950b. The new sub-genera and a new species of *Siphonosoma* (Sipunculoidea). *Ann. Mag. nat. Hist.* ser. 12, **3** : 805–808, 1 pl.

—— 1952. The sipunculid worms of California and Baja California. *Proc. U.S. natn. Mus.* **102** : 371–450, pls 18–39, 87 figs.

—— 1953. A new genus of bonellid worms (Echiuroidea). *J. Wash. Acad. Sci.* **43** : 258–259, fig. 1.

—— 1954a. A swimming *Sipunculus. Ann. Mag. nat. Hist.* ser. 12, **7** : 238–240, fig. 1.

—— 1954b. The genus *Xenosiphon. Ann. Mag. nat. Hist.* ser. 12, **7** : 311–315, pls 7–8.

FISHER, W. K. & MACGINITIE, G. E. 1928a. A new echiuroid worm from California. *Ann. Mag. nat. Hist.* ser. 10, **1** : 199–204, pl. 9.

—— 1928b. The natural history of an echiuroid worm. *Ann. Mag. nat. Hist.* ser. 10, **1** : 204–213, 1 pl., 3 figs.

FLORENTIN, R. 1902. On Cuénot's paper 'Organes agglutinants et organes ciliophagocytaires'. *Archs. Zool. exp. gén.* ser. 3, **10** : 79–99. Also *Année biol.* **7** : 334–335.

FLORKIN, M. 1932. La courbe de dissociation de l'oxyhémérythrine dans le liquide coelomique du Siponcle. *C. r. hebd. Séanc. Acad. Sci. Paris* **195** : 832–833.

—— 1933a. Recherches sur le hémérythrines. *Archs. Int. Physiol.* **36** : 247–328.

—— 1933b. Le pouvoir oxyphorique du liquide coelomique et des hématies de *Sipunculus nudus. C. r. Séanc. Soc. Biol.* **112** : 705–706.

—— 1936a. Sur la 'surcharge en urée' (Delauney) des hématies du Siponcle. Repartition de l'urée entre hématies et plasma dans les liquides coelomiques pourvus de l'hématies. *C. r. Soc. biol. Paris* **121:** 158–160.

—— 1936b. Taux des substances reductrices et fermentescibles dans les liquides organiques de l'Arénicole, du Dasybranche et du Siponcle. *C. r. Soc. biol. Paris* **123** : 1022–1024.

FLORKIN, M. & DUCHATEAU, G. 1942. Sur le metabolisme de l'azote chez le siponcle. *Archs. Int. Physiol.* **52** : 261.

FLORKIN, M. & HOVET, R. 1937. Nouvelle démonstration de la surcharge en urée des hématies du Siponcle. *Arch. Int. Physiol.* **45** : 125–127.

—— 1939. Presence d'acide allantoique dans le liquide coelomique d'Annélides et des Sipunculiens. *C. r. Séanc. Soc. Biol.* **131** : 1276–1277.

FLORKIN, M. F. & SCHEER, B. T. 1969. Annelida, Echiura and Sipuncula. *Chemical Zoology* **4**. 548 pp. Academic Press, New York and London.

FORBES, E. 1841. *A history of British starfishes.* 267 pp. London.

FORBES, E. & GOODSIR, J. 1841. On the natural history and anatomy of *Thalassema and Echiurus*. *Edinb. New Philos. J.* **30** : 369–378, pl. 7.

FRANC, A. 1960. Classe de Bivalves. [In] Grassé, *Traité de Zoologie* **5** : 1845–2133.

FUCHS, R. F. 1910. Die elektrischen Erscheinungen am glattem Muskel. *Pflügers Arch. ges. Physiol.* **136** : 65–100.

GABE, M. 1953. Données histologiques sur la neurosécrétion chez quelques Sipunculidiens. *Bull. Lab. marit. Dinard* **38** : 3–15, 1 pl.

GADD, G. G. 1911. Verzeichnis der Gephyreen des Kola-Golfes und zwei neue Species der *Phascolosoma*. *Trudy leningr. Obshch. Estest.* **42** : 79–93, German résumé: 102–105.

GADEAU DE KERVILLE, H. 1894. Recherches sur les faunes marine et maritime de la Normandie, 1er. voyage. Region de Granville et les iles Chausey. *Bull. Soc. Scient. nat Rouen*, 1er Semestre.

GARDINER, A. 1928. Notes on British Mollusca. *J. Conchol.* **18** : 245–250.

GAY, C. 1854. Historia fisica y politica de Chile. *Zoologia* **8**, suppl. : 475.

GEROULD, J. H. 1900. Observations upon the development of *Phascolosoma*. *Science, N.Y.* n. ser. **11** : 173–174 (cf. *Année Biol.* **5** : 145).

—— 1903. Studies on the embryology of the Sipunculidae. i. The embryonal envelope and its homologue. *Mark. Anniv. Vol.* **1903** : 437–452. New York, pl. 32.

—— 1904a. A key to the development of *Sipunculus nudus*. *Am. Nat.* **38** : 493–494.

—— 1904b. The development of *Phascolosoma*. *Archs. Zool. exp. gén.* ser. 4. Notes and Review. **2** : 17–29, 8 figs.

—— 1906. The development of *Phascolosoma*. 2. Studies on the embryology of the Sipunculidae. *Zool. Jb. Anat.* **23** : 77–162, pls 4–11.

—— 1908. A comparison of the cephalic organs of certain Sipunculids. *Science N.Y.* n.s. **27** : 488–489.

—— 1913. The sipunculids of the eastern coast of North America. *Proc. U.S. natn. Mus* **44** : 373–437, 16 figs, pls 58–62.

—— 1939. The eyes and nervous system of *Phascolosoma verrillii* and other Sipunculids. *Trav. Stn. zool. Wimereux* **13** : 313–325, pl. 18.

GIDEON, P. W., MENON, P. K. B., RAO, S. R. & JOSE, K. V. 1956. Occurrence of the echiuroid worm, *Ikedella misakiensis* (Ikeda) in Indian Waters. (Gulf of Kutch.) *J. Bombay nat. Hist. Soc.* **54** : 201–202.

GIDEON, P. W. 1957. On the marine fauna of the Gulf of Kutch. A preliminary survey. *J. Bombay Nat. Hist. Soc.* **54** : 690–706.

GINESTE, CH. 1901a. Sur les affinities zoologiques des genres *Pompholyxia* (Fabre-Domergue), *Kunstheria* (Delage), parasites de la cavité générale des Gephyriens. *Act. Soc. linn Bordeaux* **56** : 75–80.

—— 1901b. Les parasites de la cavité générale des Gephyriens. *Act. Soc. linn. Bordeaux* **56** : 120–126.

—— 1901c. Quelques particularités anatomiques des Sipunculides. *Act. Soc. linn. Bordeaux* **56** : 163–165.

—— 1901d. Sur les vésicules énigmatiques de la cavité générale du *Phymosoma granulatum* (F. S. Leuckart). *P. V. Soc. linn. Bordeaux* **56** : 81–84. 11 pls.

—— 1903a. Quelques caractères physiologiques des urnes Sipunculides. *Act. Soc. linn. Bordeaux* **58** : 24–27.

—— 1903b. Sur la structure histologique des canaux oesophagiens du Siponcle. *Act. Soc. linn. Bordeaux* **58** : 104–118.

—— 1903c. Quelques observations sur les vésicules énigmatiques de la cavité générale du Siponcle. *Act. Soc. linn. Bordeaux* **58** : 168–171.

—— 1903d. Études des urnes libres de la cavité générale du *Sipunculus nudus*. *Act. Soc. linn. Bordeaux* **58** : 174–184.

—— 1903e. Note préliminaire sur une *Hemsporidii* parasite des hématies. *Sipunculus nudus*. *Act. Soc. linn. Bordeaux* **58** : 237.

GISLÉN, T. 1940. Investigations on the ecology of *Echiurus*. *K. fysiogr. Sällsk. Lund Forh. N.F.* **51** (10) : 1–39, 6 pls. Also *Lunds Univ. Arsskrift. N.F.* 2, **36** (10) : 1–39, 6 pls.

GLAUS, A. 1933. Erzeugung, Organisation und Entwicklungsmechanik der Rüsselzeucht. Intersexe von *Bonellia viridis*. *Pubbl. Stn. Zool. Napoli* **13** : 39–114.

GOLDSCHMIDT, R. 1927. Bemerkungen zum Problem der Geschlechtsbestimmung be *Bonellia*. *Biol. Zbl.* **46** : 441–452.

GMELIN, J. F. 1789. *Systema Naturae* **1** (6) : 3094–3095.

GONSE, P. H. 1953. L'ovogenèse chez *Phascolosoma vulgare*, note préliminaire. *C. r. hebd. Séanc. Acad. Sci. Paris* **236** : 526–530.

—— 1954. Respiration de l'ovocyte au cours de sa croissance. *C. r. hebd. Séanc. Acad. Sci. Paris* **238** : 2350–2352.

—— 1955. Recherches sur la physiologie de l'ovogenèse chez *Phascolosoma vulgare*. *Expl. Cell Res.* **8** : 550–553, 4 figs.

—— 1956a. L'ovogenèse chez *Phascolosoma vulgare*. i. Définition cytologique des stades de croissance des ovocytes. *Acta. zool. Stockh.* **37** : 193–224, 19 figs.

—— 1956b. L'ovogenèse chez *Phascolosoma vulgare*. ii. Recherches biométriques sur les ovocytes. *Acta. zool. Stockh.* **37** : 225–233, 5 figs.

—— 1957a. L'ovogenèse chez *Phascolosoma vulgare*. iii. Respiration exogene et endogene de l'ovocyte. Effet de l'eau de mer. *Biomchim. biophys. Acta.* **24** : 267–278, 8 figs.

—— 1957b. L'ovogenèse chez *Phascolosoma vulgare*. iv. Étude chromatographique des sucres du plasma. Action des differents substrats et de malonate sur la respiration de l'ovocyte. *Biomchim. biophys. Acta.* **24** : 520–531.

GOODRICH, E. S. 1909. Notes on the nephridia of *Dinophilus* and of the larvae of *Polygordius*, *Echiurus* and *Phoronis*. *Q. Jl. microsc. Sci.* **54** : 11–118, pl. 8.

GOODRICH, HELEN P. 1950. Sporozoa of *Sipunculus*. *Q. Jl. microsc. Sci.* **91** : 469–476, 5 figs.

GRABER, V. 1873. Über die Haut einiger Sternwürmer (Gephyrea). *Sber. Akad. Wiss. Wien.* **67** : 61–78, 3 pls.

GRAFF, L. 1875. Anatomie des *Chaetoderma nitidulum* Lovén. *Z. wiss. Zool.* **26** : 166–192, pls 11–13.

GRAVELY, F. H. 1927. The littoral fauna of Krusadai Islands in the Gulf of Manaar. Gephyrea and Phoronis. *Bull. Madras Govt. Mus.* n. ser. **1** : 87–88, figs a, b.

GRAVELY, F. H. & PRASHAD, B. 1919. A note on the marine invertebrate fauna of Chandipore, Orissa, with a note on the echiuroids. *Rec. Indian Mus.* **16** : 395–402, 1 text-fig.

GRAY, J. E. 1828. *Spicilegia Zoologica* **16** : 1–20, pl. 38.

GREEFF, R. 1872. Über die borstentragenden Gephyreen. *Sber. Ges. Beförd ges. Naturw. Marburg* (1) : 106.

—— 1874. Über die Organization der Echiuriden. *Sber. Ges. Beförd. ges. Naturw. Marburg* (2) : 21–22.

—— 1877. Über den Bau und die Entwicklung der Echiuren. *Sber. Ges. Beförd. ges. Naturw. Marburg* (4) : 68–78. Also *Arch. Naturg.* **43** : 343–353.

—— 1879. Die Echiuren (Gephyrea armata). *Nova Acta Acad. Caesar Leop. Carol.* **41** : 1–172, 9 pls. Also *Nova Acta Acad. German.* **40** : 152.

—— 1880a. Über den Bau der Echiuren. *Sber. Ges. Beförd. ges. Naturw. Marburg* 1879 (4) : 41–56. Also *Archiv. naturg.* **46** : 88–93.

—— 1880b. Die Organisation des *Echiurus pallasi*. *Zeit. wiss. Zool.* **34** : 1–22.

GREIG, J. M. 1907. Invertébrés du fond. Gephyriens. [In] Duc d'Orleans *Croisière océanog. dans la mer du Gronland* **1905** : 503–567.

GRIFFIN, B. B. 1896. The history of the achromatic structures in the maturation and fertilisation of *Thalassema*. *Trans. N.Y. Acad. Sci.* **15** : 163–176.

—— 1899. Studies in maturation, fertilisation and cleavage of *Thalassema* and *Zirphaea*. *J. Morph.* **15** : 583–634.

GRIFFITH, E. 1834. Zoophytes. *Animal Kingdom* **12** : 454–456.

GRIFFITHS, B. 1892a. On the blood of the invertebra. *Proc. R. ray Soc. Edinb.* **19** : 20.

GRIFFITHS, B. 1892b. L'hémerythrine. *C. r. hebd. Séanc. Acad. Sci. Paris* **115** : 669.

GROSKOPF, W. R., HOLLEMAN, J. W., KLOTZ, I. M., KERESTZTES-NAGY, S. & MARGOLIASH, E. 1963. Amino acid composition of hemerythrin (from Sipunculid worms) in relation to sub-unit structure. *Science, N.Y.* **141** (3576) : 166–167, fig.

GROSS, W. J. 1954. Osmotic responses in the sipunculid *Dendrostomum zostericolum*. *J. exp. Biol.* **31** : 403–423, 10 figs.

GRÜBE, E. 1837. Versuch einer Anatomie des *Sipunculus nudus. Arch. Anat. Physiol.* **1837** : 237–257, pls 10–11.

—— 1868a. Beschreibungen einiger von G. Ritter von Fraunfeld gesammelten Annelida und Gephyreen des rothen Meeres. *Verh. zool.-bot. Ges. Wien* **18** : 629–650, pls 7, 8.

—— 1868b. Thätigheit der allgemeinen Naturwiss-section der schlesischen Gesellschaft im Jahre 1866. *Jber. Schles. Ges. Vaterl. Kult* **45** : 47–49.

—— 1869. Mitth. über St. Vaast-la-Hougue und seine Meeren besonders seine Annelidenfauna. *Abh. schles. Ges.* **1868–1869** : 91–128.

—— 1872. Mitth. über St. Vaast-la-Hougue und seine Meeren besonders seine Annelidenfauna. *Abh. schles. Ges.* **1869–1872** : 75–146.

GRÜBE, E. & OERSTED, A. S. 1858. Annulata oerstediana. *Vidensk. Meddr. dansk. Natur. Foren.* **1858** : 105–120 (Gephyrea).

GRUVEL, A. 1899. Sur quelques stations zoologiques de la Méditerranée. *Mem. Soc. Sci. phys. nat. Bordeaux* **5** : 31–46.

GUÉRIN-MÉNEVILLE, F. E. 1831. Zoophytes. *Iconographie du règne animal de G. Cuvier.* . . . **2**, pl. 5, figs 3–4, pl. 6, figs 1–3.

GUSTAFSSON, G. 1937. Polychaeta and Sipunculoidea from the Siberian Arctic Ocean. The Norwegian North Polar Expedition with the 'Maud'. 1918–1925. *Scient. Results Norw. N. polar Exped. Maud* **5** (17) : 1–12.

HABE, T. 1962. *Achasmea thalassemicola* sp. nov., a new commensal bibalve found in an echiuroid *Thalassema mucosum* Ikeda. *Venus* **22** : 117–119, figs 1–3.

—— 1964. Two commensal bivalves from the west coast of Kyushu, Japan. *Venus* **23** : 137–139, pl. 8.

HÄCKER, V. 1898. Die pelagischen Polychaeten und Achaeten-Larven der Plankton-exped. Ergeb. Atlantic Ocean ausgef. [in] *Hensen Ergebn. Plankton Exped. Kiel* und Leipsig **2**: 1–50, 4 pls, 8 text-figs, 1 map.

—— 1905. Berichtigung, betreffend eine Gephyreen Larve. *Zool. Anz.* **29** : 334–386.

HAECKEL, E. 1878. Die Komentenforme der Seesterne u. Generations-wechsel der Echinodermen. *Z. wiss. Zool.* **30** : 424, suppl.

HALL, V. E. 1931. The muscular activity and oxygen consumption of *Urechis caupo. Biol. Bull. mar. biol. Lab., Woods Hole* **61** : 400–416.

HALLER, B. 1889. Beiträge zur Kenntnis der Textur des Central-Nerven Systems höheren Würmer. *Arb. zool. Inst. Univ. Wien* **8** : 1–138. Also *J.R. micr. Soc.* **1890** : 177–179.

HAMMARSTEIN, O. 1915. Gephyreen von Madagascar gesammelt von W. Kaudern. 1911–1912. *Ark. Zool.* ser. 2, **9** (10) : 1–3, 1 fig.

HAMPSON, GEORGE R. 1964. Redescription of a commensal pelecypod *Rochefortia cuneata* with notes on its ecology. *Nautilus* **77** : 125–128.

HARMER, S. F. 1921. The Polyzoa of the Siboga Expedition. *Siboga Exped.* **28**c : 503–640, pls 35–41.

HARMS, W. 1920. Experimentell-morphologische Untersuchungen über ein neues neben-nierunden-ähnliches Organ bei einem Wirbellosen (*Physcosoma* sp.) im Vergleich zum Interrenalorgan der niederen Wirbelthiere. *Sber. Ges. Beförd. ges. Naturw. Marburg* **1919** : 74–84.

—— 1921. Morphologische und kausalanalytytische Untersuchungen über das Internephridial-organ von *Physcosoma lanzarotae* nov. sp. *Arch. Entw. Mech. Organ.* **47** : 307–374.

—— 1922. Bauchnervenstrang und Spindelmuskel von *Physcosoma* in Anpassung an die Formveränderungen dieses Tieres. *Zool. Anz.* **52** : 67–76, 8 text-figs.

HARMS, J. W. & DRAGENDORFF, O.1933.Die Realisation von Genen und die consecutive Adaptation.3 Mitteilung.Osmotische Untersuchungen an *Physcosoma lurco* Sel. et de Man, aus den Mangrove-Vorländern der Sunda-Inseln.*Z. wiss. Zool.***143** : 263–322.

HARTMAN, O.1944.New England Annelida.Pt. 2 (including the unpublished plates by Verrill with reconstructed captions).*Bull. Amer. Mus. nat. Hist.***82** : 327–343, pls 45–60.

—— 1959.Catalogue of the polychaetous annelids of the World.Pts 1–12.*Occ. Pap. Allan Hancock Fdn.***23** : 1–628.

HARTMAN, O. & BARNARD, J. L.1960.The benthic fauna of the deep basins of Southern California.*Allan Hancock Pacific Expedition***22** : 217–297.

HASWELL, WILLIAM A.1896.Jottings from the biological laboratory of Sydney University.4.An Australian species of *Bonellia*.*Proc. Linn. Soc. N.S.W.***10** : 331–332.

HATSCHEK, B.1881.Über Entwicklungsgeschichte von *Echiurus* und die syst. Stellung der Echiuridae.*Arb. zool. Inst. Univ. Wien.***3** : 45–79, 3 pls.

—— 1883.Über Entwicklung von *Sipunculus nudus*.*Arb. zool. Inst. Univ. Wien.***5** : 61–140, 6 pls.

HEATH, H.1910.*Pelagosphaera*, a larval Gephyrean.*Biol. Bull. mar. biol. Lab., Woods Hole***18** : 281–284.

—— 1930.A connecting link between the Annelida and the Echiuroidea (Gephyrea armata).*J. Morph.***49** : 223–249, 3 pls, 4 figs.

HECKMANN, RICHARD.1961.Preliminary studies on gregarines inhabiting *Sipunculus* in Kanohe Bay, Hawaii.*J. Protozool.***8** (suppl.) : 17 abstract.

HEDGPETH, J. W.1954.Miscellaneous vermes, Gulf of Mexico.*Fishery Bull. Fish. Wildl. Serv. U.S.***55** : 419–420.

HEDLEY, C.1915.An ecological sketch of Sydney Beaches.*Proc. Linn. Soc. N.S.W.***49** : 15–77, pls 1–7, figs 1–28.

HEIDENREICH, F.1935.Untersuchungen zur Analyse der vermännlichenden Wirkung von mit Salz-Schwefel oder Kohlensaure versetztem Seewasser auf indifferenten Bonellia-larven.*Wilhelm Roux Arch. Entw. Mech. Organ***132** : 600–615, 3 figs, 6 tables.

HERBST, C.1928.Untersuchungen zur Bestimmung des Geschlects. i. Mitteilung: Ein neuer Weg zur Lösung des Geschlechtsbestimmungsproblems bei *Bonellia viridis*.*Sber. Heidleberger Akad-Wiss. Math. Naturw. Reihe***19** (2) : 1–19.

—— 1929.Untersuchungen zur Bestimmung des Geschlecht. ii. Mitteilung: Weitere Experimente über die Vermännlichung indifferenter *Bonellia*-larven durch künstliche Mittel.*Sber. Heidleberger Akad. Wiss. Math. Naturw. Reihe***20** (16) : 1–43.

—— 1932.Untersuchungen zur Bestimmung des Geschlechts. iii. Mitteilung: Die Vermännlichung der Larven durch Kupferspuren.*Naturwissenschaften***20** : 375–379.

—— 1935.Untersuchungen zur Bestimmung des Geschlechts. iv. Mitteilung: Die Abhängigkeit des Geschlechts von Kaliumgehalt des umgebenden Mediums bei *Bonellia viridis*.*Wilhelm Roux Arch. Entw. Mech. Organ***132** : 567–599.

—— 1936.Untersuchungen zur Bestimmung des Geschlechts. v. Mitteilung: Die Notwendigkeit des Magnesiums für die Lebenserhaltung und Weiterentwicklung der *Bonellia*-larven und seine Bedeutung für die geschlechtliche Differensiehrung derselben.*Wilhelm Roux Arch. Entw. Mech. Organ***134** : 313–330.

—— 1937a.Untersuchungen zur Bestimmung des Geschlechts. vi. Mitteilung: Neue Gedanken zur Geschlechtsbestimmung bei Tieren.*Wilhelm Roux Arch. Entw. Mech. Organ***135** : 178–201.

—— 1937b.Untersuchungen zur Bestimmung des Geschlechts. vii. Mitteilung: Über die Bedeutung des SO_4-ions für die Weiterentwicklung und geschlechtliche Differenzierung der *Bonellia*-larven und den Einfluss des erhöhten Ca-Gehaltes in SO_4-armen Medium auf diese Prozesse.*Wilhelm Roux Arch. Entw. Mech. Organ***136** : 147–168, 6 figs.

—— 1938.Untersuchungen zur Bestimmung des Geschlechts. viii. Mitteilung: Die Gene als Realisatoren und die Natur der prospectiven Potenz.*Wilhelm Roux Arch. Entw. Mech. Organ***138** : 451–464.

HERBST, C. 1939. Untersuchungen zur Bestimmung des Geschlechts. ix. Mitteilung: Der Einfluss des Glycerins auf des Geschlechtsbestimmung bei *Bonellia*. *Wilhelm Roux Arch. Entw. Mech. Organ* **139** : 282–302.

—— 1940. Untersuchungen zur Bestimmung des Geschlechts. x. Mitteilung: Über *Bonellia* weibchen mit spaltförmiger Leibeshöhle und ihre Bedeutung für meine Hydrations-Theorie der Geschlechtsbestimmung. *Wilhelm Roux Arch. Entw. Mech. Organ* **140** : 252–255.

HERDMAN, W. A. 1897. Note on a new British echiuroid gephyreen with remarks on the genera *Thalassema* and *Hamingia*. *Q. Jl. microsc. Sci.* n.s. **40** : 367–384, 2 pls.

HÉRUBEL, M. A. 1902a. Sur certains éléments péritoneaux du phascolosome (*Phascolosoma vulgare* de Blainv.). *Bull. Soc. zool. Fr.* **27** : 105–114, 4 text-figs.

—— 1902b. Sur le cerveau du Phascolosome. *C. r. hebd. Seanc. Acad. Sci. Paris* **134** : 1603–1605.

—— 1903a. Sur la distribution et les affinités réciproques des Sipunculides. *Bull. Soc. zool. Fr.* **28** : 99–111, 2 figs.

—— 1903b. Première contribution à la morphologie et physiologie comparées et à la bio-statique des Sipunculides. *Bull. Soc. zool. Fr.* **28** : 111–125, 2 figs.

—— 1903c. Observations physiologiques et histologiques sur les Géphriens (dérives endotheli-aux et granules pigmentaires). *C. r. hebd. Séanc. Acad. Sci. Paris* **136** : 971–973.

—— 1904a. Sur les sipunculides nouveaux rapportés de la Mer Rouge par M. Ch. Gravier (note préliminaire). *Bull. Mus. Hist. nat. Paris* **10** : 476–480, figs 1–4.

—— 1904b. Liste des sipunculides et des echiurides rapportés par M. Ch. Gravier du Golfe de Tadjourah. *Bull. Mus. Hist. nat. Paris* **10** : 562–566.

—— 1904c. Sur une nouvelle espèce du genre *Sipunculus*. *Int. Congr. Zool.* **6** : 690–695, 1 fig.

—— 1904d. Sur les Priapulides des côtes occidentales de la Scandinavie. *Bull. Soc. zool. Fr.* **29** : 100–109, 4 figs.

—— 1904e. Sur quelques points de la morphologie comparée des Priapulides. *Bull. Soc. zool. Fr.* **29** : 126–129.

—— 1905a. Sur un nouveau siponcle de la collection du Muséum (*Sipunculus joubini* sp. nov.) *Bull. Mus. Hist. nat. Paris* **11** : 51–54, 3 figs.

—— 1905b. Sur les productions tégumentaires des sipunculides. *Bull. Soc. zool. Fr.* **30** : 90–97.

—— 1906a. Sur les sipunculides rapportés par l'Expédition Charcot. Note préliminaire. *Bull. Mus. Hist. nat. Paris* **12** : 127–128.

—— 1906b. Sur une tumeur chez un invertébré (*Sipunculus nudus*). *C. r. hebd. Séanc. Acad. Sci. Paris* **143** : 979–981.

—— 1906c. A propos de l'anatomie comparée des sipunculides. *C. r. hebd. Séanc. Acad. Sci. Paris* **142** : 651–652.

—— 1907. Recherches sur les sipunculides. *Mem. Soc. zool. Fr.* **20** : 107–418, pls 5–10 figs 1–107.

—— 1908. Expédition antarctique française (1903–1905) commandée par le Dr. Jean Charcot. Géphyriens. *Documents Scientifiques*. Maison et Cie, Paris **8** : 1–8, text-figs 1–8.

—— 1924. Quelques echiurides et sipunculides des Côtes du Maroc et du Mauritane. *Bull. Soc. Sci. nat. Phys. Maroc* **4** : 108–112, 5 figs.

—— 1925a. Description de *Phascolosoma reticulatum* n. sp. *Bull. Soc. zool. Fr.* **50** : 272–277, figs 1–6.

—— 1925b. Quelques echiurides et sipunculides de Côtes du Maroc. *Bull. Soc. Sci. nat. Phys. Maroc* **5** : 260–263.

HILTON, W. A. 1917. The central nervous system of a sipunculid. *Pomona Coll. J. Ent.* **9** : 30–35.

HIRAWA, Y. K. & KAWANURA, T. 1935. Studies on the artificial parthenogenesis of *Urechis unicinctus*. *J. Sci. Hiroshima Univ. Zool.* **4** : 35–67.

HIRAWA, Y. K. & KAWANURA, T.   1936.   Relation between maturation division and cleavage in artificially activated eggs of *Urechis unicinctus*.   *Biol. Bull. mar. biol. Lab., Wood's Hole* **70** : 344–351.

HORST, R.   1881a.   *Hamingia glacialis* sp. n. eine borstenlose Echiure.   *Zool. Anz.* **4** : 448–450.

—— 1881b.   Die Gephyrea gesammelt während der zwei ersten Fahrten des William Barents. I. Echiurida.   *Archs. néerl. Zool.* suppl. **1** (3) : 1–13, 1 pl.

—— 1882.   Die Gephyrea gesammelt während der zwei ersten Fahrten des William Barents. ii. Priapulida and Sipunculida.   *Archs. néerl. Zool.* suppl. **1** (4) : 13–40, 2 pl.

—— 1899.   *Aspidosiphon cylindricus* sp. nov.   *Notes Leyden Mus.* **20** : 195.

HUNT, O. D.   1925. Some Plymouth specimens of Echiuridae.   *Proc. S. West Nat. Un.* **1** (2) : 31.

HURSH, J. B.   1938.   The force exerted by dogfish and *Phascolosoma* muscle at different velocities of shortening.   *J. cell. comp. Physiol.* **11** : 333.

HUTTON, W. K.   1879.   Additions to the list of New Zealand worms.   *Trans. N.Z. Inst.* **12** : 277–278.

—— 1903.   On the anatomy of the gephyreen *Phascolosoma teres*. sp. n.   *Proc. zool. Soc. Lond.* **1** : 29.

HYMAN, L. H.   1959.   Phylum Sipunculida. [In] *The Invertebrates*. McGraw-Hill Book Company, New York **5** : 610–696, text-figs 213–241.

IKEDA, I.   1904.   The gephyrea of Japan.   *J. Coll. Sci. imp. Univ. Tokyo* **20** (4) : 1–87, 4 pls.

—— 1905a.   Gephyreans collected by Prof. Dean at Manjuyodi, Southern Negros (Philippine Islands).   *Annotnes zool. jap.* **5** : 169–174, pl. 8.

—— 1905b.   Key to the genera of Sipunculoidea and Echiuroidea found in Japan.   *Zool. Mag., Tokyo* **17** : 269–275, figs 325–331 (in Japanese).

—— 1907.   On three new and remarkable species of echiuroids (*B. miyajimai*, *T. taenioides*, *T. elegans*).   *J. Coll. Sci. imp. Univ. Tokyo* **21** : 1–64, 4 pls.

—— 1908a.   Note on a new deep-sea echiuroid, *Protobonellia mitsukurii* nov. gen. et sp.   *Annotnes zool. jap.* **6** : 259–265, 4 figs.

—— 1908b.   On a new echiuroid (*Hamingia ijimai*) from the Sagami Bay.   *Annotnes zool. jap.* **7** : 61–68, pl. 1.

—— 1911.   Notes on a deep-sea echiuroid, *Acanthohamingia shiplei* (nov. gen. and sp.) with remarks on the species *Hamingia ijimai* Ikeda.   *Q. Jl. microsc. Sci.* **56** : 135–147, pl. 10.

—— 1912.   Studies on some sporozoan parasites of sipunculids. The life-history of a new Actinomyxidian, *Tetraactinomyson intermedium*. gen. et sp. nov.   *Arch. Protistenk.* **25** : 240–272, pl. 20.

—— 1922.   On a case of commensalism between a simple coral and a sipunculid.   *Zool. Mag., Tokyo* **34** : 275–281 (in Japanese).

—— 1924.   Further notes on the gephyrea of Japan with descriptions of some new species from the Marshall, Caroline and Palau Islands.   *Jap. J. Zool.* **1** : 23–44, pl. 1, figs 1–19.

ILINSKAIA, N. B. & USHAKOV, B. P.   1952.   Peculiarities of the salt parabiosis (local stimulation) of the retractors of *Phascolosoma margaritaceum*.   *Dokl. Akad. Nauk. U.S.S.R.* **83** : 961–964.

IVERSON, R. M. & GIESE, A. C.   1954.   Tests for photo-reactivation in gametes of *Urechis caupo*.   *Science, N.Y.* **120** : 504.

JÄGERSTEN, G.   1963.   On the morphology and behaviour of Pelagosphaera larvae.   *Zool. Bidrag., Uppsala* **36** : 27–35, 2 figs.

JAMESON, H. L.   1899a.   *Thalassema papillosum* (delle Chiaji) a forgotten echiuroid gephyrean.   *Mitt. zool. Stn. Neapel.* **13** : 433–439, 1 pl.

—— 1899b.   Contributions to the anatomy and histology of *Thalassema neptuni* Gaert.   *Zool. Jb. anat.* **12** : 535–566, pls 28–30, 1 text-fig.

JEMEY, J. C.   1902.   Eggs of *Thalassema* from Beaufort, N.C.   *Ann. N.Y. Acad. Sci.* **14** : 137.

JOHNSON, PEACE.   1965.   Two new species of *Aspidosiphon* (Sipunculoidea).   *Ann. Mag. nat. Hist.* ser. 13, **7** : 331–335, pls 7–8.

JOHNSTON, T. HARVEY & TIEGS, O. W.   1919.   *Pseudobonellia*, a new echiuroid from the Great Barrier Reef.   *Proc. Linn. Soc. N.S.W.* **44** : 213–239, pls 9–11.

JOHNSTON, T. HARVEY & TIEGS, O. W. 1920. A new species of *Bonellia* from Port Jackson, Sydney. *Rec. Aust. Mus.* **13** : 73–76, pls 15–16.

JONES, E. M. & STEPHEN, A. C. 1955. A new species of echiuroid worm (*Ochetostoma capensis*) from Cape Province, South Africa. *Trans. R. Soc. S. Afr.* **34** : 273–278, 3 figs.

JOSÉ, K. V. 1964. The morphology of *Acanthobonellia pirotanensis* sp. nov., a bonellid from the Gulf of Kutch. *J. Morph.* **115** (1) : 53–68, 15 figs.

JOURDAIN, S. 1865. Recherches sur l'anatomie des siponcles. *C. r. hebd. Seanc. Acad. Sci., Paris*, **40** : 1042.

—— 1867. Sur quelques points de l'anatomie des siponcles. *C. r. hebd. Seanc. Acad. Sci., Paris* **29** : 871–873. Also: *Ann. nat. Hist.* **19** : 442–443.

JOURDAN, E. 1891a. Les corpuscles sensitifs et les glands cutanées des géphyriens inermes. *Annls. Sci. nat.* ser. 7, **12** : 1–13, 1 pl.

—— 1891b. Les corps jaunes des echinodermes et des géphyriens. *C. R. Ass. fr. Avanc. Sci., Marseille* **2** (1) : 240; (2) : 537.

—— 1892. De la valeur du mot 'endothelium' en anatomie à propos des cellules à cils vibratils de la cavité générale des Sipunculiens. *C. r. Séanc. Soc. Biol.* **4** : 27.

JOYSEY, K. A. 1959. Probable cirripede, phoronid and echiuroid burrows within a Cretaceous echinoid test. *Palaeontology* **1** : 397–400.

KAGAWA, Y. 1952. Reversal of the fertilisation reaction on the eggs of the echiuroid *Urechis unicinctus* (von Drasche) treated with acid seawater. *J. Gakugei Coll. Tokushima Univ. Nat. Sci.* **2** : 36–42.

KALK, M. 1954. Marine biological research at Inhaca Island Mozambique. *A. Afr. J. Sci.* **51** : 107–115.

—— 1958. Biological studies on the shore of Mozambique. I. The fauna of the intertidal rocks at Inhaca Island, Delagoa Bay. *Ann. Natal Mus.* **14** : 189–242, pls 5 and 6, 8 figs.

KEFERSTEIN, W. 1863. Beiträge zur Kenntnis der Gattung *Phascolosoma* F. S. Leuck. Untersuchungen über niedere Seethiere. *Z. wiss. Zool.* **12** : 35–51, pls 3 and 4.

—— 1865a. Beiträge zur anatomischen und systematischen Kenntnis der Sipunculiden. *Z. wiss. Zool.* **15** : 404–445, pls 31–33.

—— 1865b. Beiträge zur anatomischen und systematischen Kenntnis der Sipunculiden. *Nachr. Ges. wiss. Göttingen* **1865** : 185–209.

—— 1866. Untersuchungen über einige amerikanischen Sipunculiden. *Nachr. Ges. wiss. Göttingen* **1866** : 215–228.

—— 1867. Untersuchungen über einige amerikanischen Sipunculiden. *Z. wiss. Zool.* **17** : 44–45, pl. 6.

KEFERSTEIN, W. & EHLERS, E. 1860. Auszug aus den Untersuchungen über die Anatomie des *Sipunculus*. *Nachr. Ges. wiss. Gottingen* **1860** : 282–286.

—— 1861. Untersuchungen über die Anatomie des *Sipunculus nudus*. *Zoologische Beiträge gesammelt in Winter* 1859–1860 *in Neapel und Messina*, 35–52, pls 6–8.

KELLY, LOUISE. 1953. *The histology of the nephridia of* Golfingia gouldii. Thesis. Library, Fisk University, Nashville.

KESTEVEN, H. L. 1903. A new species of *Dendrostoma*. *Rec. Aust. Mus.* **5** : 69–73, 1 pl.

KINDLE, E. M. 1917. Notes on the bottom environment of the marine invertebrates of western Nova Scotia. *Ottawa Nat.* **30** : 149–154.

KINDLE, E. M. & WHITTACKER, E. J. 1918. Bathymetric check-list of the marine invertebrates of eastern Canada. *Contr. Can. Biol. Fish* **1917–18** : 240.

KNOX, G. A. 1957. *Urechis novae-zealandiae* (Dendy): A New Zealand echiuroid. *Trans. R. Soc. N.Z.* **85** : 141–148, 8 figs.

KNUDSEN, J. 1944. A gephyrean, a polychaete and a bivlave (*Jousseaumiellia concharum* n. sp.) living together (commensalistically) in the Indo-Malayan Seas. *Vidensk. Meddr. dansk. naturh. Foren.* **108** : 15–24, 6 figs.

KOLLER, G. 1936. Beobachtungen an den Nephridien von *Physcosoma japonicum*. **Naturwissenschaften** **24** : 827–828.

KOLLER, G. 1939a. Hormonale Regulation bei *Phascolosoma vulgare*. *Verh. dt. zool. Ges. Leipsig* **40** : 84–91, 4 figs.

—— 1939b. Über die Nephridien von *Phascolosoma japonicum*. *Verh. dt. zool. Ges. Leipsig* **41** : 440–447, 5 figs. Also: *Zool. Anz.* **12** : 440 suppl.

KOREN, J. & DANIELSSEN, D. C. 1875. Bidrag til de norske Gephyreers Naturhistorie. *Nyt. Mag. Naturvid.* **21** : 108–138.

—— 1877. Contribution to the natural history of the Norwegian Gephyrea. [In] Sars, M., *Fauna littoralis Norwegiae*, Christiania **3** : 111–156, pls 14–15, figs 18–46. Bergen.

KORN, H. 1960a. Zur Dauer Metamorphose von *Echiurus abyssalis* Skor. (Echiurida-Annelida.) *Kieler Meeresforch* **16** : 238–242, 5 figs.

—— 1960b. Ergänzende Beobachtungen zur Struktur der Larve von *Echiurus abyssalis* Skor. *Z. wiss. Zool.* **164** : 197–237, 35 figs.

KOWALEVSKY, A. 1868. Über das Männchen der *Bonellia*. *Zap. Kiev. Obshch. Estest.* **1** : 101–108 (in Russian).

—— 1870. Planariform male of *Bonellia viridis*. (In Russian.) (*See* Catta, 1875.)

—— 1872. Zur Anatomie und Entwicklung von *Thalassema*. *Z. wiss. Zool.* **22** : 284.

—— 1889. Ein Beitrag zur Kenntnis der excretions Organe. *Biol. Zbl.* **9** : 43–47, 65–76, 127–128.

—— 1901. Sur la genre *Chaetoderma*. *Archs. Zool. exp. gén.* ser. 9, **3** : 261–283, 3 pls.

KOZLOFF, E. N. 1953. *Collastma pacifica* sp. nov. a rhabdocoel turbellarian from the gut of *Dendrostoma pyroides* Chamberlain. *J. Parasit.* **39** : 336–340, 1 pl.

KROHN, A. 1839. Über das Nervensystem des *Sipunculus nudus*. *Arch. Anat. Physiol.* **1839** : 348–352.

—— 1851. Über die Larve des *Sipunculus nudus*. *Arch. Anat. Physiol.* **1851** : 368–379, pl. 16.

KUNSTLER, J. 1908a. Que sont les urnes des Siponcles ? *C. r. hebd. Séanc. Acad. Sci., Paris* **146** : 196–199, 4 text-figs.

—— 1908b. Note additionelle sur les 'urnes' des Siponcles. *C. r. Séanc. Soc. Biol.* **64** : 303–304, 1 text-fig.

KUNSTLER, J. & GRUVEL, A. 1897a. Recherches sur l'évolution des urnes. *C. r. hebd. Séanc. Acad. Sci., Paris* **124** : 309–312. Also *J. R. micr. Soc.* **1897** : 126; *Review Amer. Nat.* **31** : 541–543.

—— 1897b. Sur le développement d'elements particuliers de la cavité générale du siponcle. *P.-v. Séanc. Soc. Sci. phys. nat., Bordeaux* **1896–1897** : 57–60.

—— 1898. Nouvelles observations sur quelques stades de l'évolution des urnes. *C. r. hebd. Séanc. Acad. Sci., Paris* **126** : 970–972.

—— 1899. Recherches sur les 'coupes ciliées' der *Phymosoma granulatum*. *P.-v. Séanc. Soc. Sci. phys. nat., Bordeaux* **1898–1899** : 29–32.

LACAZE-DUTHIERS, H. DE. 1858. Recherches sur la bonellie (*Bonellia viridis*). *Ann. Sci. Nat. Zool.* ser. 4, **10** : 49–110, pls 1–4.

LADREYT, F. 1903. Sur le rôle de certains éléments figurés chez *Sipunculus nudus* L. *C. r. hebd. Séanc. Acad. Sci. Paris* **137** : 865–867.

—— 1904a. Sur le pigment de *Sipunculus nudus* L. *C. r. Séanc. Soc. biol.* **56** : 850–852.

—— 1904b. Sur les urnes de Sipunculus. *C. r. hebd. Séanc. Acad. Sci., Paris* **139** : 370–371.

—— 1905. Sur les tubes de Poli de *Sipunculus nudus* L. *Arch. Zool. exp. gén.* ser. 4, **3** : 215–222, 4 text-figs.

—— 1906. Sur certaines phénomènes de dégénérescence des globules sanguins dans le liquide coelomique de *Sipunculus nudus*. *C. r. Ass. fr. Avanc. Sci.* **34** : 601–602.

—— 1922. Sur une tumeure cancéreuse du siponcle (*Sipunculus nudus*). *Bull. Inst. océanogr. Monaco* **405** : 1–8.

LAMARCK, J. P. B. A. DE M. 1816. *Histoire naturelle des animaux sans vertébrés* **3** : 76–79.

LAMPERT, K. 1883. Über einiger neue *Thalassema*. *Z. wiss. Zool.* **39** : 334–342.

—— 1899. Étude sur quelques echinides de l'Infra-Lias et du Lias. *Bull. Soc. Sci. hist. nat. Yonne* **53** : 54.

LANCHESTER, W. F. 1905a. On a collection of sipunculids made at Singapore and Malacca. *Proc. zool. Soc. Lond.* **1905** (1) : 26–28.

—— 1905b. On the sipunculids and echiurids collected during the 'Skeat' expedition to the Malay Peninsula. *Proc. zool. Soc. Lond.* **1** : 35–41, pl. 2.

—— 1905c. The marine fauna of Zanzibar and British East Africa from collections made by C. Crossland in 1901 and 1902. Gephyrea. *Proc. zool. Soc. Lond.* **1** : 28–35, pl. 1.

—— 1908. Sipunculoidea. *Nat. Antarct. Exped.* 1901–1904, Nat. Hist. **4** : 1–6.

LANKESTER, E. R. 1873. Summary of zoological observations made at Naples in the winter of 1871–1872. *Ann. Mag. nat. Hist.* ser. 4, **11** : 81–97.

—— 1881. On *Thalassema neptuni* Gaertner. *Zool. Anz.* ser. 4, **87** : 350–356.

—— 1883. On a specimen of the gephyrean *Hamingia arctica* Kor. & Dan. from the Hardanger Fjord. *Ann. Mag. nat. Hist.* ser. 5, **11** : 37–43.

—— 1885. *Golfingia macintoshi*, a new sipunculid from the coast of Scotland. *Trans. Linn. Soc. Lond. Zool.* ser. 2, **11** : 469–474, pls 55–56.

—— 1908b. The ciliated urns of the sipunculids. *Nature, Lond.* **78** : 318.

LAFON, M. 1953. Recherches sur les sables côtiers de la Basse-Normandie et sur quelques conditions de leur peuplement zoologique. *Annls. Inst. Océanogr. Monaco* ser. 3, **28** : 113–161.

LEFEVRE, G. 1905. Artificial parthenogenesis in *Thalassema mellita*. *Science, N.Y.* n.s. **21** : 379.

—— 1906. Further observations on artificial parthenogenesis. *Science, N.Y.* n. ser. **23** : 522–524.

—— 1907. Artificial parthenogenesis in *Thalassema mellita*. *J. exp. Zool.* **4** : 91–150, 6 pls.

LEIGH-SHARPE, W. H. 1928. *Thalassema neptuni* Gaertner, a British echiuroid. *Ann. Mag. nat. Hist.* ser. 10, **2** : 499–504, pls 14–15.

LEROY, P. 1936. Les sipunculiens du Muséum National d'Histoire Naturelle de Paris. *Bull. Mus. r. Hist. nat.* ser. 2, **8** : 423–426.

—— 1942. Sipunculiens d'Indochine. Notes station maritime de Cauda. *Notes Inst. Oceanogr. Nhatrang* **40** : 1–51, pls 1–5, 12 figs.

LEUCKART, F. S. 1828. *Breves animalium quorundam maxima ex parte marinorum descriptiones*. Heidelberg: 9–23, figs 3–5.

LEUCKART, F. S. & RÜPPELL, W. P. S. 1828. Neue wirbellose Thiere des rothen Meers. [In] Rüppell, W. P. S., *Atlas zur der Reise in nordlichen Africa* **1.** Zoologie: 6–9, pl. 2, figs 1–3.

LEVINSEN, G. M. R. 1884. Systematisk geografisk Öfversight över den nordske Annulata etc. *Vidensk. Meddr. dansk. naturh. Foren.* 1883, **11** : 92–350, pls 2, 3.

—— 1887. Kara Havets Ledorme (Annulata). [In] Lutken, C. F., *Dijmna-togtets Zool.-bot. Udbytte* **1887** : 287–303, pl. 25.

LEYDIG, F. 1864. *Vom Bau des thierischen Korpers*. Tubingen. **1** : vi + 1–278.

LIGHT, S. F., SMITH, R. I., PITELKA, F. A., ABBOTT, D. P. & WEESNER, F. M. 1954. Gephyrea: 108–111, 2 figs. [In] *Intertidal invertebrates of the central Californian Coast*. 2 ed. University California Press, Berkeley and Los Angeles : 1–446, 138 figs.

LINDROTH, A. 1941. Echiurida, Sipunculida und Enteropneusta aus dem Skagerack 1933. (Festskr. tillagn. Prof. Sven Ekman.) *Zool. Bidfr. fran. Uppsala* **20** : 443–452.

LINNAEUS, C. 1766. *Systema naturae*. 12 ed.

LONGHURST, A. R. 1958. An ecological survey of the West African marine benthos. *Colonial Office Fish. Publ. London* **11** : 1–102, 11 figs.

LÖNNBERG, E. & GUSTAFSSON, G. 1939. Notes on the colour substance in *Thalassema lankesteri* Herdm. *Ark. Zool.* **32** : 1–4.

LOOSLI, M. 1935. Über die Entwicklung und den Bau der indifferenten und männlichen Larven von *Bonellia viridis* Rol. *Publ. Staz. Zool. Napoli* **15** : 16–58, 25 figs.

LOVE, W. E. 1957. The X-ray molecular weight of hemerythrin from *Phascolosoma gouldii* and some notes on the oxygenation reaction. *Biochim. Biophys. Acta.* **23** : 465–471.

LÖVEN, S. 1845. Beschreibung des *Chaetoderma nitidulum* n.g., n. sp. aus der Classe Echinodermem. *Archiv. skand. Beitr. Naturg.* **1** : 169–170, pl. 2.

McCOY, F. 1845. Contributions to the fauna of Ireland. *Ann. Mag. nat. Hist.* **15** : 270–274, pl. 16.

MacGINITIE, G. E. 1935a. Normal functioning and experimental behaviour of the egg and sperm-collectors of the Echiuroid *Urechis caupo*. *J. exp. Zool.* **70** : 341–355, 1 pl., 1 text-fig.

—— 1935b. Ecological aspects of a Californian marine estuary. *Am. Midl. Nat.* **16** : 629–765 21 figs.

—— 1935c. The fertilisation of the eggs and the rearing of the larvae of *Urechis caupo* within the blood cavity of the animal. *J. exp. Zool.* **71** : 483–487.

—— 1937a. The use of mucus by marine plankton feeders. *Science, N.Y.* **86** : 398–399.

—— 1937b. Culturing larvae of *Urechis caupo*. Class Gephyrea. [In] Galtsoff, *Cultural methods for invertebrate animals*. *Ithaca* **1937** : 197–201.

—— 1938a. Notes on the natural history of some marine animals. *Am. Midl. Nat.* **19** : 207–219, 2 pls.

—— 1938b. Experiments which cause inhibition of the function but not the actual activity of the sperms of *Urechis caupo*. *J. exp. Zool.* **79** : 237–242.

—— 1945. The size of the mesh opening in the mucous feeding nets of marine animals. *Biol. Bull. mar. biol. Lab., Wood's Hole* **88** : 107–111, 1 fig.

—— 1956. Distribution and ecology of the marine invertebrates of Point Barrow, Alaska. *Smithson. misc. Coll.* **128** (9) : 1–201, 8 pls.

MacGINITIE, G. E. & MacGINITIE, N. 1968. *Natural history of marine animals*. McGraw-Hill, New York.

McGOWAN, JOHN A. 1960. The relationship of the distribution of the planktonic worm *Poeobius meseres* Heath to the water masses of the North Pacific. *Deep-sea Res.* **6**: 125–139.

McINTOSH, W. C. 1866. Observations on the marine biology of North Uist, Outer Hebrides. *Proc. R. Soc. Edinb.* **5** : 600–614, figs 1–7.

—— 1875. *The marine invertebrates and fishes of St. Andrews.* pp. 112. Edinburgh.

—— 1922. On new and rare Polychaeta, Gephyrea etc. from various regions. *Ann. Mag. nat. Hist.* ser. 9, **9** : 1–30, 3 pls.

MACK, H. VON. 1902. Das Centralnervensystem von *Sipunculus nudus* L. (Bauchstrang). Mit besonderer Berücksichtigung des Stützgewebes. Eine histologische Untersuchung. *Arb. zool. Inst. Univ. Wien* **13** : 237–334, pls 13–17, 17 text-figs.

MACKIE, G. O. 1961. Echiuroids from the Canary Islands. *Ann. Mag. nat. Hist.* ser. 13, **3** : 247–251, 2 figs.

MAGNUS, R. 1903. Pharmakologische Untersuchungen an *Sipunculus nudus*. *Arch. exp. Path. Pharmak.* **50** : 86–122.

MANWELL, C. 1960a. Oxygen transfer systems involving haemerythrins in sipunculid worms of different ecologies. *Comp. Biochem. Physiol.* **1** : 277–285.

—— 1960b. Comparative physiology: blood pigments. *Ann. Rev. Physiol.* **22** : 191–244.

—— 1963. Genetic control of haemerythrin specificity in a marine worm. *Science* **139** (3556) : 755–758.

MARCIALIS, E. 1892. Saggio di un Catalogo metodico dei principali e piu comuni anamali invertebrati della Sardegna. *Boll. Soc. zool. ital.* **1** : 246–282.

MARCOU, J. & VOLONSKY, M. 1933. Les lignées leucocytaires des Sipunculides. *Archs. Anat. micros.* **29** : 245–260, pl. 2.

MARENZELLER, E. VON. 1888. Bericht über die Fortschritte auf dem Gebiete der Systematik, Biologie u. geogr. Verb, de Platyhel., Chaetogn., Gephyreen, Anneliden, Enteropn. u. Rotarien. *Zool. Jb. Syst.* **3** : 1015.

MARION, A. F. 1875. Du mâle planariforme de la Bonellie. *Rev. Sci. nat. par Dubrueil* **4** : 313–319.

—— 1875. Draguages au large de Marseille. *Ann. Sc. Nat. Zool.* **1875** (7) : 6–8, pls 15–18.

MARION, A. F.   1883a.   Esquisse d'une topographie zoologique du Golfe de Marseille.   *Annls. Mus. Hist. nat. Marseille* **1** : 73.

—— 1883b.   Considérations sur les faunes profondes de Méditerranée.   *Annls. Mus. Hist. nat. Marseille* **1** : 1–50.

MARRIAN, G.   1927.   A note on hemerythrin.   *J. exp. Biol.* **4** : 357–364.

MASUMI.   1960.   Studies on the fertilization in the eggs of the echiuroid worm *Urechis unicinctus*. 3.   On the growth of the egg cells suspended in the body fluid.   *J. Yokohama Munic. Univ.* (C), **95** : 1–13.

MELLO-LEITAO, A.   1955.   Equiurideos do estado do Espirito Santo.   *Revta Biol. mar.* **5** : 130–131.

MENON, P. E. B. & DATTA GUPTA, A. K.   1962.   On a new species of *Ikedosoma* (Echiuridae).   *Ann. Mag. nat. Hist.* ser. 13, **5** : 303–309, 3 figs.

MENON, P. K. B., DATTA GUPTA, A. K. & JOHNSON, P.   1964.   Report on the bonellids (*Echiura*) collected from the Gulf of Kutch and Port Blair (Andaman Islands).   *Ann. Mag. nat. Hist.* ser. 13, **7** : 49–58, 3 figs.

METALNIKOFF, S. J.   1899.   Das Blut und die Excretionsorgane von *Sipunculus nudus*.   *Mitt. zool. Stn. Neapel.* **13** : 440–447.

—— 1900.   *Sipunculus nudus*.   *Z. wiss. Zool.* **68** : 261–322, pls 17–22.

MEYER, A.   1929.   Über Cölombewimperung und cölomatische Kreislaufsystem bei Wirbellosen (Sipunculoidea, Polychaeta errantia).   *Z. wiss. Zool.* **135** : 495–538, pls 2–3, 32 text-figs.

MEYER, H.   1849.   Zur Anatomie der Sipunculiden.   *Z. wiss. Zool.* **1** : 268–269.

MICHAELSEN, W.   1889.   Die Gephyreen von Süd-Georgien nach der Ausbeute der deutschen Station von 1882–1883.   *Jb. hamb. wiss. Anst.* **6** : 73–84, 1 pl.

MICHEL, F.   1930.   Über die Larve und die Entwicklung des Männchens der *Bonellia fuliginosa* Rol.   *Pubbl. Stn. zool. Napoli* **10** : 1–47, 30 figs.

—— 1932.   Über den chemischen Schutz der *Bonellia viridis* Rol. gegen Frass.   *Pubbl. Stn. zool. Napoli* **12** : 22–30.

MINGAZZINI, P.   1905.   Un Gefireo pelagico.   *Pelagosphaera aloysii* n. gen. n. sp.   *Memorie Accad. Pont. Nuovi Lincei* **14** : 713–720.

MÖBIUS, K.   1875.   Vermes.   V.   *Kommission zur wissensch. Untersuch. des Deutschen Meere in Kiel.*   **1872–1873.**   p. 150–p. 170, 1 pl.

MOLTCANOFF, L. A.   1909.   Néphridies de *Phascolosoma spitzbergense* Théel.   *Izv. imp. Acad. Nauk.* ser. 6, **2** : 69–74.

MONRO, C. A.   1927.   On the families and genera of the class Echiuroidea.   *Ann. Mag. nat. Hist.* ser. 9, **20** : 615–620.

—— 1931.   Polychaeta, Oligochaeta, Echiuroidea and Sipunculoidea.   *Scient. Rep. Gt. Barrier Reef Exped.* **4** : 1–37, 15 figs.

MONTAGU, G.   1804.   Description of several marine animals found on the south coast of Devonshire.   *Trans. Linn. Soc. London* **7** : 61–85.

—— 1815.   Descriptions of several new or rare animals, principally marine, discovered on the south coast of Devonshire.   *Trans. Linn. Soc. Lond. Zool.* **11** (1) : 24, pl. 5, fig. 2.

MÜLLER MAX.   1852.   *Observationes anatomicae de vermibus quibusdem maritimis.*   Berlin.   **1852** : 14–22, pl. 3, figs 1–12.

MÜLLER, J.   1844.   Uber einem neuen Wurm *Sipunculus* (*Phascolosoma*) *scutatus*.   *Arch. Naturgesicht.* **10** : 166–168, pl. 5, 4 figs.

MÜLLER, O. F.   1789.   *Zoologica danica.*   **3.**   Havniae.

MÜLLICK, B. K.   1931.   Description of a new genus of Sipunculidae, and a new species of *Phascolosoma*.   *Proc. Indian Sci. Congr.* **18** (4) : 223 (abstract).

MURINA, V. V.   1957a.   Abyssal sipunculids (genus *Phascolion* Théel) of the north-western part of the Pacific, collected by 'Vitjaz' Expeditions in 1950–1955.   *Zool. Zh.* **36** : 1777–1791, 8 figs. (Russian with English summary.)

—— 1957b.   Sipunculids collected on the first trip of the Complex Antarctic Expedition of the 'OB' in 1956.   *Zool. Zh.* **36** : 992–996.   1 map (Russian with English summary).

MURINA, V. V. 1958. On the systematics of two closely related species of deep-water Sipunculids of the genus *Golfingia*, according to the materials of the 'Vitjaz' Expeditions in 1949–1955. *Zool. Zh.* **37** : 1624–1634, 1 fig. (In Russian with English summary.)

—— 1961. The geographical distribution of abyssal Sipunculida. (*Phascolion lutense* Selenka.) *Oceanol.* (Acad. Sci., S.S.S.R.) **1961** (1) : 140–142, 1 fig.

—— 1964a. New and rare species of sipunculids of the genus *Golfingia*. *Trudy Inst. Okeanol.* **69** : 216–253 (In Russian, English summary).

—— 1964b. Report on the sipunculid worms from the coast of the South China Sea. *Trudy Inst. Okeanol.* **69** : 254–270 (In Russian, English summary).

—— 1964c. On the sipunculid fauna of the Mediterranean. *Trudy sevastopol. biol. Sta.* **17** : 51–76, 20 figs.

—— 1965. Some data on the structure of Pelagosphera-sipunculid larvae. *Zool. Zh.* **44** : 1610–1618, 8 figs.

—— 1967a. Report of the sipunculid worms from the sub-littoral zone of Cuba and the Mexican Gulf. *Zool. Zh.* **46** : 1329–1339, 6 figs.

—— 1967b. On the sipunculid fauna of the littoral of Cuba. *Zool. Zh.* **46** : 35–46, 8 figs.

—— 1968. Occurrence of abyssal sipunculids in the Atlantic Ocean. *Zool. Zh.* **47** : 195–198, 1 fig.

MUTSCHELLER, F. 1935. Experimentelle Untersuchung der Organe der Weibchen von *Bonellia viridis*, deren Extracte vermännlichend wirken, auf das Vorkommen Scherwmettalen insbesondere von Kupfer. *Biol. Zbl.* **55** : 615–625.

NEWBY, W. W. 1932. The early embryology of the echiuroid, *Urechis*. *Biol. Bull.* **63** : 387–399, 5 pls.

—— 1940. The embryology of the echiuroid worm *Urechis caupo*. *Mem. Am. phil. Soc.* **16** : 1–213, 85 figs.

—— 1941. The development and structure of the slime glands of *Urechis*. *J. Morph.* **69** : 303–316, 10 figs.

NICKERSON, M. L. 1899a. Intracellular canals in the skin of *Phascolosoma*. *Zool. Jb. Anat.* **13** : 191–196, pl. 12.

—— 1899b. Intercellular differentiations in gland cells of *Phascolosoma gouldii*. *Science*, N.S. **9** : 365.

—— 1901. Sensory and glandular epidermal organs in *Phascolosoma gouldii*. *J. Morph.* **17** : 381–398, pls 34–35.

NIELSEN, B. J. 1963. Description of a new species of *Bonellia* (Echiuroidea) from Australia. *Proc. Roy. Soc. Vict.* n.s. **76** : 61–67, 3 figs, 1 pl.

NILUS, G. 1909. Notiz über *Loxosoma murmanica* und *Loxosoma brumpti*. *Trav. Soc. Imp. Natur.*, St. Petersbourg **40** : 157–166.

NOBLE, E. 1938. The life-cycle of *Zygosoma globosus* sp. n., a gregarine parasite of *Urechis caupo*. *Univ. Calif. Publs. Zool.* **43** : 41–46, 2 pls, 3 figs.

NORMAN, A. M. 1861. On echinoderms new to science from Ireland. *Ann. Mag. nat. Hist.* ser. 3, **7** : 112–114.

—— 1894. A month on the Trondhemfjord. *Ann. Mag. nat. Hist.* ser. 6, **13** : 150–164.

NOWINSKI, W. 1934. Die vermännlichende Wirkung frationeirter Darm-extracte der Weibchens auf die Larven der *Bonellia viridis*. *Pubbl. Staz. Zool. Napoli* **14** : 110–145, 13 figs.

—— 1949. Some biochemical aspects of sex determination in *Bonellia-viridis*. *Tex. J. Sci.* **1** : 103 (abstract).

OERSTED, A. S. 1844. *De regionibus marinis*. Hauniae. pp. 88.

—— 1845. Fortegnelse över Dyr samlede i Christianiafjord. *Kroyer's Nat. Tidskr.* **1** : 400–427.

OHKAWA, M. 1956. Studies on the fertilisation in an echiuroid, *Urechis unicinctus* (v. Drasche). *Zool. Mag. Tokyo* **65** : 210–218.

—— 1960. Studies on the fertilisation in eggs of the echiuroid worm, *Urechis caupo*. 3. On the growth of egg-cells suspended in the body. *J. Yokohama Munic. Univ.* ser. C, **9** : 1–13, fig. (In Japanese, English summary).

Okuda, S. 1946. The Fauna of Akkeshi Bay. 15. Gephyrea. *J. Fac. Sci. Hokkaido Univ.* ser. zool. 6, **9** : 221–224, pl. 29.

Ohuye, T. 1938. On the coelomic corpuscles in the body fluid of some invertebrates. *Sci. Rept. Tohoku Univ.* ser. 4 Biol. **12** : 203–239.

—— 1942. On the blood corpuscles and hemopoiesis of *Dendrostoma minor*. *Sci. Rept. Tohoku Univ. Biol.* ser. 4, **17** : 187–196.

Ohuye, T., Ochi, O. & Miyata, I. 1961. On the morphogenesis and histochemistry of the urn cells of the coelomic fluid of a sipunculid, *Phascolosoma scolops*. *Mem. Ehime Univ.* **2B** : 4.

Onoda, K. 1934. On *Pseudobonellia*, a new genus of bonellian Echiuroids. *Annotnes. zool. jap.* **14** : 413–424, 1 pl., 3 text-figs.

—— 1935. *Parabonellia* (nom. nov.) *misakiensis* (Ikeda) correction of my paper on *Pseudobonellia*. *Annotnes. zool. jap.* **15** : 141.

Olson, M. 1940. Histology of the retractor muscles of *Phascolosoma gouldii* Pourtalès. *Biol. Bull. mar. biol. Lab., Wood's Hole* **78** : 24–28.

Orton, J. H. 1923. Some new commensals in the Plymouth district. *Nature Lond.* **112** : 861, 1 fig.

Osburn, R. C. 1912. The Bryozoa of Woods Hole region. *Bull. Bur. Fish., Wash.* **30** : 205–261, pls 18–31.

Ostroumoff, A. A. 1909. Sur les géphyriens du nord de la Mer du Japan *Ezheg. Zool. Muz.* **14** : 319–321 (Russian, with short German summary).

Otto, A. G. 1821. Animalium maritimorum nondum editorum genera duo. *Nova acta Phys.-Med. Acad. Leop.-Carol., Verh. Natur.* **10** : 618–634, 2 pls.

Packard, A. S. 1867. Observations on the glacial phenomena of Labrador and Maine, with a view of the recent invertebrate fauna of Labrador. *Mem. Boston Soc. nat. Hist.* **1** : 210–303, pls 7 and 8.

Pallas, P. S. 1766. *Lumbricus echiurus*. *Miscellania Zoologica*. Hagae Comitum. pp. 146–151, 1 pl., 6 figs.

—— 1774. *Spicilegia Zoologica*, Berolini. (1), **10** : 1–15, 4 pls.

Pasteels, J. J. 1935. Spawning of *Thalassema neptuni*. Recherches sur la détermination de l'entrée en maturation de l'oeuf chez divers invertébrés marins. *Archs. Biol., Paris* **46** : 229–262.

Paul, G. 1910. Über *Petalostoma minuta* Keferstein und verwandte Arten, nebst Bermerkungen zur Anatomie von *Onchnesoma steenstrupi*. *Zool. Jb. Anat.* **29** : 1–50, pls 1–2.

Pearse, A. S., Humm, H. J. & Wharton, G. W. 1942. Ecology of sand beaches at Beaufort, North Carolina. *Ecol. Monogr.* **12** : 135–190, 24 figs.

Peebles, F. & Fox, D. L. 1933. The structure, functions and general reactions of the marine sipunculid worm, *Dendrostoma zostericola*. *Bull. Scripps Instn. Oceanogr. tech.* ser. **3** : 201–224, 11 figs.

Pelseneer, P. 1909. Phylogénie des lamellibranches commensaux. *Bull. Acad. Belg.* (Sci) **12** : 1144–1150.

—— 1925. Un lamellibranche commensal de Lamellibranche et quelques autres lamellibranches commensaux. *Wimereux Trav. Stat. Zool.* **9** : 164–182.

—— 1928. Les parasites des mollusques. *Bull. Soc. zool., Fr.* **53** : 158–189.

Pennant, T. 1777. *British Zoology*. Warrington and London. **4** : 31.

Perez, C. 1924. Le complexe éthologique de la Turritelle et du *Phascolion strombi*. *Bull. Soc. zool. Fr.* **49** : 341–343.

—— 1925. Sur le complexe éthologique du *Phascolion strombi*. *Bull. Soc. zool. Fr.* **50** : 74–76 3 text-figs.

Pergament, T. S. 1940. On a new genus *Nephasoma* from the Arctic Ocean. *Trans. of the Drifting Expedition of the Main Northern Passage on the Ice-breaker 'S.S. Sedov'*, **1938–40,** U.S.S.R. : 1–3.

Perrier, J. O. E. 1897. *Traité de Zoologie*, Paris. Fasc. **4** (Vers) : 1643–1662.

PETERS, W. 1850. Über die Fortpfanzungorgane des *Sipunculus*. *Arch. anat. physiol.* **1850** : 382–385, pl. 4, figs 1a–h.

PETTIBONE, M. H. 1957. Endoparasitic polychaetous annelids of the family Arabellidae with descriptions of new species. *Biol. Bull. mar. biol. Lab., Wood's Hole* **113** (1) : 170–187.

PICKFORD, G. E. 1947a. Histological and histochemical observations upon an aberrant annelid *Poeobius meseres* Heath. *J. Morph.* **80** : 287–312, pls 1–3.

—— 1947b. Echiurida and Sipunculida. *Encyclopedia Britannica* **20** : 717–718B.

POCHE, F. 1920. Über eine in Vergessenheit geratene Art der Echiuroidea. *Arch. Naturgesch.* **86** (9) : 102–104.

POPHAM, M. L. 1940. The mantle cavity of some of the Erycinidae, Montacutidae and Galeommatidae with special reference to ciliary mechanisms. *J. mar. biol. Ass. U.K.* **24** : 549–586.

POTEMKINA, V. A. 1956. Echiuroid infestation of aquatic birds. *Zh. obshch. Biol.* 1955, **12** : 28–30.

POURTALÈS, L. F. DE. 1851. On the Gephyrea of the Atlantic coast of the United States. *Proc. Am. Ass. Advmt. Sci.* for **1851** : 39–42.

PRASHAD, B. 1919a. Echiuroids from brackish water, with description of a new species from the Andamans. *Mem. Asiat. Soc. Beng.* **6** : 323–338, pl. 11.

—— 1919b. Notes on the echiuroids from Chandipore, Orissa. *Rec. Indian Mus.* **16** : 399–402.

—— 1921. On a new species of *Thalassema* from the Gulf of Mannar, with notes on Thurston's species, *T. formulosum*. *Rec. Indian Mus.* **19** (2) : 35–37.

—— 1935. On a collection of echiuroids of the genus *Thalassema* Lamarck in the Indian Museum, Calcutta. *Rec. Indian Mus.* **37** : 39–44, pl. 1.

—— 1936. On the Sipunculoidea from Indian waters in the Indian Museum, Calcutta. *Rec. Indian Mus.* **38** : 231–238, pl. 9.

PRASHAD, B. & AWATI, P. R. 1929. On a new species of the genus *Thalassema* from Bombay. *Rec. Indian Mus.* **31** : 259–262, pl. 12.

—— 1935. Reproductuve and segmental organs of *Thalassema bombayensis*. *J. Univ. Bombay* **1** : 96–107, 9 figs.

PRATT, E. M. 1898. Contributions to our knowledge of the marine fauna of the Falkland Islands. *Mem. Proc. Manchr. lit. phil. Soc.* **42** : 15–17 (Polychaeta and Gephyrea).

PRUVOT, G. 1894. Essai sur la topographie et la constitution des fonds sous-marins de la region de Banyuls. *Archs. Zool. exp. gén.* ser. 3, **2** : 599.

—— 1895. Coup d'oeil sur la distribution générale des invertébrés de la region de Banyuls (Golfe de Lion). *Archs. Zool. exp. gen.* ser. 3, **3** : 629–658.

—— 1896. Conditions générales de la vie dans les mers et principes de la distribution des organismes marins. *Année biol.* **2** : 599.

—— 1897a. Essai sur les fonds et la faune de la Manche occidentale (côtes de Bretagne), comparés à ceux du Golfe du Lion. *Archs. Zool. exp. gén.* ser. 3, **5** : 511–616.

—— 1897b. Catalogue des invertébrés benthiques du Golfe du Lion et de la Manche occidentale, avec leurs habitats, etc. *Archs. Zool. exp. gén.* ser. 3, **5** : 617–662.

QUATREFAGES, A. DE. 1847a. Memoire sur l'Echiure de Gaertner. Voyage sue les côtes de la Sicile etc. : 221, pls 25, 26. Also *Annls. Sci. Nat.* ser. 3, **7** : 307–343, pl. 6, figs 1–11.

—— 1847b. Études sur les types inférieurs de l'embranchement des Annélides. Mémoire sur l'Echiure de Pallas (*Echiurus pallasii* Quatr.). *C. r. hebd. Séanc. Acad. Sci. Paris* **24** : 776–779.

—— 1865. Notes sur la classification des Annélides. *C. r. hebd. Séanc. Acad. Sci. Paris* **40** (13) : 586–600.

—— 1865b. *Histoire naturelle des Annelés marins et d'eau douce.* Paris. **2** : 1–794, pls 1–20.

QUINTON, R. 1900. Communication osmotique, chez l'invértebré marin normal, entre le milieu de l'animal et le milieu antérieur. *C. r. hebd. Séanc. Acad. Sci. Paris* **131** : 905–908.

RAFINESQUE SCHMALZ, C. S. 1814. *Précis des découvertes et travaux zoologiques, Palerme* pp. 1–57.

RAJULA, G. S. & KRISHNAN, N. 1969. Occurrence of asexual reproduction by budding in Sipunculida. *Nature Lond.* **223** (5202) : 186.

RATHKE, H. 1843. Beiträge zur fauna Norwegens. *Nova Acta Acad. Caesar Leop. Carol.* **20** : 2–264.

REDFIELD, A. C. & FLORKIN, M. 1931. The respiratory function of the blood of *Urechis caupo*. *Biol. Bull. mar. biol. Lab., Wood's Hole* **11** : 185–210, 5 figs.

REINHARDT, J. 1851. Naturhistoriske Bidrag til en Beskrevelse of Gronland. *Geographisk og statistisk beskrevet* **2** : 45.

REMANE, A. 1933. Echiurida. [In] *Handworterbuch der Naturwissenschaften*, 2 ed : 1–6.

RETZIUS, G. 1904. Zur Kenntnis der Spermien der Evertebraten. *Biol. Unters.* **11** : 1–32, pls 1–13.

RICE, M. E. 1967. A comparative study of the development of *Phascolosoma agassizii* and *Themiste pyroides* with a discussion on the developmental patterns in Sipuncula. *Ophelia* **4** : 143–171, 4 figs.

—— 1969. Possible boring structures of sipunculids. *Amer. Zool.* **9** : 803–812, 5 figs.

—— 1970. Asexual reproduction in a sipunculan worm. *Science,* **167** : 1618–1620, 2 figs.

RICE, M. E. & STEPHEN, A. C. 1970 The type specimens of Sipuncula and Echiura described by J. E. Gray and W. Baird. *Bull. Brit. Mus. nat. Hist. Zool.* **20** (2) : 49–72, 3 pls., 29 figs.

RICKETTS, E. F. & CALVIN, J. 1952. *Between Pacific Tides. Stanford Univ., California.* Pp. 1–326, 46 pls, 112 figs (Gephyrea, para. 52, 125m, 145, 282, 306, 307, 308).

RIETSCH, M. 1884. Sur la structure histologique de la trompe de la Bonellie. *Bull. Soc. philomath Paris* ser. 7, **8** : 125–132.

—— 1886. Étude sur les géphyriens armés ou echiuriens. *Recl. Zool. suisse* **3** : 314–515, pls 17–22.

RISSO, A. 1826. *Histoire naturelle de l'Europe meridionale.* Paris and Strasbourg. **5** : 1–403, pls 10.

RITCHIE, J. 1912. The common spoon-worm, *Echiurus pallasii,* on the coast of Aberdeenshire. *Scott. Nat.* **1912** : 69.

RIVEROS-ZUNIGA, F. 1942. *Pinuca chilensis. Prnesas Universidad de Chile* : 1–15, 3 pls, Santiago.

—— 1951. *Pinuca chilensis* (Max Müller) 1852, en montemar y algunas consideraciones sinonimicas. *Revta. Biol. mar.* **3** : 1–2 : 156–157.

ROBINSON, V. C. 1927. Report on the Sipunculoidea. Zoological results of the Cambridge Expedition to the Suez Canal, 1924. *Trans. zool. Soc. Lond.* **22** : 359–360.

ROCHE, J. 1933a. Sur l'hémérythrine du siponcle. *Bull. Soc. Chim. Biol.* **15** : 1415.

—— 1933b. Sur le pigment respiratoire des hématies du siponcle (hémérythrine). *C. r. Séanc. Soc. Biol. Paris* **112** : 251–254, 2 figs.

—— 1933c. Sur les propriétés physico-chimiques de l'hémérythrine du siponcle. *C. r. Séanc. Soc. Biol.* **112** : 683–685.

ROCHE, A. & ROCHE, J. 1935. Pression osmotique et poids moleculaires de l'hémérythrine du siponcle. *Bull. Soc. Chim. Biol.* **17** : 1494. Also *C.R. Acad. Sci. Paris* **199** : 1678–1680.

ROCHE, J., CORELL, I., MACCHIA, V. & ALOG, S. 1962. Sur la fixation des hormones thyroidienne par les hématies nuclées de diverses origines. *C. r. Séanc. Soc. Biol.* **156** : 1746–1750.

ROLANDO, L. 1821. Description d'un animal nouveau qui appartient à la classe des Echinodermes. *Memorie Acad. Sci. Torino* **26** : 539–556, pl. 14, figs 1–3, pl. 15, figs 5–7.

—— 1822. Sur la *Bonellia viridis*. *J. Physique* **95** : 49–58, 2 pls.

—— 1823. Neues Thier zur Klasse der Echinodermen. Translation of Rolando, 1821. *Isis von Oken* **1** : 398.

RONDELET, G. 1555. *Universae aquatalium historiae pars altera cum veris ipsorum imaginibus* : 108–110, pls 3–4.

ROULE, L. 1896a. Sur le développement des feuillets blastodermiques chez les Géphyriens tubicoles. *C. r. hebd. Séanc. Acad. Sci. Paris* **110** : 1147–1149.

—— 1896b. Géphyriens. Resultats scientifiques de la campagne du 'Caudan' dans le Golfe de Gascogne. 1895. *Annls. Univ. Lyon* **26** : 473–474.

Roule, L. 1898a. Note préliminaire sur les espèces de géphyriens recueillies dans les explora-tions sous marines du 'Talisman' et du 'Travailleur'. *Bull. Mus. Hist. nat. Paris* **4** : 384–387.

—— 1898b. Sur les géphyriens des grands fonds de la mer. *C.R. Acad. Sci., Paris* **127** : 197–199.

—— 1907. Annélides et Géphyriens. *Expéditions scientifiques du 'Travailleur' et du 'Talisman'* **8** : 1–102, pls 1–10. Paris.

Rüppell, W. P. S. & Leuckart, F. S. 1828. *See* Leuckart & Rüppell, 1828.

Sars, M. 1851. Beretning om en i Sommernen 1849 foretagen zoologisk Reise i Lofoten og Finmarken. *Nyt. mag. Naturvid.* **6** : 121–211.

—— 1868. Bidrag til de norske Gephyriens natur. *Vid. for Handl.* Christiania.

Sato, H. 1930a. On the generic names of the Sipunculoidea of Japan. *Zool. Mag. Tokyo* **502** : 324–325 (in Japanese).

—— 1930b. Report on the biological survey of Mutsu Bay. 15. Sipunculoidea. *Sci. Rep. Tohoku Univ.* ser. 4, **5** : 1–40, 4 pls, 15 text-figs.

—— 1931. Report of the Biological Survey of Mutsu Bay. 20. Echiuroidea. *Sci. Rep. Tohoku Univ.* ser. 4, **6** : 171–184, 4 figs.

—— 1934a. On the sipunculids and echiurids of Onomichi Bay, Japan (in Japanese, English summary). *Zool. Mag. Tokyo* **46** : 245–252, 9 figs.

—— 1934b. Report on the Sipunculoidea, Echiuroidea and Priapuloidea collected by the Soyo-Maru Expedition. 1922–1930. *Sci. Rep. Tohoku Univ.* ser. 4, **9** : 1–32, 31 figs, 1 pl.

—— 1935a. *Parabonellia misakiensis* (Ikeda) found in the vicinity of the Shimoda marine biological station. *Annotnes zool. jap.* **15** : 142–144, 2 figs.

—— 1935b. Sipunculoidea and Echiuroidea of the West Caroline Islands. *Sci. Rep. Tohoku Univ.* ser. 4, **10** : 299–329, pls 2–4.

—— 1937a. Echiuroidea, Sipunculoidea and Priapuloidea obtained in North-West Honshu. *Res. Bull. Saito-Ho-on Kai Mus. (Zool.)* **12** : 137–176, 3 pls, 14 figs.

—— 1937b. Note on a new sipunculid, *Physcosoma kurilensis* n. sp. found in Shumshir Island. *Annotnes Zool. Jap.* **16** : 117–120, 4 figs.

—— 1937c. Raporto pri la Echiuroidea, Sipunculoidea kaj Priapuloidea en la Golfo de Onawaga. *Botany & Zoology, Tokyo* **5** : 1855–1859, 17 figs (in Japanese).

—— 1939. Studies on the Echiuroidea, Sipunculoidea and Priapuloidea of Japan. *Sci. Rep. Tohoku Univ.* ser. 4, **14** : 339–460, pls 19–23, 60 text-figs.

Sauvage. 1889. Contribution à la connaissance de la faune du Pas-de-Calais et des parties voisines de la Mer du Nord et de la Manche. *Bull. scient. Fr. Belg.* **20** : 104–119.

Schenck, S. L. 1875. Der grüne Färbestoff von *Bonellia viridis*. *Sber. Akad. Wiss. Wien.* **7** : 1–5.

Schindewolf, O. H. 1959. Würmer und Korallen als Synoken. Zur Kenntnis der Systeme *Aspidosiphon-Heteropsammaria* und *Hicetes-Pleurodictyum*. *Abh. math. naturw. Kl. Akad. Wiss. Mainz* **1959** : 259–328, 14 pls, 3 figs.

Schleip, W. 1934a. Die Regeneration des Rüssels von *Phascolion strombi* (Mont.) (Sipun-culidae). *Z. wiss. Zool.* **145** : 462–469, 15 figs.

—— 1934b. Die Regenerationsstrang bei *Phaccolosoma minutum* (Kef.) (Sipunculidae). *Z. wiss. Zool.* **146** : 104–122, 11 figs.

—— 1935. Die Reparationsvorgänge nach Amputation des Hinterendes von *Phascolosoma minutum* (Kef.) (Sipunculidae). *Z. wiss. Zool.* **147** : 59–76, 11 figs.

Schmarda, L. K. 1852. Zur Naturgeschichte der Adria. *Bonellia viridis*. *Denkschr. Akad. Wiss. Wien.* **4** : 117–126.

Schmidt, O. 1854. Über Sipunculiden. *Z. ges. Naturw. Halle* **3** : 5, pls 1–2, fig. 3.

—— 1865. Über den Bau un die systematische Stellung von *Aspidosiphon muelleri* Dies. (*Lesinia farcimen* Schmidt). *Mitt. naturw. Ver. Steirm.* **3** : 56–66, 1 pl.

Schmitt, J. 1904. *Monographie de l'Isle d'Anticosti*. These. Facult. Sci. Paris, Sorbonne.

Schneider, A. 1864. Über die Muskeln der Wurmer und ihre Bedeutung für das System. *Arch. anat. physiol.* **1864** : 590–597.

SCHNEIDER, R. 1912. Die neuerster Beobachtungen über natürlicher Eisenresorption in thierischen Zellkern und einige characteristiche Falle der Eisen verwerthung im Körper von Gephyreen. *Int. Stat. Neapel* **12** : 207–216.

SCHWARZE, W. 1903. Symbiosis between crabs, nereids and sipunculids. *Zool. Zentbl.* Summary, **9** : 331–334.

SCOTT, K. M. F., HARRISON, A. D. & MACNAE, W. 1952. The ecology of South African Estuaries. Pt. 2. The Klein River Estuary, Hermanus, Cape. *Trans. R. Soc. S. Afr.* **33** : 283–331.

SEDGWICK, A. 1898. A student's textbook of Zoology. **1.** Swan Sonnenschein, London.

SEILER, J. 1927. Das Problem der Geschlechtsbestimmung bei *Bonellia*. *Naturwissenschaften* **15** (2) : 33–43, 5 figs.

SEITZ, P. 1907. Der Bau von *Echiurus chilensis* (*Urechis* n. gen.). *Zool. Jb. Anat.* **24** : 323–356, 3 pls.

SELENKA, E. 1875. Eifurchung und Larvenbildung von *Phascolosoma elongatum* Kef. *Z. wiss. Zool.* **25** : 442–450, pls 29–30. Abstract *Arch. Zool. exper.* **4** : 55–58.

—— 1878. Das Männchen der *Bonellia*. *Zool. Anz.* **1** : 120–121.

—— 1885. Report of the Gephyrea collected by H.M.S. 'Challenger' during the years 1873–1876. *Rep. Scient. Res. Challenger* **13** (36) : 1–25, 4 pls.

—— 1888. On the Gephyrea of the Mergui Archipelago collected for the Trustees of the Indian Museum. *J. Linn. Soc.* (*Zool.*) **21** : 220–222.

—— 1897. Die Sipunculiden. Gattung *Phymosoma*. *Zool. Anz.* **20** : 460.

SELENKA, E., MAN, J. G. DE & BÜLOW, C. 1883. Die Sipunculiden. Reisen im Archipel Phillippinen von Dr. C. Semper. Leipzig and Wiesbaden, pt. 2, **4** (1) : 1–133, 14 pls.

SELENSKY, W. 1876. Über die Metamorphose des *Echiurus*. *Morph. Jb.* **2** : 319–327, pl. 22.

—— 1905a. Über den Bau des Prototrochs der *Echiurus*-larven. *C.R. Congr. inter. Zool.* **6** : 338–342.

—— 1905b. Über die Bildung des Mesoblasts bei den *Echiurus*-larven. *Int. Congr. Zool.* **6** : 377–381.

—— 1905c. Morphogenetische Studien au Wurmer. I. Über den Bau der *Echiurus*-larven. *Zap. imp. Acad. Nauk. phys.-math.* ser. 8, **16** (1) : 1–102, 10 pls.

—— 1907a. Über die sogenannten Urner der Sipunculiden. *Trudy imp. S. Peterb. Obshch. Estest.* **38** : 235–237 (in Russian).

—— 1907b. Über den Bau und die Entwicklung der sogenannten Urnen der Sipunculiden. *Zool. Anz.* **32** : 329–336.

—— 1908a. Über die Metamorphose des *Echiurus*. *Irv. imp. Acad. Nauk.* ser. 6, **2** : 307–328, 363–380.

—— 1908b. Untersuchungen über die sogenannten Urnen der Sipunculiden. *Z. wiss. Zool.* **90** : 436–595, 4 pls.

SENNA, A. 1906. Raccolte planktonische fatte della R. nave Liguria nel viaggio di circumnavigazione, 1903–1905. 1. Sulla struttura di alcune larve (Pelagosphaera) di Sipunculidi. *Pubbl. Ist. Studi sup. prat. Firenze, Seg. Sci.* 50–78, 2 pl.

—— 1908. Su una larva di Echiurus (*Echiurus abyssalis*) del plancton di Messina. *Monittore zool. ital.* **19** : 38–44, 2 text-figs.

SERENI, G. 1926. Le ossidasi del *Sipunculus*. *Pubbl. Stn. Zool. Napoli* **7** : 459–478.

SETNA, S. B. 1931. On three new gregarines, *Bhatiella marphysae*, n. gen. and sp., *Ferraria cornucephali* n. gen. and sp., *Extremocytes dendrostomi* n. gen. and sp. from Indian polychaetes. *Rec. Indian Mus.* **33** : 203–210, 2 pls.

SHARP, E. 1908. The echinoderms of Guernsey. *Rep. Trans. Guernsey Soc. nat. Sc.* **5** : 329–332.

SHERBORN, C. D. 1930. *Index animalium* **23** : 5826–5827.

SHIPLEY, A. E. 1890. On *Phymosoma varians*. *Q. Jl. microsc. Sci.* **31** : 1–27, pls 1–4.

—— 1891. On a new species of *Phymosoma*, with a synopsis of the genus and some account of its geographical distribution. *Q. Jl. microsc. Sci.* **32** : 111–126, pl. 11.

—— 1892a. On *Onchnesoma steenstrupi*. *Q. Jl. microsc. Sci.* **34** : 233–250, pl. 9.

SHIPLEY, A. E. 1892b. A new species of *Phymosoma*. *Proc. Camb. phil. Soc. biol. Sci.* **7** : 77–78.

—— 1893. Notes on the genus *Sipunculus*. *Proc. zool. Soc. Lond.* **1893** : 326–333, pls 25–27.

—— 1896. Gephyrea and *Phoronis*. [In] Harmer & Shipley, *Cambridge Natural History* **2** : 409–462.

—— 1898. Report on the gephyrean worms collected by Mr. Stanley Gardiner at Rotuma and Funafuti. *Proc. zool. Soc. Lond.* **1898** : 468–473, pl. 37, figs 1–12.

—— 1899a. A report on the Sipunculoidea collected by Dr. Willey at the Loyalty Islands and in New Britain. [In] A. Willey, *Zool. Res.* **2** : 151–160, pl. 18.

—— 1899b. Notes on a collection of echiurids from the Loyalty Islands, New Britain and China Straits, with an attempt to revise the group and to determine its geographical range. [In] A. Willey, *Zool. Res.* **3** : 335–356, pl. 33.

—— 1899c. Notes on a collection of gephyrean worms found at Christmas Island, Indian Ocean, by Mr. C. W. Andrews. *Pric. zool. Soc. Lond.* **1899** : 54–57.

—— 1899d. A list of the gephyrean worms of Funafuti. *Rep. Aust. Mus. Memoir* **3** : 531.

—— 1901. The abyssal fauna of the Antarctic region. *Antarctic Manual* Chap. 18, pp. 241–275.

—— 1902a. 13. Gephyrea. *Rep. Coll. nat. hist. Southern Cross Exped.* London, 284–285.

—— 1902b. Sipunculoidea, general anatomy. *Encyclopedia Britannica* suppl. London **32** : 636–638, 4 figs.

—— 1902c. Echiuroidea. [In] Gardiner, J. S., *Fauna and Geography of the Maldive and Laccadive Archipelagoes* **1** : 127–130, pl. 6.

—— 1902d. Sipunculoidea, with an account of a new genus *Lithacrosiphon*. [In] Gardiner, J.S., *Fauna and Geography of the Maldive and Laccadive Archipelagoes*. **1** : 131–140. pl. 7.

—— 1903. Report on the Gephyrea collected by Prof. Herdman at Ceylon in 1902. *Herdman Rep. Pearl Oyster Fishery* **1** (3) suppl. : 169–176, 1 pl., figs 4–10.

—— 1910. Gephyrea. [In] Harmer & Shipley, *Cambridge Natural History* (2nd ed.) **2** : 411–449.

SHITAMORI, K. 1936. Histology of the integument of *Siphonosoma cumanense* (Kef.). *J. Sci. Hiroshima Univ.* ser. B, **4** : 155–175, 2 pls, 3 figs.

SILVA, F. B. D. DE. 1934. Geschlectsbepaling bij *Bonellia* volgens de onderzoekingen van F. Baltzer. *Vakbl. Biol.* **15** : 221–228.

SKORIKOW, A. C. 1901a. Über die Gattung *Hamingia* Kor. & Dan. (Bonellidae). *Zool. Anz.* **24** : 158–160.

—— 1902. Gephyrea aus der zoologischen Ausbeute der Eisbrechers 'Ermak' im Sommer 1901. *Ezheg. zool. Muz.* **7** : 274–279, 1 chart.

—— 1906. Eine neue *Echiurus*-species aus dem Mittelmeer. *Zool. Anz.* **29** : 217–221.

—— 1909. *Echiurini* sousfamille nouveau des gephyrea armata. *Ezheg. zool. Muz.* **14** : 77–102, pl. 1 (in Russian).

—— 1910. Die Polychaeten und Gephyreen der Ostsee. *Ezheg. zool. Muz.* **15** : 207–236, 6 figs, 2 charts.

SLUITER, G. P. 1882a. Beiträge zur der Kenntnis der Gephyreen aus dem Malayischen Archipel. *Naturrk. Tijdschr. Ned. Indie* **41** : 84–110, pls 1–2, 148–150, pls 1–2.

—— 1882b. Notiz über die Segmental-Organe und Geschlechtsdrüsen einiger tropischer Sipunculiden. *Tijdschr. Ned. Dierk. Vereen* **6** : 1–20, pl. 1.

—— 1883a. Über einige Sternwürmer des indischen Archipels. *Zool. Anz.* **6** : 222–228.

—— 1883b. Über die Segmentalorgane und Geschlechts-drüsen einiger Sipunculiden des Malayischen Archipels. *Zool. Anz.* **6** : 523–527.

—— 1884. Beiträge zu der Kenntnis der Gephyreen aus dem Malayischen Archipel. *Natuurk. Tijdschr. Ned. Indie* **43** : 26–88, pls 1–3.

—— 1886. Beiträge zur der Kenntnis der Gephyreen aus dem Malayischen Archipel. *Natuurk. Tijdschr. Ned. Indie* **45** : 472–517, pls 1–4.

—— 1889. Über zwei merkwürdige Gephyreen aus des Bai von Batavia. *Natuurk. Tijdschr. Ned. Indie* **48** : 244–248, pl. 3.

SLUITER, G. P. 1891. Die Evertebraten aus der Sammlung des königlichen natuurwissen-schlaftlichen Vereins in Niederländisch Indien in Batavia. Zugleich eine Skisse der Fauna des Java-Meeres mit Beschreibung der neuen Arten. *Natuurk. Tijdschr. Ned. Indie* **50** : 102–123, 2 pls.

—— 1898. Gephyreen von Süd-Africa, nebst Bermerkungen über *Sipunculus indicus*. Beitr. zur Kenntnis der Fauna Süd-Africa. 3. Ergebn. einer Reise von Prof. Max Weber im Jahre 1894. *Zool. Jb. Syst.* **11** : 422–450, 2 figs.

—— 1900. Géphyriens (sipunculides et echiurides) provenant des campagnes de l'Hirondelle et de la Princesse Alice. 1886–1887. *Result. Camp. scient. Prince Albert I* **15** : 1–30, 3 pls.

—— 1902. Die Sipunculiden und Echiuriden der Siboga-Expedition, nebst Zusammenstellung der Überdies aus den indischen Archipel bekannten Arten. *Siboga-Expedition.* Monographie **25** : 1–53, 4 pls. Leiden. Ed. Dr. Max Weber.

—— 1912. Géphyriens (Sipunculides et Echiurides) provenant des campagnes de la Princesse Alice. 1898–1910. *Result. Camp. scient. Prince Albert I* **36** : 1–36, pl. 1, figs 1–21.

SORBY, H. C. 1875. On the colouring matter of *Bonellia viridis*. *Q. Jl. microsc. Sci.* **15** : 166–172.

SOUTHERN, R. 1908. A new Irish gephyrean. *Ir. Nat.* **17** : 83–86.

—— 1913a. Oligochaeta, Gephyrea, Hirundinea of Clare Island. *Proc. R. Ir. Acad.* **31**, pts. 48–50 : 1–14.

—— 1913b. Gephyrea of the coasts of Ireland. *Scient. Invest. Fish. Brch. Ire.* **1912** (3) : 1–46, 7 pls.

SPENGEL, J. W. 1879a. Beiträge zur Kenntnis der Gephyreen. I. Die Eibildung, die Entwicklung und das Männchen der *Bonellia*. *Mitt. zool. Stn. Neapel* **1** : 357–420, pls 8–12.

—— 1879b. Über die Organization des *Echiurus pallasii*. *Zool. Anz.* **2** : 542–547.

—— 1880. Beiträge zur Kenntnis der Gephyreen. II. Die Organization des *Echiurus pallasii*. *Z. wiss. Zool.* **34** : 460–534, 2 pls.

—— 1898. Der Name *Physcosoma*. *Zool. Anz.* **21** : 50.

—— 1907. Eine verkannte *Sipunculus*-larve. *Zool. Anz.* **31** : 97–99, 232.

—— 1912a. Einige Organisationverhältnisse von *Sipunculus*-arten und die Bedeutung für die Systematik dieser Thiere. *Verh. dt. zool. Ges.* **22** : 261–272.

—— 1912b. Über den Hautmuskelschlauch gewisser *Thalassema*-arten und seine Bedeutung für die Systematik dieser Thiere. *Verh. dtsch. zool. Ges.* **22** : 309–317.

—— 1912c. Beiträge zur Kenntnis der Gephyreen. III. Zum Bau des Kopflappens der armaten Gephyreen. *Z. wiss. Zool.* **101**: 342–385, 4 pls.

—— 1912d. Beiträge zur Kenntnis der Gephyreen. IV. Revision der Gattung *Echiurus*. *Zool. Jb. Syst.* **33** : 173–212, 1 pl.

—— 1913a. Zur Organisation und Systematik der Gattung *Sipunculus*. *Verh. dt. zool. Ges.* **23** : 68–78.

—— 1913b. Sipunculoidea. *Handbuch der Naturwissenschaften.* **9** : 97–106, 14 text-figs.

STEHLE, G. 1952. Differenzierungen des Verdauungstraktus von *Phascolosoma elongatum* Kef. (Vorläufige mitteilung). *Annls. Univ. Sarav.* **1** : 309–314, 5 figs.

—— 1953. Anatomie und Histologie von *Phascolosoma elongatum* Kef. *Annls. Univ. Sarav.* **2** : 204–256, 52 figs.

—— 1954. Die gewebezerstorende Wirkung von Cercarien in Rüssel und Gehirn verschiedenen Sipunculiden. *Z. Parasit.* **16** : 253–362, 5 figs.

STEINBECK, Q. & RICKETTS, E. F. 1941. Sipunculids : 112, 154, 155, 201, 206, 272; Echiurids : 120, 226, 239. *The Sea of Cortez.* New York : 1–598, 40 pls.

STEPHEN, A. C. 1929. A sipunculid worm (*Physcosoma granulatum*) new to the Scottish fauna. *Scott. Nat.* **1929** : 59–60.

—— 1931. A new sipunculid worm (*Phascolosoma cluthensis* sp. nov.) from the Firth of Clyde. *Scott. Nat.* **1931** : 59–61, 2 figs.

—— 1934. The Echiuridae, Sipunculidae and Priapulidae of Scottish and adjacent waters. *Proc. R. phys. Soc. Edinb.* **22** : 159–186.

STEPHEN, A. C.   1940.   On a sipunculid from the Congo coast.   *Revue Zool. Bot. Afr.* **33** : 124.
——— 1941a.   Sipunculids and echiurids of the Sir John Murray Expedition to the Red Sea and Indian Ocean.   1933–1934.   *Scient. Rep. John Murray Ezped.* **7** : 401–409, 2 pls.
——— 1941b.   The Echiuridae, Sipunculidae and Priapulidae collected by the ships of the Discovery Committee during the years 1926–1937.   *Discovery Rep.* **21** : 235–260, pls 7, 8.
——— 1942.   The South African intertidal zone and its relation to ocean currents.   Notes on the intertidal sipunculids of Cape Province and Natal.   *Ann. Natal Mus.* **10** : 245–256, pl. 11.
——— 1948.   Sipunculids.   *Rep. B.A.N.Z. Antarct. Res. Exped.* 1929–1931, ser. 5B, **4** : 213–220.
——— 1952.   The 'Manihine' Expedition to the Gulf of Aquaba.   5.   Gephyrea.   *Bull. Brit. Mus. (nat. Hist.) Zool.* **1** : 181–182.
——— 1956.   *Amalosoma eddystonense* sp. n. a new species of Bonellidae.   *J. mar. biol. Ass. U.K.* **35** : 605–608.
——— 1958.   The sipunculids of Haifa Bay and neighbourhood.   *Bull. res. Coun. Israel* **7B** (3–4) : 129–136.
——— 1960a.   Echiuroidea and Sipunculoidea from Senegal, West Africa.   *Bull. Inst. fr. Afr. Noire* **22**, ser. A (2) : 512–520.
——— 1960b.   British echiuroids, sipunculoids and priapulids with keys and notes for the identification of species.   *Linnean Soc. Lond.*, Synopsis of British Fauna **12** : 1–27, 7 figs.
——— 1961.   Sponge growing on a sipunculid.   *Scott. Nat.* **70** : 79.
——— 1965.   A revision of the phylum Sipuncula.   *Ann. Mag. nat. Hist.* ser. 13, **7** : 457–462.
——— 1966.   A collection of Sipuncula taken on the summit of the Vema sea mountain, South Atlantic Ocean.   *Ann. Mag. nat. Hist.* ser. 13, **9** : 145–148.
STEPHEN, A. C. & CUTLER, E. B.   1968.   On a collection of Sipuncula, Echiura and Priapulida from South African waters.   *Trans. roy. Soc. S. Afr.* **38** (2) : 111–121, 1 fig.
STEPHEN, A. C. & ROBERTSON, J.   1952.   A preliminary report on the Echiuridae and Sipunculidae of Zanzibar.   *Proc. R. Soc. Edinb.* **64**, sect. B (22) : 426–444, 1 pl.
STEPHENSON, T. A., STEPHENSON, A., TANDY, G. & SPENCER, M.   1931.   The structure and ecology of Low Island and other reefs.   Great Barrier Reef Exped.   1928–1929.   *Scient. Rep. Gt. Barrier Reef Exped.* **3** : 17–112.
STEUER, A.   1936.   Sipunculidea, Phoronidea, Brachiopoda, Enteropneusta und Acrania von Alexandrien in Ägypten.   *Not. Inst. Biol. Rovigno* **23** : 1–18, 4 figs.
——— 1939.   The fishing grounds near Alexandria.   18.   Sipunculoidea etc.   *Notes Mem. Fish. Res. Dir. Cairo* **30**.
STEVENS, J. L.   1952.   The structure and function of the body-wall of *Phascolosoma minutum* Kef.   *Rep. Challenger Soc.* **3** : 13 abstract.
STEWART, F. H.   1900.   Note on a variation in the number of genital pouches in *Thalassema neptuni* Gaertner.   *Ann. Mag. nat. Hist.* ser. 7, **6** : 218–219.
——— 1909a.   *Investigator sicarius*, a Gephyrean worm hitherto undescribed, the type of a new Order.   *Mem. Indian Mus.* **1** : 283–293, pl. 21, figs 1–9.
——— 1909b.   The generic name '*Investigator*', a correction.   *Rec. Indian Mus.* **3** : 183.
STIASNY, G.   1930.   Verzeichnis der Echiuridae, Sipunculidae und Priapulidae des naturhistorischen Reichsmuseum in Leiden.   *Zool. Meded. Leiden* **13** : 204–223, 4 figs.
STIMPSON, W.   1854.   Marine invertebrates of Grand Manan.   *Smithson. Contr. Knowl.* **6** : 5–76, pls 1–3.
——— 1855.   Descriptions of some new marine invertebrates from the Chinese and Japanese seas.   Gephyrea.   *Proc. Acad. nat. Sci. Philad.* **7** : 390–391.
——— 1864.   Descriptions of some new species of marine invertebrates from Puget Sound.   *Proc. Acad. nat. Sci. Philad.* **16** : 159.
STOSSICH, M.   1882.   Prospetto del la faunal del mare Adriatico.   *Bull. Soc. Adriat. Sci. nat.* **7** : 168, 2 figs.
STUDER, TH.   1879.   Die fauna von Kerguelensland.   *Arch. Naturgesch* **45** : 104–141.
TÉTRY, A.   1959.   Classe des sipunculiens.   [In] Grassé, *Traité de Zoologie* **5** (1) : 785–854 1068–1081, pl. 4 col., text-figs 575–673, 9–16 suppl.

TEUSCHER, R. 1874. Notiz über *Sipunculus* und *Phascolosoma*. *Jena Z. Naturw.* **8** : 488–489, pl. 19.

THÉEL, H. 1875a. Recherches sur le *Phascolion* (*Phascolosoma*) *strombi* (Mont.). *Bih. K. svensk. Vetensk. Akad. Handl.* **3** (3) : 1–7.

—— 1875b. Études sur les géphyriens inermes des mers de la Scandinavie, du Spitzberg et du Groenland. *Bih. K. svenska Vetensk. Akad. Handl.* 3 (6) : 1–30, pls 1–4.

—— 1905. Northern and arctic invertebrates in the collection of the Swedish State Museum. Sipunculids. *K. svenska Vetensk. Akad. Handl.* **39** : 1–130, pls 1–15.

—— 1906. Northern and arctic invertebrates in the collection of the Swedish State Museum. Priapulids. Echiurids etc. *K. svenska Vetensk. Akad. Handl.* **40** : 1–26, pls 1–2.

—— 1911. Priapulids and sipunculids dredged by the Swedish antarctic Expedition 1901–1903, and the phenomenon of bi-polarity. *K. svenska Vetensk. Akad. Handl.* **47** : 1–36, pls 1–5, 8 figs.

THOMAS, I. A. 1931. Recherches sur les vésicules énigmatiques et des urnes du Siponcle. La reproduction par bourgeonnement. *C. r. hebd. Séanc. Acad. Sci. Paris* **193** : 1462–1465, 8 figs.

—— 1932. Recherches cytologiques et expérimentales sur les vésicules énigmatiques et les urnes du Siponcle. *Arch. Zool. exp. gén.* **73** : 22–40.

THOMPSON, W. 1840. On the Mollusca of Ireland. *Ann. Mag. nat. Hist.* **5** : 101.

THORSON, G. 1957. Parasitism in the sipunculid *Golfingia procerum* (Möbius). *J. Fac. Sci, Hokkaido Univ.* ser. 6, **13** : 128–132, 1 fig.

THURSTON. 1895. Ramesvarn Island and the fauna of the Gulf of Manaar. *Madras Gov. Mus. Bull.* **3** : 79–138.

TOKIOKA, T. 1953. Invertebrate fauna of the intertidal zone of the Tokara Islands. iii. *Echiuroidea* and *Sipunculoidea*. *Publs. Seto mar. Biol. Lab.* ser. 3, **2** : 140.

TORREY, J. C. 1902a. The early development of the mesoblast in *Thalassema*. *Anat. Anz.* **21** : 247–256, 3 text-figs. Also *J.R. micr. Soc.* **1902** : 557.

—— 1902b. The cell-lineage of the mesoblast-bands and mesenchyme in *Thalassema*. *Science N.Y.* n.s. **15** : 576–577.

—— 1902c. Eggs of *Thalassema* from Beaufort N.C. *Ann. N.Y. Acad. Sci.* **14** : 137.

TOWLE, A. & GIESE, A. C. 1966. Biological changes during reproduction and starvation in the sipunculid worm, *Phascolosoma agassizii*. *Comp. Bioch. Physiol.* **19** : 667–680.

—— 1967. The annual reproductive cycle of the sipunculid *Phascolosoma agassizii*. *Physiol. Zool.* **40** : 229–237, 2 tables, 1 fig.

TURTON, W. 1807. *The British Fauna*. Pp. 118–128. Swansea.

TUZETTE, ODETTE. 1932. Survive des trompes de *Bonellia* separées du corps. *Bull. Soc. zool. Fr.* **57** : 401–408, 4 figs.

TYLER, A. 1931a. The production of normal embryos by artificial parthenogenesis in the Echiuroid *Urechis*. *Biol. Bull. mar. biol. Lab., Wood's Hole* **60** : 187–211, 38 figs, 2 pls.

—— 1931b. The relation between cleavage and total activation in artificially activated eggs of *Urechis*. *Biol. Bull. mar. biol. Lab., Wood's Hole* **61** : 45–72, 9 figs.

—— 1932a. The polarity of the eggs of *Urechis caupo*. *Biol. Bull. mar. biol. Lab., Wood's Hole* **63** : 145–148.

—— 1932b. Changes in the volume and surface of *Urechis* eggs upon fertilisation. *J. exp. Zool.* **63** : 155–173, 2 pls.

—— 1932c. The polarity of the eggs of *Urechis caupo*. *Biol. Bull. mar. biol. Lab., Wood's Hole* **63** : 145–148.

—— 1932d. Chromosomes of artificially activated eggs of *Urechis*. *Biol. Bull. mar. biol Lab., Wood's Hole* **63** : 212–217.

—— 1965. The biology and chemistry of fertilization. *Amer. Nat.* **99** : 309–334.

TYLER, A. & DESSEL, F. W. 1939. Increasing the life-span of unfertilised *Urechis* eggs by acid. *J. exp. Zool.* **81** : 459–472, 1 fig.

HH

TYLER, A. & HOROWITZ, N. H. 1938. On the energetics of differentiation. 7. Comparison of the respiratory rates of parthenogenetic and fertilised eggs of *Urechis*. *Biol. Bull. mar. biol. Lab., Wood's Hole* **74** : 99–107, 1 fig.

TYLER, A. & SCHULTZ, J. 1932. Inhibition and reversal of fertilisation in eggs of the echiuroid worm, *Urechis caupo*. *J. exp. Zool.* **63** : 509–532, 1 pl.

UEXKÜLL, J. VON Y. 1896. Zur Muskel und Nervenphysiologie von *Sipunculus nudus*. *Z. Biol.* ser. 9, **15** (2) : 1.

—— 1903. Tonusstudien. I. Die biologische Bauplan von *Sipunculus nudus*. *Z. Biol.* **44** : 269–344, 1 pl., 28 text-figs.

VALENCIENNES, A. 1854. Remarques sur la mémoire de M. Euguene Robert. *C. r. hebd. Séanc. Acad. Sci., Paris* **39** : 640–643.

VEJDOVSKY, F. 1878. Über die Eibildung und di Männchen von *Bonellia viridis* Rol. *Z. wiss. Zool.* **30** : 487–500, pl. 30, text-figs A, B. Reviews, *Rev. Int.* **1** : 722–727. *Arch. Z. exper.* **6** : 3, pl. 46.

VERRILL, A. E. 1873a. Results of recent dredging expeditions on the coast of New England. *Am. J. Sci.* ser. 3, **5** : 98–106.

—— 1873b. Report upon the invertebrate animals of Vineyard Sound and adjacent waters, etc. *Rep. U.S. Commnr. Fish.* **1872** : 295–778, pls 1–38.

—— 1874. Explorations of Casco Bay by the U.S.F.C. in 1873. *Proc. Amer. Ass. Av. Sci.* **22** : 340–393, pls 1–6.

—— 1879a. Notice of recent additions to the marine invertebrates of north-eastern America. *Proc. U.S. natn. Mus.* **2** : 163–205.

—— 1879b. Annelids, in L. Kumlien, Contributions to the Natural History of Arctic America. *Bull. U.S. natn. Mus.* **15** : 141–143.

—— 1885. Results of the explorations made by the steamer 'Albatross' off the northern coast of the U.S. in 1883. *Rep. U.S. Comm. Fish.* **1883** : 503–727, pls 1–44.

—— 1900. Additions to the Turbellaria, Nematoda and Annelida of the Bermudas, with revision of some New England genera and species. *Trans. Conn. Acad. Arts. Sci.* **10** : 595–671, pl. 70, 2 text-figs.

—— 1904. Additions to the fauna of the Bermudas from the Yale Expedition of 1901 with notes on other species. *Trans. Conn. Acad. Arts. Sci.*, **11** : 15-62, pls 1–11.

VIGNAL, W. 1887. Sur les éléments du liquide de la cavité générale des Siponcles (*Sipunculus nudus*). *C. r. Ass. fr. Avanc. Sci.* **1886** (2) : 592–593.

VOGT, C. 1876. Sur les loxosome des phascolosomes. *Arch. Zool. exp. gén.* **5** : 304–356. pls 11–14.

VOGT, K. & YOUNG, E. 1888. Vermes. *Anatomie comparée* **1** : 200–213.

VOLONSKY, M. 1933. Digestion intracellulaire et accumulation des colerants acides. Étude cytologique des cellules sanguines des Sipunculides. *Bull. Biol. Fr. Belg.* **67** : 135–275, 6 pls, 2 text-figs.

VOLONSKY, M. & MARCOU, J. 1933. Les lignes leucocytaires des sipunculides. *Archs. Anat. microsc.* **29** : 245–260.

WAHL, B. 1910. Das Genus *Collastoma*. *Sber. Akad. Wiss. Wien.* Abt. 1, **119** : 363–391.

WALCOTT, C. D. 1911. Middle Cambrian annelids. *Smithson misc. Coll.* **57** : 109–144.

—— 1931. Addenda to descriptions of Burgess Shale fossils. *Smithson. misc. Coll.* **85** (3117) : 1–46, 23 pls.

WARD, H. B. 1891. On some points in the anatomy and histology of *Sipunculus nudus*. *Bull. Mus. comp. Zool. Harv.* **21** : 143–182, pls 1–3.

WATIER, A. 1932. Une curieuse anomalie chez *Phascolosoma vulgare*. *Bull. Soc. Étude Sci. Reims* n.s. **9** : 19–20.

WEGENER, FR. 1938. Beiträge zur Kenntnis der Rüsselregeneration der Sipunculiden. *Z. wiss. Zool.* **150** : 527–565, 29 figs.

WESENBERG-LUND, E. 1925. Gephyreer. *Meddr. Gronland* **23** : 81–91 (suppl.).

—— 1928. Gephyrea and *Sternapsis*. *Zoology Faroes* (**20**) : 1–5.

WESENBERG-LUND, E. 1929. Some anatomical features subject to variation in *Phascolion strombi* Mont. *Vidensk. Meddr. dansk. naturh. Foren* **88** : 155–164, 5 figs.

—— 1930. *Priapulidae* and *Sipunculidae*. *Dan. Ingolf Exped.* Kbh. **4**, pt. 7 : 1–44, 6 pls.

—— 1932. The Godthaab Expedition 1928. Gephyrea. *Meddr. Gronland* **79**, pt. 3, : 1–18, 7 figs.

—— 1933. The collection of gephyreans in the Royal Museum of Natural History, Belgium. *Bull. Mus. r. Hist. nat. Belg.* **9** (6) : 1–16, 4 pls, 3 figs.

—— 1934. Gephyreans and Annelids. The Scoresby Sound Committee's 2nd East Greenland Expedition in 1932 to King Christian 9th's Land. *Meddr. Gronland* **104** (14) : 1–38, 9 figs.

—— 1937a. Gephyreans. The zoology of east Greenland. *Meddr. Gronland* **121** (1) : 1–25, 7 figs.

—— 1937b. Gephyrea. *Zoology Iceland* **2** (23) : 1–16, 3 text-figs.

—— 1937c. Gephyrea. *Bull. Mus. r. Hist. nat. Belg.* **13** (36) : 1–23, 10 figs.

—— 1939a. Polseorme (Gephyrea). Sipunculider, Priapulider, Echiurider. *Dan. Fauna.* **45** : 1–60, 31 figs.

—— 1939b. Norwegian gephyrea from the collections of the Zoological Museum of Trondheim. *K. norske Vidensk. Selsk. Skr.* **11** : 26–29.

—— 1939c. Gephyreans from Swedish waters in the Museum of Natural History, Gotenburg. *Goteborg K. Vetensk.-o Vitterh-Samb. Handl.* ser B, **6** : 1–35, 1 map.

—— 1939d. Echiurids collected in French Indo-China by Mr. C. Dawydoff. *Arch. Zool. exp. gén. Notes et Revue* **81** : 45–53, 6 figs.

—— 1939e. Polychètes et géphyriens de Tunise. *Bull. Stn. Océanogr. Salammbô* **39** : 1–20.

—— 1954a. *Priapuloidea, Sipunculoidea* and *Echiuroidea*. *Bull. Inst. r. Sci. nat. Belg.* **30** (16) : 1–18, 1 pl., 3 text-figs.

—— 1954b. Sipunculids and echiurids collected by G. Ransom in Oceanea in 1952. *Bull. Mus. natn. Hist. nat. Paris* ser. 2, **26** : 376–384, 6 figs.

—— 1955a. Sipunculidae. *Rep. swed. deep-sea exped. Zool.* **2** : 197–201, 1 fig.

—— 1955b. Gephyrea from Chile. Repts. Lund Univ. Chile Expedition. *Acta Univ. Lund.* n. ser. 5, **10** (51) : 1–24, 4 charts.

—— 1957a. Sipunculoidea from the coast of Israel. *Bull. Res. Coun. Israel* **6B** : 193–200. 3 figs.

—— 1957b. Sipunculoidea and Echiuroidea from the Red Sea. *Bull. Sea Fish. Res. Stn. Israel* **14** (3) : 1–15.

—— 1957c. Sipunculoidea and Echiuroidea from West Africa, together with a bibliography on gephyrea after 1920. *Bull. Inst. r. Sci. Nat. Belg.* **33** (42) : 1–24.

—— 1959a. Sipunculoidea and Echiuroidea from tropical West Africa. *Atlantide Rep.* **5** : 177–210, 16 figs.

—— 1959b. *Sipunculoidea* and *Echiuroidea* from Mauritius. *Vidensk. Meddr. dansk. naturh. Foren.* **121** : 53–73, 6 figs.

—— 1959c. Campagne 1956 de la 'Calypso' dans le Golfe de Guinée et aux Iles Principes Sao Tome et Annobon. *Sipunculoidea & Echiuroidea*. *Annls. Inst. océanogr. Monaco* N.S., **37** : 207–217.

—— 1963. South African sipunculids and echiurids from coastal waters. *Vidensk. Meddr. dansk. naturh. Foren.* **125** : 101–146, text-figs 1–12.

WHARTON, L. D. 1913. A description of some Philippine *Thalassemae* with a revision of the genus. *Philipp. J. Sci.* **8** : 243–270, 2 pls.

WHEELER, M. B. 1938. The Sir Joseph Banks Islands. Reports of the expedition of the McCoy Society for field investigations and research. *Proc. R. Soc. Vict.*, (1) **50** : 345.

WHITELEGGE, T. & HILL, J. P. 1899a. The Hydrozoa, Scyphozoa, Actinozoa and Vermes of Funafuti. *Mem. Aust. Mus.* (7) Vermes **3** : 371–394, pls 23–27.

—— 1899b. List of the marine and freshwater invertebrate fauna of Port Jackson and neighbourhood. *J. Proc. R. Soc. N.S.W.* **23** : 163–323.

WILLEMOES-SUHM, R. V. & SIEBOLD, C. T. V.   1876.   Briefe Von der Challenger-Expedition. *Z. wiss. Zool.* **27** : 97–98.

WILSON, C. B.   1890.   Our North American echiurids.   A contribution to the habits and geographical range of the group.   *Biol. Bull. mar. biol. Lab., Wood's Hole* **1** : 163–178, 5 figs.

WILCZYNSKI, J.   1914.   Über die Excretionsvorgange bei den Männchen von *Bonellia viridis*. Rol.   Note préliminaire.   *Bull. int. Acad. Pol. Sci. Lett. Cl. Sci. Math. Nat.* **1914B** : 191–196, 1 fig.

WOLFF, TORBEN.   1960.   The hadal community, an introduction.   *Deep-sea Res.* **6** : 95–124.

ZENKEVITCH, L. A.   1957.   A new genus and two new species of deep-water Echiuroidea of the Far Eastern Seas and of the north-west Pacific.   *Trudy Inst. Okeanol.* **23** : 291–295, 6 figs (in Russian).

—— 1958.   The deep-sea echiurids of the north-western part of the Pacific Ocean.   *Trudy Inst. Okeanol.* **27** : 192–203, 30 figs (in Russian).

—— 1964a.   New deep-sea echiurids from the Indian Ocean.   *Trudy Inst. Okeanol.* **69** : 178–182 (in Russian with English summary).

—— 1964b.   New representatives of deep-sea echiurids *Alomasoma belyaevi* Zenk. sp. n. and *Choanostoma filatovae* n. sp. in the Pacific.   *Zool. Zh.* **43** : 1863–1864 (in Russian with English summary).

—— 1966.   The systematics and distribution of abyssal and hadal (ultra-abyssal) Echiuroidea. *Galathea Rep.* **8** : 175–184, 4 figs.

ZENKEVITCH, L. A., BIRSTEN, J. A. & BELIAEV, G. M.   1955.   Investigations of the bottom fauna of the Kurile-Kamchatka Trench.   *Trudy Inst. Okeanol.* **12** : 345–381 (in Russian).

ZUCKERKANDL, E.   1950.   Coelomic pressures in *Sipunculus nudus*.   *Biol. Bull. mar. biol. Lab., Wood's Hole* **98** : 161–173.

ZURBUCHEN, K.   1937.   Entwicklungsmechanische untersuchungen an *Bonellia viridis*. 2. Entwicklung der Intersexe und sexuelle Variabilität bei *Bonellia viridis* in Versuchen mit abgekürztem Rüsselparasitismus.   *Pubbl. Stn. Zool. Napoli* **16** : 28–80, 27 figs.

ZURBUCHEN, K. & BALTZER, F.   1936.   Das Tempo das männlichen, weiblichen und inter-sexuelle Differenzierung bei *Bonellia viridis* und die Goldschmidtsche Theorieder Geschlechts-bestimmung.   *Revue suisse Zool.* **43** : 489–494, 1 table.

VI. INDEX OF SCIENTIFIC NAMES

Names of subfamilies and families are printed in SMALL CAPITAL letters and those of higher categories in CAPITAL letters; new names are printed in **bold** type, other valid names are printed in roman type and names listed in synonymy are printed in *italic* type.